Effects of Urbanization on Stream Ecosystems

Effects of Urbanization on Stream Ecosystems is a special project of the
Water Quality Section, American Fisheries Society

Support for publication of this book was provided by

Water Quality Section, American Fisheries Society

U.S. Geological Survey, National Water Quality Assessment Program

Effects of Urbanization on Stream Ecosystems

Edited by

Larry R. Brown
U.S. Geological Survey, Placer Hall, 6000 J Street
Sacramento, California 95819, USA

Robert H. Gray
R. H. Gray & Associates, 2867 Troon Court
Richland, Washington 99354, USA

Robert M. Hughes
Department of Fisheries and Wildlife, Oregon State University
Corvallis, Oregon 97331, USA

Michael R. Meador
U.S. Geological Survey, 12201 Sunrise Valley Drive
MS 413 Reston, Virginia 20192, USA

American Fisheries Society Symposium 47

Proceedings of the Symposium
The Effects of Urbanization on Aquatic Ecosystems
held in Quebec City, Quebec, Canada
11–12 August 2003

American Fisheries Society
Bethesda, Maryland
2005

Printed in the United States of America on acid-free paper.

Library of Congress Control Number 2005932606
ISBN 1-888569-73-5
ISSN 0892-2284

American Fisheries Society Web site: *www.fisheries.org*

American Fisheries Society
5410 Grosvenor Lane, Suite 110
Bethesda, Maryland 20814-2199
USA

Contents

Regional Comparisons

Preface

During the 2002 Annual Business meeting of the Water Quality Section (WQS) of the American Fisheries Society (AFS), Larry Brown proposed that WQS sponsor a symposium at the 2003 Annual AFS Meeting in Quebec City, Quebec, Canada on the effects of urbanization on aquatic ecosystems. The proposal was supported and Bob Hughes suggested that WQS sponsor the production of a symposium volume. Bob Gray and Mike Meador subsequently volunteered to join the project as coeditors. The symposium "The Effects of Urbanization on Aquatic Ecosystems" was well attended and covered a wide array of topics related to urbanization. This book contains chapters by many of the speakers, although some speakers chose not to contribute to the book and other authors were invited to contribute to the book after the symposium was over. As authors, we often wonder why it seems to take so long to get a book to press. As editors, we find that busy lives, long field seasons, and other aspects of the publication process all conspire to ruin the most well-planned production schedule. We thank all of the authors, the reviewers, and Aaron Lerner and Debby Lehman at AFS books for their help and persistence in producing this volume. We hope you, the reader, enjoy the book and find it useful in your professional endeavors.

Reviewer Acknowledgments

We thank the following individuals for reviewing one or more of the submitted articles.

Bob Angus
Barry Baldigo
Michael Barbour
Anne Brasher (3)
Carmen Burton
Virginia Butler
Kurt Carpenter
James Carter
Michael Chadwick
William Clark
James Congleton
Bob Daniels
Susan Davies
Wayne Davis
John Faustini
Faith Fitzpatrick
Mary Freeman
Elise Giddings
Peter Groothuis
Julie A. Hambrook Berkman
Mitchell Harris
James Harrison

Bret Harvey
Raul Henry
Ju-Chin Huang
James Karr (2)
Christopher Konrad
Scott Lankford
Michael Marchetti
Terry Maret (2)
Maurice Mettee
Karen Murray
Mike Paller
Yangdong Pan
Alison Purcell
Vincent Resh
Kurt Schwabe
Terry Short
Camm Swift
Cathy Tate
Marcos von Sperling
Ian Waite (2)
J. Alan Yeakley

Symbols and Abbreviations

The following symbols and abbreviations may be found in this book without definition. Also undefined are standard mathematical and statistical symbols given in most dictionaries.

A	ampere	J	joule
AC	alternating current	K	Kelvin (degrees above absolute zero)
Bq	becquerel	k	kilo (10^3, as a prefix)
C	coulomb	kg	kilogram
°C	degrees Celsius	km	kilometer
cal	calorie	l	levorotatory
cd	candela	L	levo (as a prefix)
cm	centimeter	L	liter (0.264 gal, 1.06 qt)
Co.	Company	lb	pound (0.454 kg, 454g)
Corp.	Corporation	lm	lumen
cov	covariance	log	logarithm
DC	direct current; District of Columbia	Ltd.	Limited
D	dextro (as a prefix)	M	mega (10^6, as a prefix); molar (as a suffix or by itself)
d	day		
d	dextrorotatory	m	meter (as a suffix or by itself); milli (10^{23}, as a prefix)
df	degrees of freedom		
dL	deciliter	mi	mile (1.61 km)
E	east	min	minute
E	expected value	mol	mole
e	base of natural logarithm (2.71828...)	N	normal (for chemistry); north (for geography); newton
e.g.	(exempli gratia) for example		
eq	equivalent	N	sample size
et al.	(et alii) and others	NS	not significant
etc.	et cetera	n	ploidy; nanno (10^{29}, as a prefix)
eV	electron volt	o	ortho (as a chemical prefix)
F	filial generation; Farad	oz	ounce (28.4 g)
°F	degrees Fahrenheit	P	probability
fc	footcandle (0.0929 lx)	p	para (as a chemical prefix)
ft	foot (30.5 cm)	p	pico (10^{212}, as a prefix)
ft^3/s	cubic feet per second (0.0283 m^3/s)	Pa	pascal
g	gram	pH	negative log of hydrogen ion activity
G	giga (10^9, as a prefix)	ppm	parts per million
gal	gallon (3.79 L)	qt	quart (0.946 L)
Gy	gray	R	multiple correlation or regression coefficient
h	hour		
ha	hectare (2.47 acres)	r	simple correlation or regression coefficient
hp	horsepower (746 W)		
Hz	hertz	rad	radian
in	inch (2.54 cm)	S	siemens (for electrical conductance); south (for geography)
Inc.	Incorporated		
i.e.	(id est) that is	SD	standard deviation
IU	international unit	SE	standard error

s	second	α	probability of type I error (false rejection of null hypothesis)
T	tesla		
tris	tris(hydroxymethyl)-aminomethane (a buffer)	β	probability of type II error (false acceptance of null hypothesis)
UK	United Kingdom	Ω	ohm
U.S.	United States (adjective)	μ	micro (10^{-6}, as a prefix)
USA	United States of America (noun)	'	minute (angular)
V	volt	"	second (angular)
V, Var	variance (population)	°	degree (temperature as a prefix, angular as a suffix)
var	variance (sample)		
W	watt (for power); west (for geography)	%	per cent (per hundred)
Wb	weber	‰	per mille (per thousand)
yd	yard (0.914 m, 91.4 cm)		

American Fisheries Society Symposium 47:1–8, 2005

Introduction to Effects of Urbanization on Stream Ecosystems

LARRY R. BROWN*

U.S. Geological Survey, Placer Hall, 6000 J Street, Sacramento, California 95819, USA

ROBERT H. GRAY

R. H. Gray & Associates, 2867 Troon Court, Richland, Washington 99354, USA

ROBERT M. HUGHES

Department of Fisheries and Wildlife, Oregon State University, Corvallis, Oregon 97331, USA

MICHAEL R. MEADOR

U.S. Geological Survey, 12201 Sunrise Valley Drive, MS 413, Reston, Virginia 20192, USA

Abstract.—The human population of the earth continues to grow, with most of that growth occurring by expansion of existing urban areas. The resulting conversion of rural land to urban land uses will affect associated streams. This book provides researchers, aquatic resource managers, land use planners, and others with results of recent studies of the effects of urbanization on stream ecosystems. In this introductory chapter, we review some of the existing literature on urbanization and highlight some issues addressed by other chapters of the book. We expect the information in this book will be helpful to new and established researchers studying effects of urbanization, as well as to managers and others interested in recent progress in the field. Communicating results of scientific research to managers and planners is essential if streams are to be protected as urban populations continue to grow.

The world's ecosystems provide a wide range of essential and economically valuable services (Costanza et al. 1997). Aquatic ecosystems provide a wide array of such services, including freshwater for agricultural, industrial and municipal uses, transportation corridors, food, opportunities for recreation and esthetic enjoyment, and waste disposal (Petts 1989). As human populations have grown, their effects on aquatic ecosystems have increased (Postel 1996, 2000; Vitousek et al. 1997; Sala et al. 2000). Freshwater ecosystems are particularly vulnerable because human populations are concentrated near waterways (Sala et al. 2000; Alberti and Marzluff 2004).

The world's urban population is increasing at a faster rate than the total population. Almost all population growth in the next 30 years is expected to occur by expansion of existing urban areas (United Nations

2004). The world's urban population was estimated to be 3 billion in 2003 and is expected to increase to 5 billion by 2030 (United Nations 2004). As rural lands surrounding urban areas are converted to urban land uses, nearby freshwater systems will experience increased stresses with a variety of consequences for biodiversity and ecosystem processes (McDonnell and Pickett 1990; Sala et al. 2000; Paul and Meyer 2001).

Previous studies have identified a wide variety of stressors affecting streams in urban areas (Paul and Meyer 2001). Urbanization can change the chemical and physical properties of stream systems (Klein 1979; Heany and Huber 1984). Large areas of impermeable surface can increase the frequency and magnitude of storm flows (Arnold et al. 1982; Booth and Jackson 1997; Trimble 1997). Excessive groundwater pumping and reduced recharge lessen base flows (Klein 1979; Finkenbine et al. 2000) and can exacerbate the effects of droughts. Modification of stream hydrology and flood management practices can alter the sedi-

* Corresponding author: lrbrown@usgs.gov

ment regime, with subsequent effects on streambed composition, and stream channel morphology (Arnold et al. 1982; Booth 1990, 1991; Booth and Jackson 1997; Finkenbine et al. 2000). Loss of riparian vegetation can increase water temperatures as stream shading is reduced (Booth 1991; Belt and O'Laughlin 1994; LeBlanc et al. 1996), reduce habitat structure for fish (Martin et al. 1986; Finkenbine et al. 2000), and change trophic processes (Kellar and Swanson 1979; Vannote et al. 1980). Concentrations of nutrients, pesticides, organic chemicals, and heavy metals are often elevated in urban runoff and treated wastewater, which are major sources of water in many urban streams (Klein 1979; Heany and Huber 1984; Field and Pitt 1990; Ahel et al. 2000; Lieb and Carline 2000; Shinya et al. 2000). These changes in physical habitat and water quality have been linked to changes in aquatic biota. Urban stormwater runoff has been recognized as an important factor affecting biota (Heany and Huber 1984), as have hydrologic and land use changes associated with urbanization (Weaver and Garman 1994; Wichert 1994, 1995; Finkenbine et al. 2000; Wang et al. 2000; Sonneman et al. 2001; Walsh et al. 2001; Wang and Lyons 2003). Understanding the effects of these stresses on aquatic assemblages will be extremely important in preserving, rehabilitating, and managing these ecosystems as urbanization proceeds (Nilsson et al. 2003; Cottingham et al. 2004).

This book provides researchers, aquatic resource managers, land-use planners, and others with results of recent studies of the effects of urbanization on stream ecosystems. The book includes case studies from all regions of the United States and one from Brazil. The studies in the United States encompass a variety of environmental settings, ranging from arid, highly urbanized Southern California to the humid southeastern and long-urbanized northeastern United States. Regional comparisons of the characteristics of urbanization and effects of urbanization on biological assemblages based on a standard study design are also included. Other studies address a range of topics, including hydrology, economics, and management and offer a variety of tools that will be useful to others embarking on studies of urban streams.

What Is Urbanization?

The most basic definition of urbanization is the transformation of land from rural land uses, such as agriculture, to urban land uses, such as housing. However, summarizing the many environmental effects of ur-

banization as a variable in scientific studies is less straightforward. Popular surrogate measures for urbanization in the recent literature include general measures of urban land use, population density, and the extent of impervious surface (Arnold and Gibbon 1996; Center for Watershed Protection 2003; Morse et al. 2003). Use of impervious surface has been especially favored because it is linked to changes in stream hydrology, which affect stream biota and a variety of stream processes (Poff et al. 1997; Konrad and Booth 2005, this volume). However, urbanization clearly has a variety of interacting effects on stream ecosystems that may be further influenced by regional and historical differences in urban development and natural factors such as climate, physiography, geologic setting, vegetation, and soils (Harding et al. 1998; Fitzpatrick et al. 2004 and 2005, this volume). Tate et al. (2005, this volume) use an urbanization intensity index originally formulated by McMahon and Cuffney (2000) to describe the characteristics of urbanization in specific study areas. Information on the specific characteristics of urbanization in particular geographic areas is especially important as researchers and resource managers try to extrapolate results of studies from smaller to larger geographic scales. Coordinated studies by Meador et al. (2005, this volume), Cuffney et al. (2005, this volume), and Potapova et al. (2005, this volume) highlight similarities and differences in responses of biotic assemblages to various characteristics of urbanization in different regions of the United States. Some of the variability observed is likely due to the fact that patterns of urbanization and environmental manifestations of those patterns are not necessarily the same from areas with different economic, social, and environmental conditions. The study by Pompeu et al. (2005, this volume) is instructive in this respect. In Brazil, environmental scientists are dealing with urban problems such as disposal of raw sewage that have been greatly reduced in the United States since implementation of the Clean Water Act. Thus, the results of studies in Brazil and the United States should only be applied across areas with caution and recognition of the similarities and differences in the characteristics of urbanization in each location.

Approaches to Studying the Effects of Urbanization

As in many other areas of stream ecology, studies of the effects of urbanization are often observational and correlative. In fact, it is difficult to imagine doing an experimental study of urbanization. Studies in this book and the literature take several approaches. In one approach, urbanization is considered a single factor and streams or stream reaches with different levels of urbanization are sampled. Biotic assemblages or other biological measures at the sampling sites are analyzed in terms of that single factor to infer effects of urbanization. In another approach, biotic assemblages or metrics are ordinated, correlated, or regressed against a variety of physical and chemical environmental factors, often including the original measure of urbanization used to design the study. Significant environmental factors are then related back to urbanization using similar correlative methods. These approaches have clearly been useful, because they form the basis of much of our existing knowledge. However, one must be cautious when generalizing across a variety of spatial scales based on individual studies with different designs (Kennen et al. 2005, this volume).

Tate et al. (2005) offer one approach to this problem by applying a single study design to studies of the effects of urbanization in three different United States cities— Birmingham, Alabama; Boston, Massachusetts; and Salt Lake City, Utah. A standard protocol based on an index of urban intensity (McMahon and Cuffney 2000; Tate et al 2005) was applied to site selection within the three cities. There was some flexibility in the final site selection and study design to account for regional environmental differences. For example, in Salt Lake City, Utah, there were few perennial streams for study because of the arid climate and a correlation between urbanization and altitude. These factors required a partially nested design (multiple sites per stream), in contrast to single-site per stream designs in the other two cities (Tate et al. 2005). Standardized sampling of stream habitat (Short et al. 2005, this volume), benthic algae (Potapova et al. 2005), benthic macroinvertebrates (Cuffney et al. 2005), and fishes (Meador et al. 2005) provided convincing comparisons of stream ecosystem responses among the three cities. Integration of the results of these studies is proceeding as the approach is applied to additional regions within the United States (Cathy Tate, U.S. Geological Survey, personal communication). Although other approaches are certainly possible, these studies represent a step toward the types of interdisciplinary efforts necessary to forecast effects of urbanization on stream ecosystems in support of proper planning and management (Benda et al. 2002; Nilsson et al. 2003).

By design, studies in this book mainly approach the effects of urbanization by assessing changes in biological assemblages. Biological assemblages are sensitive indicators of stream environmental conditions, and biotic indices are efficient ways of assessing stream condition (Karr 1991; Karr and Chu 1999; Simon 2003). However, there are many approaches to assessing effects of urbanization. Historical reconstructions of stream condition during the early stages of development are possible given sufficient historical data (MacCoy and Blew 2005, this volume). Monitoring growth and life history characteristics of fishes can be informative (e.g., Fraker et al. 2002). Limburg et al. (2005, this volume) use eastern blacknose dace *Rhinichthys atratulus* as a sentinel species to monitor inputs of anthropogenic nitrogen using stable isotope analysis in New York watersheds. Erickson et al. (2005, this volume) use several physiological endpoints to assess stress in fishes related to urban runoff. Advances in genomic tools, such as genetic microarrays (Rotchell and Ostrander 2003; Williams et al. 2003), make it possible to determine if organisms exhibit physiological responses to pollutants. In combination with passive samplers to assess the presence of hydro- phobic and hydrophilic pollutants (Huckins et al. 1993; Alvarez et al. 2004; Petty et al. 2004; Rowe et al. 2005; Rosen et al., in press), these techniques provide sensitive indicators of organism exposure to chemicals in urban runoff, beyond toxicity tests or chemical measurements of pollutant concentrations.

Indices of biotic integrity (IBIs) are a common method of assessing biotic responses to environmental stressors, including those associated with urbanization. Typically, IBIs compare index scores to a set of reference sites that represent the least disturbed condition (Karr 1991; Karr and Chu 1999; Simon 2003); however, it is often difficult to define useful reference sites. Carter and Fend (2005, this volume) apply new concepts to determining the best attainable conditions in urban areas where highly urbanized areas might not be expected to have as high a potential for ecological function as less intensively urbanized areas or areas experiencing different types of urbanization (low-density housing versus intense industrial development). In contrast, MacCoy and Blew (2005) present an example of how to use historical land survey notes to describe ecological conditions before major development occurred. Many recent studies have identified the level of watershed development at which ecological effects become evident (e. g., Wang et al. 2000; Walsh et al. 2001; Morse et al. 2003; Taylor et al. 2004). These studies hint at a more basic issue confronting managers of urban streams. What ecological services do we expect from urban streams, and how likely is it that we can protect or rehabilitate those services in urban streams?

Studies of urban streams typically focus on the form of stream responses to urban influences. Few studies have addressed the equally difficult question of what services society expects from urban streams and how much effort society is willing to expend to protect healthy streams or to rehabilitate degraded streams so they can provide the expected services. Cottingham et al. (2004) identified the lack of quantification of urban stream ecosystem goods and services as a key knowledge gap. Society is willing to expend time and money to preserve urban waterways (Dumas et al. 2005; Winternitz and Holtz 2005; both this volume) and even very highly urbanized areas, such as Southern California, can have streams with some (and often interesting) ecological function (e.g., Brown et al. 2005a; Burton et al. 2005; Lin and Ambrose 2005; all this volume). Preserving the ecological values of waterways in the face of other societal needs is difficult and requires aquatic resource scientists and managers to participate in interdisciplinary efforts that extend beyond traditional ecology and integrate topics such as economics, engineering, and the social sciences (Postel 2000; Nilsson et al. 2003). Dumas et al. (2005) introduce a number of economic methods for determining the value of ecosystem services. Winternitz and Holtz (2005) provide a case study of an ongoing and complex negotiation focused on protecting the fisheries resources of an urban California river. As these examples demonstrate, participation in interdisciplinary efforts will be challenging, especially given discipline specific knowledge gaps and mismatches of spatial and temporal scale among disciplines (Benda et al. 2002; Nilsson et al. 2003). However, integrated approaches to understanding and managing urban streams provide the greatest opportunity for developing robust, sustainable solutions.

Conclusion

Articles in this book provide invaluable background for anyone involved in or interested in urban streams. Although our knowledge of urban streams is improving, there are still considerable challenges to understanding these systems and managing them effectively (Cottingham et al. 2004). Additional studies are needed to document similarities and differences in the characteristics of urbanization and the effects of urbanization on stream ecosystems across multiple spatial scales. Differences in socioeconomic conditions between regions and countries likely affect both the valuation of stream ecosystem services and the ability to protect and rehabilitate them (Cottingham et al.

2004). Perhaps most important and most challenging and one of the principal motivations for this book, the scientific knowledge of aquatic resource scientists and managers must be made accessible to urban planners so that streams can be protected as urbanization occurs rather than attempting to rehabilitate them afterward (Karr and Chu 1999; Nilsson et al. 2003; Cottingham et al. 2004). As our knowledge improves, so will our ability to protect and rehabilitate urban streams and the valuable services they provide to urban populations.

Acknowledgments

We thank Tom Cuffney and James Carter for comments that significantly improved this manuscript. Larry Brown and Mike Meador were funded by the National Water Quality Assessment Program of the U.S. Geological Survey, during the preparation of this article. Bob Hughes was partially funded by grant #R-829498-01 from the National Center for Environmental Research (NCER) STAR Program of the U.S. Environmental Protection Agency.

References

Ahel, M., E. Molnar, S. Ibric, and W. Giger. 2000. Estrogenic metabolites of alkylphenol polyethoxylates in secondary sewage effluents and rivers. Water Science and Technology 42(7–8):15–22.

Alberti, M., and J. M. Marzluff. 2004. Ecological resilience in urban ecosystems: linking urban patterns to human and ecological functions. Urban Ecosystems 7:241–265.

Alvarez, D. A., J. D. Petty, J. N. Huckins, T. L. Jones-Lepp, D. T. Getting, J. P. Goddard, and S. E. Manahan. 2004. Development of a passive, in situ, integrative sampler for hydrophilic organic contaminants in aquatic environments. Environmental Toxicology and Chemistry 23:1640–1648.

Arnold, C. L., P. J. Boison, and P. C. Patton. 1982. Sawmill Brook: an example of rapid geomorphic change related to urbanization. Journal of Geology 90:155–160.

Arnold, C. L., and C. J. Gibbons. 1996. Impervious surface coverage: the emergence of a key environmental indicator. American Planners Association Journal 62:243–258.

Belt, G. H., and J. O'Laughlin. 1994. Buffer strip design for protecting water quality and fish habitat. Western Journal of Applied Forestry 9:41–45.

Benda, L. E., N. L. Poff, C. Tague, M. A. Palmer, J. Pizzuto, S. Cooper, E. Stanley, and G. Moglen. 2002.

How to avoid train wrecks when using science in environmental problem solving. BioScience 52:1127–1136.

Booth, D. B. 1990. Stream-channel incision following drainage-basin urbanization. Water Resources Bulletin 26:407–417.

Booth, D. B. 1991. Urbanization and the natural drainage system—impacts, solutions, and prognoses. Northwest Environmental Journal 7:93–118.

Booth, D. B., and C. R. Jackson. 1997. Urbanization of aquatic systems—degradation thresholds, stormwater detention, and the limits of mitigation. Water Resources Bulletin 33:1077–1090.

Brown, L. R., C. A. Burton, and K. Belitz. 2005a. Aquatic assemblages of the highly urbanized Santa Ana River basin, California. Pages 263–287 in L. R. Brown, R. H. Gray, R. M. Hughes, and M. R. Meador, editors. Effects of urbanization on stream ecosystems. American Fisheries Society, Symposium 47, Bethesda, Maryland.

Burton, C. A., L. R. Brown, and K. Belitz. 2005. Assessing water source and channel type as factors affecting benthic macroinvertebrate and periphyton assemblages in the highly urbanized Santa Ana River basin, California. Pages 239–262 in L. R. Brown, R. H. Gray, R. M. Hughes, and M. R. Meador, editors. Effects of urbanization on stream ecosystems. American Fisheries Society, Symposium 47, Bethesda, Maryland.

Carter, J. L., and S. V. Fend. 2005. Setting limits: the development and use of factor-ceiling distributions for an urban assessment using macroinvertebrates. Pages 179–191 in L. R. Brown, R. H. Gray, R. M. Hughes, and M. R. Meador, editors. Effects of urbanization on stream ecosystems. American Fisheries Society, Symposium 47, Bethesda, Maryland.

Center for Watershed Protection. 2003. Impacts of impervious cover on aquatic ecosystems. Center for Watershed Protection, Watershed Protection Research Monograph No. 1, Ellicott City, Maryland.

Costanza, R., R. d'Arge, R. de Groot, S. Farber, M. Grasso, B. Hannon, K. Limburg, S. Naeem, R. V. O'Neill, and J. Paruelo. 1997. The value of the world's ecosystem services and natural capital. Nature 387:253–260.

Cottingham P., C. Walsh, G. Rooney, and T. Fletcher, editors. 2004. Urbanization impacts on stream ecology – from syndrome to cure? Outcomes of workshops held at the Symposium on Urbanization and Stream Ecology, Melbourne University, Melbourne, Australia 8th – 10th December 2003. Cooperative Research Centre for Freshwater Ecology, Canberra, Australia.

Cuffney, T. F., H. Zappia, E. M. P. Giddings, and J. F.

Coles. 2005. Effects of urbanization on benthic macroinvertebrate assemblages in contrasting environmental settings: Boston, Massachusetts; Birmingham, Alabama; and Salt Lake City, Utah. Pages 361–407 in L. R. Brown, R. H. Gray, R. M. Hughes, and M. R. Meador, editors. Effects of urbanization on stream ecosystems. American Fisheries Society, Symposium 47, Bethesda, Maryland.

Dumas, C. F., P. W. Schuhmman, and J. C. Whitehead. 2005. Measuring the economic benefits of water quality improvement with benefit transfer: an introduction for noneconomists. Pages 53–68 in L. R. Brown, R. H. Gray, R. M. Hughes, and M. R. Meador, editors. Effects of urbanization on stream ecosystems. American Fisheries Society, Symposium 47, Bethesda, Maryland.

Erickson, J. W., S. J. Kenner, and B. A. Barton. 2005. Physiological stress response of brown trout to stormwater runoff events in Rapid Creek, Rapid City, South Dakota. Pages 117–132 in L. R. Brown, R. H. Gray, R. M. Hughes, and M. R. Meador, editors. Effects of urbanization on stream ecosystems. American Fisheries Society, Symposium 47, Bethesda, Maryland.

Field, R., and R. E. Pitt. 1990. Urban storm-induced discharge impacts. Water Science Technology 22(3):1–7.

Finkenbine, J. K., J. W. Atwater, and D. S. Mavinic. 2000. Stream health after urbanization. Journal of the American Water Resources Association 36:1149–1160.

Fitzpatrick, F. A., M. W. Diebel, M. A. Harris, T. L. Arnold, M. A. Lutz, and K. D. Richards. 2005. Effects of urbanization on geomorphology, habitat, hydrology, and fish index of biointegrity of streams in the Chicago area, Illinois and Wisconsin. Pages 87–115 in L. R. Brown, R. H. Gray, R. M. Hughes, and M. R. Meador, editors. Effects of urbanization on stream ecosystems. American Fisheries Society, Symposium 47, Bethesda, Maryland.

Fitzpatrick, F. A., M. A. Harris, T. L. Arnold, and K. D. Richards. 2004. Urbanization influences on aquatic communities in northeastern Illinois streams. Journal of the American Water Resources Association 40:461–475.

Fraker, M. E., J. W. Snodgrass, and F. Morgan. 2002. Differences in growth and maturation of blacknose dace (Rhinichthys atratulus) across an urban-rural gradient. Copeia 2002:1122–1127.

Harding, J. S., E. F. Benfield, P.V. Bolstad, G. S. Helfman, and E. B. D. Jones. 1998. Stream biodiversity: the ghost of land use past. Proceedings of the National Academy of Sciences 95:14843–14847.

Heany, J. P., and W. C. Huber. 1984. Nationwide assessment of urban runoff impact on receiving water quality. Water Resources Bulletin 20:35–42.

Huckins, J. N., G. K. Manuweera, J. D. Petty, D. MacKay, and J. A. Lebo. 1993. Lipid-containing semipermeable membrane devices for monitoring organic contaminants in water. Environmental Science and Technology 27:2489–2496.

Karr, J. A. 1991. Biological integrity: a long neglected aspect of water resource management. Ecological Applications 1:66–84.

Karr, J. A., and E. W. Chu. 1999. Restoring life in running waters: better biological monitoring. Island Press, Washington D.C.

Kellar, E. A., and F. J. Swanson. 1979. Effects of large organic material on channel form and alluvial process. Earth Surface Processes 4:361–380.

Kennen, J. G., M. Chang, and B. H. Tracy. 2005. Effects of landscape change on fish assemblage structure in a rapidly growing metropolitan area in North Carolina, USA. Pages 39–52 in L. R. Brown, R. H. Gray, R. M. Hughes, and M. R. Meador, editors. Effects of urbanization on stream ecosystems. American Fisheries Society, Symposium 47, Bethesda, Maryland.

Klein, R. D. 1979. Urbanization and stream quality impairment. Water Resources Bulletin 15:948–963.

Konrad, C. P., and D. B. Booth. 2005. Hydrologic changes in urban streams and their ecological significance. Pages 157–177 in L. R. Brown, R. H. Gray, R. M. Hughes, and M. R. Meador, editors. Effects of urbanization on stream ecosystems. American Fisheries Society, Symposium 47, Bethesda, Maryland.

LeBlanc, R. T., R. D. Brown, and J. E. FitzGibbon. 1996. Modeling the effects of land use changes on the water temperature in unregulated urban streams. Journal of Environmental Management 49:445–469.

Lieb, D. A., and R. F. Carline. 2000. The effects of urban runoff from a detention pond on water quality, temperature, and caged Gammarus minus (Say) (Amphipoda) in a headwater stream. Hydrobiologia 441:107–116.

Limburg, K. E., K. M. Stainbrook, J. D. Erickson, and J. M. Gowdy. 2005. Urbanization consequences: case studies in the Hudson River watershed. Pages 23–37 in L. R. Brown, R. H. Gray, R. M. Hughes, and M. R. Meador, editors. Effects of urbanization on stream ecosystems. American Fisheries Society, Symposium 47, Bethesda, Maryland.

Lin, C. J., and R. F. Ambrose. 2005. Relations between fish assemblages and urbanization in southern California coastal streams. Pages 229–238 in L. R. Brown, R. H. Gray, R. M. Hughes, and M. R. Meador, editors. Effects of urbanization on stream ecosystems. American Fisheries Society, Symposium 47, Bethesda, Maryland.

MacCoy, D., and D. Blew. 2005. Impacts of land-use changes and hydrologic modification on the lower Boise River, Idaho, USA. Pages 133–156 in L. R. Brown, R. H. Gray, R. M. Hughes, and M. R. Meador, editors. Effects of urbanization on stream ecosystems. American Fisheries Society, Symposium 47, Bethesda, Maryland.

Martin, D. J., L. J. Wasserman, and V. H. Dale. 1986. Influence of riparian vegetation on posteruption survival of coho salmon fingerlings on the west-side streams of Mount St. Helens, Washington. North American Journal of Fisheries Management 6:1–8.

McDonnell, M. J., and S. T. A. Pickett. 1990. Ecosystem structure and function along urban-rural gradients: an unexploited opportunity for ecology. Ecology 71:1231–1237.

McMahon, G., and T. F. Cuffney. 2000. Quantifying urban intensity in drainage basins for assessing stream ecological conditions. Journal of the American Water Resources Association 36:1247–1261.

Meador, M. R., J. F. Coles, and H. Zappia. 2005. Fish assemblage responses to urban intensity gradients in contrasting metropolitan areas: Birmingham, Alabama and Boston, Massachusetts. Pages 409–423 in L. R. Brown, R. H. Gray, R. M. Hughes, and M. R. Meador, editors. Effects of urbanization on stream ecosystems. American Fisheries Society, Symposium 47, Bethesda, Maryland.

Morse, C. C., A. D. Huryn, and C. Cronan. 2003. Impervious surface area as a predictor of the effects of urbanization on stream insect communities in Maine, U.S.A. Environmental Monitoring and Assessment 89:95–127.

Nilsson, C., J. E. Pizzuto, G. E. Moglen, M. A. Palmer, E. H. Stanley, N. E. Bockstael, and L. C. Thompson. 2003. Ecological forecasting and the urbanization of stream ecosystems: challenges for economists, hydrologists, geomorphologists, and ecologists. Ecosystems 6:659–674.

Paul, M. J., and J. L. Meyer. 2001. Streams in the urban landscape. Annual Review of Ecology and Systematics 32:333–365.

Petts, G. E. 1989. Perspectives for ecological management of regulated rivers. Pages 3–24 in J. A. Gore and G. E. Petts, editors. Alternatives in regulated river management. CRC Press, Boca Raton, Florida.

Petty, J. D., J. N. Huckins, D. A. Alvarez, W. G. Brumbaugh, W. L. Cranor, R. W. Gale, A. C. Rastall, T. L. Jones–Lepp, T. J. Leiker, C. E. Rostad, and E. T. Furlong. 2004. A holistic passive integrative sampling approach for assessing the presence and potential impacts of waterborne environmental contaminants. Chemosphere 54:695–705.

Poff, N. L., J. D. Allan, M. B. Bain, J. R. Karr, K. L.

Prestegaard, B.D. Richter, R. E Sparks, and J. C. Stromberg. 1997. The natural flow regime: a paradigm for river conservation and restoration. BioScience 47:769–784.

Pompeu, P. S., C. B. M. Alves, and M. Callisto. 2005. The effects of urbanization on biodiversity and water quality in the Rio das Velhas basin, Brazil. Pages 11–22 in L. R. Brown, R. H. Gray, R. M. Hughes, and M. R. Meador, editors. Effects of urbanization on stream ecosystems. American Fisheries Society, Symposium 47, Bethesda, Maryland.

Postel, S. 1996. Dividing the waters: food security, ecosystem health, and the new politics of scarcity. Worldwatch Institute, Washington, D.C.

Postel, S. L. 2000. Entering an era of water scarcity: the challenges ahead. Ecological Applications 10:941–948.

Potapova, M., J. F. Coles, E. M. P. Giddings, and H. Zappia. 2005. A comparison of the influences of urbanization in contrasting environmental settings on stream benthic algal assemblages. Pages 333–359 in L. R. Brown, R. H. Gray, R. M. Hughes, and M. R. Meador, editors. Effects of urbanization on stream ecosystems. American Fisheries Society, Symposium 47, Bethesda, Maryland.

Rosen, M. R., T. G. Rowe, S. L. Goodbred, D. O. Shipley, and J. A. Arufe. In press. Importance of land use, streamflow, and water quality on toxicity of SPMD extracts deployed in streams from the Lake Tahoe and Truckee River watersheds. In R. M. Hughes, L. Wang, and P. W. Seelbach, editors. Influences of landscapes on stream habitats and biological assemblages. American Fisheries Society, Symposium 48, Bethesda, Maryland.

Rotchell, J. M., and G. K. Ostrander. 2003. Molecular markers of endocrine disruption in aquatic organisms. Toxicology and Environmental Health B Critical Reviews 6:453–496.

Rowe, T. G., M. R. Rosen, S. L. Goodbred, and D. O. Shipley. 2005. Relation between urbanization and relative toxicity of semipermeable membrane device extracts in the Lake Tahoe basin and Truckee River watershed, Nevada and California. Journal of the Nevada Water Resources Association 2:58–89.

Sala, O. E., F. S. Chapin, III, J. J. Armesto, E. Berlow, J. Bloomfield, R. Dirzo, E. Huber-Sanwald, L. F. Huenneke, R. B. Jackson, A. Kinzig, R. Leemans, D. M. Lodge, H. A. Mooney, M. Oesterheld, N. L. Poff, M. T. Sykes, B. H. Walker, M. Walker, and D. H. Wall. 2000. Global biodiversity scenarios for the year 2100. Science 287:1770–1774.

Shinya, M., T. Tsuchinaga, M. Kitano, Y. Yamada, and M. Ishikawa. 2000. Characterization of heavy metals and polycyclic aromatic hydrocarbons in urban highway runoff. Water Science and Technology 42(7–8):201–208.

Short, T. M., E. M. P. Giddings, H. Zappia, and J. Coles. 2005. Urbanization effects on stream habitat characteristics in Boston, Massachusetts; Birmingham, Alabama; and Salt Lake City, Utah. Pages 317–332 in L. R. Brown, R. H. Gray, R. M. Hughes, and M. R. Meador, editors. Effects of urbanization on stream ecosystems. American Fisheries Society, Symposium 47, Bethesda, Maryland.

Simon, T. P., editor. 2003. Biological response signatures: indicator patterns using aquatic communities. CRC Press, Boca Raton, Florida.

Sonneman, J. A., C. J. Walsh, P. F. Breen, and A. K. Sharpe. 2001. Effects of urbanization on streams of the Melbourne region, Victoria, Australia. II. Benthic diatom communities. Freshwater Biology 46:553–565.

Tate, C. M., T. F. Cuffney, G. McMahon, E. M. P. Giddings, J. F. Coles, and H. Zappia. 2005. Use of an urban intensity index to assess urban effects on streams in three contrasting environmental settings. Pages 291–315 in L. R. Brown, R. H. Gray, R. M. Hughes, and M. R. Meador, editors. Effects of urbanization on stream ecosystems. American Fisheries Society, Symposium 47, Bethesda, Maryland.

Taylor, S. L., S. C. Roberts, C. J. Walsh, and B. E. Hatt. 2004. Catchment urbanisation and increased benthic algal biomass in streams: linking mechanisms to management. Freshwater Biology 49:835–851.

Trimble, S. W. 1997. Contribution of stream channel erosion to sediment yield from an urbanizing watershed. Science 278:1442–1444.

United Nations. 2004. World urbanization prospects: the 2003 revision. United Nations, Department of Economic and Social Affairs, Population Division, New York.

Vannote, R. L., G. W. Minshall, K. W. Cummins, J. R. Sedel, and C. E. Cushing. 1980. The river continuum concept. Canadian Journal of Fisheries and Aquatic Sciences 37:130–137.

Vitousek, P. M., H. A. Mooney, J. Lubchenco, and J. M. Melillo. 1997. Human domination of the earth's ecosystems. Science 277:494–499.

Walsh, C. J., A. K. Shape, P. F. Breen, and J. A. Sonneman. 2001. Effects of urbanization on streams of the Melbourne region, Victoria, Australia. I. Benthic macroinvertebrate communities. Freshwater Biology 46:535–551.

Wang, L., and J. Lyons. 2003. Fish and benthic macroinvertebrate assemblages as indicators of stream degradation in urbanizing watersheds. Pages 227–249 in T. P. Simon, editor. Biological response signatures: indicator patterns using aquatic communities. CRC Press, Boca Raton, Florida.

Wang, L., J. Lyons, P. Kanehl, R. Bannerman, and E. Emmons. 2000. Watershed urbanization and changes in fish communities in southeastern Wisconsin streams. Journal of the American Water Resources Association 36:1173–1189.

Weaver, L. A., and G. C. Garman. 1994. Urbanization of a watershed and historical changes in a stream fish assemblage. Transactions of the American Fisheries Society 123:162–172.

Wichert, G. A. 1994. Fish as indicators of ecological sustainability: historical sequences in Toronto area streams. Water Pollution Research Journal of Canada 29:599–617.

Wichert, G. A. 1995. Effects of improved sewage effluent management and urbanization on fish associations of Toronto streams. North American Journal of Fisheries Management 15:440–456.

Williams, T. D., K. Gensberg, S. D. Minchin, and J. K. Chipman. 2003. A DNA expression array to detect toxic stress response in European flounder (*Platichthys flesus*). Aquatic Toxicology 65:141–157.

Winternitz, L., and E. Holtz. 2005. Managing conflicts on the lower American River—can urban and agricultural demands be met while maintaining healthy fisheries? Pages 213–227 *in* L. R. Brown, R. H. Gray, R. M. Hughes, and M. R. Meador, editors. Effects of urbanization on stream ecosystems. American Fisheries Society, Symposium 47, Bethesda, Maryland.

Case Studies

American Fisheries Society Symposium 47:11–22, 2005

The Effects of Urbanization on Biodiversity and Water Quality in the Rio das Velhas Basin, Brazil

PAULO S. POMPEU* AND CARLOS BERNARDO M. ALVES

Projeto Manuelzão – Universidade Federal de Minas Gerais
Avenida Alfredo Balena, 190 /10.012 Belo Horizonte (MG) Brazil 30130-100

MARCOS CALLISTO

Universidade Federal de Minas Gerais, ICB, Departamento de Biologia Geral
Laboratório de Ecologia de Bentos, CP. 486 Belo Horizonte (MG) Brazil 30161-970

Abstract.—In Brazil, most urban sewage is discharged without treatment into rivers. This is the situation for the Rio das Velhas, which receives in its upper course the sewage of the state capital of Minas Gerais, Belo Horizonte, with more than 2.4 million inhabitants. Our study focuses on the effects of basin urbanization on aquatic biodiversity and water quality in the Rio das Velhas. We use the assemblage structure and taxonomic composition of fishes and benthic macroinvertebrates as biological indicators of water quality. Effects of Belo Horizonte's discharge included changes in water quality and declines in fish and benthos richness and diversity. However, the absence of dams in the Rio das Velhas main course, associated with connectivity with the Rio São Francisco system and tributaries in excellent condition, increase its rehabilitation potential.

Introduction

Rivers have an important role in the biosphere as conduits for water, nutrients, sediments, woody debris, and biota from the continents to the sea. They are used by humans for transportation, fisheries, hydropower, and domestic, industrial, and agricultural water supplies (Petts 1989). Rivers also support unique and complex ecological communities and often influence the structure and functioning of the surrounding terrestrial ecosystem. Because of this, and the critical role of freshwater as a human resource, ecologists are increasingly asked to assess or monitor river "health," "status," or "condition" (Bailey et al. 2004).

Changes in environmental factors often initiate qualitative modifications in species composition and biodiversity. For example, eutrophication may cause a shift in primary producers, which in turn may change faunal species composition. Through time, a sequence of modifications may give rise to a fundamentally altered trophic network structure and function (Marques et al. 2002). Many rivers, streams, lakes, and reservoirs have been damaged as a consequence of the increasing impact of human activities (McAllister et al. 1997). This situation is particularly noticeable in areas of dense human population, especially in the urban environment, where watercourses show highly degraded water quality, receiving not only a great amount of domestic and industrial wastewater, but also sediments and trash. Thus, urban rivers have been transformed, losing their natural characteristics, many of them preserving little of their original biological diversity (Shepp and Cummins 1997).

In Brazil, most urban sewage is discharged without treatment into rivers. In addition, in large cities, rivers and streams are canalized or placed below streets in culverts. Intensive urbanization along Brazilian rivers has contaminated water bodies, thereby increasing water-born diseases and altered catchment hydrography and hydrology, which in turn has increased flooding, land sliding, and siltation of navigation channels. These same physical and chemical changes in Brazil's urban rivers have also markedly altered their aquatic biota (Tundisi 2003).

For more than a century, Brazilian water resource management has been dominated by outdated legal doctrines, weak implementation of good laws, and a focus on water chemistry. Yet the most direct and ef-

---

* Corresponding author: pompeups@uai.com.br

fective measure of water body condition is the status of its living systems. These systems are the product of millennia of adaptation to climatic, geological, chemical, and biological factors. Biota integrate everything that has happened where they live, as well as what has happened upstream and upland. When something alters the landscape around rivers' headwaters, life in lowland reaches is affected (Karr and Chu 1999). Although the neotropical biogeographic area is the world's richest region for freshwater fish species (around 8,000 species, Schaefer 1998), there are few published studies regarding the effects of urbanization on neotropical aquatic fauna. Our study focuses on the effects of basin urbanization on aquatic biodiversity and water quality in the Rio das Velhas. We use the assemblage structure and taxonomic composition of fishes and benthic macroinvertebrates as biological indicators of river quality.

Methods

Study Area

The Rio São Francisco basin, with an area of 631,133 km^2, covers 7.4% of Brazil. It is situated between 21° and 7°S latitudes and receives precipitation ranging from 350 to 1,900 mm in average years. The Rio São Francisco has an average annual discharge of 100 × 10^9 m^3 with an average flow of 3.150 m^3/s at its mouth (PLANVASF 1986). The 2,900-km river crosses five Brazilian states and is the 31st longest river in the world (Welcomme 1985). Its water is used for electricity generation, irrigation, urban and industrial supplies, navigation, and fisheries (Diegues 1994).

The Rio das Velhas is the longest tributary in the São Francisco basin. It is oriented in a southwest to northeast direction and extends 761 km from its headwaters, at an altitude of 1,520 m, to its confluence with the São Francisco River, at an altitude of 478 m. The estimated average annual flow is 300 m^3/s (Q95% = 103.69 m^3/s) with a drainage area of 29,173 km^2 and a mean width of 38.3 m (CETEC 1983).

The headwaters of the Rio das Velhas are located in a transition zone between the Atlantic rainforest and cerrado, which is a common savanna-like vegetation of central Brazil. Both biomes are identified as world biodiversity hotspots because they have exceptional concentrations of endemic species undergoing rapid habitat loss (Myers et al. 2000). Below its headwaters to its mouth, it flows only through cerrado. Another vegetation formation occurs near high elevation headwaters: the "campos rupestres," or rocky shrublands, such as seen in the Rio Cipó, one of its most important tributaries. This formation is very rich in floral and faunal species, with high diversity and endemism (Costa et al. 1998).

The Rio das Velhas has significant social and economical importance. Belo Horizonte, the state capital of Minas Gerais, with more than 2.4 million inhabitants (IBGE 2000), is located about 100 km from the Rio das Velhas headwaters. The river provides most of the city's water supply. The metropolitan region of Belo Horizonte (MRBH) consists of 34 counties situated around the capital. The total human population of MRBH is approximately 4.5 million people. The sewage from 3.2 million people is collected, but only 27.5% of it receives secondary treatment. In addition, MRBH is the most industrialized region of the state. The combination of sewage and industrial waste has made the Rio das Velhas the most polluted large river of Minas Gerias State.

The effect of native Americans on the region is unknown. But the settlement of Minas Gerais (translates to General Mines) by Europeans initiated extensive mining and contributed to degradation that continues to this day. Also, gold and gem explorations in the early 16th century produced the towns of Sabará and Ouro Preto. The changes caused by mining were greatest in the gravel plains and on the riverbeds (Dean 1996). Situated on the banks of the Rio Arrudas, Belo Horizonte is located about 100 km from the Rio das Velhas headwaters, Belo Horizonte was built in 1897 to be the capital of the state of Minas Gerais. Since 1898, an industrial and urban center emerged and started a new cycle of mining activities, mainly characterized by iron mines and iron industries next to the Rio das Velhas (FUNDO-FUNDEP 2000). Presently, the Rio das Velhas is severely damaged by urbanization and mining activities in its watershed. However, well-preserved tributaries with low human density persist in the basin. The most important source of pollution is located on the river's upper course, where mining debris and most of the domestic and industrial wastewater from the MRBH are discharged.

The capital's urban concept was oriented to the rationalist philosophy of humans dominating nature (SUDECAP 2001). Therefore, the city was designed with no concern for regional hydrography (Figure 1). Small and large streams were canalized to accommodate roads, waste, and sewage. Until 2000, the flood control policy of the MRBH was rapid water evacuation through canals and revetted streambeds. About 200 km of watercourses have been canalized in the city of Belo Horizonte, representing one-third of the

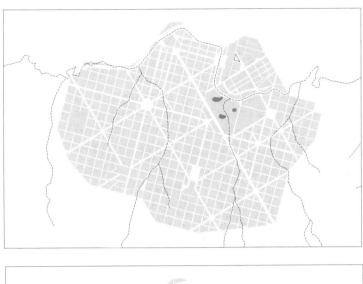

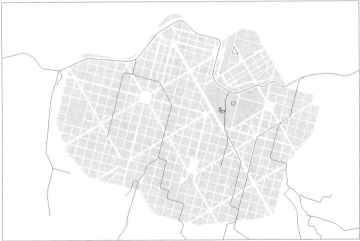

FIGURE 1. Plan of Belo Horizonte downtown, indicating the original (top) and current (bottom) stream courses.

drainages in the MRBH (SUDECAP 2001). Only recently, some streams have been chosen for environmental rehabilitation and sanitation in their natural courses.

Sampling Design

Water quality and benthos.—Water quality and benthos sampling sites included six stations along the Rio das Velhas main stem (Figure 2). In relation to the MRBH discharges, one site is located upstream (São Bartolomeu – RV-01), two in the MRBH (Sabará – RV-02 and Lagoa Santa – RV-03), and three downstream (Curvelo – RV-04, Corinto – RV-05 and Lassance – RV-06). Mean distance between sites was 59 km. For the analysis, these sites were grouped into

upper (RV-01 and RV-02), middle (RV-03 and RV-04), and lower (RV-05 and RV-06) courses.

We also sampled another 13 tributary sites in the MRBH, including one located upstream and another downstream of each sewage treatment plant that is being built in Onça and Arrudas tributaries. The sites were chosen for geographic location above and below disturbances, common physical characteristics, and ease of access. Substrate types at most sites included sand, cobble, and vegetation in canalized third- to fifth-order reaches. But there was no substantial difference in site substrate (>90% sandy bottom), and common habitat types (riffles in streams and mid-channel in rivers) were sampled at all sites. Site length was 5–10 times the average bank-full width of the stream (as suggested by Newbury 1984). Sites were located away from the influ-

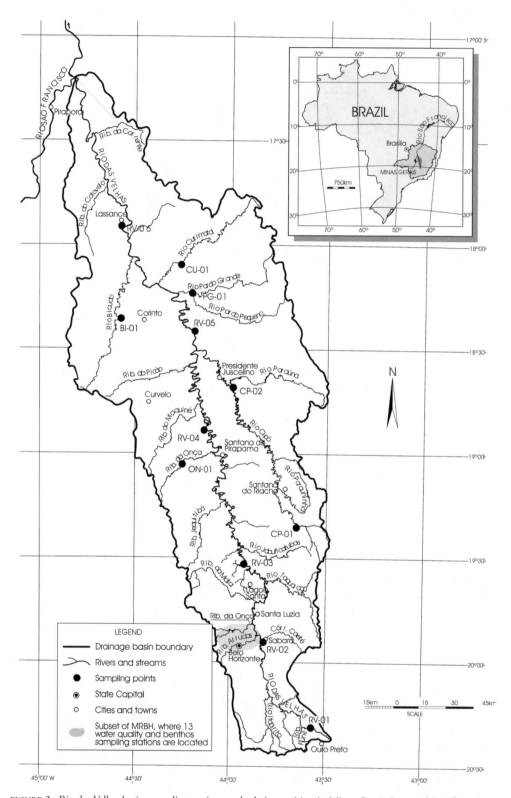

FIGURE 2. Rio das Velhas basin, sampling stations and relative position in Minas Gerais State and Brazil.

ence of tributaries or other water bodies. When a stream was sampled at more than one site, the sites were separated by a minimum of 120–150 stream widths or 10–15 pool-riffle sequences. Thus, in streams with an average width of 10 m, sites were 50–100 m long and had a minimum of 1.2 km between adjacent sites on the same stream (as suggested by Bailey et al. 2004). We sampled in the rainy and dry seasons.

Temperature, dissolved oxygen, conductivity, turbidity, and pH were measured in situ using a Horiba U-10 multi-probe and portable YSI samplers. Depth and velocity were measured with a Global Water flowmeter. We collected one water sample from each site with a Van Dorn sampler in the morning (0900–1100 hours), stored the bottles in an ice box for less than 4 h, and took samples to the metropolitan laboratory of COPASA (Companhia de Sanea-mento de Minas Gerais) for determination of total and dissolved nutrients (total-P, total-N, nitrite, nitrate, organic-N, and NH_4^+) and total dissolved solids, according to Lenore et al. (2002). For the microbiologic analyses (thermotolerant coliforms, total coliforms, *Escherichia coli* and fecal streptococcus), two subsurface water samples were taken directly into sterile glass bottles and returned to the COPASA laboratory, where they were kept on ice and processed within 8 h. Total and fecal coliforms were determined using the most probable number method (MPN; Lenore et al. 2002).

Five random sediment samples were collected at each site with a Van Veen dredge (area of 0.045 m²), without focusing on a specific habitat. In the laboratory, samples were washed through 1.00-, 0.50-, and 0.25-mm sieves, sorted under a stereomicroscope, and identified organisms were deposited in the Reference Collection of Benthic Macroinvertebrates of the Institute of Biological Sciences, Federal University of Minas Gerais, Brazil. Insects were identified to genus and others to family, according to Cranston (2000), Domínguez et al. (2001), Epler (2001), Pérez (1988), and Trivinho-Strixino and Strixino (1995). We determined granulometric composition of the sediments as proposed by Suguio (1973), and modified by Callisto and Esteves (1996). Organic matter content of sediment was determined by ashing previously dried samples in an oven at 550°C for 4 h.

Fish.—Fish sampling stations include the same six benthos and water quality sites along the Rio das Velhas mainstem and five well-preserved tributaries: Cipó (CP-01 and CP-O2), Bicudo, (BI-01), Curimataí (CU-01), Pardo Grande (PG-01), and da Onça (ON-01) rivers (Figure 2). These tributaries were included to compare main-stem sites, affected by a huge urbanized area, with water courses located in areas with low human density. Except for Rio Cipó, which was sampled five times, every sampling station was visited two or three times from 1999 to 2002, including at least one dry and one wet season.

Fish were caught with gill nets (20 m long, with 3- to 16-cm stretch mesh), seines (5 m long and 1-mm mesh), cast nets (3-cm stretch mesh), and kick nets (1-mm mesh). Gillnets were fished in the water column for 14 h overnight. Seines were used in shallow areas or littoral zones, kick nets were employed in nearshore aquatic macrophytes and in riffles, and cast nets were used in habitats too deep to wade. The three latter methods were employed for 1–3 h and used only qualitatively to maximize the number of species collected. Reaches 50–100 m were surveyed, depending on depth and water flow. All sampled fishes were identified to species and specimens were placed in the University of São Paulo Zoology Museum (MZUSP).

Results

Water Quality

The Rio das Velhas upper course waters were slightly alkaline to slightly acidic, intermediate in conductivity and total suspended solids, well oxygenated, and relatively clear (Table 1). The sediment organic matter was low. Total phosphorus and total nitrogen were also low.

The MRBH tributaries were slightly acidic to alkaline, with very low dissolved oxygen (Table 1). Comparing the sampling stations upstream and downstream of the two Belo Horizonte sewage treatment plants (STPs), substantial differences were found in pH (8.6 upstream and 7.43 downstream for Onça and 7.13 upstream and 5.8 downstream for Arrudas), with very low oxygen levels in both streams (<0.5 mg/L). In both tributaries, conductivities were relatively high (>350 µS/cm), and the waters were very turbid (>100 NTU), with high TDS (244–428 mg/L). Sediments were sandy with 0.66–48.01% dry weight of organic matter. Nutrient concentrations were high (total N = 16.66 ± 4.83 mg/L, total P = 2.16 ± 1.28 mg/L).

Baleares, Onça, and Cardoso are the most important tributaries in MRBH and showed the highest concentrations of microorganisms (>2.3 × 10⁷ coliforms/mL, >2.4 × 10⁵ *E. coliform*/mL), low oxygen levels (<2.0 mg/L), high conductivity (219 ± 187 µS/cm) and nutrient concentrations (total N = 14.3 + 6.9 mg/L, total P = 0.97 ± 1.12 mg/L), moderate turbidity (30–143 NTU), slightly acidic to slightly alkaline pH (6.8–7.7), and sandy sediments.

TABLE 1. Water quality in upper, middle, Belo Horizonte metropolitan region (MRBH) and lower das Velhas River (*, not measured).

Sampling subbasins	Depth (m)	Width (m)	Velocity (m/s)	Flow (m³/s)	pH	Conductivity (µS/cm)	Dissolved oxygen (mg/L)	TDS (mg/L)	Turbidity (NTU)	Temp (°C)	Total-N (mg/L)	Total-P (mg/L)	E. coli (N/mL)	Fecal Streptococcus (N/mL)	Sediment organic matter (% dry weight)
Upper part															
Minimum	0.5	4.5	0.58	3.11	5.9	26.5	6	44	2	18.2	0.019	0.019	2,400	1,500	0.99
Maximum	2.0	25.0	2.5	29.00	7.78	83	8.4	112	11	25.6	1.3	0.74	24,000	20,000	7.19
Mean	1.3	17.5	1.92	18.50	7.05	40.22	6.95	71.00	5.50	22.60	0.250	0.20	9,700	12,000	3.06
Standard deviation	0.8	8.5	0.70	13.5	0.65	25.68	1.19	29.10	3.94	3.18	0.75	0.36	12,000	9,500	2.20
MRBH															
Minimum	0.3	4.5	0.58	3.11	5.77	275.00	0.50	244.00	18.00	22.70	12.00	0.60	24,000	6,000	48.01
Maximum	2.5	25	2.00	29.00	8.61	603.00	4.48	428.00	120.00	27.90	24.00	5.40	98,000	200,000	0.66
Mean	2.0	12	1.57	15.50	7.46	459.50	1.73	308.60	44.30	24.49	16.66	2.16	45,000	20,000	5.74
Standard deviation	1.5	3.5	0.35	3.79	0.66	96.02	1.45	59.60	29.8	1.36	4.83	1.28	22,500	15,500	10.33
Middle part															
Minimum	0.6	25	0.44	15.00	7.33	13.5	3.2	10	3.4	23	0.019	0.019	160	56,000	0.5
Maximum	1.7	50	1.28	22.44	7.4	260	7.5	172	127	27.2	7.12	1.5	8200	6	7.81
Mean	0.71	25	0.50	20.20	7.25	146.06	5.65	116.25	49.90	25.16	2.55	0.39	2,400	11,435	4.01
Standard deviation	0.3	15	0.65	2.30	0.35	71.85	1.40	52.22	55.65	1.22	4.60	0.74	6,500	24,914	2.57
Lower part															
Minimum	1.0	30	0.16	4.75	6.7	13.00	6.2	24.00	3.4	22.00	*	0.019	0	0	0.17
Maximum	3.18	100	1.18	212.50	7.93	275.00	8.00	84.00	143.00	29.3	*	0.21	13,000	1,020	15.47
Mean	2.2	75	0.43	136.03	7.25	73.25	6.80	57.00	48.29	25.80	*	0.05	5,200	790	3.78
Standard deviation	2.5	60	0.67	67.85	0.33	81.16	0.56	23.58	52.79	2.04	*	0.07	2,420	320	4.40

The middle stretch of Rio das Velhas had slightly alkaline to slightly acidic waters, intermediate conductivity, and was well oxygenated (Table 1). A considerable number of coliform and fecal streptococus were seen, indicating contamination by directly discharged, domestic untreated sewage from the MRBH tributaries.

In the lower course of the Rio das Velhas, oxygen was 6.2 ± 0.5 mg/L at Barra do Guaicuí and 8.0 ± 0.3 mg/L, between Corinto and Augusto de Lima counties (Table 1). The sediments had low organic matter (1.15% at Corinto and Augusto de Lima, and 15.47% at Lassance), but waters showed high conductivity (275 μS/cm at Lassance) and high turbidity (143 NTU at Barra do Guaicuí).

Benthic Macroinvertebrates

Benthic macroinvertebrates were dominated by oligochaetes (87.9%), chironomids (mainly *Chironomus* and *Polypedilum* – 8.25%), and other dipterans, such as Psychodidae (3.78%). In the upper reach (RV-01, RV-02), tolerant taxa were found in high densities, mainly dominated by chironomids (*Ablabesmyia, Chironomus, Cryptochironomus, Fissimentum, Polypedilum*), psychodids, empidids, elmids, odonates, *Biomphalaria straminea,* and oligochaetes. A total of 13 taxa were found. Numerically dominant taxa included chironomids (up to 1,000 ± 250/m²), *Physa* (120,000 ± 45,000/m²), *Biomphalaria straminea* (250 ± 65/m²), and oligochaetes (4,300 ± 1,500/m²).

In the MRBH tributaries, we found 12 taxa, with numerical dominance by oligochaetes (74,000 ± 25,000/m²), chironomids (up to 13,000 ± 5,600/m², mainly *Chironomus* and *Polypedilum*), and psychodids (up to 4,000 ± 2,500/m²).

In the middle Rio das Velhas (RV-03, RV-04), we collected 21 taxa, with Sphaeriidae (1,926 ± 1,461/m²), chironomids (1,600 ± 1,300/m²), hirudineans (1,400 ± 1,800/m²), and oligochaetes (93,000 ± 60,700/m²) most abundant.

In the lower reach (RV-05, RV-06), 23 taxa were found and the introduced Asian snail *Melanoides tuberculatus* (607 ± 405/m²) was abundant, as well as Sphaeriidae (415 ± 551/m²), *Physa* (919 ± 821/m²), and Elmidae (452 ± 538/m²).

Fish

Fish and macroinvertebrates had similar distribution patterns along the Rio das Velhas main channel. Fish richness and Shannon Diversity Index of benthic macroinvertebrates decreased downstream of the MRBH streams, between sampling sites RV02 and RV03 (Figure 3). This effect was greatest during the dry season, but was moderated by water dilution in the rainy season. The effects of urbanization on the fish fauna of the main stem were also marked in comparison with tributaries. The 81 species recorded in the tributaries represent almost 83% of the total fish species of the whole basin, including native and alien records. We found 37 species (34% of local fauna) exclusively in these tributaries. The sampling stations located in the main stem also had the larger number of alien species, especially those sites located immediately downstream of Belo Horizonte (Table 2).

Discussion

According to Brazilian law, (regulation number 1469, 29 December 2000), all of the studied reaches of Rio das Velhas are inappropriate for human consumption without prior treatment and inappropriate for primary contact, aquatic sports, and bathing. The Rio das Velhas has very low potential for recreational use without further treatment by the sanitary company (COPASA-MG). Most Brazilian cities have experienced uncontrolled development and increased occupation of river margins and their floodplains. Many cities are trying to solve problems of sanitation and flooding with river canalization. Canalization increases water velocities, reducing residence time and accelerating domestic effluent and pollutant transport. Such changes also lower richness and diversity in the Rio das Velhas downstream of MRBH, highlighting the effects of sewage discharge on the main channel. However, urbanization costs are even higher in the small water courses draining the metropolitan area. Besides the poor benthos assemblage and water quality, pollution and canalization of MRBH streams have eliminated most native fish species. Only a few well-preserved headwater reaches, protected as natural reserves or water supply sources, support typical headwater fishes, such as *Trichomycterus* and *Astyanax*.

Urbanization has also changed fish assemblages in the natural lakes of the MRBH. Lagoa Santa is a shallow permanent lake located north of Belo Horizonte, inside the metropolitan region. Between 1850 and 1856, Reinhardt collected fish in Lagoa Santa (Lütken 2001). Comparisons between the historical and recent data showed that at least 70% of the original fish fauna is now extinct (Pompeu and Alves 2003). The reasons were directly related to urbanization: the obstruction and canalization of the natural connection between Lagoa Santa and the Rio das Velhas, the elimination of

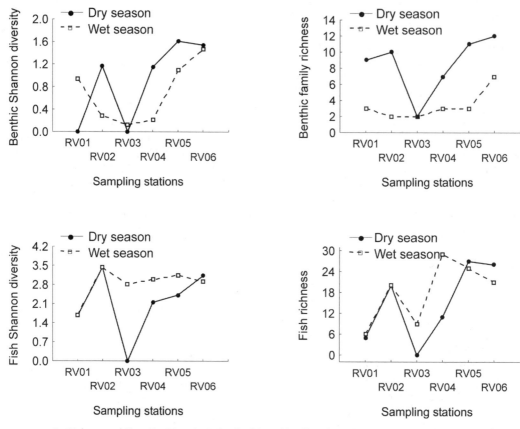

FIGURE 3. Richness and Shannon Diversity Index for fish and benthos along the Rio das Velhas main course, in the dry and wet seasons.

littoral (Cyperaceae) and submerged (Characeae) vegetation, and the introduction of alien fish species.

Another important effect of urbanization on the basin is regular fish kills, mainly in the beginning of the rainy season (Alves et al. 2000). Heavy organic discharges from the MRBH accumulate in the river bottom during the dry season. At the beginning of the summer/wet season, this material is suspended and water temperatures increase. Rapid decomposition of the organic matter depletes dissolved oxygen, causing frequent fish kills. Recent radiotelemetry studies have shown that Rio das Velhas is an important route for large migratory species from São Francisco River (A. Godinho, Universidade Federal de Minas Gerais, personal communication). Annual kills of adults and burying of the eggs and larvae lead to annual decreases of resident fish populations and those that migrate from the Rio São Francisco to spawn. However, our data indicate that the most severe effects of the MRBH urbanization on fish and benthos in the Rio das Velhas occur during the winter/dry season. Some researchers (Bozzetti and Schulz

2004; B. C. T. Pinto and F. G. Araujo, Universidade Federal Rural do Rio de Janeiro, and R. M. Hughes, Oregon State University, unpublished data) concluded the same for other rivers in southeastern Brazil, linking the effect to pollutant concentration and more efficient sampling during the dry season.

In aquatic environments, processes that determine structural diversity are closely related to the fluvial regime, which determines depth, velocity, substrate types, and channel shape (Angermeier 1997). The fluvial regime also is linked to the seasonal flood cycle, which affects sediment, organic matter fluxes, and biomass production (Junk et al. 1989). In the tropics, many fish species use river floodplains for feeding, reproduction, and refuge (Agostinho and Zalewski 1996). Fragmentation and habitat simplification are broadly described as the main threats to biodiversity conservation because they directly interfere with the rates of colonization and extinction (Kareiva et al. 1995) and are the main causes of fish species extinction in North America (Miller et al. 1989). There are no dams in the Rio das Velhas main

TABLE 2. Number of native and alien fish species per family collected at each site. See Figure 2 for locations of sample sites.

Family	Total species	Tributaries						Rio das Velhas					
		BI-01	CP-01	CP-02	CU-01	ON-01	PG-01	RV-01	RV-02	RV-03	RV-04	RV-05	RV-06
Native families	102												
Acestrorhynchyidae	1	1	–	1	1	–	1	–	–	–	–	1	–
Anostomidae	8	4	1	6	4	1	1	–	2	–	1	4	3
Apteronotidae	1	–	–	1	–	–	–	–	–	–	–	–	–
Aspredinidae	2	–	–	1	1	–	–	–	–	–	–	–	–
Auchenipteridae	1	1	–	–	–	–	1	–	–	–	–	–	–
Callichthyidae	1	–	–	–	–	–	–	–	–	1	–	–	–
Characidae	30	12	11	9	10	6	16	2	4	2	9	11	9
Cichlidae	4	–	–	–	1	–	–	2	–	1	–	3	1
Crenuchidae	3	2	3	2	3	2	2	2	1	–	–	–	2
Curimatidae	4	2	2	3	2	1	2	–	–	2	3	–	1
Engraulidae	1	–	–	–	–	–	1	–	–	–	–	–	–
Erythrinidae	2	2	1	2	1	1	1	1	1	–	1	1	1
Gymnotidae	1	1	–	1	1	1	–	–	1	1	–	1	–
Loricariidae	18	7	4	10	7	7	6	2	2	–	5	3	9
Parodontidae	4	1	1	4	2	2	2	–	1	–	1	1	3
Pimelodidae	14	7	3	10	4	6	4	1	5	–	–	5	8
Poeciliidae	1	–	1	–	–	–	1	–	–	–	–	–	–
Prochilodontidae	2	1	1	1	1	1	1	–	–	1	2	2	1
Scianidae	1	–	–	–	–	–	–	–	–	–	–	–	1
Sternopygidae	2	1	–	2	1	1	1	–	1	–	1	1	1
Trichomycteridae	1	–	1	–	–	–	–	–	–	–	–	–	–
Alien families	5												
Callichthyidae	1	1	–	–	–	–	–	–	–	1	1	–	–
Cichlidae	2	–	–	1	–	–	1	–	1	1	2	2	1
Cyprinidae	1	–	–	–	–	–	–	1	1	–	–	–	–
Poeciliidae	1	–	–	–	–	1	–	–	–	–	–	1	–
Total	107	43	29	54	39	30	40	9	20	9	27	36	41

stem and no observed changes in its flow regime. This connectivity with the Rio São Francisco system and tributaries in excellent condition, increase the rehabilitation potential of the Rio das Velhas (Pompeu et al. 2004).

In addition, there are 12 sewage treatment plants already installed within the MRBH and others are being designed and built. The DRENURBS Project (Environmental Rehabilitation and Sanitation of Valleys and Natural Riverbeds of Belo Horizonte) is also being implemented. Its main goals are water course cleaning, sediment control, institutional reinforcement by Belo Horizonte City Hall, and integration of water resources with urban scenery.

An environmental monitoring program has begun for the Rio das Velhas as part of the Manuelzão Project. Physical, chemical, and biological indicators are being used to: (1) determine the contribution of the Rio das Velhas to the condition of the Rio São Francisco; (2) identify point and diffuse pollution sources throughout the basin; (3) assess aquatic ecosystem health and environmental quality; and (4) monitor changes in water quality due to sanitation interventions and sewage treatment. The assessment and monitoring will employ modified monitoring designs and indices of biotic integrity used by the USEPA's Environmental Monitoring and Assessment Program.

The objective of the Manuelzão Project is to return the fishes to the Rio das Velhas. The project adopts the basin as a research, planning, and social mobilization unit. The basin perspective helps to integrate nature, history, environment and social relationships, and human health. Our data, collected as part of this project, contribute to the knowledge of freshwater biodiversity in the Rio das Velhas, which can be useful for Brazilian decision makers. We are using the Reference Condition Approach (RCA, least disturbed sites) of Hughes (1995) and Bailey et al. (2004) for biological assessment in the Rio das Velhas basin. The RCA has a number of key features that make it useful for our purposes: (1) It defines and quantifies ecosystem health; (2) it incorporates variation among healthy ecosystems; and (3) it uses the deviation of a test site from Reference Condition to measure the effect of stressors on the ecosystem. We measure variability in benthos and fishes among sites in "Reference Condition" in four subbasins (Taquaraçú, Paraúna, Curimataí, and Itabirito). These reference subbasins are minimally exposed to human stressors such as effluent discharges or land uses that often disturb ecosystems. We plan to elaborate, test, and validate an empirical model to explain as much of the variability in the reference site biota as possible, based on the environmental characteristics of the sites.

Acknowledgments

We are grateful to Bob Hughes, who invited us to write this chapter and for his editorial suggestions. Also, we thank Sílvia Magalhães for her help on the map and providing geographical information about the basin; Mark Bowen for suggestions on the manuscript; Luiz Felipe Mascarenhas Horta for his help with the translation; and Karina Moreyra, Juliana França, Wander Ferreira, and Pablo Moreno for the water and benthos sampling. We also thank Projeto Manuelzão para Revitalização da Bacia do Rio das Velhas (UFMG), Fundo-Fundep de apoio acadêmico 1999, CNPq, FAPEMIG, CAPES, U.S. Fish & Wildlife Service, Pad Award, Padi Foundation, and Fundação O Boticário de Proteção à Natureza (grant No. 0472002) for the logistics and financial support.

References

Agostinho, A. A., and M. Zalewski. 1996. A planície alagável do alto rio Paraná: importância e preservação. Editora da Universidade Estadual de Maringá, Maringá, Brazil.

Alves, C. B. M., C. A. M. Estanislau, M. A. R. Araújo, M. V. Polignano, and P. S. Pompeu. 2000. Projeto S.O.S. Rio das Velhas: estudo das possíveis causas das mortandades de peixes na sub-bacia. Technical report. Projeto Manuelzão/IEF, Belo Horizonte, Brazil.

Angermeier, P. L. 1997. Conceptual roles of biological integrity and diversity. Pages 49–65 in J. E. Williams, C. A. Wood, and M. P. Dombeck, editors. Watershed restoration: principles and practices. American Fisheries Society, Bethesda, Maryland.

Bailey, R. C., R. H. Norris, and T. B. Reynoldson. 2004. Bioassessment of freshwater ecosystems—using the reference condition approach. Kluwer Academic Publishers, Boston.

Bozzetti, M., and U. H. Schulz. 2004. An index of biotic integrity based on fish assemblages for subtropical streams in southern Brazil. Hydrobiologia 529:133–144.

Callisto, M., and F. A. Esteves. 1996. Composição granulométrica do sedimento de um lago amazônico impactado por rejeito de bauxita e em um lago natural. Acta Limnologica Brasiliensi 8:115–126.

CETEC. 1983. Diagnóstico ambiental do Estado de Minas Gerais. Fundação Centro Tecnológico de Minas Gerais, Série de Publicações Técnicas/SPT-010, Belo Horizonte, Brazil.

Costa, C. M. R., G. Herrmann, C. S. Martins, L. V. Lins, and I. R. Lamas. 1998. Biodiversidade em Minas Gerais: um atlas para sua conservação. Fundação Biodiversitas, Belo Horizonte, Brazil.

Cranston, P. S. 2000. Identification guide to the Chironomidae of New South Wales. CSIRO Division of Entomology, AWT – Australian Water Technologies Insight, West Ryde, Austrália.

Dean, W. 1996. A ferro e fogo. A história da devastação da mata atlântica brasileira. Companhia das Letras, São Paulo, Brazil.

Diegues, A. C. 1994. An inventory of Brazilian wetlands. IUCN, Glang, Switzerland.

Domínguez, E., M. D. Hubbard, M. L., Pescador, and C. Molineri. 2001. Ephemeroptera. Guía para la determinación de los artrópodos bentónicos sudamericanos. Pages 17–54 in H. R Fernández and E. Domínguez, editors. Universidad Nacional de Tucumán, Tucuman, Argentina.

Epler, J. H. 2001. Identification manual for the larval chironomidae (Diptera) of North and South Carolina. North Carolina Department of Environmental and Natural Resources, Palatka.

FUNDO-FUNDEP. 2000. Integração homem natureza e seus efeitos na saúde: uma intervenção interdisciplinar na bacia do rio das Velhas. Universidade Federal de Minas Gerais/Projeto Manuelzão, Belo Horizonte, Brasil.

Hughes, R. M. 1995. Defining accetable biological status by comparing with reference conditions. Pages 31–47 in W. S. Davis, and T. P. Simon, editors. Biological assessment and criteria: tools for water resource planning and decision making. Lewis Publishers, Boca Raton, Florida.

IBGE (Instituto Brasileiro de Geografia e Estatística). 2000. Sinopse preliminar do censo demográfico. Instituto Brasileiro de Geografia e Estatística, Rio de Janeiro, Brazil.

Junk, W. J., P. B. Bayley, and R. E. Sparks. 1989. The flood pulse concept in river-floodplain systems. Canadian Special Publications in Fisheries and Aquatic Sciences 106:110–127.

Kareiva, P., D. Skelly, and M. Ruckelshaus. 1995. Reevaluating the use of models to predict the consequenses of habitat loss and fragmentation. Pages 156–166 in T. A. Pickett, R. S. Ostfeld, M. Shachak, and G. E. Likens, editors. The ecological basis of conservation: heterogeneity, ecosystems, and biodiversity. Chapman and Hall, New York.

Karr, J. R. and E. W. Chu. 1999. Restoring life in running waters—better biological monitoring. Island Press, Washington D.C.

Lenore, S. C., E. G. Arnold, and D. E. Andrew. 2002. Standard methods for the examination of water and wastewater: user guide. American Public Health Association, Washington, D.C.

Lütken, C. F. 2001. Peixes do Rio das Velhas: uma contribuição para a ictiologia do Brasil. Pages 23–164 in C. B. M. Alves and P. S. Pompeu, editors. Peixes do Rio das Velhas: passado e presente. Editora Segrac, Belo Horizonte, Brazil.

Marques, J. C., M. A. Pardal, S. N. Nielsen, and S. E. Jorgensen. 2002. Applications of holistic ecological indicators of ecosystem integrity: a case study in the Mondego Estuary. Pages 551–564 in M. A. Pardal, J. C. Marques, and M. A. Graça, editors. Aquatic ecology of the Mondego River basin—global importance of local experience. Universidade de Coimbra, Coimbra, Portugal.

McAllister, D. E., A. L. Hamilton, and B. Harvey. 1997. Global freshwater biodiversity: striving for the integrity of freshwater ecosystems. Sea Wind 11(3):1–142.

Miller, R. R., J. D. Williams, and J. E. Williams. 1989. Extinctions of North American fishes during the past century. Fisheries 14(6):22–30.

Myers, N., R. A., Mittermeier, C. G. Mittermeier, G. A. B. Fonseca, and J. Kent. 2000. Biodiversity hotspots for conservation priorities. Nature (London) 403:853–858.

Newbury, R. W. 1984. Hydrologic determinants of aquatic insect habitats. Pages 323–357 in V. H. Resh and D. M. Rosenberg, editors. The ecology of aquatic insects. Praeger, New York.

Pérez, G. P. 1988. Guía para el studio de los macroivertebrados acuáticos del departamento de Antioquia. Editorial Presencia Ltda.Bogotá, Colombia.

Petts, G. E. 1989. Perspectives for ecological management of regulated rivers. Pages 3–24 in J. A. Gore and G. E. Petts. Alternatives in regulated river management. CRC Press, Boca Raton, Florida.

PLANVASF (Plano Diretor para o Desenvolvimento do Vale do São Francisco). 1986. Plano Diretor para o Desenvolvimento do Vale do São Francisco. Companhia para o Desenvolvimento do Vale do São Francisco, Brasília, Brazil.

Pompeu, P. S., and C. B. M. Alves. 2003. Local fish extinction in a small tropical lake in Brazil. Neotropical Ichthyology 1(2):133–135.

Pompeu, P. S., C. B. M. Alves, and R. Hughes. 2004. Restoration of the das Velhas River basin, Brazil: challenges and potential. Pages 589–594 in D. Garcia de Jalon Lastra and P. V. Martinez, editors. Aquatic habitats: analysis & restoration. Proceedings of the Fifth International Symposium on Ecohydraulics, September 2004, Madrid, Spain, Volume 1. International Association of Hydraulic Engineering & Research, Madrid.

Schaefer, S. A. 1998. Conflict and resolution: impact of

new taxa on phylogenetic studies of the neotropical cascudinhos (Siluroidea: Loricariidae). Pages 375–400 *in* L. R. Malabarba, R. E. Reis, R. P. Vari, Z. M. S. Lucena, and C. A. S Lucena, editors. Phylogeny and classification of neotropical fishes. EDIPUCRS, Porto Alegre, Brazil.

Shepp, D. L., and J. D. Cummins. 1997. Restoration in an urban watershed: Anacostia River of Maryland and the District of Columbia. Pages 297–317 *in* J. E. Williams, C. A. Wood, and M. P. Dombeck, editors. Watershed restoration: principles and practices. American Fisheries Society, Bethesda, Maryland.

SUDECAP. 2001. Drenurbs-BH: Programa de recup-

eração ambiental e saneamento dos fundos de vale e dos córregos em leito natural de Belo Horizonte – Termo de Referência, Belo Horizonte, Brazil.

Suguio, K. 1973. Introdução à sedimentologia. Edgard Blucher Ltd., EDUSP, São Paulo, Brazil.

Trivinho-Strixino, S., and Strixino, G. 1995. Larvas de Chironomidae (Diptera) do estado de São Paulo: guia de identificação e diagnose dos gêneros. editor. UFSCar, São Carlos, Brazil.

Tundisi, J. G. 2003. Água no século XXI: enfrentando a escassez. editor. Rima, São Carlos, Brazil.

Welcomme, R. L. 1985. River fisheries. FAO Fisheries Technical Paper 262.

American Fisheries Society Symposium 47:23–37, 2005

Urbanization Consequences: Case Studies in the Hudson River Watershed

Karin E. Limburg*, Karen M. Stainbrook

State University of New York, College of Environmental Science & Forestry
241 Illick Hall, Syracuse, New York 13210, USA

Jon D. Erickson

The Rubenstein School of Environment and Natural Resources, University of Vermont
344 George D. Aiken Center, 81 Carrigan Drive, Burlington, Vermont 05405, USA

John M. Gowdy

Economics Department, Russell Sage Laboratory, Rensselaer Polytechnic Institute
110 8th Street, Troy, New York 12180, USA

Abstract.—Parcel by parcel, urban/suburban development is one of the most active converters of land in the Hudson River Valley in New York State. We are taking an integrative approach to understanding the drivers of and responses to urbanization, by studying how economy drives land use change and how that, in turn, affects downstream indicators of ecosystem state. The ultimate goal of the project is to provide a tool for policymakers, illustrating consequences of different development strategies. In this paper, we discuss synoptic ecological assessments of two major Hudson River tributaries in Dutchess County, the Wappinger Creek and Fishkill Creek watersheds. Physical, chemical, geographic, and biotic indices are compiled, creating a multivariate data set. These data, when set into a geographic information database, provide a spatial response to land use. Application of a regionally calibrated index of biotic integrity showed little relationship to urbanization, although some component metrics indicated a response. Chemical or biogeochemical indicators were more reflective of urbanization gradients. A hierarchy of responses, beginning with physicochemical and moving up to fish assemblages, reflected decreasing responses to urbanization. However, fish densities and the stable isotopic ratios of nitrogen determined in a sentinel species (eastern blacknose dace *Rhinichthys atratulus*) were significantly affected by urbanization. Longitudinal gradients of elevation were identified as strong drivers of development, potentially confounding relationships of land-use attributes and ecological responses.

Introduction

The transformation of land into urban and suburban uses is one of the fastest alterations of the American landscape today, producing cumulative ecological stress. The causes are numerous but generally involve choices made in piecemeal fashion, rather than by some concerted effort such as regional planning. Kahn (1966) referred to "the tyranny of small decisions," which describes the evolution of unintended economic consequences of decisions made on the basis of short-term, marginal gains. Odum (1982) applied this concept to the general problem of environmental degradation, and Ehrlich and Ehrlich (1981) used the analogy of an airplane's loss of structural integrity (the "rivet-popping hypothesis") to the disintegration of ecosystems and consequent loss of species. All point out the mismatch between maximizing individually based, short-term economic benefits and long-term social welfare, including environmental quality.

In this context, we have studied nested economic and ecological systems in the Hudson River Valley of New York State. Our research has focused on characterizing the structure of the economy of Dutchess

---

* Corresponding author: KLimburg@esf.edu

County and understanding how economic and social change affect land development and how these pressures on the landscape may affect the ecological status (physical, chemical, and biological) of two streams, Fishkill Creek and Wappinger Creek. One goal is to elucidate, through integrated studies, the connections between what society does and how, ultimately, ecosystems respond. However, a more pertinent goal is to envision policy options and create tools for decision makers. We hypothesized that ecological integrity would reflect urbanization in the Fishkill Creek and Wappinger Creek watersheds. Although the focus of this paper is to present and discuss the ecological results, we include a brief presentation of the overall methodology. Further details on overall and specific approaches may be found in Erickson et al. (2005). Specific questions we address in this paper include

1. Does an urban-to-rural gradient in ecosystem health occur in the study area?
2. Is the Fishkill Creek watershed, closer to the New York City metropolitan area, more degraded than the Wappinger Creek watershed, as measured by metrics of ecosystem health? and
3. How do natural physiographic factors affect our ability to detect urbanization impacts?

Study Area

Dutchess County, New York (2,077 km²) is located on the eastern side of the Hudson River Estuary (Figure 1). Within the county, the Wappinger Creek (547 km²) and Fishkill Creek (521 km²) watersheds compose more than half of the drainage area. Physiographically, the county and its watersheds belong to the eastern Great Lakes and Hudson lowlands (western county) and Northeastern highlands (eastern county) ecoregions (EPA 2002). Both Wappinger and Fishkill creeks arise in eastern highlands and drain southwest into the Hudson River.

Dutchess County was principally agrarian until the mid-20th century, but today supports a 203-sector economy (Erickson et al. 2005), dominated by large industries such as semiconductors (notably IBM). Development is heaviest in the southwestern part of the county, focused around the cities of Poughkeepsie, Wappingers Falls, and Beacon. New York City, 120 km to the south, is a source of jobs, first and second homeowners, and tourists, serving as another driver of development in southern Dutchess County.

Methods

Economic and Land-Use Change Models

The economy of Dutchess County was described with a social accounting matrix or SAM (Pyatt and Round 1985). This is an extension of the traditional Leontief input–output matrix (Leontief 1966), which tracks the flows of dollars through industrial sectors. The SAM includes household and government transactions, which can be disaggregated to reveal demographic detail as needed. Data for the Dutchess County SAM were obtained from a regional database (IMPLAN or Impact Analysis for PLANning; Minnesota IMPLAN Group, Inc. 2004) and Bureau of Labor statistics (Nowosielski 2002). A geographical information system (GIS) was also developed and coupled to the SAM in order to reference, geographically, where household institutions and businesses occur. Further geographic detail can be built into the GIS.

A drawback of input-output models is that they are static in nature, so tracking the temporal dynamics of an economy is difficult. To explore some of the temporal consequences of economic growth, specifically the development of new residential housing (a major component of sprawl), a probabilistic model of land-use change was developed for the Wappinger Creek watershed (Polimeni 2002); Polimeni did not develop a model for the Fishkill Creek watershed, due to lack of data, but our research group is currently expanding the database to include this second watershed. Land classified as vacant (vacant-residential, agricultural, or private forest tax parcels) in the 2001 tax rolls provided the source for conversion. Change was modeled with a binomial logit regression that took account of both tax parcel and neighborhood characteristics, as defined by census blocks. These included land assessment value, distance to nearest central business district, household income, and population growth. Biophysical data on slope, soils, wetland vegetation, riparian corridors, and agricultural land further refined estimates of "developable" land. Monte Carlo simulations that specified particular constraints (e.g., do not develop wetland parcels) generated probabilities of land conversion (Polimeni 2002; Erickson 2005).

Ecological Assessments

Thirty-three stream sites (Figure 2) were surveyed within the Wappinger and Fishkill creeks in 2001 and 2002, in order to quantify physical, chemical, and biological attributes composing ecological integ-

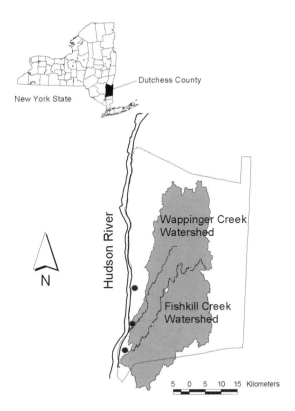

FIGURE 1. Map of Dutchess County, New York, showing the Wappinger and Fishkill watersheds. Major cities, indicated by black dots, are, from north to south, Poughkeepsie, Wappingers Falls, and Beacon.

rity. These included both main-stem sites as well as sites located within subcatchments, generally near their confluences with the main stem. Most were selected in order to make comparisons with earlier studies (Stevens et al. 1994; DCEMC 2000). We followed and modified slightly U.S. Geological Survey (USGS) stream habitat sampling protocols (Fitzpatrick et al. 1998), dividing up a 150-m stream reach into five sections and conducting assessments for stream and riparian zone physical characteristics. Due to limited resources, we made four synoptic surveys of water quality, choosing the period May–August to cover wet and dry months. Chlorophyll-a was quantified by fluorometry (Welschmeyer 1994). Phosphorus was analyzed following Langner and Hendrix (1982) and Clesceri et al. (1998), and total N, NO_2, NO_3, and NH_4 were measured with a Bran-Lubbe autoanalyzer, also following standard protocols (Clesceri et al. 1998). Fish were sampled with a backpack electroshocker, sampling 150 m of stream in a single pass without block nets. All fish were identified to species, counted, and released. Macroinvertebrates were collected by kick-sampling following Barbour et al. (1999), subsampled (combining methods from

Barbour and Gerritsen 1996; Courtemanch 1996; Vinson and Hawkins 1996) and identified to family. Insect taxa were used to compute metrics for benthic macroinvertebrate indices (Bode et al. 1996; Riva-Murray et al. 2002).

A number of indices and metrics were used to quantify fish and macroinvertebrate assemblage integrity, sensu Karr (1981, 1991). For both, regionally calibrated indices of biotic integrity (IBI) were computed (Bode et al. 1996; Daniels et al. 2002; Riva-Murray et al. 2002). In addition to the IBIs, metrics were examined individually. For fish, this included species richness, diversity, density (number per area), and percent of assemblage that was composed of centrarchids. For invertebrates, percent dominance of the three most abundant taxa, Ephemeroptera-Plecoptera-Trichoptera (EPT), family richness and diversity (H'), density of organisms, family (Hilsenhoff) biotic index, percent model affinity, and biotic assessment profile were computed (Hilsenhoff 1988; Bode et al. 1996; Hauer and Lamberti 1996; Riva-Murray et al. 2002). Percent model affinity (PMA) is a measure of how closely the assemblage reflects an idealized or "model community"

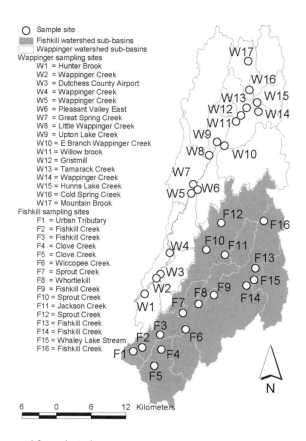

FIGURE 2. Stream sites used for ecological assessments.

in the absence of disturbance, while biotic assessment profile scales and combines results from EPT, dominance, species richness, and PMA.

In addition, a cosmopolitan fish species (eastern blacknose dace *Rhinichthys atratulus*) was assayed as a biogeochemical tracer of anthropogenic N (McClelland et al. 1997) by means of stable isotope analysis. Three to five individuals were collected from as many sites as possible, dried (50°C), pulverized, and analyzed at the Alaska Stable Isotope Facility with a Thermo-Finnigan Delta[Plus] mass spectrometer coupled to a Carlo-Erba C:N analyzer. Results were expressed as $\delta^{15}N$, or $[(^{15}N/^{14}N_{sample} \div {}^{15}N/^{14}N_{standard}) - 1] \times 1,000$ (Peterson and Fry 1987).

Geographic Analyses

A GIS was developed to delineate catchments, provide physiographical data (e.g., elevation), and incorporate land cover, population density, and highway density to relate to our ecological assessments. Site locations were recorded with a Garmin 12XL geographi-

cal positioner. Elevation was derived from Dutchess County 1:24,000 scale quad (30-m resolution) digital elevation maps (DEM) downloaded from the Cornell University Geospatial Information Repository (CUGIR; CUGIR 2003). Site distance from the mouth of each main stem was derived from hydrography shape files downloaded from CUGIR. Stream segments (km) were summed from the confluence of the Hudson River to each sampling site.

Wappinger Creek watershed delineations were obtained from the Dutchess County Watershed Program (DCEMC 2000). Fishkill Creek watershed and subbasin areas (draining to the sampling sites) were delineated, and associated maps were created using Better Assessment Science Integrating Point and Nonpoint Sources (BASINS) within the Automated Watershed Delineation platform (EPA 2001). The BASINS software uses neighborhood operations, where calculations and "decisions" (for water flow direction, inflow, and accumulation) are made for each cell in the DEM based on the values in the eight cells that are spatially adjacent (Jensen and Domingue 1988).

Land use was classified with Multi-Resolution Land Characteristics Consortium (MLRC) National Land Cover Data (NLCD) derived from Landsat-5 Thematic Mapper (TM) satellite imagery. The 1992 NLCD were downloaded from an EPA Web site (http://www.epa.gov/mrlc/nlcd.html) and the 2001 NLCD were provided by M. Hall (State University of New York, College of Environmental Science and Forestry, Syracuse, personal communication). The 2001 NLCD map was created using satellite imagery from three seasons and classified into the 1992 NLCD categories. The satellite images from May 2001 were primarily used to create the map because the April 2001 satellite image was fairly snow-covered; therefore, the analysis omitted leaf-off imagery (important for accurately defining roadways; however, we are confident that this did not unduly bias our estimates of road densities). Distinguishing among agricultural pastureland, row crops, and urban and recreational grasses proved difficult. However, county-level agricultural data showed that crop- and pasturelands in 1992 and 2000 were similar (31,282 ha in 1992 versus 31,404 ha in 2000; NYNASS 1999, 2002). Therefore, as a conservative estimate, we assumed that crop- and pastureland covers were the same in 2001 as in 1992.

Land use areas for 1992 and 2001 were calculated with ArcView 3.3 (Hutchinson and Daniels 1997). Road maps for the year 2000 (road maps were not available for 1992 or 2001 to match the NLCD) were downloaded from the CUGIR. From these maps, we calculated total road length (km) and density (km/km^2) for each subbasin.

Statistical Analysis

Statistical analyses were conducted with Statistica 6.0 (Statsoft 2003). Data were examined for homogeneity of variance and were log-transformed as necessary (e.g., road density). Pearson correlations were performed to explore relationships between anthropogenic disturbance indices (percent of land cover in urban and suburban uses, population density, and road density) and physical, chemical, biological, and biogeochemical parameters. Analysis of variance (ANOVA) was used to test for differences between the Fishkill Creek and Wappinger Creek watersheds; analysis of covariance (ANCOVA) was used when comparisons by watershed involved continuous variables. Linear and nonlinear regression analyses were performed to examine relationships between anthropogenic disturbance indices and ecological response variables. Principal components analysis (PCA) was used to examine relationships among anthropogenic indices, land covers, and physical factors, in order to select a reduced set of explanatory variables. P-values less than 0.05 were accepted as significant.

Results

Land use shifted in both watersheds toward increasing urbanization and suburban development over the period 1992–2001. The spatial pattern of land use change over that period is striking (Figure 3) and shows most of the increase in urban/suburban lands in the upper-mid portions of both watersheds. Much of this growth was along the Taconic Parkway, a north–south thoroughfare used to commute to downstate metropolitan centers (White Plains and New York City, primarily). During our field surveys of 2001, we observed dozens of new homes being constructed within a few kilometers of the parkway. Note, though, that urbanization occurred throughout the watersheds, with no subbasin gaining forest or farmland over this period (Figure 3).

Urbanization indices showed some cross correlations, and some habitat variables had significant correlations with highway density (Table 1). However, taken in the aggregate across all 33 field sites, many of the correlations were nonsignificant, even while the sign of correlation was often as expected. For example, percent canopy cover over streams was negatively (but not significantly) correlated with population density, highway density, and percent of land in urban and suburban use. Urbanization indices were all negatively correlated with elevation (Table 1).

Examining chemical and biological response variables, generally more of the chemical indicators responded significantly to urbanization than did biotic ones (Table 2). For example, total N, percent inorganic N (NO_2, NO_3, and NH_4 as a percent of the total, reflecting fertilizers and sewage inputs), total P, and August conductivity (when flows were lowest and dissolved salts highest during our study) all were positively and significantly correlated with urban and suburban land use. Within the indicators of macroinvertebrate assemblage integrity, the EPT index, percent model affinity, and biotic assessment profile were negatively, significantly correlated with urban and suburban land use and positively, but not significantly correlated with percent of the catchment in forest. None of the fish assemblage metrics showed significant correlations with any land use or with other metrics of human activity, such as highway

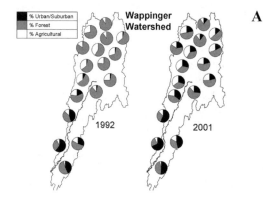

A

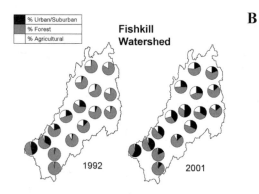

B

FIGURE 3. Maps showing percentages of land in urban/suburban, agricultural, and forested uses for (A) the Wappinger Creek and (B) Fishkill Creek watersheds, in 1992 and 2001.

density (Table 2). Only one assemblage characteristic, the percent of fishes caught that were centrarchids, showed a significant, negative correlation with elevation. A biogeochemical response variable, the stable isotopic ratios of nitrogen measured in a single, cosmopolitan fish species (eastern blacknose dace),

correlated significantly and positively with urban and suburban lands and highway density, and negatively with forested land and elevation (Table 2).

Statistics presented in the aggregate, combining data from both watersheds, conceal detail about how variables respond differently in the two watersheds and how knowledge of particular circumstances helps to explain observed patterns. For example, nitrogen concentrations across the two watersheds (Figure 4) show a complex pattern. Sites F12, F10, and F7, all with moderately elevated N, drain a predominantly agricultural subcatchment (Sprout Creek). Sites W14 and F11 are both located at recreation areas, which receive many visitors in the summer and have restroom facilities near the streams. Site W15 is approximately 1 km downstream from a dude ranch, the horse paddock of which was in direct contact with the stream, and sites W11, W9, and W7 all drain predominantly agricultural subcatchments. Nevertheless, despite the somewhat checkerboard nature of N values reflecting various land uses, total N concentrations tended to increase downstream towards the more urbanized areas (Figure 4).

Other response variables reflected the "individual character" of each watershed. For example, chlorophyll-a values had a stronger correlation with total P than with total N, evidence that P is limiting in the streams, as is generally the case in freshwater (Wetzel 2001). However, the slopes and intercepts of the chlorophyll-TP regressions were different (ANCOVA, $P < 0.01$; Figure 5), suggesting that Fishkill Creek, overall, is less able to use this nutrient in autochthonous production.

Another example of different responses between watersheds is seen in the temperature excursion data (maximum–minimum values recorded in our surveys; Figure 6), which may be interpreted as an index of

TABLE 1. Pearson correlation matrix of elevation (m), three indices of urbanization (population density in people/km^2, highway density in km/km^2 of each subcatchment, and percent of watershed in urban and suburban use), and three habitat indicators (percent embeddedness of the streambed, percent canopy cover, and bank-full stream width (m)) for sites in the Wappinger and Fishkill drainages. Correlation coefficients in bold are significant ($P < 0.05$).

	Elevation	Population density	Highway density	% urban + suburban	% embeddedness	% canopy cover
Population density	**−0.60**					
Highway density	**−0.55**	**0.77**				
% urban + suburban	**−0.59**	**0.77**	**0.67**			
% embeddedness	−0.12	0.19	**0.38**	0.29		
% canopy cover	**0.38**	−0.18	−0.26	−0.30	−0.14	
Bank-full width	**−0.40**	0.16	**0.39**	−0.02	0.19	−0.23

TABLE 2. Pearson correlations of selected response variables on land-use type, highway density, and elevation. Chemical variables are based on May–August means unless otherwise noted. Correlation coefficients in bold are significant ($P < 0.05$). "Transient" species are as defined in Daniels et al. (2002).

Response variable	% forested	% agri-culture	% urban + suburban	Highway density (km/km^2)	Elevation (m)
Chemistry					
Total N	**−0.53**	0.07	**0.53**	0.35	−0.35
% inorganic N	−0.35	0.10	**0.42**	**0.41**	−0.10
Total P	−0.22	−0.32	**0.55**	0.30	**−0.58**
August conductivity	**−0.40**	−0.24	**0.71**	**0.52**	**−0.58**
Temperature	0.11	0.06	−0.19	−0.05	−0.16
Max–min temperature	−0.01	−0.16	0.14	**0.42**	−0.21
Chlorophyll-a	−0.16	0.08	−0.005	−0.14	−0.21
Macroinvertebrate assemblage					
Species richness/area	−0.16	0.09	0.35	0.06	0.33
Diversity (H')	0.17	−0.14	−0.26	−0.18	0.01
EPT index	0.34	−0.25	**−0.42**	−0.27	0.05
% model affinity	0.32	0.11	**−0.53**	−0.32	**0.43**
Biotic assessment profile	0.22	0.11	**−0.52**	−0.35	0.31
Fish assemblage					
Species richness/area	−0.27	0.16	0.15	−0.26	0.16
Diversity (H')	0.27	−0.24	−0.31	−0.16	−0.08
Density (#/m^2)	−0.12	0.27	−0.14	**−0.42**	0.27
IBI	−0.18	0.05	−0.20	−0.27	−0.11
IBI, excluding transients	−0.18	0.27	−0.26	−0.31	0.15
% centrarchids	−0.07	−0.02	0.03	0.32	**−0.38**
Eastern blacknose dace δ^{15}N	**−0.61**	0.09	**0.63**	**0.57**	**−0.55**

stream thermal constancy. Temperature differentials (ΔT) in the Fishkill Creek watershed were nearly double those in the Wappinger (Fishkill Creek mean ΔT = 10.4°C ± 0.7 [±SE]; Wappinger Creek mean ΔT = 5.9°C ± 0.7). Most Wappinger Creek sites trended to lower differentials moving away from the Hudson River (and up-elevation), but this was not the case for Fishkill Creek sites (ANCOVA: overall R^2 = 0.67, $P < 0.001$). The sites circled in Figure 6 are all located in the region of the county where we observed most construction ongoing in 2001. Site W10, which drains a primarily forested subcatchment, nevertheless is near the Taconic Parkway. Site W16, Cold Spring Creek, ironically was one of the warmest streams in our August survey, and we observed water withdrawals both by truck and farm ponds in the vicinity.

Principal component analyses confirmed covariation of many factors, such as highway density with population density and urban and suburban lands. Hence, a PCA was conducted with only five variables—elevation, highway density, discharge normal-ized to watershed area, percent agriculture, and percent forest—that were selected as representative of land use, physiography, and habitat. The first principal component, accounting for 41.3% of the variance and representing a gradient of urbanization and elevation, was used as a new independent variable against which fish assemblage metrics were regressed. A significant relationship was found between the first principal component and the N stable isotope ratios in eastern blacknose dace (Figure 7; combined R^2 = 0.55, $P < 0.001$). In this case, the regression lines for each watershed had nearly identical intercepts and slopes, with the Fishkill Creek samples being slightly enriched in ^{15}N isotopes. A weaker (R^2 = 0.17), but still significant ($P < 0.05$) relationship was found between fish species richness normalized to watershed area and the first principal component as well. None of the other fish assemblage metrics were significantly related to this factor.

Our initial hypothesis was that the Fishkill Creek watershed would be more urbanized and, as such, would show signs of greater ecological degradation. To examine this, we conducted an ANOVA on three

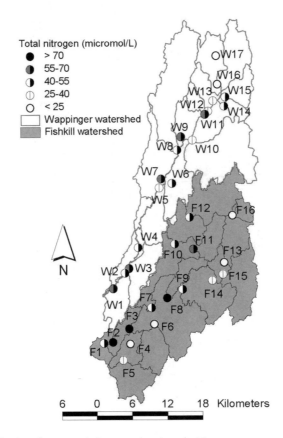

FIGURE 4. Spatial distribution of mean total nitrogen values (μmoles/L).

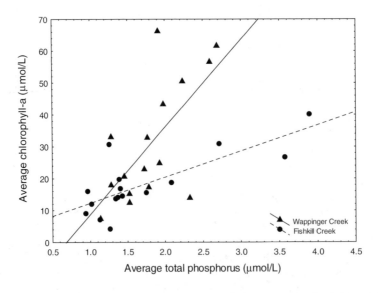

FIGURE 5. Relationship of chlorophyll a (μmol/L) to total P (μmol/L) at Wappinger Creek (triangles) and Fishkill Creek (circles) sites. Mean values, May–August.

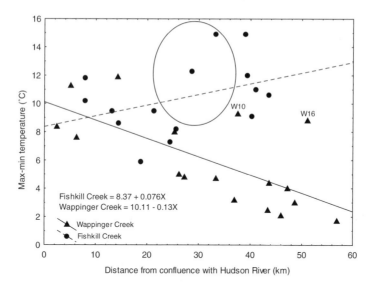

FIGURE 6. Maximum–minimum temperature differentials versus site distance from the Hudson River, Wappinger (triangles) and Fishkill (circles) watersheds.

physical habitat, six chemical, six macroinvertebrate, and seven fish assemblage response variables (Table 3). Most of the means were not significantly different, with a few notable exceptions. Aside from thermal excursions and chlorophyll-a (reported above), three macroinvertebrate assemblage indices were significantly different ($P < 0.05$) and one was marginally signifi-

cant ($P < 0.053$). All macroinvertebrate assemblage variables showed poorer ecological integrity in Fishkill Creek than Wappinger Creek. Of the fish assemblage variables, only densities showed a significant difference between watersheds, with Fishkill Creek having less than half the mean density of fish seen in Wappinger Creek.

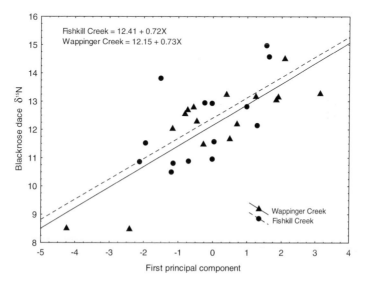

FIGURE 7. Regressions of the nitrogen stable isotope ratios of eastern blacknose dace versus the first principal component from a PCA analysis that examined elevation, highway density, discharge normalized to watershed area, percent agriculture, and percent forest.

TABLE 3. Means, SE, and results of one-way ANOVAs between Wappinger Creek and Fishkill Creek watersheds for selected response variables. Variables with statistically different means ($P < 0.05$) are highlighted in bold.

Response variable	Wappinger		Fishkill		df	F	P
	Mean	SE	Mean	SE			
Physical habitat							
% silt and sand	17.8	2.97	25.6	3.07	31	3.37	0.08
% embeddedness	44.7	4.15	53.5	4.27	31	2.21	0.15
% canopy cover	69.5	3.25	67.4	3.25	31	0.21	0.65
Chemical							
Max–min temperatures	**5.9**	0.71	**10.4**	0.76	30	18.48	0.001
Chlorophyll-a (mmol/L)	**30.0**	3.68	**18.1**	3.79	31	5.08	0.03
% inorganic N	62.5	4.17	71.0	4.29	31	1.98	0.17
Total P (μmol/L)	2.1	0.24	1.7	0.24	31	0.93	0.34
Total N (μmol/L)	44.2	5.45	49.0	5.62	31	0.38	0.54
August conductivity (mS/cm)	471.7	44.6	502.7	46.1	29	0.23	0.63
Macroinvertebrate assemblage							
% dominance	**61.8**	2.09	**70.1**	2.16	29	7.51	0.01
Diversity (H')	**0.93**	0.03	**0.84**	0.03	29	5.33	0.03
% model affinity	**55.8**	2.42	**48.2**	2.50	29	4.74	0.04
Biotic assessment profile	7.2	0.32	6.2	0.33	29	4.08	0.053
EPT index	52.4	4.69	44.2	4.69	28	1.52	0.23
Taxa richness/watershed area	0.83	0.20	0.63	0.21	29	0.47	0.50
Fish assemblage							
Density (#/m²)	**0.23**	0.04	**0.11**	0.04	31	5.19	0.03
Species richness/watershed area	0.31	0.06	0.20	0.06	31	1.50	0.23
IBI, excluding transients	36.9	1.82	35.4	1.88	31	0.36	0.55
% centrarchids	10.5	3.49	7.5	3.60	31	0.35	0.56
IBI	37.5	1.87	36.4	1.93	31	0.18	0.67
Diversity (H')	0.65	0.06	0.68	0.06	31	0.16	0.69
Blacknose dace δ15N	12.1	0.38	12.2	0.41	29	0.067	0.80

Some of the ecological data showed nonlinear trends when plotted against urbanization indices, suggestive of a threshold response. We present fish density as an example. Fish densities, when plotted against percent of watersheds in urban and suburban uses, highway density, or population density appeared to show nonlinear, inverse relationships, but the data were scattered. We selected the best relationship (highest proportion of variance explained in nonlinear least-squares regression), which was highway density as the independent variable (Figure 8). Realizing that all these variables were in some way confounded by elevation, we regressed log-transformed highway density on elevation ($R^2 = 0.55$, $P < 0.001$) and used the standardized residuals of this analysis as a new independent variable. This effectively removes the influence of elevation on highway density. The new response also appears nonlinear, but now, Fishkill Creek sites tend to cluster in areas with "higher than expected" road densities (adjusting for elevation), whereas Wappinger Creek sites distribute at "lower than expected" road densities and show more variation in fish density (Figure 9).

Discussion

Over the past two or three decades, land use change in Dutchess County has followed a pattern of economic downturn for farms, reversion of abandoned fields to secondary forest, sale, and development into new housing or, less frequently, commercial property. Most of the new growth is spreading north and east. Housing booms in the mid-1980s, and again in 1998–2001, reflected economic development often tied to industries such as IBM. Downsizing by the IBM corporation was also responsible for a development slowdown in the early 1990s (Lynch 2000). Farmland statistics (NYNASS 1999) show that most of the acreage losses were not from active croplands—which increased slightly over the 1990s—but rather from wooded areas, and areas that had buildings on them. We feel satisfied that our GIS analysis picked

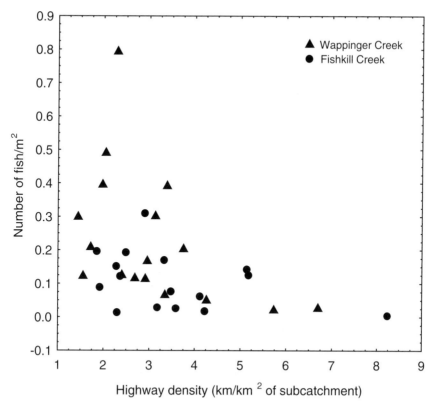

FIGURE 8. Fish densities observed at sites in the Fishkill Creek (circles) and Wappinger (triangles) Creek versus highway densities.

up most of the changes in land use between 1992 and 2001 (Figure 3).

Although suburban growth is clearly happening in many parts of the Wappinger Creek and Fishkill Creek watersheds, the ecological responses were often complex and rarely clear. When plotted against land use, most of the response variables showed much scatter and low, if any, correlations. There appeared to be a hierarchy of responses, going from chemical to organismal, where chemistry reflected land use characteristics, macroinvertebrates did to some extent as well, but fish assemblages (representing a part of the ecosystem that was more displaced from primary production processes) were relatively insensitive.

The regional IBI (Daniels et al. 2002), which had been calibrated, in part, in the Hudson River drainage, appeared relatively insensitive to anthropogenic disturbance, but this could have been due to the limited range of values. Most of our sites fell into the range of IBI scores corresponding to fair to poor conditions. When IBIs are calibrated, care is taken to include sites at the extremes of environmen-

tal quality. Our collection of stream sites, while encompassing one or two highly degraded and one or two relatively undisturbed sites, did not possess as clear a gradient of variation in fish assemblage structure. Some of the sites were surprising in their scores: for instance, a site near a county airport, in a suburban area, had the highest IBI score for the Wappinger Creek watershed.

Several of the stream macroinvertebrate indices appeared to be more sensitive to indicators of urbanization. Some of the reasons for the discrepancy may lie in the scale at which fish and macroinvertebrates experience the environment. Stream insects presumably have smaller spatial ranges than do fish, and so their assemblages may be more constrained by streamwater chemistry. Fish, which can move greater distances, can seek refuge from unsuitable conditions. One of the ameliorating factors for the fish assemblages we surveyed may have been the presence of riparian vegetation, and reasonably high canopy cover over the streams, resulting in shading during the record drought of 2001.

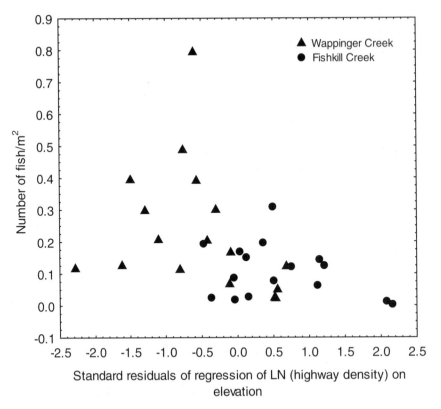

FIGURE 9. Fish densities observed at sites in Fishkill Creek (circles) and Wappinger Creek (triangles), plotted against the standardized residuals from a regression of log-transformed highway densities on elevation.

The strong relationship of eastern blacknose dace nitrogen stable isotope ratios to urbanization indices is in agreement with results obtained in coastal catchments on Cape Cod, where organisms in more urbanized watersheds had higher $\delta^{15}N$ values than those in less disturbed watersheds (McClelland et al. 1997). The heavier, less abundant ^{15}N isotope tends to accumulate in trophic transfers and under circumstances where much N processing occurs; for example, Caraco et al. (1998) found that $\delta^{15}N$ values increased as leaf litter was decomposed and the dissolved inorganic N remineralized. Sewage tends to have elevated $\delta^{15}N$ as well, whereas artificial fertilizers, manufactured by the Haber-Bosch process of fixing atmospheric N, have $\delta^{15}N$ values closer to the atmospheric value of zero (McClelland et al. 1997). Seston and periphyton (unpublished data) also showed increasing $\delta^{15}N$ with urbanization indices, but with more scatter. The weaker relationships probably resulted from different sources of organic matter contributing to the seston and different species of periphyton. Thus, standardizing on a particular species, as well as a particular life stage (we

chose adult eastern blacknose dace, although juveniles were occasionally assayed as well), is useful.

Eastern blacknose dace was a sentinel species in our study, and this represents a novel combination of the sentinel species and the stable isotopic methods for impact assessments. Eastern blacknose dace are cosmopolitan in Hudson Valley streams and, thus, provide a useful species to track. Fraker et al. (2002) used eastern blacknose dace as an indicator species in the Baltimore, Maryland vicinity, finding that fish in more urbanized areas put on most of their growth and matured in the first year of life, while fish in more rural environments continued to grow through age 2, and most matured in that year as well. Fitzgerald et al. (1999) also found utility in the sentinel species approach because their sentinel organism (creek chub *Semotilus atromaculatus*) was sensitive to water quality and was also ubiquitous in the small streams they were surveying.

A nonlinear, inverse response of fish densities to highway densities was detected. Similarly, Limburg and Schmidt (1990) found an inverse response of larval fish density and percent of land in urban and suburban use in 16 Hudson River tributaries studied in the late 1980s. The ultimate cause may only be speculated on, but could relate to the effects of impervious surface, which affect hydrology, chemistry, and geomorphology of streams (Klein 1979; Walsh 2000; CWP 2003). Reviewing the ecological effects of roads, Forman and Alexander (1998) noted that increased peak flows occur at road densities greater than 2–3 km/km^2, promoting more scouring and erosion. Within our own data set, 16 sites had road densities greater than 3 km/km^2, but consistently low fish densities occurred at sites where subcatchment highway densities exceeded 4 km/km^2 (Figure 8).

Fish densities may vary as a function of position in the watershed, with increases in smaller, higher elevation streams confounding urbanization indices. Therefore, further exploration of this relationship included an attempt to adjust highway densities for the observed, nonlinear decline in highway densities with elevation (a proxy for many other geographic factors, such as distance from the river mouth and stream order), by extracting the standardized residuals of the latter relationship and using them as a new independent variable. In this analysis, a new pattern emerged, showing that the Fishkill Creek watershed had higher than expected road densities and low densities of fish and that the Wappinger Creek watershed sites had lower than expected road densities and generally higher densities of fish. In a sense, then, the Fishkill Creek watershed is "over-built" and the Wappinger Creek watershed is "under-built," and in the road-denser drainage, fish densities were lower. The historic pattern of settlement by humans in this part of the Hudson Valley follows longitudinal gradients, with access to the Hudson River (for trade) at one end and higher elevation lands, with upland soils less suited for agriculture, at the other. This pattern is likely common to many areas and implies that urbanization trends may be conflated with strong, longitudinal gradients.

In this study, as in many others (this volume), complex and often diffuse patterns of ecological response to urbanization appear to be the result of historical contingencies (Harding et al. 1998), patchworks of land uses, and unexplained variation, presenting challenges that even multidisciplinary approaches find difficult to resolve (Nilsson et al. 2003). Some of the uncertainty may ultimately be explained by zoning regulations, as these are implemented town by town on individual tax parcels, implemented as parcels come up for sale and new regulations take effect. The spatial configurations of urban and suburban land development may also produce different ecosystem responses (Kleppel et al.

2004). Thus, more work could focus on the relationship of zoning and ecological responses, but would entail site-specific knowledge of what regulations apply.

The approach used here indicates that Fishkill Creek is the more ecologically degraded of the two, but also that moderate impact is occurring to Wappinger Creek as well. Given that most growth in the Wappinger watershed is predicted to occur in its northern and eastern parts (Polimeni 2002), planners and citizens there might take note of the Fishkill watershed as a vision of the "business as usual" development trajectory.

Future work in our project will include more historic ecological comparisons with data from the 1980s, as well as further integrating the ecological, economic, and land use change studies. At a very practical level, we are currently working with planners and an intermunicipal citizens' council to develop a new policy tool, using Multi-Criteria Decision Assessment (Erickson et al. 2005). This is a stakeholder-based approach that helps to elicit their preferences, whether explicit or hidden, and work towards compromise in conflict resolution. We will test the approach for its value as a means for managers and citizens to come together for prioritizing watershed management goals.

Acknowledgments

We are grateful for the help of D. Burns, L. Vasilakos, S. Patterson, T. Lynch, W. Relyea, A. Nowosielski, J. Polimeni, I. Ascencio, and G. Lange for fieldwork assistance; K. Schulz, E. Bridger, C. Dabney, A. Storch, and M. Cail for help in the laboratory; N. Haubenstock and T. Howe for conducting the stable isotope analysis; and M. Hall for providing satellite images and interpreted land use (project funded by U.S. Forest Service Grant No. 01-DG-11130144–254). We thank R. Schmidt, R. Daniels, K. Riva-Murray, K. Schulz, and D. Swaney for insightful discussions, and for the comments of two external reviewers and our editors. This work was supported by grants from the Hudson River Foundation and the National Science Foundation (Project No. DEB-0238121).

References

Barbour, M. T., J. Gerritsen, B. D. Snyder, and J. B. Stribling. 1999. Rapid bioassessment protocols for use in streams and wadeable rivers: periphyton, benthic macroinvertebrates, and fish. United States Environmental Protection Agency, Office of Water, Washington, D.C.

Barbour, M. T., and J. Gerritsen. 1996. Subsampling of benthic samples: a defense of the fixed-count method. Journal of the North American Benthological Society 15:386–391.

Bode, R.W., M. A. Novak, and L. E. Abele. 1996. Quality assurance work plan for biological stream monitoring in New York State. New York State Department of Environmental Conservation, technical report, Albany.

Caraco, N. F., G. Lampman, J. J. Cole, K. E. Limburg, M. L. Pace, and D. Fischer. 1998. Microbial assimilation of DIN in a nitrogen rich estuary: implications for food quality and isotope studies. Marine Ecology Progress Series 167:59–71.

Clesceri, L. S., A. E. Greenberg, and A. D. Eaton, editors. 1998. Standard methods for the examination of water and wastewater, 20th edition. American Public Health Association, Washingon, D.C.

Courtemanch, D. L. 1996. Commentary on the subsampling procedures used for rapid bioassessments. Journal of the North American Benthological Society 15:381–385.

CUGIR (Cornell University Geospatial Information Repository). 2003. Available: http://cugir.mannlib.cornell.edu (January 2004).

CWP (Center for Watershed Protection). 2003. Impacts of impervious cover on aquatic ecosystems. Center for Watershed Protection, Watershed Protection Research Monograph No. 1, Ellicott City, Maryland.

Daniels, R. A., K. Riva-Murray, D. B. Halliwell, D. L. Miller, and M. D. Bilger. 2002. An index of biological integrity for northern mid-Atlantic slope drainages. Transactions of the American Fisheries Society 131:1044–1060.

DCEMC (Dutchess County Environmental Management Council). 2000. Natural resource management plan for the Wappinger Creek watershed. Dutchess County Environmental Management Council, Millbrook, New York.

Ehrlich, P. R., and A. H. Ehrlich. 1981. Extinction: the causes and consequences of the disappearance of species. Ballantine, New York.

EPA (Environmental Protection Agency). 2001. Better Assessment Science Integrating Point and Nonpoint Sources (BASINS) Version 3.0. Users' Manual 823B01001. United States Environmental Protection Agency, Office of Water, Washington, D.C.

EPA (Environmental Protection Agency). 2002. Level III ecoregions of the United States. Revised August 2002. United States Environmental Protection Agency, National Health and Environmental Effects Research Laboratory. Available: kgsweb.uky.edu/download/geology/useco.pdf (January 2004).

Erickson, J. D., K. Limburg, J. Gowdy, K. Stainbrook A. Nowosielski, C. Hermans, and J. Polimeni. 2005. Anticipating change in the Hudson River watershed: an ecological economic model for integrated scenario analysis. Pages 341–370 in R. Bruins and M. Heberling, editors. Economics and ecological risk assessment: applications to watershed management. CRC Press, Boca Raton, Louisiana.

Fitzgerald, D. G., R. P. Lanno, and D. G. Dixon. 1999. A comparison of a sentinel species evaluation using creek chub (*Semotilus atromaculatus* Mitchill) to a fish community evaluation for the initial identification of environmental stressors in small streams. Ecotoxicology 8:33–48.

Fitzpatrick, F. A., I. R. Waite, P. T. D'Arconte, M. R. Meador, M. A. Maupin, and M.E. Gurtz. 1998. Revised methods for characterizing stream habitat in the National Water-Quality Assessment Program. United States Geological Survey Water Resources Investigations 98–4052, Raleigh, North Carolina.

Forman, R. T. T., and L. E. Alexander. 1998. Roads and their major ecological effects. Annual Review of Ecology and Systematics 29:207–231.

Fraker, M. E., J. W. Snodgrass, and F. Morgan. 2002. Differences in growth and maturation of blacknose dace (*Rhinichthys atratulus*) across an urban-rural gradient. Copeia 2002:1122–1127.

Harding, J. S., E. F. Benfield, P. V. Bolstad, G. S. Helfman, and E. B. D. Jones, III. 1998. Stream biodiversity: the ghost of land use past. Proceedings of the National Academy of Science USA 95:14843–14847.

Hauer, F. R., and G. A. Lamberti. 1996. Methods in stream ecology. Academic Press, San Diego, California.

Hilsenhoff, W. L. 1988. Rapid field assessment of organic pollution with a family-level biotic index. Journal of the North American Benthological Society 7:65–68.

Hutchinson, S., and L. Daniels. 1997. Inside ArcView GIS. 2nd edition. OnWord Press, Santa Fe, New Mexico.

Jensen, S. K., and J. O. Domingue. 1988. Extracting topographic structure from ditigal elevation data for geographic information systems analysis. Photogrammetric Engineering and Remote Sensing 53:1593–1600.

Kahn, A. 1966. The tyranny of small decisions: market failures, imperfections, and the limits of economics. Kyklos 19:23–47.

Karr, J. R. 1981. Assessment of biotic integrity using fish communities. Fisheries 6(6):21–27.

Karr, J. R. 1991. Biological integrity: a long-neglected aspect of water resource management. Ecological Applications 1:66–84.

Klein, R. D. 1979. Urbanization and stream quality impairment. Water Resources Bulletin 15:948–963.

Kleppel, G. S., S. A. Madewell, and S. E. Hazzard. 2004. Responses of emergent marsh wetlands in upstate New York to variations in urban typology. Ecology and Society 9(5): 1. Available: http://www.ecologyandsociety.org/vol9/iss5/art1 (December 2004).

Langner, C. L., and P. F. Hendrix. 1982. Evaluation of a persulfate-digestion method for particulate nitrogen and phosphorus. Water Research 16:1451–1454.

Leontief, W. W. 1966. Input-output economics. Oxford University Press, Oxford, UK.

Limburg, K. E., and R. E. Schmidt. 1990. Patterns of fish spawning in Hudson River tributaries: response to an urban gradient? Ecology 71:1238–1245.

Lynch, E. 2000. Merchants cheer, but some residents wary of growth. Poughkeepsie Journal, October 11, 2000.

McClelland, J. W., I. Valiela, and R. H. Michener. 1997. Nitrogen-stable isotope signatures in estuarine food webs: a record of increasing urbanization in coastal watersheds. Limnology and Oceanography 42:930–937.

Minnesota IMPLAN Group, Inc. 2004. IMpact Analysis for PLANning website. Available: http://www.implan.com/index.html (July 2004).

Nilsson, C., J. E. Pizzuto, G. E. Moglen, M. A. Palmer, E. H. Stanley, N. E. Bockstael, and L. C. Thompson. 2003. Ecological forecasting and the urbanization of stream ecosystems: challenges for economists, hydrologists, geomorphologists, and ecologists. Ecosystems 6:659–674.

Nowosielski, A. 2002. Geo-referenced social accounting with application to integrated watershed planning in the Hudson River Valley. Doctoral dissertation. Rensselaer Polytechnic Institute, Troy, New York.

NYNASS (New York Agricultural Statistics Service). 1999. New York county estimates 1992–1999. Farms, farmland, major crops, livestock and milk. Compiled and issued by New York Agricultural Statistics Service. New York State Department of Agriculture and Markets, Division of Statistics, Albany.

NYNASS (New York Agricultural Statistics Service). 2002. New York county estimates 2000–2001. Farms, farmland, major crops, livestock and milk. Compiled and issued by New York Agricultural Statistics Service. New York State Department of Agriculture and Markets, Division of Statistics, Albany.

Odum, W. E. 1982. Environmental degradation and the tyranny of small decisions. BioScience 32:728–729.

Peterson, B. J., and B. Fry. 1987. Stable isotopes in ecosystem studies. Annual Review of Ecology and Systematics 18:293–320.

Polimeni, J. 2002. A dynamic spatial simulation of residential development in the Hudson River Valley, New York State. Doctoral dissertation. Rensselaer Polytechnic Institute, Troy, New York.

Pyatt, G., and J. Round. 1985. Social accounting matrices: a basis for planning. World Bank, Washington, D.C.

Riva-Murray, K., R. W. Bode, P. J. Phillips, and G. L. Wall. 2002. Impact source determination with biomonitoring data in New York State: concordance with environmental data. Northeastern Naturalist 9:127–162.

Statsoft. 2003. Statistica Version 6.1. Statsoft, Tulsa, Oklahoma.

Stevens, G., R. E. Schmidt, D. R. Roeder, J. S. Tashiro, and E. Kiviat. 1994. Baseline assessment of tributaries to the Hudson (BATH): water quality, fishes, macroinvertebrates, and diatoms in Fishkill Creek, Quassaic Creek, and Moodna Creek. Hudsonia Ltd., Annandale, New York.

Vinson, M. R., and C. P. Hawkins. 1996. Effects of sampling area and subsampling procedure on comparisons of taxa richness among streams. Journal of the North American Benthological Society 15:392–399.

Walsh, C. J. 2000. Urban impacts on the ecology of receiving waters: a framework for assessment, conservation and restoration. Hydrobiologia 431:107–114.

Welschmeyer, N. A. 1994. Fluorometric analysis of chlorophyll *a* in the presence of chlorophyll *b* and pheopigments. Limnology and Oceanography 39:1985–1992.

Wetzel, R. G. 2001. Limnology, 3rd edition. Academic Press, New York.

American Fisheries Society Symposium 47:39–52, 2005
© 2005 by the American Fisheries Society

Effects of Landscape Change on Fish Assemblage Structure in a Rapidly Growing Metropolitan Area in North Carolina, USA

Jonathan G. Kennen*

U.S. Geological Survey, 810 Bear Tavern Road, Suite 206, West Trenton, New Jersey 08628, USA

Ming Chang

U.S. Environmental Protection Agency, Office of Environmental Information
1200 Pennsylvania Avenue NW, Mail Code #2842T, Washington, D.C. 20460, USA

Bryn H. Tracy

North Carolina Department of Environment and Natural Resources, Environmental Sciences Section
1621 Mail Service Center, Raleigh, North Carolina 27699, USA

Abstract.—We evaluated a comprehensive set of natural and land-use attributes that represent the major facets of urban development at fish monitoring sites in the rapidly growing Raleigh-Durham, North Carolina metropolitan area. We used principal component and correlation analysis to obtain a nonredundant subset of variables that extracted most variation in the complete set. With this subset of variables, we assessed the effect of urban growth on fish assemblage structure. We evaluated variation in fish assemblage structure with nonmetric multidimensional scaling (NMDS). We used correlation analysis to identify the most important environmental and landscape variables associated with significant NMDS axes. The second NMDS axis is related to many indices of land-use/land-cover change and habitat. Significant correlations with proportion of largest forest patch to total patch size ($r = -0.460$, $P < 0.01$), diversity of patch types ($r = 0.554$, $P < 0.001$), and population density ($r = 0.385$, $P < 0.05$) helped identify NMDS axis 2 as a disturbance gradient. Positive and negative correlations between the abundance of redbreast sunfish *Lepomis auritus* and bluehead chub *Nocomis leptocephalus*, respectively, and NMDS axis 2 also were evident. The North Carolina index of biotic integrity and many of its component metrics were highly correlated with urbanization. These results indicate that aquatic ecosystem integrity would be optimized by a comprehensive integrated management strategy that includes the preservation of landscape function by maximizing the conservation of contiguous tracts of forested lands and vegetative cover in watersheds.

Introduction

Conversions of rural and forest lands to urban land degrade streams (Booth and Jackson 1997; Kennen 1999; Wang et al. 2000, 2001) by altering the composition, structure, and function of aquatic ecosystems (Frissell et al. 1986; Jones and Clark 1987; Richards and Host 1994; Richards et al. 1997; Lammert and Allan 1999; Kennen and Ayers 2002; Roy et al. 2003). Landscape changes associated with urbanization include terrestrial habitat loss, landscape

fragmentation, increased impervious surface area, increased storm runoff, reduced groundwater recharge, and riparian habitat loss (Wang and Lyons 2003). Urbanization is linked consistently to stream degradation, which results from increased peak flows, stream power and stream sedimentation, reduced base flows, and modified instream habitat and substrate complexity (Klein 1979; Schueler 1994; Booth and Jackson 1997; Wang et al. 2000, 2001; Kennen and Ayers 2002; Walters et al. 2003). These changes are accentuated when connected forests and undeveloped lands are replaced with a patchwork of smaller and smaller interspersed parcels of lands fragmented

---

* Corresponding author: jgkennen@usgs.gov

by urban land uses. The changes not only modify the landscape in measurable ways, but also increase the extent of stream ecosystem degradation. Riparian areas are particularly susceptible to urbanization impacts and habitat fragmentation. Loss of riparian vegetation can destabilize stream banks, increase summer water temperatures and diel fluctuations, alter the recharge of shallow aquifers, and reduce the effectiveness of these natural filters (Karr and Gorman 1975; Kleiss et al. 1989; Jensen and Platts 1990). Loss of riparian vegetation results in increased surface runoff, increased erosion and sedimentation, and reduced woody debris and leaf litter that are used by many aquatic organisms for food and shelter (Finkenbine et al. 2000). Declines of native fish, amphibian, and aquatic invertebrate assemblages have been linked to deterioration of riparian habitats (Dodd and Smith 2003).

Terrestrial habitat fragmentation results in smaller habitats suitable for survival and fewer corridors suitable for dispersal and migration (Noss 1987). It is one of the most commonly cited threats to loss of biological diversity (D'Eon et al. 2002), and its effects on terrestrial systems have been extensively studied (Saunders et al. 1991; Brooker and Cale 1999; McCoy and Mushinsky 2000). How forest fragmentation affects water quality and stream processes is less well known; however, such understanding is important for evaluating the ways in which humans can minimize their impacts on aquatic ecosystems. Thus, the goal of this study was to evaluate the effects of urban development on fish assemblage structure. Our specific objectives were to (1) identify a subset of urbanization indicators (e.g., land use/land cover, fragmentation indices, riparian habitat) that extract most of the variation along a disturbance gradient, and (2) determine correlations between those urbanization indicators and variations in fish assemblage structure.

Study Area

The Raleigh-Durham, North Carolina study area (RDU; Figure 1) covers approximately 8,579 km², has a population of nearly 1.5 million and is the second fastest growing metropolitan area in the United States (http://www.census.gov/prod/www/statistical-abstract-O2.html). In addition, this area was the third most sprawling metropolitan area of 83 measured in the conterminous United States and Hawaii (Ewing et al. 2002). Population in the study area doubled from 1970 to 2000, and the amount of urbanized land increased by 150% over the same time period.

The study area is primarily within the Northern Outer Piedmont level IV ecoregion with small parts in the Triassic Basins, the Carolina Slate Belt, and the Rolling Coastal Plain (Griffith et al. 2002). All of the streams have moderate gradients. Streams in the Northern Outer Piedmont have mostly cobble, gravel, and sandy substrates. Streams in the Triassic Basins tend to have mostly sand and clay substrates; however, substrates in the Carolina Slate Belt are composed primarily of boulders and cobbles, and those in the Rolling Coastal Plain have sandy substrates. Natural forest vegetation in the study area typically includes mixed stands of hardwoods and some pines. Land use/land cover (LU/LC) is deciduous forest, pine plantations, pasture, row crops, and hay; cattle and poultry production is common. Landscapes in the RDU have changed from lightly harvested forests interspersed with light residential and agricultural lands to heavily urbanized landscapes with ever smaller parcels of intensively harvested forests. Annual precipitation and runoff in the study area are about 103 and 38 cm per year, respectively.

Methods

Study Design

The RDU comprises the contiguous metropolitan area plus a surrounding 32-km buffer inclusive of the major drainage basins. The conservative 32-km buffer was chosen to incorporate projected urban growth of these metropolitan areas beyond the year 2000 and to evaluate the effects of expanding urban development on aquatic communities. Thirty-nine sites were selected on the basis of a stratified approach designed to control for natural environmental differences (Figure 1). Site selection was intended to exhibit a range of urban LU/LC from low to high and to minimize nested catchments (i.e., spatial autocorrelation). Catchments in rapidly growing regions of the study area were targeted, and natural variability associated with elevation, slope, stream size, substrate, and physiographic region was minimized.

ATtILA

The Analytical Tools Interface for Landscape Assessments (ATtILA) program was used to generate a comprehensive list of landscape metrics. Analytical Tools Interface for Landscape Assessments is an ArcView

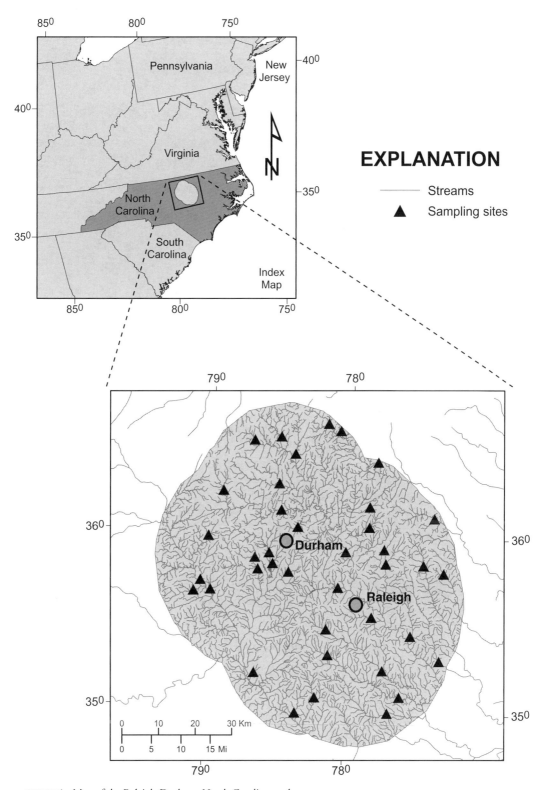

FIGURE 1. Map of the Raleigh-Durham, North Carolina study area.

extension that allows users to calculate and evaluate many types of landscape attributes (Ebert and Wade 2004). Four different metric groups can be calculated by ATtILA, including landscape characteristics, riparian characteristics, human stress, and physical characteristics. Data on LU/LC, elevation, slope, and precipitation are in raster format; stream and road data are lines; and population and census data are in polygon format for ATtILA. The LU/LC is the core input and is represented by specific land-use codes. Coding also can be customized to aggregate similar land-use components for metric calculation. Numerous land-use, diversity, and forest patch metrics were calculated for this study. Forest fragmentation was classified into five categories as defined in Riitters et al. (2000). Many small patches are representative of a fragmented forest, whereas larger patches represent a clumped or contiguous distribution of land uses that provide essential habitat and connected corridors for many interior species. Proportions of land-cover types in the riparian zone also were evaluated (Ebert and Wade 2004). Human-stress metrics, such as amount of impervious surfaces, road density, and population density, were derived from census and roads data. Many physical characteristics, such as elevation, stream slope, density, and length also were included in the assessment. Although not indicators of disturbance, these metrics were used to evaluate whether natural factors accounted for a part of the variation along significant ordination axes.

Digital Data Used in Watershed Assessment

Digital LU/LC, census, and transportation data were aggregated for this study. The 1990s land cover for the RDU was derived from the 1992 National Land Cover Data for North Carolina at 30-m resolution. The 2000 RDU northeastern area land coverage was derived from the 1999 Neuse River basin (NRB) land cover and was used for all areas it covers within the RDU study area. Landsat Enhanced Thematic Mapper Plus was used for the remaining area to perform an unsupervised classification to create 150 clusters. Each cluster was labeled for the land cover it contained and was then combined according to similar land-cover types to create a recoded thematic image. The NRB land-cover classification was recoded to match the desired scheme and resampled at 15–30-m resolution. The study area imagery then was processed into the common Albers Conical Equal Area projection with mosaic processing. The finished product was clipped to the RDU study-area boundary

and used to derive many of the LU/LC and fragmentation metrics.

Fish Assemblage Sampling

Wadeable streams (4–12 m wide) were sampled from 1991 to 2000 using a two-pass procedure with dual backpack electrofishing units and two netters. All collections were made at base flow, and reach length was scaled to a distance 20 times the mean channel width (average length = 180 m; Leopold et al. 1992; Meador et al. 1993; NCDENR 2001a). At each representative reach, all available macro- and microhabitats were sampled (e.g., riffles, pools, runs, snags, undercuts, deadfalls, and quiescent leaf-covered substrates). Block nets were not used. Juvenile and adult fish were collected, and readily identifiable fish were examined for external anomalies (sores, lesions, fin damage, skeletal abnormalities), measured (total length to the nearest 1 mm), and then released. Those fish that were not readily identifiable (e.g., *Notropis* spp.) were preserved in 10% formalin and returned to the laboratory for identification, examination, and total length measurement. Year-0 fish were excluded from all analyses because they pose several challenges when applying index of biotic integrity (IBI) metrics (Angermeier and Karr 1986; Angermeier and Schlosser 1987).

North Carolina Index of Biotic Integrity

The North Carolina index of biotic integrity (NCIBI) is a modification of the IBI initially proposed by Karr (1981) and Karr et al. (1986). The IBI is a quantitative measure that can be used to distinguish among a range of conditions (poor through excellent). It preserves the integrity of the data and incorporates professional judgment (Miller et al. 1988). Although Karr's (1981) original IBI was designed for use in warmwater systems in the Midwest, many regional applications have been presented (e.g., Fausch et al. 1984; Miller et al. 1988; Halliwell et al. 1999; Daniels et al. 2002). Like most biomonitoring tools, the IBI is based on the premise that pristine systems have biological characteristics that can be accurately measured and that departure from these characteristics is directly related to the severity of degradation (Fausch et al. 1990; Bramblett and Fausch 1991). The IBI used to assess North Carolina streams consists of 12 metrics that retain many of Karr's standard components, including species richness and composition, trophic composition, and fish abundance and condition. Additional information on the development of the NCIBI and species classifications can be found in NCDENR (2001a).

Physical Habitat Assessment

We employed a habitat assessment procedure (NCDENR 2001b), which is a modification of the U.S. Environmental Protection Agency rapid bioassessment protocols (Barbour et al. 1999) to evaluate channel modification, proportion of instream habitat types, type of bottom substrate, pool variety, bank stability, light penetration, and riparian zone conditions at stream reaches. Piedmont streams of moderate to high quality have sticks, leafpacks, snags, undercut banks, root mats, gravels and cobbles with low embeddedness, frequent pools and riffles of varying depths and widths, stable banks with a moderate to full tree canopy, and an intact riparian zone with no or rare breaks in the forest cover. In contrast, Piedmont streams of low to poor quality have a sand substrate, embedded riffles, if present, and incised, sparsely vegetated banks.

Data Analysis

A combination of correlation, regression, and multivariate analyses was used to quantify the variation in the landscape, environmental quality, and fish assemblage structure and to identify possible linkages among these attributes.

Fish assemblages were analyzed on the basis of species composition. Species composition was calculated as relative abundance (i.e., proportion of total catch) of various species, which provides detailed information on species tolerance of environmental conditions and is useful in identifying environmental determinants of assemblage structure (Poff and Allan 1995; Walters et al. 2003). Rare species that accounted for less than 0.1% of overall abundance and that were present in less than 5% of the samples were excluded from multivariate analyses. This approach reduced the number of fish taxa from 76 to 57. However, all fish species were used in the calculation of the NCIBI.

Patterns in fish assemblage structure among the sites were examined using nonmetric multidimensional scaling (NMDS; McCune and Mefford 1999; McCune et al. 2002). The distance measure used was Sorensen, and all NMDS procedures (Kruskal 1964a, 1964b; Mather 1976) were performed using PC-ORD software (McCune and Mefford 1999). Forty runs and 400 iterations were made using real data

with a final instability of 0.00005. Stress was evaluated using a Monte Carlo test ($P < 0.05$) that was based on 50 randomized runs and indicated that the 3-dimensional solution was the best solution and could not have occurred by chance alone. Higher dimensions did little to improve the model. The NMDS analysis allowed us to determine which environmental variables accounted for the majority of the variability in the distribution of fish species in ordination space (e.g., Roy et al. 2003; Walters et al. 2003). Because NMDS axes are acquired independently of gradient length and amount of variance explained, it was important to establish which of the NMDS axes accounted for the primary gradient.

A total of 126 environmental variables were evaluated for this study. We used principal components analysis (PCA; SAS Institute Inc. 1989) in combination with collinearity assessment to isolate a subset of variables that accounted for the greatest proportion of variance while minimizing redundancy. Distributions of all response and explanatory variables used in the PCA analysis were evaluated for normality and were appropriately transformed when necessary. Variables based on amount of land use in a basin were standardized by basin area (percentage data) and arcsine square-root transformed. We conducted PCA on the correlation matrix and evaluated the significance of principal components using the broken stick method (Jackson 1993). The broken stick method is used to determine statistically significant principal component axes by comparing the observed eigenvalues to the eigenvalues from random data. In addition, by using the correlation matrix, we ensured that all the environmental variables contributed equally to the PCA and that the contributions were scale-independent (Legendre and Legendre 1998; Olden and Poff 2003). Loadings of the environmental variables on each significant principle component were used to identify variables that extracted dominant patterns of variation. A Spearman rank correlation matrix (SAS Institute Inc. 1989) of the environmental variables was examined to eliminate redundant variables with an r greater than 0.80. We used a combination of correlation and linear regression analysis to link environmental variables with changes in fish assemblage structure. Axis 2 from the NMDS analysis was correlated with environmental variables, NCIBI metric scores, and fish species. Linear regression analysis was used to directly link changes in sensitive species abundance with the disturbance gradient and to evaluate the relation between urban land use and the NCIBI. The later analyses were used to exemplify the strength of relations between key land use stressors and fish assemblage structure.

Results

Environmental Disturbance Gradient

The NMDS identified three primary gradients that together accounted for 88% of the variance in the analytical data set. The first and third axes accounted for a significant but small proportion of variance (6% and 15%, respectively) and were not considered for further analysis. The second axis accounted for 67% of the fish assemblage variation.

Data reduction using PCA and correlation analysis reduced the environmental data to nonredundant subsets of 35 and 28 variables, respectively. Of these, only 12 habitat and landscape variables (Table 1) were significantly ($P < 0.05$) related to the extracted NMDS axis 2 scores for the fish assemblage. Nonmetric multidimensional scaling axis 2 correlated most strongly with specific environmental disturbance variables. In particular, population density, percent urban land cover, and diversity of patch types were positively related, and variables such as proportion of largest forest patch to total forest area, and the percent of forest land were negatively related to NMDS axis 2 (Table 1). Habitat variables most significantly related to NMDS axis 2 include light penetration, riffle habitats, and riparian zone vegetation width (Table 1). Natural environmental factors such as stream slope, length, density, and elevation accounted for an insignificant amount of the variation in NMDS axis 2 scores (Table 1).

Linking Fish Assemblage and Landscape Change

More than 30,700 fish representing 76 species in 12 families were collected (Table 2); however, only 57 species met the censoring criteria and were retained for ordination analysis. The most commonly collected

TABLE 1. Spearman's correlation coefficients of selected environmental variables and NMDS ordination axis 2 (***, $P < 0.001$; **, $P < 0.01$; *, $P < 0.05$).

Variable	NMDS axis 2	Mean	Standard deviation	Minimum	Maximum
Population density in watershed (people/km^2)	0.385*	153.0	3,150.7	8.5	5,509.2
Urban land cover (%)	0.357*	23.36	21.17	2.70	81.13
Area of watershed classified as edge forest (%)	−0.404**	23.27	6.51	6.47	32.70
Amount of largest forest patch to total forest area (%)	−0.460**	76.39	23.13	29.50	99.55
Number of forest patches in watershed	0.371*	264.4	204.5	24.0	1,120.0
Patch Diversity (Shannon-Wiener)	0.554***	0.95	0.17	0.49	1.18
Area of watershed classified as patch forest (%)	0.395*	2.93	1.24	0.57	5.76
Latitude (decimal degrees)	−0.380*	356,758	3,175	352,800	362,000
Forest land cover (%)	−0.408**	58.94	16.30	18.57	87.41
Riffle habitat[a]	−0.302*	5.34	2.74	0.00	10.00
Light penetration[a]	−0.530***	8.11	2.51	2.00	10.00
Density of riparian vegetation[a]	0.347*	4.36	0.91	2.00	6.00
Mean slope (%)	−0.073	4.48	1.22	2.41	7.50
Stream length (km)	0.100	81.85	42.69	9.53	211.39
Stream density (kilometers of stream/km^2)	0.093	0.13	0.01	0.00	0.32
Mean elevation (m)	−0.023	121.90	39.40	56.21	201.69
Bottom substrate[a]	0.071	6.88	1.92	3.00	13.00

[a] Nominal variables derived from visual characterization of habitat condition (NCDENR 2001b).

TABLE 2. Occurrence frequency, total abundance, tolerance, and trophic guild of fish species collected in the Raleigh-Durham study area. Only those species included in the ordination analysis are shown.

Family name *Scientific name*	Common name	Occurence frequency	Total abundance	Tolerance[a]	Trophic guild[a]
Anguillidae					
Anguilla rostrata	American eel	22	409	Intermediate	Piscivore
Clupeidae					
Dorosoma cepedianum	gizzard shad	4	70	Intermediate	Omnivore
Cyprinidae					
Clinostomus funduloides	rosyside dace	7	48	Intermediate	Insectivore
Cyprinella analostana	satinfin shiner	23	942	Tolerant	Insectivore
C. nivea	whitefin shiner	3	318	Intermediate	Insectivore
Cyprinus carpio	common carp	3	37	Tolerant	Omnivore
Luxilus albeolus	white shiner	29	3,841	Intermediate	Insectivore
Lythrurus matutinus	pinewoods shiner	19	565	Intolerant	Insectivore
Nocomis leptocephalus	bluehead chub	29	4,708	Intermediate	Omnivore
N. raneyi	bull chub	8	386	Intermediate	Omnivore
Notemigonus crysoleucas	golden shiner	12	87	Tolerant	Omnivore
Notropis alborus	whitemouth shiner	2	37	Intermediate	Insectivore
N. altipinnis	highfin shiner	8	284	Intermediate	Insectivore
N. amoenus	comely shiner	8	139	Intermediate	Insectivore
N. cummingsae	dusky shiner	3	77	Intermediate	Insectivore
N. hudsonius	spottail shiner	4	44	Intermediate	Omnivore
N. procne	swallowtail shiner	26	3,324	Intermediate	Insectivore
N. scepticus	sandbar shiner	2	37	Intermediate	Insectivore
N. volucellus	mimic shiner	5	109	Intolerant	Insectivore
Semotilus atromaculatus	creek chub	15	149	Tolerant	Insectivore
Catostomidae					
Catostomus commersonii	white sucker	9	27	Tolerant	Omnivore
Erimyzon oblongus	creek chubsucker	25	249	Intermediate	Omnivore
Hypentelium nigricans	northern hog sucker	15	183	Intermediate	Insectivore
Moxostoma collapsum	notchlip redhorse	16	182	Intermediate	Insectivore
M. pappillosum	V-lip redhorse	7	39	Intermediate	Insectivore
M. cervinum (sometimes called *Scartomyzon cervinus*	blacktip jumprock (formerly black jumprock)	11	203	Intermediate	Insectivore
Ictaluridae					
Ameiurus catus	white catfish	2	7	Tolerant	Omnivore
A. natalis	yellow bullhead	25	104	Tolerant	Omnivore
A. nebulosus	brown bullhead	10	16	Tolerant	Omnivore
A. platycephalus	flat bullhead	11	39	Tolerant	Insectivore
Ictalurus punctatus	channel catfish	8	20	Intermediate	Omnivore
Noturus insignis	margined madtom	30	639	Intermediate	Insectivore
Esocidae					
Esox americanus	redfin pickerel	19	95	Intermediate	Piscivore
Umbridae					
Umbra pygmaea	eastern mudminnow	2	11	Intermediate	Insectivore
Aphredoderidae					
Aphredoderus sayanus	pirate perch	24	137	Intermediate	Insectivore
Fundulidae					
Fundulus rathbuni	speckled killifish	7	195	Intermediate	Insectivore
Poeciliidae					
Gambusia holbrooki	eastern mosquitofish	22	384	Tolerant	Insectivore

TABLE 2.   Continued.

Family name *Scientific name*	Common name	Occurence frequency	Total abundance	Tolerance[a]	Trophic guild[a]
Centrarchidae					
Ambloplites cavifrons	Roanoke bass	5	89	Intermediate	Piscivore
Centrarchus macropterus	flier	7	21	Intermediate	Insectivore
Enneacanthus gloriosus	bluespotted sunfish	9	28	Intermediate	Insectivore
Lepomis auritus	redbreast sunfish	38	4,727	Tolerant	Insectivore
L. cyanellus	green sunfish	31	688	Tolerant	Insectivore
L. gibbosus	pumpkinseed	25	347	Intermediate	Insectivore
L. gulosus	warmouth	22	67	Intermediate	Insectivore
L. macrochirus	bluegill	36	3,117	Intermediate	Insectivore
L. microlophus	redear sunfish	16	191	Intermediate	Insectivore
Lepomis sp.	Hybrid sunfish	8	30	Tolerant	Insectivore
Micropterus salmoides	largemouth bass	28	172	Intermediate	Piscivore
Pomoxis nigromaculatus	black crappie	9	30	Intermediate	Piscivore
Percidae					
Etheostoma collis	Carolina darter	2	11	Intermediate	Insectivore
E. flabellare	fantail darter	6	232	Intermediate	Insectivore
E. nigrum	johnny darter	19	1,136	Intermediate	Insectivore
E. olmstedi	tessellated darter	20	581	Intermediate	Insectivore
E. vitreum	glassy darter	12	84	Intermediate	Insectivore
Perca flavescens	yellow perch	6	80	Intermediate	Piscivore
Percina nevisense	chainback darter	18	89	Intolerant	Insectivore
P. roanoka	Roanoke darter	22	856	Intolerant	Insectivore

[a] North Carolina Department of Environment and Natural Resources 2001a.

family was the Centrarchidae. Redbreast sunfish was the most abundant fish (N = 4,727) and was found at all but one site. Bluegill and green sunfish were collected at 36 and 31 sites, respectively (Table 2). In addition, two common cyprinids (white shiner and bluehead chub) occurred at 29 of the sites sampled. Highly significant relations were found between NMDS axis 2 and the abundance of redbreast sunfish (r^2 = 0.70) and bluehead chub (r^2 = 0.65; Figure 2). In total, the abundance of 11 fish species was significantly correlated with NMDS axis 2 (Table 3).

The NCIBI was significantly related to the amount of watershed urbanization (N = 39, r^2 = 0.44, P < 0.0001; Figure 3). Sites with the highest NCIBI scores typically fell in watersheds with a high percentage of forest and a low percentage of urban land. Four of the NCIBI component metrics were significantly related to NMDS axis 2, including percentage of tolerant individuals, percentage of omnivorous and herbivorous individuals, percentage of insectivorous individuals, and percentage of piscivorous individuals (Table 4).

Discussion

Our analyses identified ecologically relevant landscape and habitat factors that were directly related to changes in fish assemblage structure across a disturbance gradient in North Carolina streams (Table 1). Many of the fragmentation, patch, and riparian metrics accounted for a significant amount of the variability in fish assemblage structure and were important in differentiating fish assemblages along a disturbance gradient. For example, the percentage of the watershed classified as patch forest, the diversity of patch types, and the number of forest patches in the watershed were significant indicators of watershed change and were directly related to NMDS axis 2. In contrast, factors such as the proportion of largest forest patch to total forest area, the percent of the watershed classified as forest, and the amount of riffle habitat were inversely related to NMDS axis 2. The direct link from forest fragmentation, habitat loss, and changes in patch dynamics to ecological consequence for many terrestrial species is well established (e.g., Saunders et al. 1991; Andren 1994; Debinski and Holt 2000; Trombulak

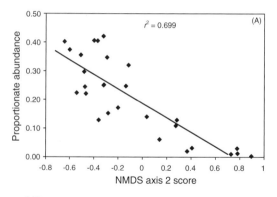

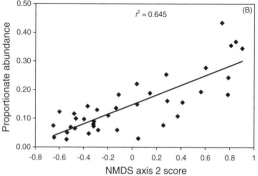

FIGURE 2. Regression relation between NMDS axis 2 scores and proportionate abundance of redbreast sunfish (A) and bluehead chub (B).

and Frissell 2000). However, lotic systems also are linked directly and indirectly to terrestrial ecosystem fragmentation (Conroy et al. 2003).

The same anthropogenic processes that affect terrestrial species by reducing landscape connectivity,

TABLE 3. Significant correlations (Spearman's rho) between relative abundance of fish species collected from the Raleigh-Durham study area and NMDS ordination axis 2. Tolerance classes are defined in Table 2.

Species	r	P
Bluehead chub	−0.616	<0.001
Redbreast sunfish	0.697	<0.001
American eel	0.492	0.001
White shiner	−0.484	0.002
Bull chub	0.466	0.003
Tessellated darter	0.419	0.008
Satinfin shiner	0.379	0.017
Dusky shiner	0.376	0.018
Bluespotted sunfish	0.344	0.032
Speckled killifish	−0.336	0.036
Largemouth bass	0.326	0.043

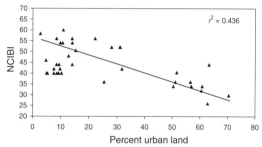

FIGURE 3. Regression relation between percent urban land and the North Carolina index of biotic integrity (NCIBI).

habitat availability, and increasing patch diversity can have a quantifiable effect on aquatic assemblage structure. One possible scenario is that as fragmentation increases, forested watershed and riparian areas become more and more discontinuous and patchy. This process results in the loss of protective forested areas that can alter riparian conditions by reducing buffering capacity and ultimately modifying water quality and aquatic assemblage structure.

Results of previous investigations indicate that aquatic-assemblage health is affected negatively by the alteration of forested and agricultural lands (Benke et al. 1981; Garie and McIntosh 1986; Jones and Clark 1987; Kennen 1999). Roth et al. (1996) indicate that the amount of forested land in a basin was posi-

TABLE 4. Correlation coefficients (Spearman's rho) between NCIBI metrics and NMDS ordination axis 2. Metrics with a significant correlation ($P < 0.05$) with NMDS axis 2 are in bold.

Metric	r	P
Number of species	0.338	0.838
Number of fish	−0.184	0.262
Number of darter species	−0.027	0.872
Number of sunfish species	−0.049	0.766
Number of sucker species	−0.135	0.411
Number of intolerant species	0.021	0.899
Percentage of tolerant individuals	**0.609**	<0.001
Percentage of omnivorous and herbivorous individuals	**−0.500**	0.001
Percentage of insectivorous individuals	**0.463**	0.003
Percentage of piscivorous individuals	**−0.467**	0.003
Percentage of diseased fish	−0.053	0.341
Percentage of species with multiple age-groups	−0.231	0.156

tively related to fish-assemblage IBI scores. May et al. (1997) report that stream buffer width, vegetative condition, and longitudinal connectedness of buffer vegetation were altered as the level of development in a watershed increased. Urbanization fragments landscapes and riparian corridors and greatly reduces the amount of mature vegetation in watersheds. In addition, soil erosion during and after development activities affects vegetative cover by promoting the movement of invasive species, increasing pathogens, inhibiting vegetative regeneration, and increasing foliar damage (Schlosser and Karr 1981; Reid 1993). Consequently, fragmentation of forested areas and a concomitant reduction in canopy cover can result in changes in stream temperature and habitat structure, which can alter the structure and function of the fish assemblage.

In the RDU, sensitive species such as the bluehead chub, which typically occur in clear creeks and small rivers with medium to fast current and a substrate composed of rock, gravel, or sand (Rohde et al. 1994), decreased in abundance across the disturbance gradient (Figure 2). In contrast, the opportunistic and tolerant redbreast sunfish, which occurs throughout the mid-Atlantic region in lotic systems (Rohde et al. 1994), increased in abundance with increasing watershed disturbance. Abundance of other tolerant and intermediate tolerant species, such as the tessellated darter *Etheostoma olmstedi*, satinfin shiner *Cyprinella analostana*, and the bull chub *Nocomis raneyi*, increased along the disturbance gradient (Table 3). In contrast, intermediate species such as the white shiner and speckled killifish *Fundulus rathbuni* decreased. In addition, the NCIBI metric percentage of tolerant individuals was significantly related to the disturbance gradient (Table 4), further supporting the linkage between landscape change and watershed disturbance.

In this study, fragmentation of the landscape associated with the loss of forested lands, changes in patch dynamics, and an increase in developed lands appeared to promote highly tolerant aquatic species. In contrast, species sensitive to environmental disturbance became much less prevalent (Figure 2; Table 3). This is only one of many processes associated with landscape disturbance that are known to degrade stream condition. Other pressures that can affect native species include impoundments, streamflow regulation, and water-resource development. These practices can have profound effects on the structure, function, and resilience of lotic systems (Conroy et al. 2003), yet often are essential to meet the water needs of a growing population. Consequently, changes in

aquatic species composition throughout this and other regions are the legacy of historical management practices.

Linking the effects of landscape fragmentation in a spatial context to ecological consequences is often a difficult task for aquatic ecologists. Moreover, translating the effects into procedures that can be used in management is even more complicated because ecological complexity tends to blur results with patterns and processes that can be difficult to distinguish because of the high level of variability inherent in aquatic ecological data. This tendency is apparent in these data because the strongest relations with metrics and landscape and habitat variables, although significant, account for only a part of the overall variability in the fish assemblage data. However, management of forest and riparian fragmentation may become necessary if ecosystem function is to be maintained, especially for aquatic systems that exhibit a response to landscape change. Additionally, an increase in patch diversity indicates that greater attention be given to the prevention of perforated landscape conditions, especially those along the stream corridor that may result in modification in aquatic-assemblage structure. Some development practices promote habitat fragmentation and this process ultimately may jeopardize the conservation goals of many state agencies (Keitt et al. 1997) by creating smaller and smaller noncontiguous forested areas in watersheds. This approach is in direct contrast to "smart growth" efforts that support "green infrastructure" (that is, large conservation areas, connected forest and riparian corridors, and green belts) that promote the maintenance and restoration of intact forests and riparian areas that have consistently been shown to be protective of stream integrity (e.g., Karr and Gorman 1975; Kleiss et al. 1989; Leavitt 1998).

The results of this study indicate that smart growth policies complemented by low-impact development and open-space preservation appear to promote the retention of sensitive species. Watershed-level low-impact development patterns likely result in improved sediment mitigation, hydrologic stability, and biotic integrity because these approaches protect larger tracts of land and preserve critical ecological functions (i.e., they maximize open space and minimize impervious cover). Thus, natural landscapes that maintain contiguous areas of forest in a watershed and along the stream corridor are important for the maintenance of ecosystem health. Nonproactive growth policies that promote or allow scattered development eventually replace naturally vegetated areas with impervious surfaces and increase the volume and frequency of stormwater runoff following a rain event. The resulting hydrologic alteration is but one of the many consequences of urban growth that have been linked to changes in the composition, structure, and function of aquatic systems (see Ward and Stanford 1989; Richter et al. 1996; Bunn and Arthington 2002; Wang and Lyons 2003). Structurally engineered stormwater-management measures (e.g., swales, retention basins) often have been used to control the environmental impact of new development; however, few have demonstrated the long-term ability to control the movement of contaminants or maintain ecosystem integrity (Coffman and Smith 1996; Maxted and Shaver 1998). These results indicate that for preservation of open land to be most effective as a management tool, the preserved forest and riparian lands not only need to be large enough to serve an environmental function, but also should be connected. To manage aquatic ecosystem integrity in a comprehensive, integrated manner, resource managers will need to consider restoration of the hydrologic regime, protection of ground-and surface water quality by minimizing disturbance to the riparian corridor, and preservation of landscape function by maximizing the conservation of contiguous tracts of forested lands and vegetative cover in watersheds.

Acknowledgments

The authors thank Cary Roberts of the U.S. Environmental Protection Agency (USEPA) for aggregating ATtILA metrics and Wayne Davis for his insightful comments. Karen Murray and Robert Goldstein of the U.S. Geological Survey provided many helpful suggestions that greatly improved the manuscript. Although the research described in this paper was partially funded by the USEPA, it has not been subjected to the agency's required peer and policy review process and, therefore, does not necessarily represent the views of the USEPA; no official endorsement by the USEPA should be inferred. The use of trade, product, or firm names in this report is for descriptive purposes only and does not imply endorsement by the U.S. Government.

References

Andren, H. 1994. Effects of habitat fragmentation on birds and mammals in landscapes with different proportions of suitable habitat. Oikos 71:344–366.

Angermeier, P. L., and J. R. Karr. 1986. Applying an index of biotic integrity based on stream-fish communities: considerations in sampling and interpretation. North American Journal of Fisheries Management 6:418–429.

Angermeier, P. L., and I. J. Schlosser. 1987. Assessing biotic integrity of the fish community in a small Illinois stream. North American Journal of Fisheries Management 7:331–338.

Barbour, M. T., J. Gerritsen, B. D. Snyder, and J. B. Stribling. 1999. Rapid bioassessment protocols for use in streams and wadeable rivers: periphyton, benthic macroinvertebrates, and fish, 2nd edition. U.S. Environmental Protection Agency, EPA 841-B-99–002, Washington, D.C.

Benke, A. C., G. E. Willke, F. K. Parrish, and D. L. Stites. 1981. Effects of urbanization on stream ecosystems. Georgia Institute of Technology, Report ERC07–81, Atlanta.

Booth, D. B., and C. R. Jackson. 1997. Urbanization of aquatic systems: degradation thresholds, stormwater detection, and the limits of migration. Journal of the American Water Resources Association 33:1077–1090.

Bramblett, R. G., and K. D. Fausch. 1991. Variable fish communities and the index of biotic integrity in a western Great Plains river. Transactions of the American Fisheries Society 120:752–769.

Brooker, L. B., and P. Cale. 1999. Animal dispersal in fragmented habitat: measuring habitat connectivity, corridor use, and dispersal mortality. Conservation Ecology 3(1):4.

Bunn, S. E., and A. H. Arthington. 2002. Basic principles and ecological consequences of altered flow regimes for aquatic biodiversity. Environmental Management 30:492–507.

Coffman, L. S., and J. Smith. 1996. Environmentally sensitive low-impact development. Proceedings of Watershed 96, Water Environment Federation, June 8–12, Baltimore, Maryland.

Conroy, M. J., C. R. Allen, J. T. Peterson, L. Pritchard Jr., and C. T. Moore. 2003. Landscape change in the southern Piedmont: challenges, solutions, and uncertainty across scales. Conservation Ecology 8(2):3.

Daniels, R. A., K. Riva-Murray, D. B. Halliwell, D. L. Vana-Miller, and M. D. Bilger. 2002. An index of biological integrity for northern mid-Atlantic slope drainages. Transactions of the American Fisheries Society 131:1044–1060.

Debinski, D. M., and R. D. Holt. 2000. A survey and overview of habitat fragmentation experiments. Conservation Biology 14:342–353.

D'Eon, R. G., S. M. Glenn, I. Parfitt, and M-J Fortin. 2002. Landscape connectivity as a function of scale and organism vagility in a real forested landscape. Conservation Ecology 6(2):10.

Dodd, C. K., Jr., and L. L. Smith. 2003. Habitat destruction and alteration: historical trends and future prospects for amphibians. Pages 94–112 *in* R. D. Semlitsch, editor. Amphibian Conservation, Smithsonian Institution Press, Washington, D.C.

Ebert, D. W., and T. G. Wade. 2004. Analytical Tools Interface for Landscape Assessment (ATtILA), user manual, Version 3.0. U.S. Environmental Protection Agency, Office of Research and Development, National Exposure Research Laboratory, Environmental Sciences Division, Landscape Ecology Branch, Las Vegas, Nevada.

Ewing, R., R. Pendall, and D. Chen. 2002. Measuring sprawl and its impact, Smart Growth America, Washington, D.C. Available: http://www.smartgrowthamerica.org/sprawlindex/MeasuringSprawl.PDF (February 2004)

Fausch, K. D., J. Lyons, J. R. Karr, and P. L. Angermeier. 1990. Fish communities as indicators of environmental degradation. Pages 123–144 *in* S. M. Adams, editor. Biological indicators of stress in fish. American Fisheries Society, Symposium 8, Bethesda, Maryland.

Fausch, K. D., J. R. Karr, and P. R. Yant. 1984. Regional application of an index of biotic integrity based on stream fish communities. Transactions of the American Fisheries Society 113:39–55.

Finkenbine, J. K., J. W. Atwater, and D. S. Mavinic. 2000. Stream health after urbanization. Journal of the American Water Resources Association 36:1149–1160.

Frissell, C. A., W. J. Liss, C. E. Warren, C. E., and M. D. Hurley. 1986. A hierarchical framework for stream habitat classification: viewing streams in a watershed context. Environmental Management 10:199–214.

Garie, H. L., and A. McIntosh. 1986. Distribution of benthic macroinvertebrates in a stream exposed to urban runoff. Water Resources Bulletin 22:447–455.

Griffith, G., J. Omernik, and J. Comstock. 2002. Ecoregions of North Carolina. U.S. Environmental Protection Agency, Office of Research and Development, NHEERL, Western Ecology Division, Corvallis, Oregon.

Halliwell, D. B., R. W. Langdon, R. A. Daniels, J. P. Kurtenbach, and R. A. Jacobson. 1999. Classification of freshwater fish species of the northeastern United States for use in the development of indices of biological integrity, with regional applications. Pages 301–333 *in* T. P. Simon, editor. Assessing the sustainability and biological integrity of water resources using fish communities. CRC Press, Boca Raton, Florida.

Jackson, D. A. 1993. Stopping rules in principal compo-

nents analysis: a comparison of heuristical and statistical approaches. Ecology 74:2204–2214.

Jensen, S. E., and W. S. Platts. 1990. Restoration of degraded riverine/riparian habitat in the Great Basin and Snake River region. Pages 367–404 *in* J. A. Kusler and M. E. Kentula, editors. Wetland creation and restoration: the status and the science, Island Press, Washington, D.C.

Jones, R. C., and C. C. Clark. 1987. Impact of watershed urbanization on stream insect communities. Water Resources Bulletin 23:1047–1055.

Karr, J. R. 1981. Assessment of biotic integrity using fish communities. Fisheries 6(6):21–27.

Karr, J. R., K. D. Fausch, P. L. Angermeier, P. R. Yant, and I. J. Schlosser. 1986. Assessing biological integrity in running water: a method and its rationale. Illinois Natural History Survey Special Publication 5, Champaign.

Karr, J. R., and O. T. Gorman. 1975. Effects of land treatment on the aquatic environment. Pages 4–1 to 4–18 *in* U.S. Environmental Protection Agency nonpoint source pollution seminar, Report 905/9–75-007, Washington, D.C.

Keitt, T. H., L. U. Dean, and B. T. Milne. 1997. Detecting critical scales in fragmented landscapes. Conservation Ecology 1(1):4.

Kennen, J. G. 1999. Relation of macroinvertebrate community impairment to catchment characteristics in New Jersey streams. Journal of the American Water Resources Association 35:939–955.

Kennen, J.G., and M. A. Ayers. 2002. Relation of environmental characteristics to the composition of aquatic assemblages along a gradient of urban land use in New Jersey, 1996–98. U.S. Geological Survey Water-Resources Investigations Report 02–4069, Trenton, New Jersey.

Klein, R. D. 1979. Urbanization and stream quality impairment. Water Resources Bulletin 15:948–963.

Kleiss, B. A., E. E. Morris, J. F. Nix, and J. W. Barko. 1989. Modification of riverine water quality by an adjacent bottomland hardwood wetland. Pages 429–438 *in* D. W. Fisk, editor. Proceedings of wetlands: concerns and successes. American Water Resources Association, TPS 89–3, Bethesda, Maryland.

Kruskal, J. B. 1964a. Multidimensional scaling by optimizing goodness of fit to nonmetric hypothesis. Psychometrika 29:1–27.

Kruskal, J. B. 1964b. Nonmetric multidimensional scaling: a numerical method. Psychometrika 29:115–129.

Lammert, M., and J. D. Allan. 1999. Assessing biotic integrity of streams: effects of scale in measuring the influence of land use/cover and habitat structure on fish and macroinvertebrates. Environmental Management 23:257–270.

Leavitt, J. 1998. The functions of riparian buffers in urban watersheds. Master's thesis. University of Washington, Seattle.

Legendre, P., and L. Legendre. 1998. Numerical ecology. Elsevier, Amsterdam.

Leopold, L. B., M. G. Wolman, and J. P. Miller. 1992. Fluvial process in geomorphology. Dover Publications, Inc., New York.

Mather, P. M. 1976. Computational methods of multivariate analysis in physical geography. Wiley, London.

Maxted, J. R., and E. Shaver. 1998. The use of retention basins to mitigate stormwater impacts on aquatic life. Pages 494–512, in, L. A. Roesner, editor. Effects of watershed development and management on aquatic ecosystems. American Society of Civil Engineers, New York.

May, C. W., R. R. Horner, J. B. Karr, B. W. Mar, and E. G. Welch. 1997. Effects of urbanization on small streams in the Puget Sound lowland ecoregion. Watershed Protection Techniques 2:483–493.

McCoy, E. D., and H. R. Mushinsky. 2000. Effects of fragmentation on the richness of vertebrates in the Florida scrub habitat. Ecology 75:446–457.

McCune, B., J. B. Grace, and D. L. Urban. 2002. Analysis of ecological communities. MjM Software Design, Gleneden Beach, Oregon.

McCune, B., and M. J. Mefford. 1999. PC-ORD –multivariate analysis of ecological data Version 4.25. MjM Software, Gleneden Beach, Oregon.

Meador, M. R., T. R. Cuffney, and M. E. Gurtz. 1993. Methods for characterizing stream habitat as part of the National Water-Quality Assessment Program. U.S. Geological Survey Open-File Report 93-408, Raleigh, North Carolina.

Miller, D. L., P. M. Leonard, R. M. Hughes, J. R. Karr, P. B. Moyle, L.H. Schrader, B. A. Thompson, R. A. Daniels, K. D. Fausch, G. A. Fitzhugh, J. R. Gammon, D. B. Halliwell, P. L. Angermier, and D. O. Orth. 1988. Regional application of an index of biotic integrity for use in water resource management. Fisheries 13(5):12–20.

NCDENR (North Carolina Department of Environment and Natural Resources). 2001a. Standard operating procedure: biological monitoring, stream fish community assessment and fish tissue. North Carolina Department of Environment and Natural Resources, Raleigh. Available: http://www.esb.enr.state.nc.us/BAU.html (December 2003)

NCDENR (North Carolina Department of Environment and Natural Resources). 2001b. Standard operating procedures for benthic macroinvertebrates. North Carolina Department of Environment and Natural Resources, Raleigh. Available: http://www.esb.enr.state.nc.us/BAU.html (December 2003)

Noss, R. F. 1987. Corridors in real landscapes: a reply to Simerloff and Cox. Conservation Biology 1:159–164.

Olden, J. D., and N. L. Poff. 2003. Redundancy and the choice of hydrologic indices for characterizing streamflow regimes. River Research and Applications 19:101–121.

Poff, N. L., and J. D. Allan. 1995. Functional organization of stream fish assemblages in relation to hydrological variability. Ecology 76:606–627.

Reid, L. 1993. Research and cumulative watershed effects. U.S. Forest Service, Pacific Southwest Research Station, General Technical Report PSW-GTR-141, Albany, California.

Richards, C., R. J. Haro, L. B. Johnson, and G. E. Host. 1997. Catchment and reach-scale properties as indicators of macroinvertebrate species traits. Freshwater Biology 37:219–230.

Richards, C., and G. E. Host. 1994. Examining land influences on stream habitats and macroinvertebrates: a GIS approach. Water Resources Bulletin 30:729–738.

Richter, B. D., J. V. Baumgartner, J. Powell, and D. B. Braun. 1996. A method for assessing hydrologic alteration within ecosystems. Conservation Biology 10:1163–1174.

Riitters, K., J. Wickham, R. O'Neill, B. Jones, and E. Smith. 2000. Global-scale patterns of forest fragmentation. Conservation Ecology 4(2):3.

Rohde, F. C., R. G. Arndt, D. G. Lindquist, and J. F. Parnell. 1994. Freshwater fishes of the Carolinas, Virginia, Maryland, and Delaware. The University of North Carolina Press, Chapel Hill.

Roth, N. E., J. D. Allan, and D. E. Erickson. 1996. Landscape influences on stream biotic integrity assessed at multiple spatial scales. Landscape Ecology 11:141–156.

Roy, A. H., A. D. Rosemond, M. J. Paul, D. S. Leigh, and J. B. Wallace. 2003. Stream macroinvertebrate response to catchment urbanisation (Georgia, U.S.A.). Freshwater Biology 48:1–18.

SAS Institute Inc. 1989. SAS/STAT® users guide, version 6, 4th edition, volume 2. SAS Institute Inc., Cary, North Carolina.

Saunders, D. A., R. J. Hobbs, and C. R Margules. 1991. Biological consequences of ecosystem fragmentation: a review. Conservation Biology 5:18–32.

Schlosser, I. J., and J. R. Karr. 1981. Riparian vegetation and channel morphology impact on spatial patterns of water quality in agricultural watersheds. Environmental Management 5:233–243.

Schueler, T. 1994. The importance of imperviousness. Watershed Protection Techniques 1:100–111.

Trombulak, S. C., and C. A. Frissell. 2000. Review of ecological effects of roads on terrestrial and aquatic communities. Conservation Biology 14:18–30.

Walters, D. M., D. S. Leigh, M. C. Freeman, B. J. Freeman, B. J., and C. M. Pringle. 2003. Geomorphology and fish assemblages in a Piedmont river basin, U.S.A. Freshwater Biology 48:1950–1970.

Wang, L., J. Lyons, P. Kanehl, R. Bannerman, and E. Emmons. 2000. Watershed urbanization and changes in fish communities in southeastern Wisconsin streams. Journal of the American Water Resources Association 36:1173–1189.

Wang, L., J. Lyons, P. Kanehl, and R. Bannerman. 2001. Impacts of urbanization on stream habitat and fish across multiple spatial scales. Environmental Management 28:255–266.

Wang, L., and J. Lyons. 2003. Fish and benthic macroinvertebrate assemblages as indicators of stream degradation in urbanizing watersheds. Pages 227–249 in T. P. Simon, editor. Biological response signatures: indicator patterns using aquatic communities. CRC Press, Boca Raton, Florida.

Ward, J. V., and J. A. Stanford. 1989. Riverine ecosystems: the influence of man on catchment dynamics and fish ecology. Canadian Special Publications in Fisheries and Aquatic Sciences 106:56–64.

American Fisheries Society Symposium 47:53–68, 2005

Measuring the Economic Benefits of Water Quality Improvement with Benefit Transfer: An Introduction for Noneconomists

CHRISTOPHER F. DUMAS, PETER W. SCHUHMANN

Department of Economics and Finance, University of North Carolina at Wilmington
Wilmington, North Carolina 28403-5945, USA

JOHN C. WHITEHEAD*

Department of Economics, Appalachian State University, Boone, North Carolina 28608-2051, USA

Abstract.—In this paper, we provide an introduction to water quality benefit estimation for noneconomists. Net water quality benefits are typically measured using the concept of consumer surplus, which is estimated using a number of economic valuation methodologies. These are divided into direct and indirect methods. Direct methods involve questioning survey respondents to determine their consumer surplus. Indirect methods use data from consumer market behavior to estimate economic values. When limited time or funding preclude costly data collection and the development of new consumer surplus estimates, the method of benefit transfer is used to tailor preexisting consumer surplus estimates to fit new policy situations. We provide an example of benefit transfer by estimating the value of water quality improvements for the Cape Fear River in North Carolina. Benefit transfer methods are used with three valuation approaches to estimate the benefits of water quality improvement.

Introduction

Urbanization has negative impacts on river and stream water quality and associated economic benefits. This chapter will describe categories of water quality benefits, discuss the economic methodologies commonly used to estimate the values of these benefits, explore the relatively new techniques of benefit transfer used to estimate benefits of a given water quality improvement using information from other locations or time periods, and apply benefit transfer techniques in a case study of the benefits of water quality improvement in the Cape Fear River basin, North Carolina. The discussion illustrates how economic methodologies can be used to document the economic benefits of maintaining water quality and associated ecological functions.

Water quality provides two broad classes of economic benefits, withdrawal benefits, and instream benefits (Feenberg and Mills 1980). Withdrawal benefits include municipal water supply and domestic

use (e.g., household drinking, cooking, washing, and cleaning) benefits, agricultural irrigation and livestock watering benefits, and industry process water benefits. If water quality is low, withdrawn water must be treated before it can be used, and the economic benefits (net of treatment costs) associated with its use are lower. Instream benefits (i.e., the benefits of water quality arising from water left "in the stream" and not withdrawn) include two subcategories: use benefits and nonuse benefits. Instream use benefits include swimming, boating, and sport-fishing benefits—benefits associated with direct human interaction with water in the stream/river. Other instream use benefits include the esthetic value of water quality that may accrue to nearby picnickers, streamside trail hikers, and streamside property owners. Instream *nonuse* benefits of water quality include stewardship value, altruistic value, bequest value, and existence value. Nonuse benefits accrue to individuals regardless of whether or not they have direct interaction with water. Stewardship value arises from a belief (often moral or religious) that humans are responsible for maintaining some level of water quality even in cases where no withdrawal or

* Corresponding author: whiteheadjc@appstate.edu

instream use benefits result. Altruistic value arises from the enjoyment some people receive from simply knowing that other people enjoy withdrawal or instream use benefits. Bequest value arises from a belief that current human generations are responsible for maintaining some level of water quality to "bequest" to future human generations. Existence value arises from the enjoyment some people receive from simply knowing that some level of environmental quality exists. If water quality is allowed to deteriorate, then stewardship, bequest, and existence goals may not be met, and associated benefits fall.

The impacts of urbanization on water quality benefits are mediated by aquatic ecosystems. Increases in stream nutrient levels that lead to algae blooms can reduce swimming and boating benefits. Reductions in dissolved oxygen that lead to fish kills can reduce fishing and streamside property value benefits. Increases in disease-causing bacteria due to urban and suburban storm water runoff can increase water treatment costs and reduce swimming, fishing, and boating benefits. Reductions in aquatic species populations or diversity caused by stream sedimentation or toxic chemical discharges can reduce stewardship, altruistic, bequest, and existence values. Economic valuation methodologies typically trace changes in water quality variables through changes in aquatic ecosystem parameters to changes in economic benefits. Often, it is a change in an aquatic ecosystem parameter, such as a fish population, algae population, or disease-causing bacteria population, that is the ultimate cause of a change in economic benefits.

The economic valuation methodologies vary depending on the category of water quality benefit. Appropriate methodologies are used to estimate the benefits arising from each category, and the resulting benefits are then added to arrive at a measure of the overall value of water quality. Market prices can be used together with traditional economic valuation and benefit cost analysis methodologies to derive estimates of most withdrawal benefits. However, many instream benefits lack direct market prices and have public good characteristics that make benefit estimation using traditional economic methodologies difficult. Specifically, many instream benefits exhibit the public good characteristics of *nonrivalry* and *nonexcludability*. Nonrivalry means that more than one consumer can enjoy the quality of a given body of water at the same time (whether or not this enjoyment is associated with direct use). Nonexcludability means that it is difficult (costly) to prevent one individual from enjoying the benefits created by another individual's

actions. If individuals cannot be excluded, then they will not pay prices to gain the benefits (instead, they will "free ride"), and therefore, price data will not be available.

This paper will focus on the estimation of the instream benefits of water quality changes because these types of benefits are more difficult to estimate and they are most pertinent to the theme of this book. Instream benefits are typically estimated using nonmarket valuation methodologies. Nonmarket techniques have been developed to estimate economic values in situations where direct market prices are lacking and where public good characteristics are significant. Nonmarket valuation methodologies include direct or stated preference and indirect or revealed preference approaches. The contingent valuation, contingent behavior, and conjoint/choice analysis methods are examples of direct approaches. The travel cost, averting behavior, and hedonic price methods are indirect approaches. Each of these methods requires primary data collection. When the cost of primary data collection is prohibitive and/or time is short, the benefit transfer approach can be used to develop economic benefit estimates.

With benefit transfer, benefit estimates from existing direct or indirect valuation case studies are spatially and/or temporally transferred to a new case study. There are four types of benefit transfer approaches: benefit estimate transfer, benefit function transfer, meta-analysis, and preference calibration. Benefit estimate transfer uses summary measures of the environmental benefit estimates directly. Researchers simply obtain a benefit estimate from a similar study conducted elsewhere and use it for the current policy analysis case study. With benefit function and meta-analysis transfer, researchers use statistical models to transfer benefits. Characteristics of the current policy situation or case study (e.g., population demographics, site characteristics) are substituted into a statistical model to translate benefit estimates more accurately. Preference calibration uses an analytical model to reconcile existing benefit estimates derived from different methodological approaches and develop consistent benefit estimates for the new policy study.

The remainder of this paper is organized as follows. In the second section of the paper, we present the economic theory and some definitions used in benefit–cost analysis and describe the water quality valuation methodologies. In the third section, we discuss the benefit transfer approach to estimating water quality benefits. In the fourth section, we present a case study: water quality improvement in the Cape

Fear River. In this example, benefit transfer methods are used with three valuation approaches to estimate the benefits of water quality improvement. The fifth section is a summary of our findings.

Economic Theory

Whenever a government project or policy is implemented, there are economic winners and losers. The economic efficiency criterion requires that the gains to the winners exceed the losses imposed on the losers. Economic efficiency is one of several criteria (others include equity and risk) used to assess the desirability of government projects, such as water quality improvement projects. Benefit–cost analysis is a method used to calculate and compare monetary gains and losses for the purpose of assessing efficiency (Boardman et al. 2001). When government pursues a water quality improvement policy, such as the regulation of polluting firms or the implementation of urban land use controls (e.g., zoning), gains and losses are distributed to consumers and firms. Losses are typically relatively straightforward to measure by considering reductions in firm profits and increases in consumer costs. However, gains are often more difficult to measure, especially when they come in the form of public goods such as water quality.

The concept of consumer surplus is the basis for measuring net economic benefits. Considering a market good, for example a car, the consumer surplus is the difference between what the consumer is willing (and able) to pay and the market price (amount actually spent) for the car. Consumer surplus is also called net willingness to pay (net WTP) since it is willingness to pay net of the costs. The consumer may be willing and able to pay the manufacturer's suggested retail price of $35,000 for a new Ford Mustang. However, if the agreed-upon price is $31,000 then the consumer surplus is $4,000—the difference between the consumer's maximum willingness to pay and the market price.

Nonmarket goods such as water quality also provide consumer surplus (Freeman 1993). In the context of water quality valuation, suppose a catch-and-release freshwater angler is willing and able to pay up to $125 for a good day of urban fishing. If the cost of the day trip is $25, then his consumer surplus is $125 – $25 = $100. Now suppose that a zoning law is enacted that leads to a water quality improvement that, in turn, increases the angler's expected catch per trip. With the increase in expected catch, the angler's willingness to pay might increase to, say, $160. If so, the angler's consumer surplus per trip after the water quality improvement is $160 – $25 = $135. The angler's economic gain from the water quality improvement is the change is his or her consumer surplus, or $135 – $100 = $35. The empirical challenge, of course, is to determine the angler's willingness to pay and consumer surplus before and after the water quality change.

Economics students may remember the graphical depiction of demand and consumer surplus (Figure 1). The demand curve (denoted D_1) is a downward sloping line with market price on the vertical axis and quantity purchased/consumed on the horizontal axis. The demand curve slopes downward due to the fact that lower prices are required to convince consumers to purchase larger quantities. Typically, the position of the demand curve is estimated using data on market prices and quantities purchased by the consumer. The rectangle below the current market price is the initial expenditure on the good (i.e., the product of price per unit and quantity of units purchased, noted as EXP in Figure 1). Changes in consumer surplus and not changes in expenditures (DEXP) should be used in benefit–cost analysis (Edwards 1991). In Figure 1, consumer surplus (CS) is the triangular area above the current market price and below the demand curve. The area of the consumer surplus triangle increases or decreases with changes in demand (i.e., with shifts in the position of the demand curve). Changes in consumer income, prices of related goods, consumer tastes, or most importantly for the present discussion, the quality of the good can cause shifts in demand. For example, an improvement in quality would increase demand, shifting it to the right (from D_1 to D_2 as shown in Figure 1). When the demand curve shifts to the right the associated consumer surplus area increases (DCS). This change in consumer surplus is the change in net economic benefits from the quality improvement. In practice, changes in consumer surplus have been found to be good approximations of more theoretically correct measures of economic benefit (Willig 1976; Randall and Stoll 1980). See Johansson (1987) for additional detail on the theory of environmental valuation.

Estimation of consumer surplus is relatively straightforward if market data exist. Typically, the demand curve equation is estimated statistically using data on market prices, quantities purchased by consumers, and other related variables such as consumer incomes and prices of related goods. Without market data, a number of methodologies have been developed to estimate consumer surplus. Consumer sur-

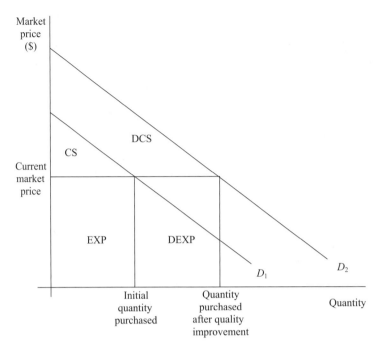

FIGURE 1. Relations among demand (*D*), consumer surplus (CS), and expenditure (EXP).

plus for nonmarket goods such as water quality improvements can arise from two sources: *use value* and *nonuse value*. Both use and nonuse values can be estimated using direct and indirect methodologies, although the latter are typically better suited for the estimation of use values, while the former are better suited for estimating nonuse values.

Indirect "Revealed Preference" Methods

The travel cost method (Bockstael 1995) is a revealed preference method that is most often used to estimate the benefits of outdoor recreation (e.g., improved fishing opportunities following water quality improvement). The travel cost method begins with the insight that the major cost of outdoor recreation is the travel and time costs incurred to get to the recreation site. Since individuals reside at varying distances from the recreation site, the variation in distance and the number of trips taken are used to trace out a demand curve for the recreation site. The demand curve is then used to derive the consumer surplus associated with using the site. With data on appropriate demand curve shift variables (i.e., independent variables such as measures of water quality), the economic benefits (i.e., changes in consumer surplus) associated with changes in the

shift variables (i.e., changes in water quality) can be derived.

A variation of the travel cost method is the random utility model (RUM) (e.g., Bockstael et al. 1989). Unlike the traditional travel cost model which focuses on one recreation site, a RUM uses information from multiple recreation sites. Individuals choose a recreation site based on differences in trip costs and site characteristics (e.g., water quality) between the alternative sites. Statistical analysis of the relationship between site characteristics and recreationists' site choices enables estimation of any consumer surplus changes arising from any changes in site characteristics, such as water quality.

The averting behavior method (Smith 1991) begins with the recognition that individuals seek to protect themselves when faced with environmental risk such as contaminated drinking water. Defensive behavior requires expenditures that would not normally be made. For example, purchases of bottled water or water filters may increase when the risk of contaminated drinking water increases. These increases in expenditures represent a lower bound on the economic benefits of policy that reduces drinking water risk.

The hedonic price method (Palmquist 1991; Freeman 1993) exploits the relationship between characteristics of land and labor markets, including water quality, and housing prices and wages. For example, land parcels in close proximity to water bodies with high quality water command higher prices than parcels adjacent to water with lower quality. Job markets with greater environmental amenities (such as high quality water) are associated with lower wages relative to other job markets because individuals are willing to accept lower wages in order to gain greater amenities. Housing and labor market differences can therefore be used to trace out the demand for water quality and used to measure economic benefits.

The travel cost, averting behavior, and hedonic methods are considered indirect valuation methods because they estimate the benefits of water quality improvement (or other nonmarket goods) through an examination of demands for related goods such as recreational trips and housing. The major strength of indirect approaches is that they are based on data reflecting actual market choices, where individuals bear the actual costs and benefits of their actions. However, indirect methods are generally only suitable for the estimation of use value, as nonuse value may not be reflected in market choices and behavior. The major weakness of indirect approaches is their reliance on historical data. Policies often are beyond the range of historical experience. For example, few residents of an urban area located near a long-degraded stream may have experienced a fishable stream. Without variation in the historical water quality data, it is difficult to predict how an improvement in water quality would shift the residents' demand curve and change their consumer surplus. Analysis of the economic benefits of water quality policy is often difficult when indirect valuation methods are used exclusively.

Direct "Stated Preference" Methods

The contingent valuation method (Mitchell and Carson 1989; Bateman and Willis 1999) is a stated preference approach that directly elicits willingness (and ability) to pay statements from survey respondents. In other words, respondents are directly asked about their willingness to pay (i.e., change in consumer surplus) for environmental improvement or willingness to accept (i.e., amount of monetary compensation required to allow) environmental degradation.

The method involves the development of a hypothetical market via in-person, telephone, mail, or other types of surveys. In the hypothetical market respondents are informed about the current prob-

lem and the policy designed to mitigate the problem. The state of the environment before and after the policy is described. Other contextual details about the policy are provided such as the policy implementation rule (e.g., majority voting) and the payment vehicle (e.g., increased taxes or utility bills). Finally, a hypothetical question is presented that asks respondents to choose between improved water quality with increased costs or the status quo. The choice is often framed as a referendum vote in order to make the situation more realistic. Respondents can be presented with multiple scenarios and make multiple choices. Statistical analysis of these data leads to the development of willingness to pay and consumer surplus estimates.

The contingent behavior approach is similar to the contingent valuation method in that it involves hypothetical questions. In contrast, the questions involve changes in hypothetical behavior instead of hypothetical changes in willingness to pay. For example, respondents can be asked about hypothetical recreation trips with and without water quality improvements (Whitehead et al. 2000). Conjoint analysis is a type of contingent behavior approach that asks about hypothetical recreation site choice and other discrete choices (Louviere 1988; Adamowicz et al. 1999). Again, respondents can be presented with multiple scenarios and make multiple choices. Contingent behavior and conjoint analysis responses are treated as behavioral data and are analyzed using the same statistical methods as are used in the indirect approaches.

A strength of the direct or stated preference approaches is their flexibility. Water quality policies are often new policies with no historical precedent. Absent a natural policy experiment, the historical (i.e., revealed preference) data does not contain observations related to the policy. Direct approaches can be used to construct realistic policy scenarios for any new policy. Oftentimes, hypothetical choices are the only way to gain policy relevant nonmarket benefit information. Another strength of the direct approaches, especially contingent valuation, is the ability to measure nonuse values, such as the value of improving aquatic ecosystems. The major weakness of the direct approaches is their hypothetical nature. Respondents are placed in unfamiliar situations in which complete information may not be available. At best, respondents give truthful answers that are limited only by their unfamiliarity. At worst, respondents give unconsidered answers due to the hypothetical nature of the scenario.

Benefit Transfer

The benefit transfer approach to environmental valu-ation was developed for situations in which the time and/or money costs of primary data collection for original direct and indirect studies are prohibitive. With benefit transfer, environmental benefit estimates from existing case studies (i.e., the study sites) are spatially and/or temporally transferred to a new, policy case study (i.e., the policy site). The more com-mon type of benefit transfer is the spatial transfer, where consumer surplus from the study site is trans-ferred to the policy site at the same point in time. Less common is the temporal transfer in which con-sumer surplus from one time period is transferred to another time period.

Benefit transfer has been widely used to inform policy analysis since the 1950s (Smith 1992; Bergstrom and DeCivita 1999). Yet, it was not until a 1992 special issue of *Water Resources Research* that attention was focused on the theory and practice of benefit trans-fer (Brookshire and Neil 1992). Research focusing on benefit transfer has rapidly increased since the special issue. Four benefit transfer methodologies have emerged: benefit estimate transfer, benefit function transfer, meta-analysis transfer, and most recently, pref-erence calibration transfer. Each of these transfer meth-odologies can be used to transfer benefit estimates obtained from a variety of benefit estimation method-ologies, such as travel cost, contingent valuation, and hedonic valuation.

Brouwer (2000) proposes some necessary condi-tions for a valid benefit transfer. First, consumer sur-plus from the study site must be theoretically and methodologically valid. Second, the populations in the study and policy sites must be similar. Third, the difference between prepolicy and postpolicy quality (or quantity) levels must be similar across study and policy sites. Fourth, the study and policy sites must be similar in terms of environmental characteristics. Fifth, the distribution of property rights and other institu-tions must be similar across sites. Accuracy of benefit transfer will suffer if any of these conditions is vio-lated. Yet, as will be shown below, the degree to which accuracy is impacted depends greatly upon the mea-sures used and the assumptions made.

Benefit Estimate and Function Transfer

Benefit function transfer should be distinguished from benefit estimate transfer. Benefit *estimate* transfer uses environmental benefit estimates developed for a study site at the policy site. Researchers simply obtain a benefit estimate from a similar study conducted else-where and use it for the current policy analysis case study (e.g., Luken et al. 1992). In contrast, benefit *function* transfer uses a statistical model of benefits developed at the study site to estimate benefits at the policy site (e.g., Desvousges et al. 1992). Character-istics from the policy site are substituted into the model from the study site to tailor benefit estimates for the policy site.

Loomis (1992) argues that benefit function trans-fer can be more powerful than benefit estimate trans-fer in situations where demographic or environmental quality factors (for example) at the study site differ from those at the policy site. However, empirical re-sults concerning the superiority of benefit function transfer are mixed. In a study of Wisconsin lake recre-ation, Parsons and Kealy (1994) find that benefit func-tion transfer estimates are within 4% of the original model estimates, while benefit estimate transfers are within 34%. Brouwer and Spaninks (1999) also find that benefit function transfer is more accurate (within 22%) than benefit estimate transfer. Loomis (1992) finds that recreational fishing benefits developed us-ing the travel cost method transfer from one state to another with between 5% and 15% accuracy. Loomis et al. (1995) find that per capita reservoir recreation benefit estimates from a travel cost model transfer ac-curately across sites.

In contrast, Barton (2002) finds that benefit es-timate transfer, with transfer errors of 20% and 30%, outperforms benefit function transfer in the case of water quality improvements in Costa Rica. In a study of marine recreational fishing using the contingent valuation method, Downing and Ozuna (1996) find that few benefit functions transfer and, of those that do, few benefit estimates generated from the benefit functions transfer accurately. Similarly, in a study of recreation sites in Arizona and New Mexico using con-tingent valuation, Kirchhoff et al. (1997) find that between 55% and 90% of the benefit function trans-fer estimates are not accurate.

Meta-Analysis Transfer

Meta-analysis is a general term for any methodology that summarizes results from several studies. In the case of environmental benefit transfer, benefit esti-mates gathered from several studies serve as the de-pendent variable in regression analysis, and character-istics of the individual studies (e.g., water quality, type of survey methodology) serve as the independent variables. Benefit transfer using meta-analysis has three advantages over benefit function transfer (Shrestha and Loomis 2001). First, by employing a large number of studies, benefit estimates will be more rigorous. Second, meta-analysis may be used to control for differences in functional form and other methodological differences across studies (Smith and Kaoru 1990a). Third, differences between the study site and the policy site can be better controlled.

Several meta-analysis studies focus on one valuation method and one type of environmental commodity. Smith and Kaoru (1990a, 1990b) conducted a meta-analysis of the benefit estimates derived from travel cost recreation demand models. Smith and Huang (1993, 1995) conducted a meta-analysis of air quality benefits derived from hedonic property value models. These studies confirm that study methodology influences benefit transfer estimates. The authors recommend that meta-analysis be used as a complement to other benefits transfer methods. Smith and Osborne (1996) conducted a meta-analysis of air visibility benefits. They found that benefit estimates tend to conform to important economic principles that confirm their validity, but this conclusion is subject to variation in research methods used in the studies. Loomis and White (1996) conducted a meta-analysis of studies of rare and endangered species. Their model is able to explain more than 50% of the variation in these values. They conclude that meta-analysis is a promising technique for benefit transfer.

Two meta-analysis studies compare alternative environmental valuation methods for a single environmental commodity. Walsh et al. (1992) conducted a meta-analysis of outdoor recreation value estimates from travel cost and contingent valuation studies. Woodward and Wui (2001) conducted a meta-analysis of studies of wetland values using travel cost, contingent valuation and other methods. Both studies conclude that the contingent valuation method tends to generate lower benefit estimates relative to other methods. A similar result is found by Carson et al. (1996).

Rosenberger and Loomis (2000) compare national and census region meta-analysis functions. The national and census region models produce benefit estimates that differ from those in the original studies by 54% and 71%, respectively. Benefit transfers are more accurate for activities with many existing studies in the database, such as fishing, than for activities with only a few studies, such as skiing. Shrestha and Loomis (2001) use results from U.S. studies to forecast benefits for international policy sites. They find

that average prediction error is between 24% and 30% after adjusting for inflation and exchange rates.

Finally, Smith and Pattanayak (2002) provide a review of the meta-analysis literature. They argue that few existing meta-analyses should be used for benefit transfer due to inconsistent definitions of the benefit estimates (e.g., pooling estimates from contingent valuation and travel cost methods) and environmental commodities (e.g., value derived for use versus nonuse values).

Preference Calibration Transfer

Smith et al. (2002) and Pattanayak et al. (in press) argue that a new approach to benefit transfer, preference calibration, is needed because the majority of the evidence appears to indicate that benefit function transfer is not accurate. As with benefit function transfer, preference calibration exploits benefit estimates from other studies. In contrast, preference calibration uses estimates from multiple methods to develop a preference function consistent with economic theory. Importantly, preference calibration ensures that benefit estimates do not violate the consumer's ability to pay requirement when the scale of the environmental change is large. In other words, preference calibration ensures that consumers can afford to pay the amounts indicated by the transferred willingness to pay estimates.

Smith et al. (2002) used preference calibration to estimate the benefits of improved water quality using contingent valuation, travel cost demand, and hedonic property value studies. They found that conventional benefit estimate transfer understate benefits by 83% for the travel cost studies and 3% for the hedonic property value studies. Conventional transfer overstate benefits by 64% for the contingent valuation study. Pattanayak et al. (in press) found that conventional benefit estimate transfer understate water quality benefits by 66% for travel cost studies and 16% for contingent valuation studies. The contingent valuation method performs better in the second study because it includes nonuse values as well as use values.

An Assessment

Three preferred types of benefit transfer are emerging: benefit function transfer, meta-analysis transfer, and preference calibration. Meta-analysis transfer has several advantages over benefit function transfer. A major advantage is that meta-analysis is able to control for differences in study methodologies. However, meta-analysis suffers from (1) reporting errors and omissions in the original studies, (2) inconsistent definitions of environmental commodities and values, and (3) large random errors. In addition, the development of a meta-analysis function is costly in terms of time and money relative to benefit function transfer due to the larger number of studies required.

Preference calibration has been proposed as a solution to the problems associated with benefit function transfer and meta-analysis transfer. A major benefit of preference calibration is its recognition that willingness to pay is constrained by income in situations involving large changes in policy variables. However, there are several problems with preference calibration. Preference calibration does not tailor the benefit estimates to the demographics and other characteristics of the policy site as does benefit function transfer and meta-analysis transfer. Preference calibration is more time consuming than benefits function transfer due to the increased analytical burden. Also, preference calibration has yet to be vetted by tests of transfer accuracy.

Numerous and restrictive conditions are necessary for the successful application of each of the three emerging benefit transfer methods. It is not surprising that many studies evaluating benefit transfer methods reject transfer accuracy. In other words, the differences between benefits from a primary study and transferred benefits are statistically significant. Nonetheless, the benefits from a primary study and transferred benefits are typically of the same order of magnitude and differences are typically much less than 100%. When primary data collection is not feasible, there are no current alternatives to benefit transfer. The practice of benefit transfer is sure to continue.

Policy Study: Cape Fear River

In this section, we use benefit transfer methods to estimate the benefits of hypothetical water quality improvement policies for residents of an urban area. Although it would be an interesting methodological exercise to estimate the benefits of a water quality improvement *for the same policy* using alternative benefit transfer methods to test their validity, the purpose of this paper is to illustrate the empirical use of existing methods. Given the limited scope of this study, we do not employ the time-intensive meta-analysis or preference calibration approaches to benefit transfer. Instead, we apply the benefit estimate and benefit function transfer approaches using the travel cost, hedonic price, and contingent valuation methods of estimating will-

ingness to pay and consumer surplus. The analysis illustrates how the benefit transfer approaches are used in combination with the valuation methods to obtain benefit estimates.

The case study site is the portion of the lower Cape Fear River that flows through New Hanover County, located in the southeastern corner of North Carolina. The Cape Fear River basin is the largest river basin in North Carolina (North Carolina Department of Environment and Natural Resources 2000). It originates near Greensboro and flows east past the Chapel Hill-Durham area and southeast to Wilmington (population = 75,838) in New Hanover County (population = 165,712) where it drains into the Atlantic Ocean. The Cape Fear River basin is comprised of the Haw, Deep, upper Cape Fear, Black, northeast Cape Fear, and lower Cape Fear watersheds.

The Cape Fear River is subject to point-source water pollution from industrial and municipal waste treatment facilities and nonpoint source pollution from agricultural runoff, storm water runoff from urban and suburban areas, and sediment from newly urbanizing areas. As of 1999, there were 280 point-sources of wastewater in the Cape Fear River basin permitted under the National Pollutant Discharge Elimination System (NPDES), with a total permitted flow of 1.34 million m^3/d (353 million gallons/d, MGD) (North Carolina Department of Environment and Natural Resources 2000). Of these, 58 were major sources, each emitting more than 3,700 m^3/d (1 MGD). The lower Cape Fear contains more than 50% of the agricultural hog production operations in North Carolina. Nutrients from treated hog waste sprayed onto field crops as fertilizer flow into tributary waters during high rainfall events. Although one-half of the land area is forested, the Cape Fear River basin is a rapidly urbanizing area. For example, Wilmington experienced significant economic growth during the 1990s, its population increasing by 29.4%. Land clearing and construction activities associated with development increase the sediment load in the river. As of 1999, 623 general stormwater permits (typically construction projects affecting two or more hectares) and forty-eight individual (large municipal and industrial) stormwater permits were issued within the basin under the stormwater program of the 1990 Clean Water Act.

Multiparameter water quality sampling for the Cape Fear River has been conducted by the Lower Cape Fear River Program (LCFRP) since June 1995 (Mallin et al. 2002). The LCFRP currently encompasses 35 water sampling stations throughout the Cape

Fear, Black, and northeast Cape Fear River watersheds. The LCFRP sampling program includes physical, chemical, and biological water quality measurements, analyses of the benthic and epibenthic macroinvertebrate assemblages, and assessment of the fish assemblages.

The main-stem lower Cape Fear River is characterized by somewhat turbid water containing high levels of inorganic nutrients. It is fed by two large blackwater rivers (the Black and northeast Cape Fear rivers) that have low levels of turbidity, but darkly colored water (due to naturally occurring tannins), with less inorganic nutrient content than the main stem. While nutrients are reasonably high in the river channels, algal blooms are rare because light is attenuated by water color or turbidity and flushing is high. Periodic algal blooms are seen in the tributary stream stations, some of which are impacted by point source discharges. Below some point sources, nutrient loading can be high and fecal coliform contamination occurs. Other stream stations drain blackwater swamps or agricultural areas, some of which periodically show elevated pollutant loads or effects.

During the 2001–2002 sampling period, a prolonged drought had a significant positive effect upon water quality. As a result of the drought conditions, a considerably lower number of stations were impaired by fecal coliform contamination than in the past several years. The impaired locations were a mixture of areas impacted by point and nonpoint source inputs. Against this background, we estimate the benefits of water quality improvement with the benefit transfer approach.

Benefit Estimate Transfer: Travel Cost Method

To illustrate a temporal benefit estimate transfer using the travel cost method of valuation, we apply estimates of the benefits of ambient water quality improvements in river basins and watersheds in North Carolina from Phaneuf (2002). Phaneuf (2002) used data from the Environmental Protection Agency's (EPA) national water-based recreational survey, which are combined with chemical measures of water quality. The random utility model (RUM) version of the travel cost method is employed to model behavioral responses to changes in water quality in order to aid in the design and implementation of total maximum daily load (TMDL) policies in North Carolina. As noted above, given that travel costs serve as an implicit price of a recreation visit, changes in

recreational site choices in response to changes in water quality can be used to estimate the use value of water quality improvements.

Phaneuf (2002) estimated the benefits of four potential changes: the loss of individual watersheds from recreation use, water quality improvements in individual watersheds, water quality improvements across an entire river basin, and reductions in ammonia and phosphorous. The specific water quality improvement for the second of these measures is defined as a reduction in pollution loadings such that a maximum of 10% of monitoring station readings for pH, dissolved oxygen, phosphorous, and ammonia are out of compliance for the watershed and is most applicable for our purposes here—to illustrate benefits transfer for a specific watershed. In addition to quantifying the value of reductions in pollutant loadings using individual measures of the pollutants, Phaneuf (2002) also derived the willingness to pay for the same improvements as measured by the EPA's index of watershed indicators (IWI) (U.S. Environmental Protection Agency 2002). This index is a scale of 1–6, with 1 indicating the highest water quality.

For the watersheds in the Cape Fear River basin, willingness to pay per trip to maintain (i.e., to prevent the loss of) existing recreation access is $0.29 for the upper Cape Fear River, $0.39 for the lower Cape Fear River, and $0.80 for the northeast Cape Fear River (Phaneuf 2002). Further, the willingness to pay per trip for the water quality *improvement* was found to be $0.10 for the upper and lower Cape Fear River and $0.24 for the northeast Cape Fear River. The mean willingness to pay per trip estimates across all watersheds in the state were $0.41 for access and $0.17 for the improvement. The ranges of these estimates were $0.05 to $2.91 and $0.00 to $1.44.

Phaneuf (2002) found that the per trip willingness to pay for a reduction in pollution loadings such that a maximum of 10% of readings are out of criteria for the entire Cape Fear River basin (as opposed to a single watershed within the basin) are between $1.00 and $6.29, depending on the specification of the statistical model and which water quality data are used. The per trip willingness to pay value found using the IWI is $2.25 (Phaneuf 2002). In terms of the benefits transfer, a lower bound on the aggregate benefits of basin-wide improvements over the entire season is approximated by multiplying these per trip benefits by the total number of freshwater angling days in North Carolina. The U.S. Fish and Wildlife Service estimated that 675,000 resident anglers fished 11.4 million freshwater days in North Carolina in 2001

(U.S. Department of the Interior, Fish and Wildlife Service and U.S. Department of Commerce, U.S. Census Bureau 2002). These estimates lead to an aggregate value of $31.8 million (2003 dollars) for the basin-wide water quality improvements using the IWI estimate. Using the range of values estimated for the 10% out-of-criteria improvements, this annual aggregate benefit measure is between $14.1 million and $88.9 million (2003 dollars).

We also obtain an aggregate estimate for New Hanover County by using data on North Carolina freshwater angler-days and population estimates for the state and county (New Hanover County contains approximately 2% of the North Carolina population). Assuming that the proportion of anglers in the population is constant across counties, this amounts to 13,500 resident anglers fishing 228,000 freshwater days in New Hanover County. These estimates lead to an aggregate value of $636,000 (2003 dollars) for the basin-wide water quality improvements using the IWI estimate. Using the range of values estimated for the 10% out-of-criteria improvements, the value to New Hanover County anglers is between approximately $283,000 and $1.86 million (2003 dollars).

Benefit Function Transfer: Hedonic Price Method

The existing hedonic studies of the value of water quality typically use water clarity or fecal coliform as a measure of water quality. We select fecal coliform, a group of bacteria widely used as an indicator of the presence of disease-producing bacteria, as our measure of water quality for the hedonic analysis. Water clarity would not be a good measure of water quality for the New Hanover county area, as several tributaries of the Cape Fear River are naturally low-visibility, low-clarity waters in their pristine states (due to naturally occurring tannins in the water). Fecal coliform measurements vary by an order of magnitude above and below the state health standard for human contact waters (200 CFU/100 mL) in the Lower Cape Fear River. During the 2001–2002 monitoring period, the state standard was exceeded six times (North Carolina Department of Environment, Health, and Natural Resources 1996). (The standard is typically violated more frequently; the 2001–2002 period had a relatively low number of violations due to low runoff conditions during a drought.)

For the benefit transfer application, we select Leggett and Bockstael's (2000) hedonic pricing study of the effect of fecal coliform water pollution on Chesa-

peake Bay shoreside property values. In addition to its focus on fecal coliform pollution, Leggett and Bockstael (2000) utilized relatively recent data (late 1990s) and considered coastal estuarine properties in the mid-Atlantic region of the United States, properties similar to those in our study region. We recalibrate the Leggett and Bockstael (2000) hedonic price model to New Hanover conditions. The recalibration accounts for differences in parcel area, distance to urban centers, and baseline fecal coliform levels between the Leggett and Bockstael (2000) study area and New Hanover County. The model is not recalibrated for differences between the two study areas in neighborhood land uses or distances to point sources of water pollution. For these variables, we use the mean values from Leggett and Bockstael (2000).

Land parcel and tax data for 2001 were provided by the New Hanover County Planning Department. Industrial, government, commercial and utility right-of-way parcels are excluded from the analysis. The remaining 334 residential and residential/farm parcels adjacent to the Cape Fear and northeast Cape Fear rivers in New Hanover County in 2001 occupy a total of 3,554 ha. The mean land value per parcel (excluding the value of any structures) is approximately $121,000 for residential land use (n = 331) and $300,000 for residential/farm land use (n = 3). Fecal coliform is measured at LCFRP water quality monitoring field station NAV, just north (upstream) of Wilmington, North Carolina. From 1997–2002, monthly average fecal coliform readings varied from a minimum of 6 CFU/100 mL to a maximum of 4,453 CFU/100 mL, depending on season, rainfall, and point source and nonpoint source pollution discharges, with a geometric mean of 31 CFU/100 mL.

The policy scenario consists of a hypothetical water quality program that would prevent deterioration of water quality from a baseline yearly median fecal coliform count of 40 CFU/100 mL, a level approximating current conditions, to the level of the state health standard for human contact waters, 200 CFU/100 mL. Using the Leggett and Bockstael (2000) model recalibrated for the Cape Fear region, we found that the 334 riverfront residential properties in New Hanover County have an aggregate land value (excluding the value of any structures) of approximately $42.4 million (2003 dollars) under baseline water quality conditions of 40 CFU/100 mL. If water quality were allowed to deteriorate to the level of the state health standard for human contact waters (200 CFU/100 mL), land value would fall to an estimated level of $39.1 million, a loss of $3.3 million.

This is equivalent to a 7.7% decrease in land value. The maximum decrease in value for any single property is $510,000 (for a 538-ha parcel slated for subdivision), the minimum decrease is $12, the mean decrease is $9,800, and the median decrease is $4,400.

Benefit Function Transfer: Contingent Valuation Method

The contingent valuation method literature contains a number of studies that estimate the economic values of river water quality. Several of these are focused on North Carolina river basins, but none focuses on the Cape Fear River basin. A recent study estimated the economic value of water quality protection in the Catawba River basin (Kramer and Eisen-Hecht 2002). The Catawba River basin is similar to the Cape Fear River basin in that it originates near an urban area, Charlotte, and flows southeast to the Atlantic coast. It differs in that the Catawba River basin is dominated by reservoirs and most of the basin is located in South Carolina. Nevertheless, we choose this as the study site due to its similarities to the policy site and the richness of the statistical valuation function relative to other North Carolina river basin valuation studies.

Kramer and Eisen-Hecht (2002) used a combination of mail and telephone survey methods. The sample is mailed an information booklet that describes a water quality management plan for the Catawba River. The booklet includes maps that show the potential deterioration in water quality given current population and land use changes as predicted by a water quality model. The proposed management plan would focus on several water quality problems: sediment, nutrients, toxic substances, bacteria, and viruses. The management plan would include the use of best management practices for construction and agriculture within the basin, develop a basin-wide land use plan, improve and increase the capacity of sewage treatment plants within the basin, and provide for the purchase and protection of land that is important for the protection of water quality.

Respondents were asked to vote for or against the management plan given that it would be financed by a specified increase in state income taxes over the following 5 years. The specified increase in state income taxes varied across survey respondents, ranging from $5 to $250 per year. Without further water quality information, the contingent valuation method cannot be used to place a monetary value on a specific water quality improvement (i.e., a change in pH or fecal coliform units). The benefit estimate from this application of the contingent valuation method is the willingness to pay for protection of current water quality with the proposed water quality management plan. Additional information from the water quality model that was used to estimate the potential degradation in water quality could be used to develop estimates for specific improvements. However, this level of analysis is beyond the scope of this paper.

Kramer and Eisen-Hecht (2002) statistically analyzed the survey data to develop a willingness to pay model. The model includes a number of variables that can be used to examine the validity of the hypothetical votes. For example, the probability of a vote for the management plan should fall as the tax amount increases and should rise with increases in respondent income. Such results were obtained in this study and indicate that respondents responded rationally to the stated cost of the policy relative to their income levels. These results strongly suggest that the hypothetical votes reveal valid economic values for Catawba River water quality.

Kramer and Eisen-Hecht (2002) estimated that respondent annual willingness to pay is $194 (1998 $) for 5 years for the Catawba River. The Catawba River willingness to pay model is calibrated for New Hanover County residents. Calibration involves substitution of relevant values from the policy site (New Hanover County) for the values used in the study site (Catawba River basin).

There are no objective measures for New Hanover County residents for most variables in the willingness to pay model. For these variables, we used the mean values from the Catawba River basin sample (Eisen-Hecht and Kramer 2002). These include study specific variables, such as knowledge and attitudes about water quality, and variables specific to the survey design. The willingness to pay also includes a variable for whether the respondent is from North Carolina or South Carolina. We set this variable equal to South Carolina, assuming that downstream New Hanover County residents are more similar to respondents in South Carolina than the upstream, urban North Carolina respondents. This choice has significant effects on willingness to pay. The alternative assumption would decrease annual willingness to pay estimates by almost $62.

For the demographic variables measuring respondent age, education, sex, and household income, we developed estimates of the mean values for New Hanover County residents 18 years or older using U.S. Census Bureau data. We assume that respondents would rate the use of the river as important and that drinking water is important. In order to differentiate between use and nonuse values, we alternatively assumed that altruistic, bequest, and existence values are zero and positive. The means from the Catawba River sample are used for all other variables.

Assuming that the willingness to pay functions for the Catawba River and the Cape Fear River are similar, these estimates represent the willingness to pay of New Hanover County residents to maintain water quality through a Cape Fear River basin-wide management plan. The willingness to pay of New Hanover County households is $175 per person, per year, for 5 years when nonuse values are equal to zero and $326 per person, per year, for 5 years when nonuse values are positive (2003 dollars). When nonuse value is considered the residual between total value and use value, this implies that nonuse values are 46% of the total value.

Comparison of Methods

The benefits of water quality improvement in the Lower Cape Fear River varied with method (Table 1). Willingness to pay estimates developed from the travel cost, hedonic price, and contingent valuation methods are aggregated by the number of New Hanover County angler-days (n = 13,500), New Hanover County residential properties in vicinity of the Cape Fear River (n = 334 properties), and New Hanover County households (n = 68,183), respectively. The raw value estimates from the transfer studies are not directly comparable for two reasons. First, the estimates refer to different time periods: the contingent

valuation estimates are annual values for each of 5 years, the travel cost estimates are annual values received each year in perpetuity, and the hedonic price method estimate is a capitalized, present value. To make the estimates comparable, we calculated the present value of the annual amounts (using a 5-year time horizon for the contingent valuation estimates and a 30-year time horizon for the travel cost method), and we annualized the hedonic price method estimate.

Second, each benefit transfer example focuses on a different policy context. The travel cost method willingness to pay estimate is appropriate for a policy that leads to a reduction in pollution loadings such that a maximum of 10% of readings are out of criteria for the entire Cape Fear River basin (as measured by a one unit change in a water quality index). In contrast, the hedonic price method and contingent valuation method estimates are appropriate for a water quality management plan that protects the current level of water quality, though the two estimates are based on different definitions of the current level of water quality and different definitions of the water quality management plan.

We used two discount rates for the present value calculations. The first discount rate, 2%, is a frequently used approximation of the real discount rate based on market interest rates and is recommended by the Congressional Budget Office (Hartman 1990). The second and higher discount rate, 7%, is required for benefit–cost analysis by the U.S. Office of Management and Budget (Office of Management and Budget 1992). The higher rate is based on the

TABLE 1. Aggregate benefits for Lower Cape Fear River water quality (millions of 2003 dollars).

Method	Aggregation	Policy	Annual			Present value		
			Unadjusted	CBO[a]	OMB[b]	Unadjusted	CBO[a]	OMB[b]
Travel cost	228,000 angler-days	Avoidance of 10% of water quality monitoring stations being out of compliance	$0.64				$14.33	$7.94
Hedonic price	334 properties	Protection of water quality to avoid increase in fecal coliform from current level		$0.15	$0.27	$3.30		
Contingent valuation	68,183 households	Protection of current water quality with a water quality management plan	$22.20				$104.62	$91.01

[a] Value adjusted based on the Congressional Budget Office discount rate of 2%.

[b] Value adjusted based on the U.S. Office of Management and Budget discount rate of 7%.

market rate of return of housing and corporate borrowing costs.

With discount rates of 2% and 7% the present value of aggregate benefits for anglers using the travel cost method are $14 million and $8 million. The hedonic price method gives the present value (capitalized value) of aggregate benefits for *riverfront* property owners directly; this value is $3.30 million. Using the hedonic price method estimate of $3.30 million and discount rates of 2% and 7%, the annualized value of the aggregate benefits for property owners are $0.15 million per year and $0.27 million per year. Using the contingent valuation method and discount rates of 2% and 7%, the present value of aggregate benefits (total value including nonuse value) for all households in the county (not just riverfront) are $105 million and $91 million.

This comparison illustrates the limitations of the alternative methods. The travel cost and hedonic price methods are applicable to particular populations and are not able to measure nonuse values. The contingent valuation method can be used to estimate nonuse values and is applicable to the entire population that might enjoy nonuse values. However, it is difficult to disentangle use and nonuse values from the total value estimate with the contingent valuation method.

It is tempting to add the estimates from the three methods to generate an estimate of the total benefit of the water quality improvement. However, this temptation is misguided for two reasons. First, the benefit estimates are for different policies as described above. Second, the total benefit estimate would be prone to double counting of benefits. The travel cost method primarily estimates the water quality benefits that are enjoyed by those who participate in outdoor recreation. The hedonic price method estimates the benefits of water quality improvements that accrue to property owners. Since proximity to recreation sites is an incentive for property owners to purchase housing near water, the benefits accruing to property owners might include recreation benefits. The contingent valuation method estimates the use values, including recreation benefits, for the general population. Adding the benefits from the travel cost method, the hedonic price method, and the contingent valuation method might include recreation benefits for three overlapping populations.

Summary

In this paper, we provide an accessible primer on the economics of water quality valuation. Consumer surplus, the net benefits of a particular good, can be estimated using a number of valuation methodologies, including direct and indirect methods. These methods typically require the collection of new data. Yet, policy analysis is often constrained by time and money. In these situations, benefit transfer methods can be used to develop estimates of consumer surplus for policy analysis. Benefit transfer involves the recalibration of existing consumer surplus estimates. Existing estimates are tailored to fit a new policy situation. We provide an example of benefit transfer by estimating the value of water quality improvements for the Cape Fear River in North Carolina. Benefit transfer methods are used with three valuation approaches (travel cost, hedonic pricing, and contingent valuation) to estimate the benefits of water quality improvements.

The successful application of benefit transfer methods remains a challenge. Brouwer (2000) provides some restrictive conditions for a successful benefit transfer. Many studies evaluating benefit transfer methods that adhere to most of Brouwer's (2000) conditions reject the statistical accuracy of benefit transfer estimates. However, benefit transfer methods typically obtain accuracy within an order of magnitude. The role of the benefit estimate in the policy process and the costs of a wrong decision are the two major issues that must be addressed when deciding whether to use a benefit transfer method instead of collecting primary data (Bergstrom and DeCivita 1999). Typically, benefit cost analysis is only one input into the policy decision process. When government water quality policy decisions do not hinge on whether the present value of net benefits is positive or negative, in other words, when the benefit cost analysis is advisory, the use of benefit transfer is an acceptable approach to obtain order of magnitude estimates of benefits.

When major government decisions are made, such as reauthorization of the Clean Water Act, the costs of a wrong decision could be in the millions, or even billions, of dollars. When determining whether to conduct a study based on primary data, the cost of the study must be compared to the potential cost of a wrong decision. For example, a benefit cost analysis that uses benefit transfer to estimate benefits may conclude that the present value of net benefits of a policy is $2 million. Based on the criterion of efficiency, the policy analyst would recommend that the policy should be pursued. However, a benefit cost analysis that uses new, primary data to estimate benefits may conclude that the present value of net benefits of the same policy is −$2 million. In this case, the policy analyst would recommend that the policy should not be pursued. If the study based on new, primary data costs $500,000, then it is an investment with a net gain of $1.5 million (i.e., the $0.5 million study prevents a $2 million mistake). In this case, the study based on new, primary data are preferred to benefit transfer. For most water quality policies the costs of a wrong decision are much smaller. In many of these cases, the benefit transfer approach may be preferred.

References

Adamowicz, W. L., P. C. Boxall, J. J. Louviere, J. Swait, and M. Williams. 1999. Stated-preference methods for valuing environmental amenities. Pages 460–479 in I. J. Bateman and K. G. Willis, editors. Valuing environmental preferences: theory and practice of the contingent valuation method in the US, EU, and developing countries. Oxford University Press Inc., New York.

Barton, D. N. 2002. The transferability of benefit transfer: contingent valuation of water quality improvements in Costa Rica. Ecological Economics 42:147–164.

Bateman, I. J., and K. G. Willis. 1999. Valuing environmental preferences: theory and practice of the contingent valuation method in the US, EU, and developing countries. Oxford University Press, New York.

Bergstrom, J. C., and P. DeCivita. 1999. Status of benefit transfer in the United States and Canada: a review. Canadian Journal of Agricultural Economics 47:79–87.

Boardman, A. E., D. H. Greenberg, A. R. Vining, and D. L. Weime. 2001. Cost-benefit analysis: concepts and practice, 2nd edition. Prentice Hall, Upper Saddle River, New Jersey.

Bockstael, N. E. 1995. Travel cost models. Pages 655–671 in D. W. Bromley, editor. Handbook of environmental economics. Blackwell Scientific Publications, Cambridge, Massachusetts.

Bockstael, N. E., K. E. McConnell, and I. E. Strand. 1989. A random utility model for sportfishing: some preliminary results for Florida. Marine Resource Economics 6:245–260.

Brookshire, D. S., and H. Neil. 1992. Benefit transfers: conceptual and empirical issues. Water Resources Research 28:651–655.

Brouwer, R. 2000. Environmental value transfer: state of the art and future prospects. Ecological Economics 32:137–152.

Brouwer, R., and F. A. Spaninks. 1999. The validity of environmental benefits transfer: further empirical testing. Environmental and Resource Economics 14:95–117.

Carson, R. T., N. E. Flores, K. M. Martin, and J. L. Wright. 1996. Contingent valuation and revealed preference methodologies: comparing the estimates for quasi-public goods. Land Economics 72:80–99.

Desvousges, W. H., M. C. Naughton, and G. R. Parsons. 1992. Benefit transfer: conceptual problems in estimating water quality benefits using existing studies. Water Resources Research 28:675–683.

Downing, M., and T. Ozuna, Jr. 1996. Testing the reliability of the benefit function transfer approach. Journal of Environmental Economics and Management 30:316–322.

Edwards, S. F. 1991. A critique of three "economics" arguments commonly used to influence fishery allocations. North American Journal of Fisheries Management 11:121–130.

Eisen-Hecht, J. I., and R. A. Kramer. 2002. A cost-benefit analysis of water quality protection in the Catawba basin. Journal of the American Water Resources Association 38:453–465.

Feenberg, D., and E. S. Mills. 1980. Measuring the benefits of water pollution abatement. Academic Press, New York.

Freeman, A. M., III. 1993. The measurement of environmental and resource values: theory and methods. Resources for the Future, Washington, D.C.

Hartman, R. T. 1990. One thousand points of light seeking a number: a case study of CBO's search for a discount rate policy. Journal of Environmental Economics and Management 18:S3–S7.

Kirchhoff, S., B. G. Colby, and J. T. LaFrance. 1997. Evaluating the performance of benefit transfer: an empirical inquiry. Journal of Environmental Economics and Management 33:75–93.

Kramer, R. A., and J. I. Eisen-Hecht. 2002. Estimating the economic value of water quality protection in the Catawba River basin. Water Resources Research 38:1182–1191.

Johansson, P.-O. 1987. The economic theory and measurement of environmental benefits. Cambridge University Press, New York.

Leggett, C. G., and N. E. Bockstael. 2000. Evidence of the effects of water quality on residential land prices. Journal of Environmental Economics and Management 39:121–144.

Loomis, J. B. 1992. The evolution of a more rigorous approach to benefit transfer: benefit function transfer. Water Resources Research 28:701–705.

Loomis, J. B., Roach, F. Ward, and R. Ready. 1995. Testing transferability of recreation demand models across regions: a study of corps of engineers reservoirs. Water Resources Research 31:721–730.

Loomis, J. B., and D. S. White. 1996. Economic benefits of rare and endangered species: summary and meta-analysis. Ecological Economics 18:197–206.

Louviere, J. J. 1988. Conjoint analysis modeling of stated preferences: a review of theory, methods, recent developments and external validity. Journal of Transport, Economics and Policy 10:93–119.

Lower Cape Fear River Program. 2003. University of North Carolina at Wilmington, Wilmington, North Carolina. Available: http://www.uncw.edu/cmsr/aquaticecology/lcfrp/. (October 2003)

Luken, R. A., F. R. Johnson, and V. Kibler. 1992. Benefits and costs of pulp and paper effluent controls under the Clean Water Act. Water Resources Research 28:665–674.

Mallin, M. A., M. H. Posey, T. E. Lankford, M. R. McIver, H. A. CoVan, T. D. Alphin, M. S. Williams, and J. F. Merritt. 2002. Environmental assessment of the lower Cape Fear River system, 2001–2002. University of North Carolina at Wilmington, Center for Marine Science, CMS Report Number 02–02, Wilmington.

Mitchell, R. C., and R. T. Carson. 1989. Using surveys to value public goods: the contingent valuation method. Resources for the Future, Washington, D.C.

North Carolina Department of Environment and Natural Resources. 2000. Cape Fear River basinwide water quality plan. North Carolina Department of Environment and Natural Resources, Raleigh.

North Carolina Department of Environment, Health, and Natural Resources. 1996. Water quality progress in North Carolina, 1994–1995 305(b) Report. North Carolina Department of Environment and Natural Resources, Division of Water Quality, Report No. 96–03, Raleigh.

Office of Management and Budget. 1992. Circular no. A-94, revised (Transmittal Memo No. 64). Available: http://www.whitehouse.gov/omb/circulars/a094/a094.html. (October 2003)

Palmquist, R. B. 1991. Hedonic methods. Pages 77–120 in J. B. Braden and C. D. Kolstad, editors. Measuring the demand for environmental quality. Elsevier, New York.

Parsons, G. R., and M. J. Kealy. 1994. Benefits transfer in a random utility model of recreation. Water Resources Research 30:2477–2484.

Pattanayak, S. K., V. K. Smith, and G. Van Houtven. In press. Improving the practice of benefits transfer: a preference calibration approach. In S. Navrud and R. Ready, editors. Environmental value transfers: issues and methods. Kluwer, Dordrecht, Netherlands.

Phaneuf, D. J. 2002. A random utility model for total maximum daily loads: estimating the benefits of watershed-based ambient water quality improvements. Water Resources Research 38:1254–1264.

Randall, A., and J. R. Stoll. 1980. Consumer's surplus in commodity space. American Economic Review 70:449–455.

Rosenberger, R. S., and J. B. Loomis. 2000. Using meta-analysis for benefit transfer: in-sample convergent validity tests of an outdoor recreation database. Water Resources Research 36:1097–1107.

Shrestha, R. K., and J. B. Loomis. 2001. Testing a meta-analysis model for benefit transfer in international outdoor recreation. Ecological Economics 39:67–83.

Smith, V. K. 1991. Household production functions and environmental benefit estimation. Pages 41–76 in J. B. Braden and C. D. Kolstad, editors. Measuring the demand for environmental quality. Elsevier, New York.

Smith, V. K. 1992. On separating defensible benefit transfers from 'smoke and mirrors.' Water Resources Research 28:685–694.

Smith, V. K., and J.-C. Huang. 1993. Hedonic models and air quality: twenty-five years and counting. Environmental and Resource Economics 36:23–36.

Smith, V. K., and J.-C. Huang. 1995. Can markets value air quality? a meta-analysis of aedonic property value models. Journal of Political Economy 103:209–227.

Smith, V. K., and Y. Kaoru. 1990a. Signals or noise? explaining the variation in recreation benefit estimates. American Journal of Agricultural Economics 72:419–433.

Smith, V. K., and Y. Kaoru. 1990b. What have we learned since Hotelling's letter? A meta-analysis. Economics Letters 32:267–272.

Smith, V. K., and L. L. Osborne. 1996. Do contingent valuation estimates pass a 'scope test'? a meta-analysis. Journal of Environmental Economics and Management 31:287–301.

Smith, V. K., and S. K. Pattanayak. 2002. Is meta-analysis a Noah's ark for non-market valuation? Environmental and Resource Economics 22:271–296.

Smith, V. K., G. Van Houtven, and S. K. Pattanayak. 2002. Benefit transfer via preference calibration: 'prudential algebra' for policy. Land Economics 78:132–252.

U.S. Department of the Interior, Fish and Wildlife Service and U.S. Department of Commerce, U.S. Census Bureau. 2002. 2001 National survey of fishing, hunting, and wildlife-associated recreation. Washington, D.C.

U.S. Environmental Protection Agency. 2002. Index of

watershed indicators: an overview. Washington, D.C.

Walsh, R. G., D. M. Johnson, and J. R. McKean. 1992. Benefit transfer of outdoor recreation demand studies, 1968–1988. Water Resources Research 28:707–713.

Whitehead, J. C., T. C. Haab, and J.-C. Huang. 2000. Measuring recreation benefits of quality improve-ments with revealed and stated behavior data. Resource and Energy Economics 22:339–354.

Willig, R. D. 1976. Consumers' surplus without apology. American Economic Review 66:589–597.

Woodward, R. T., and Y.-S. Wui. 2001. The economic value of wetland services: a meta-analysis. Ecological Economics 37:257–270.

American Fisheries Society Symposium 47:69–85, 2005

Urbanization Effects on Fishes and Habitat Quality in a Southern Piedmont River Basin

DAVID M. WALTERS*,[1]

Institute of Ecology, The University of Georgia, Athens, Georgia 30602, USA

MARY C. FREEMAN

USGS Patuxent Wildlife Research Center, The University of Georgia, Athens, Georgia 30602, USA

DAVID S. LEIGH

Department of Geography, The University of Georgia, Athens, Georgia 30602, USA

BYRON J. FREEMAN

Institute of Ecology and Museum of Natural History, The University of Georgia, Athens, Georgia 30602, USA

CATHERINE M. PRINGLE

Institute of Ecology, The University of Georgia, Athens, Georgia 30602, USA

Abstract.—We quantified the relationships among urban land cover, fishes, and habitat quality to determine how fish assemblages respond to urbanization and if a habitat index can be used as an indirect measure of urban effects on stream ecosystems. We sampled 30 wadeable streams along an urban gradient (5–37% urban land cover) in the Etowah River basin, Georgia. Fish assemblages, sampled by electrofishing standardized stream reaches, were assessed using species richness, density, and species composition metrics. Habitat quality was scored using the Rapid Habitat Assessment Protocol (RHAP) of the U.S. Environmental Protection Agency. Urban land cover (including total, high-, and low-density urban) was estimated for the drainage basin above each reach. A previous study of these sites indicated that stream slope and basin area were strongly related to local variation in assemblage structure. We used multiple linear regression (MLR) analysis to account for this variation and isolate the urban effect on fishes. The MLR models indicated that urbanization lowered species richness and density and led to predictable changes in species composition. Darters and sculpin, cyprinids, and endemics declined along the urban gradient whereas centrarchids persisted and became the dominant group. The RHAP was not a suitable indicator of urban effects because RHAP-urban relationships were confounded by an overriding influence of stream slope on RHAP scores, and urban-related changes in fish assemblage structure preceded gross changes in stream habitat quality. Regression analysis indicated that urban effects on fishes accrue rapidly (<10 years) and are detectable at low levels (~5–10% urbanization). We predict that the decline of endemics and other species will continue and centrarchid-dominated streams will become more common as development proceeds within the Etowah basin.

* Corresponding author: walters.davidm@epa.gov
[1] Present address: US EPA National Exposure Research Laboratory, Mail Stop 642, 26 West Martin Luther King Drive, Cincinnati, Ohio 45268, USA. Phone: 513-569-7302

Introduction

Protecting stream resources from human impacts increasingly depends on understanding the linkages between urban land use and stream systems. Relatively low levels of basin urbanization (e.g., 10–20%) cause major changes in stream hydrology, geomorphology, water quality, and stream communities (Baer and Pringle 2000; Paul and Meyer 2001). Urban land cover, or associated variables such as impervious surface area, is linked to declines in fish richness, diversity, density, and biomass as well as changes in population structure of fishes and trophic structure of assemblages (Klein 1979; Scott et al. 1986; Lenat and Crawford 1994; Weaver and Garman 1994; Yoder and Rankin 1996). Urbanization is also associated with declines in biotic integrity, with increases in tolerant and exotic taxa, and with decline or extirpation of sensitive species (Wang et al. 1997; Boet et al. 1999; Onorato et al. 2000; Wang et al. 2000; Wolter et al. 2000).

In this study, we investigated the effects of urbanization on stream fishes in a southern Piedmont drainage characterized by exceptional species endemism as well as by local variation in assemblage composition. The southern Piedmont is among the most rapidly developing areas of the United States (USDA 2000), and increasing urbanization will likely affect fish assemblages. Although biotic integrity is known to decrease with urban sprawl (e.g., Steedman 1988; Wang et al. 1997), it is less clear if specific taxa (such as endemic species) vary predictably with increasing urban land cover. In addition, Walters et al. (2003a) found that reach-level variation in assemblage structure was strongly linked to stream slope and associated benthic habitat variables in this Piedmont system. This led us to investigate whether an effect of increasing urban land cover on fishes would be detectable given spatial variation in fish assemblages driven by geomorphology. Spatial variation is a common feature of stream communities (Allan 1995); however, most prior studies of urbanization effects on fishes have been limited to gradients in single streams or comparisons between urban and reference drainage basins (Paul and Meyer 2001). Studies of urban gradients and fishes in multiple basins are rare and have mostly focused on agricultural-dominated areas of the upper Midwest (e.g., Steedman 1988; Wang et al. 1997, 2000). Comparable studies are lacking for the southern Piedmont.

Linking land use change with stream communities and habitat is a critical step in aquatic resource management (Jacobson et al. 2001). If habitat quality changes predictably with urban land cover and fish assemblages shift in response to habitat quality, then habitat quality assessment can be used as an indirect measure of urban effects on stream biota. However, studies in the Midwest have found that habitat quality is a suitable indicator of agricultural impacts but poorly reflects urban effects on stream biota (Roth et al. 1996; Wang et al. 1997, 2001). If urbanization effects on biota precede gross structural changes to streams, then we could expect to find streams in urbanizing catchments with altered biotic assemblages that also appear to have high habitat quality. Conversely, strong correlations among fish assemblage structure, urban land cover, and stream habitat quality would support the use of habitat indices in streams draining urbanizing catchments.

Temporal components of land cover change on streams have received less attention than spatial components (Allan and Johnson 1997; Harding et al. 1998). Streams clearly respond to urbanization, but the timing of the response is poorly understood and basic questions remain unanswered. It is unknown whether fishes respond to disturbance during the initial development phase (e.g., increased sediment loading) or to the chronic, long-term effects of increased urban cover (e.g., altered hydrology and poor water quality). If urban effects accrue rapidly, then fish assemblages in recently urbanized catchments should exhibit changes in structure comparable to those with a longer history of equivalent levels of urbanization. Understanding how quickly streams respond is important for managing aquatic resources in urbanizing landscapes.

Urbanizing rural catchments in the southern Piedmont present a unique setting to examine the complex spatial and temporal aspects of urban impacts on aquatic systems. This study addresses the following questions: (1) How do fish assemblages change along an urban gradient?, (2) Does a widely-used measure of habitat quality reflect urbanization effects on fish assemblages?, and (3) How quickly do fishes respond to urban development?

Study Area

This study was conducted in wadeable tributaries in the Piedmont province of the Etowah River basin, which forms part of the upper Coosa River drainage. Portions of the Etowah basin lie in the Blue Ridge, Ridge and Valley, and Piedmont physiographic provinces of the southern Appalachian highlands (Figure 1). The southern Appalachian highlands are a center of stream fish biodiversity and endemism (Williams et

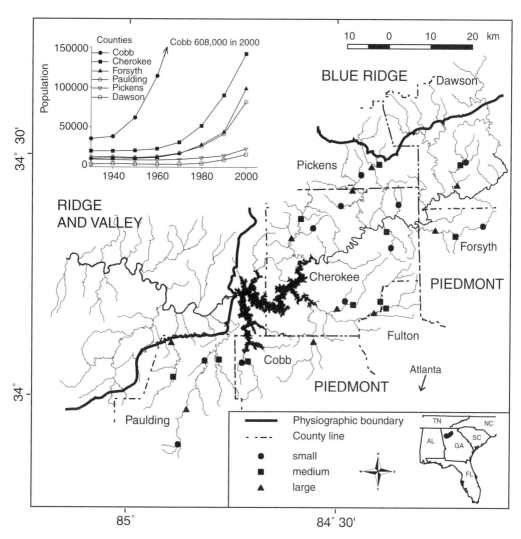

FIGURE 1. Map of sample sites in the Etowah River basin. The inset graph shows population growth 1930–2000 (U.S. Census Office 1930–2000) for counties in the study area except for Fulton County, which was strongly influenced by the population of Atlanta. Population growth in Fulton County basins in this study is similar to the trend observed for neighboring Cherokee County.

al. 1992; Warren and Burr 1994; Warren et al. 2000), and Burkhead et al. (1997) estimated that 91 species from 18 families are native to the Etowah system. The most diverse families are Cyprinidae (31 species), Percidae (19 species), and Centrarchidae (13 species). Warren et al. (1997) classified 16 species of the Tallapoosa and Coosa River systems as endemic, a level of endemic species richness unsurpassed in southeastern river systems.

Land cover in the Etowah basin is a mixture of forest, agriculture, and urban development (Leigh et al. 2001). Agricultural land use is primarily pasture

for hay production and grazing, and row crops are a minor component. Recent urban development in the basin is driven by population increases fueled by the spread of metropolitan Atlanta. Several counties have experienced exponential population growth that began in the 1970s and 1980s. The southern most counties near Atlanta show the greatest population increases (Figure 1, inset graph), and two of these, Forsyth and Paulding, were among the 10 fastest growing counties in the United States in 1997 (USCB 1998).

We randomly selected 30 Etowah basin streams ranging from 0% to 37% urban land cover. Streams were stratified into small, medium, and large basin size groups of approximately 15, 50, and 100 km² (±26%) (Figure 1; Appendix 1). All sample reaches are in the Piedmont, but two catchments have headwaters in the Blue Ridge.

Methods

Fish Sampling and Assemblage Variables

Fishes were sampled during summer base flow conditions in 1999 and 2000. Reaches of 200, 300, and 400 m were sampled in small, medium, and large streams, respectively. These reaches were approximately 40 times the average base flow wetted channel width within each stream size-group, which is slightly longer than the 35 times stream width recommended by Simonson and Lyons (1995) to assess fish assemblages in wadeable streams. Reaches were sampled in a single pass (Simon and Lyons 1995) using a crew of four to six persons equipped with a backpack electrofisher, seine, and dip nets. Reaches were divided into two sections of equal length. The first half of the reach (i.e., 20 times mean width) was sampled to obtain quantitative catch data for calculating relative abundances (Angermeier

and Smogor 1995). Large individuals (>20 cm) and fishes with protected status were counted and released. All other fishes were euthanized and preserved for laboratory identification. The second half of the reach was sampled to improve our estimate of site species richness, and we retained voucher specimens of species not observed in the first half of the reach.

Assemblage variables used for analyses included richness and density as well as the relative contribution of selected taxonomic groups (Table 1). Centrarchids, darters, and cyprinids were selected as the primary taxonomic groups because they account for more than 70% of the species we collected, and these account for much of the among-site variance in species composition in these streams (Walters et al. 2003a). Sculpin were included with darters because they use similar benthic habitats and prey (Etnier and Starnes 1993). We also included insectivorous cyprinids, a subgroup of cyprinids commonly used as a positive indicator in biotic indices (Miller et al. 1988), based on diet information in Etnier and Starnes (1993) (Appendix 2). In addition to these major species groups, we included a category for endemic species, those fishes distributed primarily in the upper Alabama River basin above the Fall Line (Appendix 2).

TABLE 1. Fish assemblage variables used in correlation and regression analysis. Scatterplots and trial and error were used to identify the best transformations for richness and density (Ott 1988).

Fish assemblage variable	Description	Transformation
Richness[a]	total species	$\log_{10}(x)$
Density[b]	fishes/m²	$x^{0.25}$
Number of species[a]		
darters and sculpin		none
centrarchids		none
cyprinids		none
insectivorous cyprinids		none
endemic species		none
Proportion of species[a]		
darters and sculpin	# (darter and sculpin spp.)/richness	none
centrarchids	# centrarchid spp./richness	none
cyprinids	# cyprinid spp./richness	none
insectivorous cyprinids	# insectivorous cyprinid spp./richness	none
endemic species	# endemic spp./richness	none
Relative abundance[b]		
darters and sculpin	abundance/total catch	none
centrarchids	abundance/total catch	arc-sine(square-root (x))
cyprinids	abundance/total catch	none
insectivorous cyprinids	abundance/total catch	none
endemic species	abundance/total catch	none (unable to normalize)

[a] Calculated from total reach (40× stream width).

[b] Calculated from first half of reach (20× stream width). See Methods for details.

We designated endemics based on distributional information provided by Mettee et al. (1996). All endemics were either darters or cyprinids except for *Cottus carolinae zopherus*, a taxonomically distinct form of banded sculpin endemic to the upper Coosa system (Etnier and Starnes 1993).

The contribution of each species group to the population was calculated as the number of species, the proportion of total richness, and the proportion of total catch (relative abundance) (Table 1). Measures of proportional richness are not commonly used in assemblage studies. We used these variables because they can identify groups that persist relative to other species and they can identify patterns in species composition even if overall richness is similar among sites. Numbers of species and proportional richness were derived from species lists compiled from the entire sampled reach (i.e., 40 times stream width). Relative abundance was calculated using catch data from the first half of each reach. Relative abundance of darters was calculated without blackbanded darter *Percina nigrofasciata*, a species that is widespread and locally common in the Etowah system (Walters et al. 2003a).

Stream and Catchment Characteristics

Stream slope and basin area were the only geomorphic variables compiled for this study. We included these variables in this study because a prior multivariate analysis of these streams identified slope and basin area (a surrogate for stream size) as the primary predictors of fish assemblages (Walters et al. 2003a). Stream slope was surveyed with an electronic total station over reaches scaled to approximately 20 times the average base flow width for streams in each size-class (i.e., 100-, 150-, and 200-m reaches). Slope was measured as the average gradient through the tops of riffles. ArcView software was used to calculate area and percentage of urban land cover for catchments. Catchment boundaries upstream of sample sites were delineated on digital raster graphics of the latest 7.5 minute USGS quadrangles.

We used the USEPA Rapid Habitat Assessment Protocol (RHAP) to assess stream habitat quality (Barbour et al. 1999). The RHAP uses 10 metrics to assess the condition of various stream habitat parameters, including benthic habitat quality, channel and bank condition, instream habitat heterogeneity, and riparian vegetation. Each metric is scored on a continuous scale ranging from 0 to 20 based on a visual assessment of the habitat feature. Metric scores were averaged for an overall RHAP score. We assessed habitat metrics over the entire reach sampled for fishes. The RHAP was usually calculated the same day as fish sampling and was always evaluated at base flow to allow comparisons among all sites. Two to four investigators completed RHAP at each site, and final scores were based on the mean of multiple assessments.

Land cover data were derived from Landsat TM images from June 1987 and July 1997 (Lo and Yang 2000). The images have 25-m resolution and overall land cover classification accuracy of about 90%, based on visual interpretation of color infrared aerial photographs (Lo and Yang 2000). Two urban land cover types were classified. High-density urban (HDU) has approximately 80–100% ground coverage with construction material and includes commercial buildings, parking lots, residential development within city cores, and multi-lane highways. Low-density urban (LDU) is roughly 50–80% construction material and is characterized by single or multiple family housing developments and two-lane roads. The LDU and HDU were summed to calculate the total basin percent coverage of urban land cover (U). Totals from 1987 were subtracted from 1997 totals to calculate the percentage of basin area converted during the decade. Three rural basins had slightly less (e.g., <2%) urban land cover in 1997 than 1987. We attributed this decline to small error in the accuracy of the data rather than actual loss of urban land. For these catchments, we assigned a value of 0 for 1987–1997 change. We limited our spatial scale to land cover of the entire catchment to assess the total impact of urbanization within a basin (Wang et al. 1997).

Data Analysis

Normality of all variables was checked using the Kolmogorov-Smirnov test using SigmaStat 4.0 and transformations were applied if needed (Table 1). Land cover percentages were converted to decimal proportions and transformed using arc-sine (square-root (x)) for correlation analysis (Sokal and Rohlf 1995). Untransformed land cover data were used in some scatter plots to illustrate trends and identify possible thresholds in the response of dependent variables. Land cover variables covary to some extent because as one element increases, others decline (Cain et al. 1997). The urban variables used in this study suffer from a lack of independence. For instance, all 1987 urban cover is contained in the 1997 urban cover because urbanized land seldom reverts to agricultural or forested cover. We used correlation analysis to quantify colinearity among land cover variables.

Relationships among fishes, land cover, stream slope, basin area, and habitat quality were quantified using correlation analysis, linear regression, and non-linear regression. We report actual probability values for tests, unadjusted for potential inflation of type I error rate resulting from multiple analyses derived from a single dataset. If scatter plots indicated nonlinear relationships between variables, curves were fit to the data using nonlinear equations derived from Sigma Plot 4.0. Scatterplots were evaluated to identify categories of nonlinear equations (e.g., polynomial and sigmoidal) that provided the most realistic fit to the data. Equations were applied to the data and were evaluated based on minimizing sum of squares error, maximizing r^2, and homoscedasticity of residuals. If multiple equations provided similar results for these criteria, the simplest model was selected.

We used forward stepwise multiple regression analysis to build predictive models for proportional richness, relative abundance, and RHAP. This procedure is recommended for exploratory analyses of large data sets (Neter et al. 1996) and allowed us to partition the variance in dependent variables relative to geomorphology and urban land cover. We set $P = 0.1$ to enter or remove variables. Variables were not included in the models unless they were significant at $P = 0.05$ and explained more than 4% of the variance in dependent variables. The analyses were conducted using JMP 5.0 (Freund et al. 2003). We transformed slope using $\log_{10}(x)$, a robust and widely used transformation for nonlinear data (Ott 1988), in multiple linear regression analysis. Other nonlinear equations provided a better fit for some dependent variables, but these transformations (e.g.,

sigmoidal) were variable specific and complicated comparisons among models (Walters 2002). Additionally, geomorphic analysis at these sites showed that $\log_{10}$ was an appropriate transformation for linking stream slope with other physical variables such as particle size distribution (Walters et al. 2003a).

Results

Land Cover Characteristics

The LDU accounted for about 87% of urban land cover (Figure 2). Mean U across basins nearly doubled from around 8% to 15% from 1987 to 1997. Mean HDU only increased from 1.1% to 1.7% over the decade, so most of the increase in U resulted from low-density housing development. Land cover variables demonstrated a high degree of colinearity ($r = 0.70$–0.99, Table 2), and correlation was highest among categories within a single year ($r = 0.85$–0.99). Correlations of 1987 and 1997 land cover with the 1987–1997% urban change were weaker, although all correlations with 1997 land cover were significant (Table 2). Basin area and slope were generally uncorrelated with urban cover except for a weak negative correlation between slope and 1987–1997 LDU.

Correlations of Fishes and RHAP with Urban Land Cover, Basin Area, and Slope

Assemblage variables were significantly correlated with urban land cover, RHAP, and geomorphic variables (Figure 3). Urban land cover (1997 U) was unrelated

TABLE 2. Correlation matrix (Pearson's r) of independent variables. Land cover abbreviations: U, urban; HDU, high-density urban; LDU, low-density urban. All land-cover variables are arc-sine (square-root (x)) transformed percentages. Correlations significant at $P < 0.05$ (uncorrected for Type I error rate) are in bold; $P < 0.01$ are in bold and italics; $P < 0.001$ are in bold, italics, and underlined ($n = 30$ sites).

	Basin area (km²)	$\log_{10}$ slope	1987% U	1987% HDU	1987% LDU	1997% U	1997% HDU	1997% LDU	1987–1997% U	1987–1997% HDU	1987–1997% LDU
$\log_{10}$ slope	**−0.37**										
1987 U	−0.10	0									
1987 HDU	−0.18	0.10	***0.90***								
1987 LDU	−0.07	−0.02	***0.99***	***0.86***							
1997 U	−0.11	−0.17	***0.85***	***0.75***	***0.85***						
1997 HDU	−0.22	0.04	***0.82***	***0.86***	***0.78***	***0.84***					
1997 LDU	−0.08	−0.20	***0.83***	***0.70***	***0.83***	***0.99***	***0.78***				
1987–1997 U	−0.04	−0.35	**0.36**	0.28	**0.38**	***0.79***	**0.50**	***0.82***			
1987–1997 HDU	−0.11	−0.03	0.35	0.31	0.34	***0.58***	***0.74***	**0.53**	**0.56**		
1987–1997 LDU	−0.04	**−0.37**	0.35	0.26	**0.36**	***0.77***	0.43	***0.81***	***0.99***	**0.46**	
RHAP	−0.08	***0.66***	***−0.47***	**−0.42**	***−0.47***	***−0.56***	***−0.48***	***−0.56***	***−0.47***	−0.31	**−0.46**

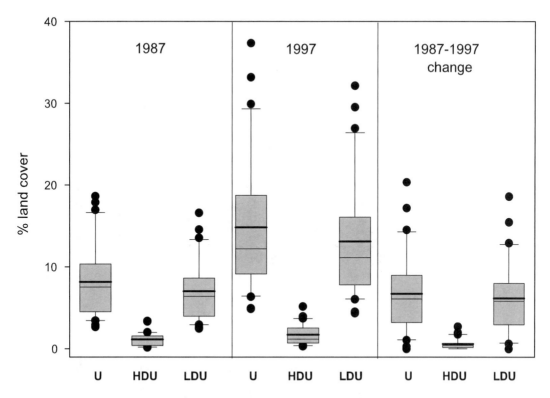

FIGURE 2. Box and whisker plots of total urban (U), high-density urban (HDU), and low-density urban (LDU) for basins upstream of 30 sample reaches in Etowah River tributaries. Top and bottom boundaries of the box indicate 75th and 25th percentiles, respectively. Within the boxes, thin lines indicate the median and thick lines indicate the mean. Whiskers above and below the box indicate the 90th and 10th percentiles.

to richness and density but was significantly related to changes in species composition. Centrarchids increased with 1997 U, whereas measures (e.g., relative abundance) of all other species groups showed significant declines. Correlations between fishes and RHAP showed the opposite trend (Figure 3). All groups except centrarchids were positively correlated with habitat quality. Assemblage structure also varied with stream geomorphology. Changes in species composition with slope showed a similar pattern to those for RHAP scores. All groups increased with stream slope except for centrarchids. Basin area, a surrogate for stream size, correlated positively with richness and negatively with density but with few of the species composition variables.

The patterns in species composition identified by correlation analysis suggested that the effects of urbanization, habitat quality, and stream slope were interrelated. To better illustrate these relationships we selected proportion of endemic species, the fish variable best predicted by independent variables, for further analysis. Scatterplots of untransformed data show significant, nonlinear declines of proportion of endemic species

and RHAP with urban land cover (Figure 4A, B). Because proportion of endemic species was strongly associated with RHAP ($r = 0.84$, Figure 3), this suggested that RHAP would be a suitable indicator of urban effects on fishes. However, stream slope was an even better predictor of proportion of endemic species and RHAP (Figure 4C, D). Both variables demonstrated a strong positive sigmoidal response with slope and a predictable coarsening of the stream bed.

Multiple Linear Regression Models of Fishes and Habitat Quality

We used multiple linear regression analysis to test the hypothesis that urban land cover explained variance remaining after accounting for effects of slope and/or basin area on fish assemblage variables and RHAP scores. Drainage area and slope were the primary predictors of RHAP and most fish assemblage variables (Table 3). After accounting for variation attributable to stream slope and basin area, urban land cover was significantly related to all of the dependent variables

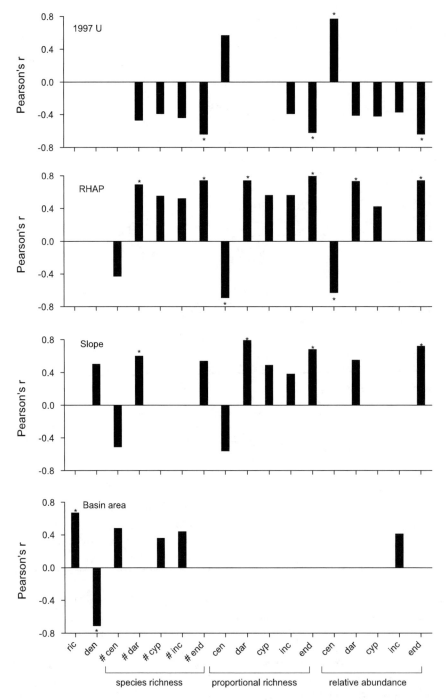

FIGURE 3. Bar charts depicting significant correlations (Pearson's *r*) of fish assemblage variables and 1997 urban land cover, RHAP, stream slope, and basin area (*n* = 30 sites). Values for relative abundance of endemics are Spearman's *r* because this variable was nonnormal. Bars are not shown for nonsignificant correlations (|*r*| < 0.36). Due to spatial and temporal colinearity among urban variables, only results for 1997 U are shown. Other urban variables showed an identical trend with slight variation in *r* values (Walters 2002). Asterisks indicate *P* < 0.0001. *P*-values are uncorrected for multiple comparisons and are shown as a rough guide to correlation strength. Variable abbreviations: ric, richness; den, density; cen, centrarchids; dar, darters and sculpin; cyp, cyprinids; inc, insectivorous cyprinids; end, endemics.

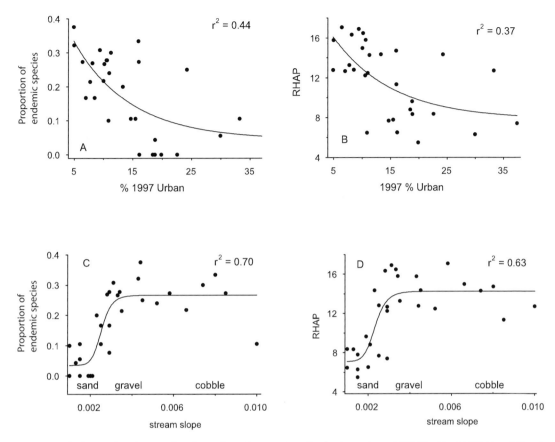

FIGURE 4. Scatterplots showing the relationships of proportion of endemic species and RHAP with 1997 U (A and B) and stream slope (C and D) (n = 30 sites). Slope explains about 85% of the variance in mean particle size in these streams (Walters et al. 2003a), so the increase in proportion of endemic species and RHAP also corresponded with a predictable coarsening of the streambed. Particle size-classes corresponding with mean particle size for streams of a given slope are labeled on the x-axis for C and D. Nonlinear curves were fit to the data using Sigma Plot 4.0. Three parameter exponential decay models were fit to 1997 urban land cover data and four parameter sigmoidal models were fit to slope data. (A) $y = 0.044 + 0.481 e^{(-0.103 \cdot \%1997 \text{ urban})}$;

(B) $y = 7.832 + 13.249 e^{(-0.0962 \cdot \%1997 \text{ urban})}$; (C) $y = 0.0356 + 0.231 \cdot \text{slope}^{\frac{10.492}{0.0025^{10.492} + \text{slope}^{10.492}}}$; (D) $y = 7.097 + 7.158 \text{ slope}^{\frac{8.591}{0.0023^{8.591} + \text{slope}^{8.591}}}$.

except relative abundance of insectivorous cyprinids. Centrarchids increased with urban land cover whereas RHAP, richness, density, darters and sculpin, endemics, cyprinids, and insectivorous cyprinids declined. Models for cyprinids and insectivorous cyprinids were the weakest among species groups, and urban land was unrelated to relative abundance of insectivorous cyprinids. The high-density urban variable was selected in 7 of the 11 models that included land cover.

Urbanization was most strongly associated with increasing centrarchid relative abundance and declining proportional richness of endemics (Figure 3). We plotted the residuals from the linear regression of these variables against $\log_{10}$slope (independent variable) and

1997 U to illustrate spatial and temporal trends in the response of these species groups (Figure 5A, B). Catchments were categorized as having more than 10% U in 1987, less than 10% U in 1987 but more than 10% in 1997, and less than 10% U in 1997. Catchments with more than 10% U in 1987 tended to have the highest urban cover, indicating that the most heavily urbanized catchments have also been urbanized for the longest time. The largest residuals in both models were from the most developed basins. At levels greater than 15% U, most residuals from the centrarchid model were positive and all but three residuals from the endemic model were negative. Thus, for basins with more than 15% U, observed

Table 3. Multiple linear regression models of RHAP and fish variables. Transformations for dependent variables are given in Table 1. Land cover variables were transformed by arc-sine (square-root(x)). Only 1997 urban and 1987–1997 land cover change variables were used due to strong colinearity between the 1987 and 1997 datasets. The relative abundance of endemics could not be normalized and is not included in this analysis. F-values are given for the whole model; P-values are uncorrected for multiple comparisons and shown as a rough guide to correlation strength (n = 30 sites and eight predictor variables).

Independent variable	Variables in model	Trend	Cumulative r^2	P	F
RHAP	$\log_{10}$ slope	+	0.43	<0.001	28.55
	97 HDU	−	0.68	<0.001	
richness	basin area	+	0.45	<0.001	14.96
	$\log_{10}$ slope	+	0.59	0.02	
	97 HDU	−	0.63	0.03	
density	basin area	−	0.50	<0.001	25.29
	97 U	−	0.65	0.002	
Proportion of species					
darters and sculpin	$\log_{10}$ slope	+	0.63	0.001	28.80
	97 HDU	−	0.68	0.02	
centrarchids	$\log_{10}$ slope[a]	−	0.31	0.001	16.48
	97 U	+	0.54	<0.001	
cyprinids	$\log_{10}$ slope	+	0.24	0.006	7.73
	87–97 HDU	−	0.35	0.04	
insectivorous cyprinids	$\log_{10}$ slope[a]	+	0.15	0.04	6.29
	97 HDU	−	0.32	0.009	
	basin area	+	0.44	0.03	
endemics	$\log_{10}$ slope	+	0.46	<0.001	36.09
	97 HDU	−	0.73	<0.001	
Relative abundance					
darters and sculpin	$\log_{10}$ slope	+	0.30	0.04	9.35
	97 LDU	−	0.41	0.002	
centrarchids	$\log_{10}$ slope[a]	−	0.08	0.12	20.00
	97 U	+	0.63	<0.001	
	87–97 HDU	+	0.70	0.02	
cyprinids	87–97 HDU	−	0.2	0.01	7.05
insectivorous cyprinids	basin area	+	0.017	0.26	5.56

[a] $\log_{10}$ slope manually entered into because scatterplots of $\log_{10}$ slope versus these variables showed clear relationships (D.M.W., unpublished data).

centrarchid relative abundance is usually higher and the proportion of endemic species is consistently lower than predicted by slope.

Urbanization led to higher relative abundance of centrarchids even in steeper streams with relatively high habitat quality. We compared the relative abundance of fishes from two sites of similar size, slope, and RHAP scores but different levels of urban cover. Site 111 had the steepest slope we observed (0.01, Figure 5C) and plots as a positive residual in Figure 5B. Slope accurately predicted relative abundance of centrarchids we observed at site 20 (slope = 0.007). Centrarchids were 59.2% of the catch at site 111 in contrast to the general trend for lower centrarchid relative abundance at higher slope streams.

Discussion

Fish Assemblage Response to Basin Urbanization

Our results showed that urbanization effects on fishes are detectable even in systems with strong geomorphic controls on fish assemblages. Stream size predicted richness and density, whereas species composition changed along a slope gradient from darter, sculpin, cyprinid complexes characterized by a high degree of endemism to assemblages dominated by centrarchids. As urban land cover increased, richness and density declined, and centrarchids became the dominant group as other species declined or were locally extirpated. By

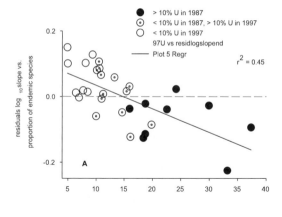

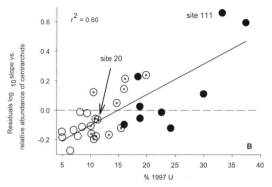

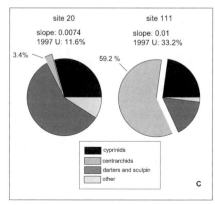

Figure 5. Linear regression of percentage 1997 U versus residuals from slope models of the proportional richness of endemics (A) and the relative abundance of centrarchids (B) (*n* = 30 sites). Basins are coded based on 1987 and 1997 urban land cover data. Panel C compares the relative abundance of major taxonomic groups and characteristics of two sites identified in (B).

disrupting geomorphic control of among-site differences in fishes, urban development homogenizes (sensu McKinney and Lockwood 2001) fish faunas at the broader scale of the Etowah basin (Walters et al.

2003b). Observed assemblages are characteristic of what we would expect in smaller, low slope streams (i.e., low richness, low endemism, and centrarchid dominance).

Darters and sculpin and endemics as a group declined with increasing urban land cover. Similar results were reported for darters in urban streams in Alabama (Onorato et al. 2000) and for the response of endemics to catchment disturbance in southern Appalachia (Scott and Helfman 2001). Darters are considered to be sensitive to disturbance (Kuehne and Barbour 1984; Jenkins and Burkhead 1994), and endemics suffer a higher degree of imperilment and extinction risk than other taxa (Meffe and Carrol 1994; Angermeier 1995). All metrics related to darters and sculpin increased with stream slope. Six of these species were included in the endemic group (Appendix 2), and the endemics showed a similar trend. These species likely increase with slope due to their dependence on coarse stream beds commonly associated with high quality benthic habitat. All of these species demonstrate a high degree of benthic specialization (Etnier and Starnes 1993; Jenkins and Burkhead 1994; Burkhead et al. 1997). They spawn on or in coarse particles, feed benthically or primarily on benthic macroinvertebrates, and are morphologically adapted (e.g., reduced air bladder, large pectoral fins, or dorsoventral compression, Helfman et al. 1997) for high-velocity, riffle-run habitats prevalent in steep streams.

Centrarchid relative abundance and proportional richness increased with urban land cover. We analyzed data published by Weaver and Garman (1994, Table 2) for six reaches in a Piedmont stream in Virginia and found the same trend. According to these data, centrarchid proportional richness increased from 0.24 to 0.41 and relative abundance almost doubled from 0.25 to 0.48 following urban development. These increases in relative abundance occurred even though absolute abundance was lower. As in the Etowah streams, these increases occurred because centrarchids persisted in urban streams whereas other fishes declined more precipitously or were extirpated altogether. Even though centrarchid species richness was not correlated with urban land cover, all 11 species except for longear sunfish *Lepomis megalotis* were collected in streams with more than 20% urban land cover.

Our findings contribute to a growing body of evidence that centrarchids are more resilient to disturbance than other stream fishes (Detenbeck et al. 1992). Centrarchids increase with turbidity, bed sedimentation, riparian deforestation, and agricultural land cover in other southeastern river systems (Jones et al. 1999;

Meyer et al. 1999; Walser and Bart 1999). Waite and Carpenter (2000) also found that introduced populations of centrarchids increased along disturbance gradients in the Willamette River basin, Oregon. Centrarchid species richness was used as a positive indicator of stream condition in the original index of biotic integrity and in subsequent regional variations (Karr 1981; Miller et al. 1988; Shaner 1999; Schleiger 2000). Our results, together with the studies reviewed above, suggest that the use of centrarchids as a positive indicator may be inappropriate for measures of stream health.

Cyprinids and insectivorous cyprinids were the least correlated with geomorphic and urban land cover gradients (i.e., multiple linear regression models r^2 = 0.20–0.34). Models for these groups may be weak because these fishes respond to variables we did not consider in this analysis (e.g., water chemistry and predation pressure) or because different cyprinid species exhibit too much ecological variability to model effectively as a group. Based on life history information provided in Jenkins and Burkhead (1994) and Etnier and Starnes (1993), the cyprinids we collected belong to six spawning guilds, three feeding guilds, and prefer habitats ranging from pools to riffles (Walters et al. 2003a). We developed much stronger models for centrarchids, darters and sculpin, and endemics, and these species have greater within-group ecological similarity than cyprinids (Walters et al. 2003a).

Numerous studies document declines in fish richness, abundance, and biotic integrity with urbanization (e.g., Lenat and Crawford 1994; Onorato et al. 2000; Wang et al. 2000). After accounting for changes in richness associated with geomorphic controls, urban land cover only explained about 5% of the total variance in richness among sites. These results support the findings of Scott and Helfman (2001) that human disturbance of southern Appalachian streams may lead to minor changes in species richness but major changes in species composition. Measures of fish assemblage health such as the index of biotic integrity (IBI, Karr 1981) are designed to account for variability associated with stream size. Our results indicate that stream slope may also warrant consideration for species composition metrics, at least in wadeable Piedmont streams.

Habitat Quality as an Indicator of Urban Effects

The RHAP scores were not a suitable indicator of urban impacts because significant changes in fish assemblages precede gross changes in habitat quality. This finding supports the hypothesis of Wang et al. (1997)

that communities are more sensitive to urban impacts related to altered water quality and hydrology than those related to habitat alteration. The disconnection between urbanization, fishes, and RHAP was most apparent in high-slope streams that had relatively high habitat quality but drastically altered species composition. Wang et al. (1997) also showed that fish-urban-habitat quality relationships were confounded in high gradient, rocky streams in Wisconsin. In their case, high slope streams had higher habitat and biotic integrity than predicted by urban land cover. The inability of existing habitat quality indices to serve as an indicator of urban impacts in our Piedmont streams is similar to results published for streams in the upper Midwest (Roth et al. 1996; Wang et al. 1997, 2001).

Our regression analyses indicated that RHAP scores did decline with urban land cover, but urban effects were subtle compared with the overriding influence of stream slope. The strong correspondence between slope and RHAP likely exists because slope is a primary determinant of benthic habitat variation at these sites (Walters et al. 2003a) and RHAP includes several metrics to assess benthic habitat quality (e.g., epifaunal substrate, sediment deposition, and embeddedness; Barbour et al. 1999). Because steep streams naturally score higher, RHAP will likely underestimate human disturbance in these systems. We documented this in a higher slope, urbanized stream (site 111). Rapid Habitat Assessment Protocol scores remained high even though the fish assemblage showed a clear shift to centrarchid dominance. Alternatively, steep streams may be more resilient to some types of disturbance (e.g., excessive sediment inputs) and maintain higher quality habitats relative to low slope streams (Wang et al. 1997). The range of urban land cover in our study was 5–37%, and most of this land was converted within the last 20 years. We predict that more obvious changes in stream habitat (e.g., severe bank erosion and channel incision) will be prevalent as urban land cover increases or as catchments are urbanized for longer time periods.

Temporal and Spatial Aspects of Fish Assemblage Response

We were unable to statistically isolate temporal changes in fish assemblages due to colinearity among urban land cover variables. However, our results did show that fishes responded to low levels of urbanization, and we can infer that the response was rapid (i.e., <10 years) given the rate of development in the Etowah River system. For example, the residual analysis showed that effects were most pronounced for basins that (1) had more than 10% U for at least 10 years, or (2) had more than 15% U. In 1987, only three of the study basins had more than 15% U. By 1997, 13 basins exceeded this level, and the mean across basins was 15%. Our results are consistent with other studies that found that stream ecosystems respond strongly to low levels of urban land cover or impervious surface coverage (Klein 1979; Booth and Jackson 1997; Wang et al. 2001; and studies reviewed by Paul and Meyer 2001). The pace of urban development has not slowed since 1997, and most of these basins will surely surpass 15% U within the next decade. Given this scenario, we predict that the decline of endemics and other species groups will become more acute and that centrarchid-dominated streams will become the norm within the Etowah basin.

Colinearity among urban variables also hindered our ability to isolate the relative impacts of HDU and LDU on the Etowah streams. For example, LDU was the dominant form of urban land cover in these catchments but was statistically indistinguishable from the total U. However, HDU variables were selected most frequently by the forward stepwise procedure even though HDU accounted for a small fraction of total U. This suggests that HDU may have a disproportionate impact on stream systems compared with LDU. High-density urban has a higher proportion of impervious surface coverage, a key element of the urban landscape that contributes to stream degradation (Klein 1979; Arnold and Gibbons 1996; Booth and Jackson 1997). High- and low-density urban land cover may affect stream systems differently, but we could not isolate these effects at the basin scale.

Acknowledgments

Funding was provided by a grant from the U.S. Environmental Protection Agency (EPA R826597–01–0) with additional support from the University of Georgia Research Foundation and the Georgia Museum of Natural History. We thank A. Bearden, T. Burgess, K. Costly, L. Ormes, and M. Paul for help in the field; C. P. Lo for land cover data; K. Blocksom for statistical advise; and G. Helfman and A. Rosemond for commenting on an earlier version of this manuscript. Although the research described in this article has been funded in part by the U.S. Environmental Protection Agency, it has not been subjected to the agency's required peer and policy review and therefore does not necessarily reflect the views of the agency, and no official endorsement should be inferred.

References

Allan, J. D. 1995. Stream ecology: structure and function of running waters, 1st edition. Chapman & Hall, New York.

Allan, J. D., and L. B. Johnson. 1997. Catchment-scale analysis of aquatic ecosystems. Freshwater Biology 37:107–111.

Angermeier, P. L. 1995. Ecological attributes of extinction-prone species: loss of freshwater fishes of Virginia. Conservation Biology 9:143–158.

Angermeier, P. L., and R. A. Smogor. 1995. Estimating number of species and relative abundances in stream-fish communities: effects of sampling effort and discontinuous spatial distributions. Canadian Journal of Fisheries and Aquatic Sciences 52:936–949.

Arnold, C. L., and C. J. Gibbons. 1996. Impervious surface coverage: the emergence of a key environmental indicator. Journal of the American Planning Association 62:243–258.

Baer, K. E., and C. M. Pringle. 2000. Special problems of urban river conservation: the encroaching megalopis. Pages 381–398 in P. J. Boon, B. R. Davis, and G. E. Potts, editors. Global perspectives on river conservation. Wiley Ltd., London.

Barbour, M. T., J. Gerritsen, B. D. Snyder, and J. B. Stribling. 1999. Rapid bioassessment protocols for use in wadeable streams and rivers: periphyton, benthic macroinvertebrates, and fish, 2nd edition. EPA 841-B-99–002, Office of Water, Washington, D.C.

Boet, P., J. Belliard, R. Berrebi-dit-Thomas, and E. Tales. 1999. Multiple human impacts by the city of Paris on fish communities in the Seine River basin, France. Hydrobiologia 410:59–68.

Booth, D. B., and C. R. Jackson. 1997. Urbanization of aquatic systems: degradation thresholds, stormwater detection, and the limits of mitigation. Journal of the American Water Resources Association 33:1077–1090.

Burkhead, N. M., S. J. Walsh, B. J. Freeman, and J. D. Williams. 1997. Status and restoration of the Etowah River, an imperiled southern Appalachian ecosystem. Pages 375–444 in G. W. Benz and D. E. Collins, editors. Aquatic fauna in peril, the southeastern perspective. Southeast Aquatic Research Institute, Lenz Design and Communication, Decatur, Georgia.

Cain, D. H., K. Riitters, and K. Orvis. 1997. A multiscale analysis of landscape statistics. Landscape Ecology 12:199–212.

Detenbeck, N. E., P. W. Devore, G. J. Niemi, and A. Lima. 1992. Recovery of temperate-stream fish communities from disturbance - a review of case-studies and synthesis of theory. Environmental Management 16:33–53.

Etnier, D. A., and W. C. Starnes. 1993. The fishes of Tennessee. The University of Tennessee Press, Knoxville.

Freund, R. J., R. C. Littell, and L. Creighton. 2003. Regression using JMP. Wiley-Interscience, New York.

Harding, J. S., E. F. Benfield, P. V. Bolstad, G. S. Helfman, and E. B. D. Jones, III. 1998. Stream biodiversity: the ghost of land use past. Proceedings of the National Academy of Sciences 95:14843–14847.

Helfman, G. S., B. B. Collette, and D. E. Facey. 1997. The diversity of fishes. Blackwell Scientific Publications, Malden, Massachusetts.

Jacobson, R. B., S. D. Femmer, and R. A. McKenney. 2001. Land use changes and the physical habitat of streams - a review with emphasis on studies within the U.S. Geological Survey Federal-State Cooperative Program. U.S. Geological Survey, Circular 1175, Reston, Virginia.

Jenkins, R. E., and N. M. Burkhead. 1994. Freshwater fishes of Virginia. American Fisheries Society, Bethesda, Maryland.

Jones, E. B. D., III, G. S. Helfman, J. O. Harper, and P. V. Bolstad. 1999. Effects of riparian forest removal on fish assemblages in southern Appalachian streams. Conservation Biology 13:1454–1465.

Karr, J. R. 1981. Assessment of biotic integrity using fish communities. Fisheries 6(6):21–27.

Klein, R. D. 1979. Urbanization and stream quality impairment. Water Resources Bulletin 15:948–963.

Kuehne, R. A., and R. W. Barbour. 1984. American darters. University of Kentucky Press, Lexington.

Leigh, D. S., B. J. Freeman, M. C. Freeman, E. K. Kramer, A. D. Rosemond, M. J. Paul, C. M. Pringle, D. M. Walters, A. Roy, and C. P. Lo. 2001. Overview of land cover and geomorphic indicators of biotic integrity in the Etowah River basin, Georgia. Pages 225–228 in K. J. Hatcher, editor. 2001 Georgia water resources conference. Institute of Ecology, The University of Georgia, Athens.

Lenat, D. R., and J. K. Crawford. 1994. Effects of landuse on water-quality and aquatic biota of 3 North-Carolina Piedmont Streams. Hydrobiologia 294:185–199.

Lo, C. P., and X. Yang. 2000. Mapping the dynamics of land use and land cover change in the Atlanta Metropolitan Area using the time sequential Landsat images. In Proceedings of the Annual Meeting of the American Society of Photogrammetry and Remote Sensing (CD-ROM), Bethesda, Maryland.

McKinney, M. L., and J. L. Lockwood. 2001. Biotic homogenization: a sequential and selective process. Pages 1–17 in J. L. Lockwood and M. L. McKinney, editors. Biotic Homogenization. Kluwer Academic/Plenum Publishers, New York.

Meffe, G. K., and C. R. Carrol. 1994. Principals of conservation biology. Sinauer Associates Inc, Sunderland, Massachusetts.

Mettee, M. F., P. E. O'Neil, and J. M. Pierson. 1996. Fishes of Alabama and the Mobile basin. Oxmore House Inc, Birmingham, Alabama.

Meyer, J. L., A. B. Sutherland, K. H. Barnes, D. M. Walters, and B. J. Freeman. 1999. A scientific basis for erosion and sedimentation standards in the Blue Ridge physiographic province. Pages 321–324 in K. J. Hatcher, editor. 1999 Georgia Water Resources Conference. The University of Georgia, Institute of Ecology, Athens.

Miller, D. L., P. M. Leonard, R. M. Hughes, J. R. Karr, P. B. Moyle, L. H. Schrader, B. A. Thompson, R. A. Daniels, K. D. Fausch, G. A. Fitzhugh, J. R. Gammon, D. B. Halliwell, P. L. Angermeier, and D. J. Orth. 1988. Regional applications of an index of biotic integrity for use in water resource management. Fisheries 13(5):12–20.

Neter, J., M.H. Kutner, C.J. Nachtsheim, and W. Wasserman. 1996. Applied linear statistical models, 4th edition. WCB/McGraw-Hill, Boston.

Onorato, D., R. A. Angus, and K. R. Marion. 2000. Historical changes in the ichthyofaunal assemblages of the upper Cahaba River in Alabama associated with extensive urban development in the watershed. Journal of Freshwater Ecology 15:47–63.

Ott, R. L. 1988. An introduction to statistical methods and data analysis, 4th edition. Duxbury Press, Belmont, California.

Paul, M. J., and J. L. Meyer. 2001. Streams in the urban landscape. Annual Review of Ecology and Systematics 32:333–365.

Roth, N. E., J. D. Allan, and D. L. Erickson. 1996. Landscape influences on stream biotic integrity assessed at multiple spatial scales. Landscape Ecology 11:141–156.

Schleiger, S. L. 2000. Use of an index of biotic integrity to detect effects of land uses on stream fish communities in west-central Georgia. Transactions of the North American Fisheries Society 129:1118–1133.

Scott, J. B., C. R. Steward, and Q. J. Stober. 1986. Effects of urban-development on fish population-dynamics in Kelsey Creek, Washington. Transactions of the American Fisheries Society 115:555–567.

Scott, M. C., and G. S. Helfman. 2001. Native invasions, homogenization, and the mismeasure of integrity of fish assemblages. Fisheries 26(11):6–15.

Shaner, B. L. 1999. Development of a standardized index of biotic integrity for the Piedmont region of Georgia. Pages 287–290 in K. J. Hatcher, editor. 1999 Georgia water resources conference. The University of Georgia, Institute of Ecology, Athens.

Simon, T. P., and J. Lyons. 1995. Application of the index of biotic integrity to evaluate water resource integrity in freshwater ecosystems. Pages 245–262 *in* W. S. Davis and T. P. Simon, editors. Biological assessment and criteria: tools for water resource planning and decision making. CRC Press, Boca Raton, Florida.

Simonson, T. D., and J. Lyons. 1995. Comparison of catch per effort and removal procedures for sampling stream fish assemblages. North American Journal of Fisheries Management 15:419–427.

Sokal, R. R., and F. J. Rohlf. Biometry. 3rd edition. Freeman, New York.

Steedman, R. J. 1988. Modification and assessment of an index of biotic integrity to quantify stream quality in southern Ontario. Canadian Journal of Fish and Aquatic Sciences 45:492–501.

USCB (U.S. Census Bureau). 1998. U.S. Department of Commerce News. CB98–41, Washington D.C.

U.S. Census Office. 1930–2000. Census of the United States. Department of the Interior, Washington, D.C.

USDA (U.S. Department of Agriculture). 2000. 1997 National resource inventory. Percent change in developed land area. Available: http://www.nhq.nrcs.usda.gov/land/ meta/m5010.html (August 2002).

Waite, I. R., and K. D. Carpenter. 2000. Associations among fish assemblage structure and environmental variables in Willamette basin streams, Oregon. Transactions of the American Fisheries Society 129:754–770.

Walser, C. A., and H. L. Bart, Jr. 1999. Influence of agriculture on in-stream habitat and fish community structure in Piedmont watersheds of the Chattahoochee River system. Ecology of Freshwater Fish 8:237–246.

Walters, D. M. 2002. Influence of geomorphology and urban land cover on fish assemblages in the Etowah River system, Georgia. Doctoral dissertation. The University of Georgia, Athens. Available: http://www.galileo.usg.edu/express?link=getd (September 2003).

Walters, D. M., D. S. Leigh, M. C. Freeman, B. J. Freeman, and C. M. Pringle. 2003a. Geomorphology and fish assemblages in a Piedmont river basin, U.S.A. Freshwater Biology 48:1950–1970.

Walters, D. M., D. S. Leigh, and A. B. Bearden. 2003b. Urbanization, sedimentation, and the homogenization of fish assemblages in the Etowah River basin, USA. Hydrobiologia 494:5–10.

Wang, L. Z., J. Lyons, and P. Kanehl. 2001. Impacts of urbanization on stream habitat and fish across multiple spatial scales. Environmental Management 28:255–266.

Wang, L. Z., J. Lyons, P. Kanehl, R. Bannerman, and E. Emmons. 2000. Watershed urbanization and changes in fish communities in southeastern Wisconsin streams. Journal of the American Water Resources Association 36:1173–1189.

Wang, L. Z., J. Lyons, P. Kanehl, and R. Gatti. 1997. Influences of watershed land use on habitat quality and biotic integrity in Wisconsin streams. Fisheries 22(6):6–12.

Warren, M. L., Jr., B. M. Burr, S. J. Walsh, J. H.L. Bart, R. C. Cashner, D. A. Etnier, B. J. Freeman, B. R. Kuhajda, R. L. Mayden, H. W. Robison, S. T. Ross, and W. C. Starnes. 2000. Diversity, distribution, and conservation status of the native freshwater fishes of the southern United States. Fisheries 25(10):7–31.

Warren, M. L., Jr., P. L. Angermeier, B. M. Burr, and W. R. Haag. 1997. Decline of a diverse fish fauna: patterns of imperilment and protection in the southeastern United States. Pages 105–164 *in* G. W. Benz and D. E. Collins, editors. Aquatic fauna in peril, the southeastern perspective. Southeast Aquatic Research Institute, Lenz Design and Communication, Decatur, Georgia.

Warren, M. L., Jr., and B. M. Burr. 1994. Status of freshwater fishes in the United States: overview of an imperiled fauna. Fisheries 19(1):6–18.

Weaver, L. A., and G. C. Garman. 1994. Urbanization of a watershed and historical changes in a stream fish assemblage. Transactions of the American Fisheries Society 123:162–172.

Williams, J. D., J. M. L. Warren, K. S. Cummings, J. L. Harris, and R. J. Neves. 1992. Conservation status of freshwater mussels of the United States and Canada. Fisheries 18:6–22.

Wolter, C., J. Minow, A. Vilcinskas, and U. A. Grosch. 2000. Long-term effects of human influence on fish community structure and fisheries in Berlin waters: an urban water system. Fisheries Management and Ecology 7:97–104.

Yoder, C. O., and E. T. Rankin. 1996. Assessing the condition and status of aquatic life designated uses in urban and suburban watersheds. Pages 201–227 *in* L. A. Roesner, editor. Effects of watershed development and management on aquatic ecosystems. American Society of Civil Engineers, New York.

Appendix 1. Characteristics of study streams and catchments in the Etowah River basin. Attributes shown include scores for Rapid Habitat Assessment Protocol (RHAP) and percent urban land cover in total urban (U), high-density urban (HDU), and low-density urban (LDU) in 1987 and 1997.

Site	Name	Basin area (km²)	Reach slope	RHAP	1987%			1997%		
					U	HDU	LDU	U	HDU	LDU
1	Pumpkinvine Cr.	16.6	0.0029	12.2	2.9	0.3	2.6	10.5	1.0	9.5
3	Avery Cr.	22.3	0.0015	5.5	7.5	1.3	6.2	19.8	4.0	15.9
4	Smithwick Cr.	15.6	0.0023	14.4	8.2	1.3	6.9	13.3	1.1	12.1
5	McCanless Cr.	13.1	0.0031	16.9	5.8	0.2	5.6	9.4	0.9	8.5
6	Bluff Cr.	14.5	0.0035	13.3	6.6	0.6	6.0	7.7	1.1	6.6
7	Settingdown Cr.	17.1	0.0020	6.5	9.9	1.5	8.4	16.1	2.0	14.1
8	Conns Cr.	14.9	0.0058	17.1	3.7	0.5	3.2	6.4	0.3	6.1
9	Polecat Branch	11.3	0.0085	11.3	17.9	3.3	14.6	16.0	3.7	12.3
10	Burt Cr.	12.2	0.0080	14.7	5.9	1.2	4.7	15.9	3.2	12.7
11	Raccoon Cr.	50.7	0.0034	15.8	4.1	0.2	3.9	10.6	0.6	9.9
12	Little Pumpkinvine	52.0	0.0045	14.3	13.6	2.0	11.5	24.2	2.4	21.8
13	Chicken Cr.	59.1	0.0015	6.3	12.7	1.3	11.5	29.9	3.0	26.9
14	Little River	52.8	0.0025	7.7	7.6	0.8	6.8	14.6	0.7	13.9
15	Mill Cr.	50.7	0.0015	7.8	9.4	1.3	8.1	15.4	1.3	14.2
16	Smithwick Cr.	38.6	0.0052	12.5	7.7	1.1	6.6	11.0	0.8	10.2
17	Shoal Cr.[a]	53.2	0.0029	12.7	3.7	0.3	3.4	7.0	0.5	6.5
18	Settingdown Cr.	53.6	0.0019	9.6	10.1	2.0	8.1	18.7	2.6	16.2
19	Darnell Cr.	60.3	0.0044	12.8	2.7	0.2	2.5	4.9	0.3	4.6
20	Shoal Cr.[b]	53.8	0.0074	14.3	4.7	0.7	4.0	11.2	1.2	10.0
21	Pumpkinvine Cr.	125.7	0.0010	6.5	6.4	0.4	5.9	10.8	1.0	9.9
22	Raccoon Cr.	108.5	0.0028	16.3	4.1	0.2	3.9	8.1	0.4	7.7
24	Settingdown Cr.	96.1	0.0021	8.8	10.4	1.9	8.6	18.4	2.3	16.1
25	Little River	122.1	0.0010	8.4	10.5	1.2	9.4	22.6	1.8	20.7
26	Mill Cr.	84.6	0.0013	8.3	10.3	1.4	8.9	18.8	2.0	16.8
27	Shoal Cr.[a]	101.9	0.0025	12.8	5.4	0.4	5.0	8.5	0.6	7.9
28	Sharp Mountain Cr.	103.9	0.0066	15.0	9.7	2.0	7.7	10.0	2.6	7.4
29	Long Swamp Cr.	77.4	0.0043	15.8	3.5	0.5	2.9	5.0	0.6	4.4
30	Shoal Cr.[b]	90.7	0.0033	16.5	4.7	0.7	4.1	10.1	1.1	9.0
101	Little Allatoona Cr.	14.8	0.0029	7.4	17.0	3.4	13.6	37.3	5.2	32.2
111	Allatoona Cr.	48.4	0.0100	12.7	18.6	2.0	16.6	33.2	3.6	29.5

[a] Cherokee County
[b] Dawson County

Appendix 2. Fishes collected in the Etowah River basin.

Family name		Family name	
Scientific name	Common name	*Scientific name*	Common name
Petromyzontidae		**Salmonidae**	
Ichthyomyzon sp.		*Onchorhynchus mykiss*	rainbow trout
Cyprinidae		**Fundulidae**	
Campostoma oligolepis	largescale stoneroller	*Fundulus stellifer*	southern studfish
Cyprinella callistia	Alabama shiner[a]	**Poeciliidae**	
C. trichroistia	tricolor shiner[a, b]	*Gambusia affinis*	western mosquitofish
C. venusta	blacktail shiner[a]	*G. holbrooki*	eastern mosquitofish
Hybopsis lineapunctata	lined chub[a, b]	**Cottidae**	
Luxilus zonistius	bandfin shiner[a]	*Cottus carolinae zopherus*	Coosa banded sculpin[b]
Nocomis leptocephalus	bluehead chub	**Centrarchidae**	
Notemigonus crysoleucas	golden shiner	*Ambloplites ariommus*	shadow bass
Notropis chrosomus	rainbow shiner[a, b]	*Lepomis auritus*	redbreast sunfish
N. longirostris	longnose shiner[a]	*L. cyanellus*	green sunfish
N. lutipinnis	yellowfin shiner[a]	*L. gulosus*	warmouth
N. stilbius	silverstripe shiner[a]	*L. macrochirus*	bluegill
N. xaenocephalus	Coosa shiner[a, b]	*L. megalotis*	longear sunfish
Phenacobius catostomus	riffle minnow[a, b]	*L. microlophus*	redear sunfish
Pimephales vigilax	bullhead minnow	*Micropterus coosae*	redeye bass (also known as Coosa bass)
Semotilus atromaculatus	creek chub	*M. punctulatus*	spotted bass
Catostomidae		*M. salmoides*	largemouth bass
Hypentelium etowanum	Alabama hog sucker	*Pomoxis nigromaculatus*	black crappie
Minytrema melanops	spotted sucker	**Percidae**	
Moxostoma duquesnei	black redhorse	*Etheostoma etowahae*	Etowah darter[b]
M. erythrurum	golden redhorse	*E. jordani*	greenbreast darter[b]
M. poecilurum	blacktail redhorse	*E. scotti*	Cherokee darter[b]
Ictaluridae		*E. stigmaeum*	speckled darter
Ameiurus brunneus	snail bullhead	*Percina kathae*	Mobile logperch
A. natalis	yellow bullhead	*P. nigrofasciata*	blackbanded darter
A. nebulosus	brown bullhead	*P. palmaris*	bronze darter[b]
Ictalurus punctatus	channel catfish	*P.* sp. cf. *P. macrocephala*	"bridled darter" [b]
Noturus leptacanthus	speckled madtom		

[a] Insectivorous cyprinid

[b] Endemic species

American Fisheries Society Symposium 47:87–115, 2005

Effects of Urbanization on the Geomorphology, Habitat, Hydrology, and Fish Index of Biotic Integrity of Streams in the Chicago Area, Illinois and Wisconsin

Faith A. Fitzpatrick*, Matthew W. Diebel,

U.S. Geological Survey, 8505 Research Way, Middleton, Wisconsin 53562, USA

Mitchell A. Harris, Terri L. Arnold,

U.S. Geological Survey, 1201 West University Avenue, Suite 100, Urbana, Illinois 61801, USA

Michelle A. Lutz, and Kevin D. Richards

U.S. Geological Survey, 8505 Research Way, Middleton, Wisconsin 53562, USA

Abstract.—Effects of urbanization on geomorphic, habitat, and hydrologic characteristics and fish biotic integrity of 45 streams in the Chicago area were examined by the U.S. Geological Survey from 2000 to 2001. An agricultural to urban land-cover gradient approach was used. Landscape characteristics such as texture of surficial deposits, slope, riparian land cover, and stream network position also were examined to determine if these factors influenced the effects of urbanization. Among geomorphic characteristics, channel enlargement occurred in urban streams with a high percent of watershed clayey surficial deposits. Other geomorphic and habitat characteristics such as stream power, fine substrate, and amount of riffles did not correlate with percent watershed urban land but instead correlated with reach slope. Bank erosion, habitat variability, and two habitat indexes did not correlate with watershed urban land. Below 30% watershed urban land, the unit area discharge for a 2-year flood increased with increasing urban land; however, above 30% urban land, unit area discharges for a 2-year flood were variable, most likely due to variations in stormwater management practices, point-source contributions, and the transport index. Streams with greater than 33% watershed urban land had low base flow, but the effects of urbanization on base flow were offset by point-source contributions. Fish index of biotic integrity (IBI) scores were low in streams with greater than 25% watershed urban land. Fish IBI scores also were low in streams with high percentages of watershed clayey surficial deposits and enlarged channels. The amount of riparian forest/wetland buffer had no moderating effect on geomorphic/habitat/hydrologic characteristics and fish IBI scores. Variations in the texture and topography of glacial landforms affected reach slope and some habitat characteristics. Longitudinal profiles were useful for distinguishing differences in local geologic settings among sampled sites.

Introduction

Urbanization is a major concern for water-resource managers, engineers, geomorphologists, and aquatic ecologists (Leopold 1968; American Society of Civil Engineers, Urban Hydrology Research Council 1969; Spieker 1970; The H. John Heinz II Center for Science, Economics and the Environment 2002). Urban development affects stream hydraulics and

sediment input, transport, and deposition, thereby altering aquatic habitat and the resident community of aquatic organisms (Garie and McIntosh 1986; Yoder and Rankin 1997; Kennen 1999; Paul and Meyer 2001; and references within). Few studies have been able to integrate multiple spatial scales of landscape characteristics and urban indicators with reach-scale geomorphic, hydrologic, habitat, and aquatic biota characteristics in order to distinguish cause and effect from simple correlations (Roesner and Bledsoe 2003).

* Corresponding author: fafitzpa@usgs.gov

Land-cover gradient and space-for-time approaches have been used to examine urbanization effects on aquatic communities, habitat, geomorphic, and hydrologic conditions (Booth and Reinelt 1993; Dreher 1997; Wang et al. 2001). Various measures have been used to represent urbanization, including imperviousness (total and effective), amount of urban land, population density, and combinations of urban indicators (Schueler 1994; Booth and Jackson 1997; McMahon and Cuffney 2001; Gergel et al. 2002). Past studies of streams showed that biotic integrity degrades at relatively low levels of urbanization (Booth and Reinelt 1993; Booth and Jackson 1997; Maxted and Shaver 1997; Wang et al. 2000, 2001). Near the Chicago area, fish index of biotic integrity (IBI) scores tended to be low in watersheds with greater than 10–20% urban land and about 100–200 people/km^2 (Dreher 1997; Wang et al. 1997; Fitzpatrick et al. 2004). Urbanization in the Chicago area is occurring on previously agricultural land; thus, urbanized streams are potentially affected by historical agricultural practices. The percent watershed agricultural land is a major factor affecting fish, macroinvertebrate, and habitat integrity in previously forested watersheds (Richards et al. 1996; Roth et al. 1996; Wang et al. 1997; Fitzpatrick et al. 2001; Stewart et al. 2001). However, some agricultural streams near the Chicago area have high biotic integrity (Dreher 1997; Wang et al. 1997; Fitzpatrick et al. 2004). Agricultural streams with relatively steep slopes and rocky substrates were more likely to have good habitat quality and biotic integrity than streams with relatively flat slopes and sandy substrates (Wang et al. 1997). The steep, rocky streams also were less likely to be channelized than flat, sandy streams.

In urban development, impervious surface area (roads, sidewalks, driveways, parking areas, rooftops) increases, which decreases infiltration and increases the rate and volume of surface runoff. Pervious surfaces are compacted by construction equipment and removal of topsoil. Drainage networks are extended through ditching and construction of storm sewers. These factors result in changes in the frequency, duration, and size of floods (Hollis 1975; Booth 1990; Booth and Jackson 1997; Konrad 2003). Flood peaks in northeastern Illinois potentially have increased three-fold due to urbanization (Allen and Bejcek 1979), and relative increases may be greater for small, frequent floods than for large, infrequent floods (Krug and Goddard 1986; Konrad 2003). Decreases in infiltration may result in decreases in the water table and ultimately decreases in base flow (Finkenbine et al.

2000). However, these offsets may be compensated for by contributions from point sources (LaTour 1993). In the Chicago area, point-source discharges may originate from outside the watershed (beyond both surface- or groundwater contributing areas) because the major source for drinking water is Lake Michigan. Although storm-water detention basins and other control measures are common in urban areas, they may not meet their design goals of controlling surface runoff (Booth and Jackson 1997; Finkenbine et al. 2000).

Early in urbanization, upland sources and available sediment may increase due to clearing of vegetation. Sediment loads may increase during initial construction and decrease to predevelopment loads after construction (Wolman 1967; Wolman and Schick 1967; Colosimo 2002). In Wisconsin, sediment loads were 10 times larger from watersheds with residential construction than from rural or urban watersheds (Owens et al. 2000). Channel and flood-plain processes of sediment erosion, transport, and deposition also may change to accommodate changes in the size, duration, and frequency of floods.

Channel erosion (through incision or widening) or sedimentation may result from urban development (Wolman 1967; Wolman and Schick 1967; Guy 1970; Graf 1975; Roberts 1989; Booth 1990; Gregory et al. 1992; Booth and Jackson 1997; Trimble 1997; Colosimo 2002). Channel enlargement (increase in channel size through incision or widening) commonly occurs in urbanizing streams (Hammer 1972; Doll et al. 2002; Center for Watershed Protection 2003). However, geomorphic processes following urbanization are highly variable both in space and time (Gregory and Madew 1982) and stability cannot be predicted by the magnitude of urbanization or the rate of ongoing land-cover change (Henshaw and Booth 2000). Channel and watershed slope, stream network position, base level, phase of urban development, distance to urban land, riparian conditions, erodibility potential of the channel bed and banks, local sediment transport characteristics, proximity of geomorphic thresholds, and history of past disturbances influence whether and where hydrologic changes associated with urbanization lead to channel erosion or sedimentation (Knight 1979; Bledsoe and Watson 2001). In addition, geomorphic conditions may or may not stabilize after one or two decades of constant land cover (Finkenbine et al. 2000; Henshaw and Booth 2000; Bledsoe and Watson 2001).

Some studies show relations among stream habitat indexes and metrics and urban development, whereas other studies do not (Booth and Jackson 1997; Paul and Meyer 2001; Wang et al. 2001; Rogers et al. 2002; Fitzpatrick et al. 2004). Habitat indexes are not always a good indicator of geomorphic responses to urbanization possibly because the component metrics are not unique in describing geomorphic processes and (or) metrics are not sensitive enough to quantify urban-related geomorphic change (Fitzpatrick et al. 2004). Some studies looked at individual metrics forming a habitat index, including measures of riffle/pool quality, bank stability, embeddedness, amount of fine substrate, and amount of large woody debris (Finkenbine et al. 2000; Paul and Meyer 2001; Center for Watershed Protection 2003). In the Pacific Northwest, increased bank erosion and lack of large woody debris corresponded to increases in urbanization (Booth 1991; Finkenbine et al. 2000). The amount of fine substrate may decrease from altered hydrology (Finkenbine et al. 2000). The Center for Watershed Protection (2003) noted that little data are available for urbanization effects on riparian shading, wetted perimeter, velocity/depth regimes, riffle frequency, and sediment deposition in pools.

A major goal of our study was to integrate geomorphic, habitat, hydrologic, fish, landscape, and urban-indicator data from a range of spatial scales to better understand how the interactions of these factors affect channel conditions and biotic integrity of Chicago area streams (Figure 1). A major hypothesis for the study was that reach-scale geomorphic, habitat, and hydrologic characteristics are affected by urbanization. Landscape characteristics or physiographic setting possibly moderate these effects. A second hypothesis is that fish biotic integrity is ultimately affected by urbanization through proximate effects from changes in geomorphic, habitat, and hydrologic characteristics.

Study Area

Sampled streams are within the Des Plaines and Fox River watersheds, two major tributaries to the upper Illinois River (Figures 1 and 2). The Des Plaines River basin contains the intensely urban downtown area, older suburbs of Chicago, and some expanding suburbs and rural areas. The Fox River drains the western suburbs of Chicago where rapid expansion of residential areas has been occurring since the early 1980s. The northern parts of the Des Plaines and Fox River basins are in expanding suburbs of the Milwaukee,

Wisconsin metropolitan area. The climate of the study area is humid continental with an average annual temperature (1961–1990) of 9°C and average annual precipitation of 89 mm.

The physiographic setting of the study area is composed of two sections: the Great Lakes section, which encompasses all of the Des Plaines River basin and the northern half of the Fox River basin; and the Till Plains section, which covers the southern half of the Fox River basin (Fenneman 1938; Leighton et al. 1948; Arnold et al. 1999). Bedrock geology mainly consists of limestone and dolomite in both basins (Willman et al. 1975; Wisconsin Geological and Natural History Survey 1981) and is buried by unconsolidated Quaternary deposits ranging in thickness from 0 to more than 120 m (Soller and Packard 1998). Deposits are thin or absent along the upper parts of the Fox River in Wisconsin, the lower valley of the Fox River upstream of its confluence with the Illinois River, and in portions of the lower Des Plaines River, the Chicago River, and the Calumet basins. The distribution of Quaternary deposits is highly variable and complex, but the deposits generally consist of clayey till in the Des Plaines River basin, glacial lake clay in the Chicago River and Calumet basins, sandy and loamy till and outwash sand and gravel in the upper Fox River basin, and loamy till in the lower Fox River basin (Willman 1971; Richmond et al. 2001) (Figure 2). Outwash sand and gravel are found along the main stem of the Des Plaines River. Streams sampled in both basins have relatively low slopes (0.01–0.8%).

Land cover in the study area consists of mainly agricultural and urban land with small amounts of forest and wetland, mainly occurring in county forest preserves (Figure 1). For the 45 sampled streams, percent watershed urban land ranged from 0% to 92% and agricultural land ranged from 0% to 99% (Table 1). Forest preserves are common in the Chicago area and forest and wetland within a 60-m riparian zone along the entire stream network ranged from 2% to 49% (Table 1).

Potentially impaired water uses (Illinois Environmental Protection Agency 2002) occurred in urban streams in the Des Plaines River basin with greater than about 30% watershed urban land, although there were exceptions (Table 1). Hickory Creek and Sugar Run have impairments and less than 30% watershed urban land. Sawmill Creek, East Branch Du Page River, and Poplar Creek (74%, 73%, and 38% watershed urban land, respectively) had no listed impairments. Impairment in the urban streams

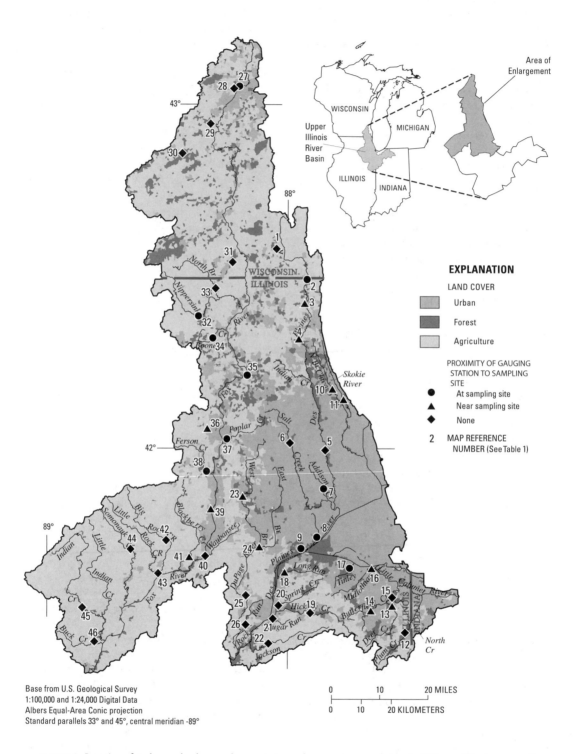

FIGURE 1. Location of study area, land-cover characteristics, and stream sites sampled in the Chicago, Illinois metropolitan area.

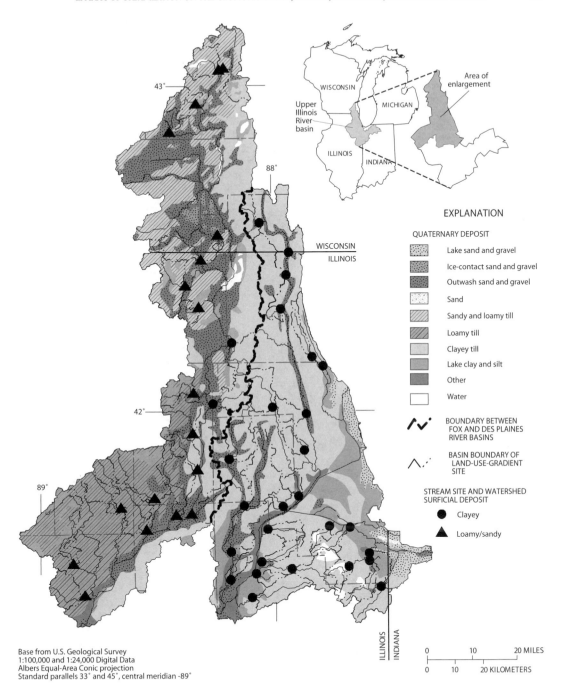

FIGURE 2. Quaternary deposits and sites grouped by texture of surficial deposits for streams in the Chicago area.

most commonly occurred from municipal point sources, construction, land development, urban run-off/storm sewers, hydromodification, channelization, habitat modification, and bank modification. No impairments were listed Fox River tributaries in Illi-nois, and no impairment data were available for Wisconsin streams.

A variety of storm-water controls are used in the Chicago area. Wet and dry storm-water detention ponds of various sizes are numerous because of the

TABLE 1. Map reference number, site name, drainage area, watershed land cover, population density, and potential causes for physical impairments (Illinois Environmental Protection Agency 2002) for sampled sites in the Chicago area. Sites with U.S. Geological Survey (USGS) streamflow gauging stations are **bolded**. Impairment data are not available for Wisconsin streams.

Map reference number (see Figure 1)	Site name	Drainage area (km²)	Watershed urban land (%)	Watershed agriculture land (%)	Forest/ wetland in 60-m stream network buffer (%)	1980 population density (people/ km²)	1990 population density (people/ km²)	2000 population density (people/ km²)	Potential causes for impairments[a]
1	Brighton Cr.	66	7	62	28	52	80	100	na
2	**Des Plaines R.**	318	5	78	17	50	52	70	**None**
3	Mill Cr. (Des Plaines)	169	10	68	21	164	164	311	None
4	Bull Cr.	20	27	52	31	238	337	453	None
5	Willow Cr.	56	86	0	9	555	454	510	1, 5
6	Salt Cr.	128	73	5	17	1,029	1,159	1,236	1, 5, 6, 7, 8, 9
7	**Addison Cr.**	47	92	0	7	1,609	1,597	1,689	**1, 4, 5, 6, 7, 8, 10, 11, 12**
8	**Flag Cr.**	43	87	0	14	1,130	1,205	1,299	**1, 2, 3, 5, 6, 7, 10, 11**
9	**Sawmill Cr.**	33	74	1	33	706	850	900	**None**
10	**N Br Chicago R.**	48	33	21	49	342	252	334	**1, 4, 5, 6, 7, 10, 11**
11	**Skokie R.**	62	60	11	25	752	678	756	**1, 2, 3, 4, 5, 7, 8, 9, 10, 11**
12	Plum Cr.	85	8	64	35	69	72	88	None
13	**Deer Cr**	62	26	51	32	341	302	311	**1, 5, 6, 7**
14	**Butterfield Cr.**	48	38	40	16	537	606	667	**2, 3, 5, 6, 7, 10, 11, 12**
15	North Cr.	58	35	44	24	678	679	710	2, 3, 5, 6, 7, 10, 11
16	**Midlothian Cr.**	51	72	13	16	1077	1346	1451	**2, 3, 5, 6, 7, 10, 11, 12**
17	**Tinley Cr.**	29	57	10	35	826	1005	1115	**2, 3, 5, 6, 7, 10, 11, 12**
18	**Long Run**	61	29	45	34	183	343	473	**None**
19	Hickory Cr.	127	21	59	25	211	260	352	1, 2, 3, 4, 5, 6, 9
20	Spring Cr.	47	11	59	36	186	149	204	None
21	Sugar Run	33	17	77	13	192	214	253	2, 3, 5, 14
22	Jackson Cr.	113	4	93	5	75	76	133	None
23	**W Br. Du Page R.**	157	58	23	18	800	1,036	1,289	**1, 2, 3, 5, 13**
24	E Br. Du Page R.	206	73	5	22	1,054	1,202	1,300	None
25	Lily Cache Cr.	114	19	69	10	366	377	636	na

TABLE 1. Continued.

Map reference number (see Figure 1)	Site name	Drainage area (km²)	Watershed urban land (%)	Watershed agriculture land (%)	Forest/wetland in 60-m stream network buffer (%)	1980 population density (people/km²)	1990 population density (people/km²)	2000 population density (people/km²)	Potential causes for impairments[a]
26	Rock Run	37	52	33	25	594	717	909	1, 2, 3, 5
27	Fox R.	203	30	44	30	244	268	320	na
28	Pewaukee R.	98	19	56	17	188	193	290	na
29	Genesee Cr.	72	7	62	31	66	94	110	na
30	Jericho Cr.	32	3	72	34	69	66	96	na
31[b]	Bassett Cr.	–	–	–	–	–	–	–	–
32	Nippersink Cr.	219	4	87	9	72	81	100	None
33	N Br. Nippersink Cr.	167	6	75	20	46	64	83	None
34	Boone Cr.	40	3	61	26	54	47	56	None
35	Flint Cr.	96	31	32	36	210	303	341	None
36	Tyler Cr.	81	3	87	12	29	39	49	None
37	**Poplar Cr.**	**94**	**38**	**40**	**22**	**541**	**748**	**881**	**None**
38	**Ferson Cr.**	**134**	**17**	**70**	**19**	**84**	**142**	**242**	**None**
39	Mill Cr. (Fox)	80	16	74	14	196	174	311	None
40	Waubansee Cr.	77	21	72	7	205	317	646	None
41	**Blackberry Cr.**	**174**	**7**	**83**	**15**	**98**	**103**	**155**	**None**
42	Big Rock Cr.	273	1	95	7	24	22	24	None
43	Little Rock Cr.	196	4	92	10	23	53	60	None
44	Somonauk Cr.	96	1	94	9	24	16	18	None
45	Indian Cr.	326	1	93	12	15	14	16	None
46	Buck Cr.	103	0	99	2	6	5	5	None

[a] Causes for impairment: 1, Municipal point source; 2, construction; 3, land development; 4, combined sewer overflow; 5, urban runoff/storm sewers; 6, hydromodification; 7, channelization; 8, upstream impoundment; 9, flow regulation/modification; 10, habitat modification; 11, bank modification/destabilization; 12, riparian vegetation removal; 13, highway/road/bridge construction; 14, agriculture/nonirrigated crop production

[b] Site 31, Bassett Creek, was dropped from analysis because of close proximity to a waste-water treatment plant.

low permeability of clayey surficial deposits. Combined-sewer systems are used in the city of Chicago and in many of the suburbs. Historically, the capacity of combined-sewer systems was often exceeded resulting in releases of untreated sewage to streams. To avoid this, Chicago's Tunnel and Reservoir Plan (TARP) system was developed and consists of drop shafts, tunnels, and reservoirs designed to capture and hold overflows from combined sewers and convey them to wastewater treatment plants (Terrio 1994). Six study streams are part of the TARP system: Willow Creek, Salt Creek, Addison Creek, Flag Creek, North Creek, and Midlothian Creek. There are five major wastewater treatment plants for the Metropolitan Water Reclamation District of Greater Chicago. Two of these are located in the watersheds of Willow Creek and Salt Creek.

Methods

Study Design

Our study was part of a larger study of urbanization effects on stream ecosystems conducted by the National Water-Quality Assessment (NAWQA) Program of the U.S. Geological Survey (USGS). From 2000 to 2001, we examined the effects of urbanization on biological, chemical, hydrologic, geomorphic, and habitat characteristics of 46 streams in the Chicago area in the Des Plaines and Fox River basins (Table 1; Figure 1) (Adolphson et al. 2002). The NAWQA program also conducted similar studies in other major urban areas of the United States during the same time period (Couch and Hamilton 2002).

Streams with historical streamflow or biological data were preferred. Streams without point sources were desirable, but in intensive urban areas point sources could not be avoided. However, one rural stream, Bassett Creek (site 31), was dropped because a wastewater treatment plant was located immediately upstream of the sampling location; thus, the data set was reduced to 45 streams. Drainage areas ranged from 20 to 326 km^2 (Table 1).

Streams were grouped into two categories based on texture of watershed surficial deposits. Streams with greater than 60% clayey till, lake clay, and silt were grouped as clayey streams (n = 28). Streams with greater than 60% loam, sand, or gravel deposits were classified as loamy/sandy streams (n = 17). All 26 streams in the Des Plaines River basin and 2 eastern tributaries to the Fox River were grouped as clayey streams (Figure 2). The remaining 17 streams in the Fox River basin were loamy/sandy streams.

The 45 streams also were grouped into three categories based on percentage of watershed urban land and population density (U.S. Bureau of the Census 2001) (Figure 3). Rural streams had less than 9% watershed urban land and population densities less than 150 people/km^2 (n = 16). Rural/urbanizing streams had 9–33% watershed urban land and population densities of 150–600 people/km^2 (n = 15). Urban streams had greater than 33% watershed urban land and greater than 600 people/km^2 (n = 14). Only clayey streams had greater than 33% watershed urban land.

Data Collection

Urban indicators and landscape characteristics.— Urban indicators and landscape-scale characteristics mainly were derived from overlays of thematic maps with watershed boundaries using a geographic information system (GIS). Urban indicators included percent watershed urban land, estimated imperviousness, upstream distance to urban land from sampling site, population density, road density, and point-source discharge information. Percent watershed land cover was calculated from 1993 30-m Multi-Resolution Land Cover (MRLC) data (Vogelmann et al. 2001) using a GIS. The land-cover data included four categories of urban land cover: low intensity residential, high intensity residential, commercial/industrial/transportation, and urban/recreational grasses. Percent forest and wetland for a 60-m buffer on each side of the stream along the entire stream network upstream of the sampling site was calculated from MRLC data. The MRLC land-cover data were used to calculate distance from the sampling site to the nearest upstream urban land. An estimate of total impervious area was calculated using U.S. Department of Agriculture, Soil Conservation Service (1986) estimates of percent impervious area for different types of urban land uses.

Population density data were from the U.S. Bureau of Census 1980, 1990, and 2000 population data (U.S. Bureau of the Census 1985, 1991, 2001). Changes in population density (as raw values and as percent change) were calculated.

The 1999 Topologically Integrated Geographic Encoding and Referencing (TIGER) system line files (U.S. Bureau of the Census 1999) were used to estimate road area and length (Adolphson et al. 2002). Road density was calculated by dividing road area by drainage area.

Point-source discharge data were obtainable only

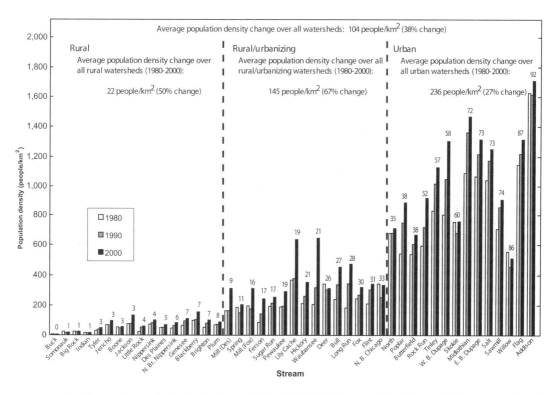

FIGURE 3. Changes in population density from 1980 to 2000 (U.S. Bureau of the Census 1985, 1991, 2001) and percent urban land (values given above histograms) in 1993 (Vogelmann et al. 2001) for 45 streams in the Chicago area.

for Illinois streams. Average monthly discharges for 2000 were obtained for each watershed (Charles Avery, U.S. Geological Survey, personal communication).

Data for landscape characteristics, which included Quaternary deposits (texture of surficial deposits), bedrock geology, bedrock depth less than 15 m, drainage area, stream slope (calculated for the length of stream between 10% and 85% of total stream length in the basin), drainage density, relief ratio (minimum elevation subtracted from maximum elevation in the watershed, divided by watershed length), cumulative stream length, and a transport index (drainage density × relief ratio), were obtained from Adolphson et al. (2002, and references within). Similar to land cover data, percentages for surficial deposits, bedrock geology, and bedrock depth were calculated for a 60-m buffer on each side of the stream along the entire stream network upstream of the sampling site. The 1:24,000 National Elevation Dataset (NED) Digital Elevation model (DEM) (U.S. Geological Survey 2001), GIS, and the BasinSoft Program were used to delineate stream networks and calculate selected watershed-scale geomorphic characteristics (Harvey and Eash 1996;

Fitzpatrick et al. 1998). Sinuosity for a segment encompassing the sampled reach was measured from 1:24,000 NED DEM (U.S. Geological Survey 2001) data.

Longitudinal profiles were constructed for a subset of streams. Profiles extend from the headwaters to the first major confluence downstream of the sampled reach. Stream lengths were measured with a map measurer between contour lines on USGS 7.5-min topographic maps. Longitudinal profiles were used to identify changes in slope usually related to glacial landforms or spatial position within the stream network.

Geomorphic characteristics.—Channel geometry and water-surface slope were surveyed once between November 2000 and May 2001 at three generally equidistant cross sections in a stream reach using an electronic Total Station or an auto-level. Reach length was 20 times the channel width, or a minimum of 150 m, and cross sections generally were located in runs. Approximately 20 points were surveyed along each transect. End points for cross sections extended into the flood plain or above bank-full stage. A combination of field indicators were used to identify bank-full stage along each reach and included the top of coarse deposits associated with point bars (minimum elevation); occurrence of a sharp break in slope of the bank above the low-flow water surface where slope changes from vertical to more horizontal; changes in vegetation, such as a change from herbaceous to tree species; and for undercut banks, the top of the undercut (minimum bank-full elevation) (Harrelson et al. 1994; Fitzpatrick et al. 1998).

Channel roughness was estimated in the field using Coon's (1998) adaptation of Cowan's (1956) method. Comparison with photos in Hicks and Mason (1998), Coon (1998), Arcement and Schneider (1987), and Barnes (1967) provided additional guidance.

The U.S. Army Corps of Engineers' HEC-RAS (v. 3.0) computer program (Brunner 2001) was used to estimate average bank-full channel area, width, depth, velocity, shear stress, and unit-channel-area stream power. Inputs to the HEC-RAS model include channel geometry, roughness, and reach water-surface slope. Bank-full area was normalized by drainage area prior to analysis because of its dependence on watershed size.

Stream competence describes the maximum particle size (D) that a stream is capable of transporting under a given flow and was calculated by the formula $D = T_c/4$, for coarse, noncohesive beds where D is mean grain diameter (ft) that can be transported and T_c is critical shear stress (lb/ft^2) (Anderson et al. 1970; Chang 1992). Critical shear stress values were calculated from HEC-RAS hydraulic models for cross-section data from the stream reach. An estimate of erosivity potential of the channel at bank-full flow was calculated as the ratio of maximum particle size (mm) transported at bank-full flow divided by average substrate particle size (mm) measured for the reach from transect-point data from the habitat assessments.

Habitat characteristics.—Habitat assessments were conducted in July 2000 along the same reach used for the surveys of channel geometry and slope using NAWQA protocols (Fitzpatrick et al. 1998). Data included both qualitative and quantitative observations of channel, substrate, bank, and habitat cover conditions at 11 transects distributed equally along the reach; data were also collected at five points (two bank and three instream) along each transect. Bank-full width and depth were measured and bank-full area and bank-full width/depth ratios were calculated for each transect and averaged. Coefficient of variation of bank-full width/depth ratio was calculated and gives an indication of variability in the shape of the channel.

Presence/absence of erosion at the intersection of each transect with the bank was noted and the length of bank erosion occurring along the transect line was measured. Presence and depth of loose silt was measured at each transect point.

Dominant riparian land cover within a 30-m buffer was recorded for each transect endpoint, and the open canopy angle was measured at the center of each transect. The percentage of endpoints with disturbed riparian land cover was calculated for each reach. Disturbed land cover included cropland, pasture, farmsteads, residential, commercial, or transportation. Undisturbed land cover was considered to be grassland, shrubs and woodland, or wetland.

Metrics of wetted channel shape and shape variability were calculated. A channel-shape index (CHANSH) was calculated for each transect by the equation CHANSH = $(W/D)^{(D/Dmax)}$, where W = wetted width, D = average depth, and $Dmax$ = maximum depth (Armantrout 1998). Smaller values of CHANSH indicate relatively narrow/deep or pool-like conditions, whereas larger values indicate more wide/shallow or riffle-like conditions. This index provides a measure of relative occurrence of macrohabitat conditions (Terry Short, U.S. Geological Survey, personal communication). Coefficient of variation of channel-shape index provides a measure of habitat variability.

Presence/absence of instream habitat cover for fish, including woody debris, was recorded at each of three in-channel points along transects. In shallow streams, woody debris in less than 0.3 m of water was not considered habitat cover. Many shallow streams had abundant woody debris; thus, the percent woody debris was a small fraction of the possible total.

Two habitat indexes were calculated, the USEPA's rapid bioassessment protocol (RBP; Barbour et al. 1999) and Wisconsin Department of Natural Resources (WDNR) habitat index; (WIHAB; Simonson et al. 1994). These indexes are commonly used in other habitat studies of Midwestern streams. The RBP index is intended to quantify the quality of habitat for the broader aquatic community, whereas the WDNR index is intended to quantify the quality of habitat for fish. Each index contained multiple metrics (10 in the RBP and 7 in the WDNR) that were combined to give a cumulative assessment of habitat quality for wadeable streams. Scores range from 0 to 170 for the RBP index and from 0 to 100 for the WDNR index. High scores reflect excellent habitat quality for both indexes. The RBP incorporates adjustments for streams with high and low slopes. Minor modifications were made to the calculation techniques for WIHAB because NAWQA data collection varied from WDNR protocols (archives are available as unpublished files, U.S. Geological Survey, Middleton, Wisconsin, 2002). For example, the riffle:riffle ratio metric for the WIHAB index was not measured; instead, the relative number of geomorphic channel units in a reach (riffle, run, pools) was substituted.

Hydrologic characteristics.—Hydrologic data included discharge measurements at all sites at the time of ecological sampling in July 2000, HEC-RAS modeled bank-full and base flow, and daily streamflow data from 1985 to 2000 for 15 streams with USGS streamgauges (Table 1). Bank-full flows were modeled in HEC-RAS by adjusting discharge to match observed bank-full stage indicators. Bank-full flows were normalized by drainage area.

Of the 15 gauged sites, 13 are on clayey streams (12 in the Des Plaines River basin and 1 in the Fox River basin). The time period 1985–2000 was selected for analysis of gauging-station data because it reflects recent urbanization. Flood-frequency analyses of gauging-station data followed guidelines in Interagency Advisory Committee on Water Data (1982) to fit logarithms of annual peak flows to a Pearson Type III distribution. Estimates of flood peaks with a 2-year recurrence interval were used because past studies showed that small, frequent floods were increased more by urbanization than large, infrequent floods (Krug and Goddard 1986). Streamflow data from the gauges were used to estimate base flow in 2001.

Discharge was measured in streams during ecological sampling; however some streams were sampled during falling stages following summer thunderstorms and thus did not represent base flow. By matching water-surface elevations during base flow conditions obtained from cross-section surveys, HEC-RAS was used to estimate base flow for streams sampled at falling stages. HEC-RAS estimates were compared to discharge measurements collected during ecological sampling and to base flow discharges from the 15 gauging stations. The base flow variable was estimated from comparisons of the three sources. Flow variability was calculated as the ratio of HEC-RAS derived bank-full flow to estimated base flow. Flow data were normalized by drainage area to remove effects of watershed size on relations with other characteristics. In Illinois streams with point sources, monthly point-source discharges for 2000 were subtracted from estimated base flow to calculate an adjusted base flow variable that more closely reflected groundwater contributions.

Fish index of biotic integrity.—Fish-assemblage data were collected during low flow by three agencies: the USGS (2 sites sampled in 2000 and 22 sites sampled in 2001), the Illinois Department of Natural Resources (IDNR) (17 sites sampled during the period from 1995 to 1999), and the WDNR (5 sites sampled in July 1997). The USGS used a barge or backpack electroshocker to sample one pass of the entire stream reach and then conducted supplementary riffle kicks and seine hauls (Meador et al. 1993). The IDNR collected fish in a single pass using a backpack electroshocker, barge electroshocker, or electric seine (Bertrand et al. 1996). The WDNR used a barge or backpack electroshocker to sample all major habitats in a stream reach. The reach length for WDNR sampling was determined by stream size, which is based on stream width (Lyons 1992). Fish data for the Addison Creek site were collected near but not at the same reach as the other samples.

A revised fish IBI is being reviewed for use in Illinois (Hite and Bertrand 1989; Roy Smogor, Illinois Environmental Protection Agency, personal communication). A draft version of the revised Illinois IBI was used in our study. Ten metrics are used in the revised IBI, of which six are based on richness, three on trophic or reproductive structure, and one on tolerance. Metric values are scaled according to geographic region, stream size, and slope; scores for the revised IBI can range from 0 to 60. High scores reflect high fish biotic integrity.

Statistical Analyses

Statistical analyses included correlation and redundancy analysis. When examining relations among physical characteristics at multiple spatial scales, reach-scale geomorphic, habitat, and hydrologic characteristics and fish IBI scores were considered dependent variables and urban indicator, landscape characteristics, and reach-scale riparian land-cover data were considered independent variables. Reach-scale slope was considered an independent variable because most Chicago area streams are not alluvial and flow on glacial deposits, bedrock, or thin fluvial deposits in poorly developed valleys.

Spearman rank correlation and principle components analysis (PCA) (Iman and Conover 1983) were used to reduce the number of variables (Table 2). Some geomorphic and habitat characteristics were retained for analysis, such as bank erosion, canopy angle, and occurrence of woody debris, because little is known about how they respond to urbanization (Table 2).

TABLE 2. Selected urban indicators and landscape characteristics used to determine urbanization effects on the geomorphic, habitat, and hydrologic characteristics and fish index of biotic integrity of 45 Chicago area streams.

Type of variable	Abbreviation	Median	Minimum	Maximum	Correlated variables
Urban indicators					
Watershed urban land (%) (square-root transformed)	URBANLU	19	0	92	Watershed industrial lands; population density, impervious area, road density
Population density change, 1980–2000 (%)	POPDENP	158	–117	1,266	Population density change by area
Mean upstream distance of urban land (km)	URBANDIS	10.2	2.4	25.3	Road area, road length
Landscape characteristics					
Drainage area (km²) (log-10 transformed)	DRAIN	81.2	20.1	326.1	Stream order, cumulative stream length
Watershed clayey surficial deposits (%)	WATCLAY	71	0	100	Soil permeability
Drainage density (km/km²)	DRAINDEN	1.34	1.08	1.44	None
Watershed slope (%)	WATSLOP2	1.31	0.20	3.36	None
Transport index *1,000 (km⁻¹) (log-10 transformed)	TRANSIN	4.77	1.23	10.05	Relief ratio
Sinuosity (ratio)	SINUOS	1.3	1.1	2.0	None
Coarse deposits within 60-m stream network buffer (%) (log-10 transformed)	BUFCOARS	2	0	96	Coarse deposits in watershed
Forest and wetland within 60-m stream network buffer (%)	BUFFOWE	19	2	49	None
Disturbed land cover in 30-m buffer (%) (log-10 trans.)	RIPLU	5	0	100	None
Average open canopy angle (°)	CANOPY	48	2	145	None
Geomorphic characteristics					
Reach slope, low-flow water surface (%) (square-root transformed)	SLOPELO	0.20	0.01	0.79	Segment and bank-full slope, velocity, power, stress, bank-full flow/drainage area, competence
Bank-full channel area/drainage area (m²/km²) (square-root transformed)	BFAREADA	0.11	0.030	0.43	Channel area, bank-full flow
Stream power (N/(m s))	POWER	12	0.097	149	None
Erosivity potential at bank-full flow (ratio) (inverse square-root transformed)	EROSBF	1.5	0.4	88.7	None
Habitat characteristics					
Fine substrate (%) (log-10 transformed)	FINES	27	3	100	Amount and type of geomorphic units, substrate texture, embeddedness, silt depth, roughness, Wisconsin habitat index
Average bank-full channel width/depth (ratio) (log-10 transformed)	BWDRAT	11	2	31	Shape index, bank-full surface area, wetted width/depth ratio, coefficient of variation of canopy

TABLE 2. Continued.

Type of variable	Abbreviation	Median	Minimum	Maximum	Correlated variables
Coefficient of variation of average bank-full channel width/depth (ratio)	BWDRATCO	25	9	86	None
Average bank erosion (m) (square-root transformed)	EROSION	2.6	0.0	11.3	Bank stability index, coefficient of variation of silt depth
Amount if riffle in reach (%)	RIFFLE	20	0	59	None
Coefficient of variation of wetted channel shape index	CHANSHCO	36	13	87	None
Woody debris (%)	WOODDEBR	11	0	71	None
USEPA rapid bioassessment protocol habitat index	RBPHABIN	118	67	154	Wisconsin habitat index
Wisconsin habitat index	WIHAB	45	20	68	RBPHABIN
Hydrologic characteristics					
Bank-full flow/drainage area ($m^3/s/km^2$) (square-root transformed)	BFLOWDA	0.10	0.011	0.42	None
Estimated base flow at time of cross section surveys (m^3/s) (log-10 transformed)	FLOWXS	0.42	0.06	2.4	None
Estimated base flow/drainage area ($m^3/s/km^2$) (log-10 transformed)	FLOWXSDA	0.0044	0.00061	0.030	None
Bank-full flow/estimated low flow (ratio) (square-root transformed)	FLOWVAR1	24.0	2.0	153.8	None
Estimated base flow - average 2000 point source flow (m^3/s) (log-10 transformed)	FLOWXS_P	0.31	−0.45	2.3	None
2-year flood peak (m^3/s)	Q2	20	6.7	28	None
2-year flood peak/drainage area ($m^3/s/km^2$) (log-10 transformed)	Q2DA	0.27	0.081	0.68	None
Fish					
Revised fish index of biotic integrity	FISHIBI	33	6	57	None

Spearman correlation analysis was used to identify relations among the remaining 34 variables for all 45 streams. For individual correlations the critical ρ is 0.29 for $P = 0.05$, but with Bonferroni adjustments for multiple tests, the critical ρ is 0.55 for $P = 0.05$.

Spearman correlation analysis was conducted separately for groups of clayey and loamy/sandy streams. The 17 loamy/sandy streams all had less than 33% urban land, so only the 15 clayey streams with less than or equal to 33% watershed urban land were included in these comparisons. With Bonferroni adjustments for multiple tests, the critical ρ values for 17

and 15 streams, 34 variables, and $P = 0.05$, are 0.81 and 0.84, respectively.

Redundancy analysis (RDA) was used to determine the relative effects of urban indicators and landscape characteristics on geomorphology, habitat, hydrology, and fish biotic integrity. Redundancy analysis is a direct gradient analysis that describes variation between a linear response data set (in this case the geomorphic, habitat, and hydrologic characteristics and fish IBI) and a predictor data set (urban indicators and landscape characteristics) (Hill 1979; Ter Braak 1986; Ter Braak and Smilauer 1998). Characteristics with nonnormal distributions were transformed prior to the RDA (Table 2). A subset of 11 urban indicators and landscape characteristics; 10 geomorphic, habitat, and hydrologic characteristics; and the revised fish IBI were selected for the RDA based on correlation analysis and the need recognized in the literature for more information about their response to urbanization. Response characteristics were plotted in ordination diagrams (biplots) with vectors representing gradients for selected predictor characteristics using a symmetric focus for scaling. Length and direction of the arrows on a biplot indicate relative strength of relations among characteristics. Arrows that plot closely to each other are positively correlated. Arrows that plot directly opposite each other are negatively correlated. Arrows that plot at right angles to each other are not correlated. Thus, proximity of a geomorphic, habitat, or hydrologic characteristic to certain urban or landscape characteristics in an RDA biplot represent relative influences of the independent variable on the dependent variable. Proximity of dependent variables to each other identifies those that behave similarly. Monte Carlo permutation tests were used to determine whether the RDA axes were significant ($P \leq 0.05$).

Results

Urban Indicators

For all 45 streams, watershed urban land, total imperviousness, and 1980, 1990, and 2000 population density were positively correlated ($\rho \geq 0.95$). Watershed urban land also positively correlated with road density ($\rho = 0.88$). Thus, watershed urban land was used as a surrogate variable to represent the amount of urbanization. Two other urban indicator variables did not correlate with watershed urban land—percent change in population density from 1980 to 2000 and mean upstream distance to urban land (Table 3). Urban sites had the highest numerical change in population density (236 people/km²), but rural/urbanizing sites had the highest percent change in population density (67%) (Figure 3).

Landscape Characteristics

There was a general lack of correlations between urban indicators and landscape characteristics (Table 3). The positive relation between clayey surficial deposits and watershed urban land was an artifact of having a full agricultural to urban land-cover gradient (0–92%)

for clayey streams and only a partial gradient (0–31%) for loamy/sandy streams. Upstream distance to nearest urban land was positively correlated with drainage area; thus, this variable was dependent on watershed size. Streams with steep watershed slopes had high percent forest/wetland in the stream network buffer (Figure 4). This relation was affected by the amount of urbanization, with rural streams showing more of a relation than urban streams. There was no relation between percent of disturbed riparian land cover in the sampled reach and percent forest/wetland within the full stream network buffer or percent watershed urban land (Table 3). Instead, streams with less than 5% and greater than 80% watershed urban land appeared to have more disturbed riparian buffers (Figure 5A). Correlation analyses for separate groups of clayey and loamy/sandy streams (standardized for range of percent watershed urban land) showed similar results to correlations when all streams were grouped together (Tables 4 and 5).

Geomorphic/Habitat Characteristics

In general, there was a lack of correlations among urban indicators, landscape characteristics, and geomorphic/habitat characteristics. Only unit-area bank-full channel area (normalized by drainage area) positively correlated with watershed urban land and clayey surficial deposits and negatively correlated with watershed size (Table 3; Figure 5B). The two habitat indexes did not correlate with watershed urban land (the RBP index is shown in Figure 5C). For the subgroup of clayey streams, only the amount of woody debris negatively correlated with the transport index (Table 4).

Relations among geomorphic and habitat characteristics were more numerous for the group of all streams (Table 3) compared to the subgroups of clayey or loamy/sandy streams (Tables 4 and 5). Stream power positively correlated with reach slope for all groups. For the group of all streams, streams with high percent fine-grained substrate had flat reach slopes, low stream power, and high erosivity potential. Streams with relatively high reach slopes had high percentages of riffles (Figure 6). The two habitat indexes correlated with each other and the WIHAB correlated with percent fines, which is a metric included in the index (Simonson et al. 1994).

Hydrologic Characteristics

Hydrologic characteristics did not correlate with any urban indicators for the group of all streams or sub-

TABLE 3. Spearman rank correlations among selected multi-scale geomorphic, habitat, and hydrologic characteristics and watershed characteristics for 45 streams in the Chicago area. Correlation coefficients shown have $P \leq 0.05$ unadjusted for multiple comparisons; bolded correlation coefficients have $P \leq 0.05$ based on Bonferroni adjustments.

	Urban indicators			Landscape characteristics										Geomorphic characteristics									Habitat characteristics				Hydrologic characteristics							Fish
	URBANLU	POPDENP	URBANDIS	DRAIN	WATCLAY	DRAINDEN	WATSLOP2	TRANSIN	SINUOS	BUFCOARS	BUFFOWE	RIPLU	CANOPY	SLOPELO	BFAREADA	POWER	EROSBF	FINES	BWDRAT	BWDRATCO	EROSION	RIFFLE	CHANSHCO	WOODEBR	RBPHABIN	WIHABIN	BFLOWDA	FLOWXS	FLOWXSDA	FLOWVAR1	FLOWXS_P	Q2	Q2DA	FISHIBI
URBANLU	1.00																																	
POPDENP	–	1.00																																
URBANDIS	–	–	1.00																															
DRAIN	-0.39	–	–	1.00																														
WATCLAY	**0.58**	–	**0.73**	-0.38	1.00																													
DRAINDEN	–	–	–	–	–	1.00																												
WATSLOP2	–	0.30	–	–	0.34	0.54	1.00																											
TRANSIN	-0.32	–	–	–	-0.42	–	–	1.00																										
SINUOS	–	–	–	–	–	–	–	–	1.00																									
BUFCOARS	–	0.40	–	–	-0.47	–	–	0.30	-0.32	1.00																								
BUFFOWE	0.40	–	–	-0.39	0.31	–	**0.56**	–	-0.32	–	1.00																							
RIPLU	–	–	–	–	–	–	–	–	–	–	–	1.00																						
CANOPY	-0.34	–	–	0.39	–	–	–	–	–	–	-0.31	–	1.00																					
SLOPELO	0.29	–	–	-0.42	–	–	–	0.44	–	–	–	–	-0.37	1.00																				
BFAREADA	**0.59**	-0.30	-0.35	**-0.64**	**0.59**	–	–	–	–	-0.40	–	–	–	–	1.00																			
POWER	–	–	–	–	–	–	0.29	–	–	–	–	–	-0.37	**0.84**	–	1.00																		
EROSBF	–	–	–	-0.34	–	–	-0.35	-0.30	–	–	–	–	–	–	0.59	–	1.00																	
FINES	-0.36	–	–	–	–	–	–	-0.29	-0.29	–	–	–	–	-0.56	–	**-0.65**	0.60	1.00																
BWDRAT	-0.33	0.37	–	0.53	-0.40	–	–	-0.34	–	–	–	–	–	0.48	-0.45	0.35	–	–	1.00															
BWDRATCO	–	–	–	–	–	–	–	0.39	–	–	–	–	–	–	–	–	–	–	0.40	1.00														
EROSION	–	–	–	0.39	–	–	-0.30	-0.44	–	-0.44	–	–	–	–	–	–	–	–	-0.35	-0.35	1.00													
RIFFLE	–	–	–	–	–	–	–	–	–	–	–	–	–	**0.71**	–	**0.70**	–	**-0.66**	–	0.30	–	1.00												
CHANSHCO	-0.33	–	–	0.34	–	–	–	–	–	–	–	–	–	0.30	–	–	–	–	–	0.39	–	0.38	1.00											
WOODEBR	–	–	–	–	–	–	–	–	–	–	–	–	–	-0.30	–	–	–	–	–	–	–	-0.33	–	1.00										
RBPHABIN	0.38	–	–	–	–	0.30	0.42	–	–	0.29	–	–	–	0.38	–	0.39	–	-0.53	0.36	0.39	-0.39	0.45	–	–	1.00									
WIHABIN	0.46	–	–	–	–	–	0.49	–	–	–	–	-0.42	–	0.34	–	0.60	–	-0.58	–	0.31	–	0.43	–	–	**0.60**	1.00								
BFLOWDA	0.46	–	-0.38	**-0.66**	0.35	–	**0.61**	–	–	-0.32	–	–	-0.36	0.46	**0.87**	**0.60**	–	–	-0.34	–	0.29	–	–	–	–	–	1.00							
FLOWXS	–	0.40	**0.69**	**0.69**	–	–	–	–	–	–	–	–	0.33	-0.42	-0.30	-0.29	–	–	0.53	–	–	–	–	–	–	–	-0.41	1.00						
FLOWXSDA	–	–	–	–	–	–	–	–	–	–	–	–	–	0.45	0.54	0.54	–	–	–	–	0.29	0.34	–	–	–	–	**0.71**	**0.72**	1.00					
FLOWVAR1	-0.51	–	-0.52	–	–	-0.32	-0.29	–	–	-0.34	–	–	–	–	-0.37	–	–	–	-0.42	–	–	–	–	–	–	–	-0.40	**-0.81**	**-0.65**	1.00				
FLOWXS_P	–	–	0.54	–	–	0.34	0.34	–	–	0.50	–	–	0.39	0.41	0.42	0.42	–	–	0.49	–	–	–	–	–	–	–	–	**-0.69**	0.46	**-0.60**	1.00			
Q2	-0.31	0.31	–	-0.48	0.35	–	0.50	–	–	–	-0.51	–	0.39	0.41	0.42	0.33	–	–	0.50	0.61	-0.68	–	–	–	–	–	–	0.39	–	–	–	1.00		
Q2DA	0.48	-0.35	**-0.87**	**-0.89**	0.35	–	0.52	–	–	–	–	–	–	0.41	**0.85**	–	–	–	**0.70**	0.50	–	–	–	-0.30	**0.78**	0.37	**0.90**	**-0.65**	**0.79**	-0.35	**0.78**	–	1.00	
FISHIBI	**-0.81**	0.29	–	0.43	**-0.57**	–	–	–	–	–	–	–	–	–	-0.49	–	–	–	–	–	–	–	–	–	0.36	–	-0.31	–	–	–	–	0.47	0.40	1.00

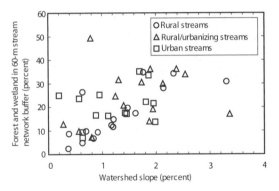

FIGURE 4. Plot of watershed slope and percent forest and wetland in the 60-m stream network buffer for 45 rural, rural/urbanizing, and urban streams in the Chicago area.

groups of clayey or loamy/sandy streams (Tables 3, 4, and 5; Figures 5D, E). Unit-area bank-full flow was negatively correlated with watershed size and positively correlated to unit-area bank-full channel area, stream power, flow variability, and unit-area 2-year flood peaks. Two-year flood peaks positively correlated with drainage density, watershed slope, and transport index. Unit-area 2-year flood peaks were positively correlated with stream power and negatively correlated with drainage area.

Examination of the effects of urbanization on base flow is complicated because most urban streams in the Chicago area have point source contributions that augment base flow (Figure 7). A scatter plot of streams with less than 3% of base flow resulting from point-source contributions and watershed urban land illustrates that rural and rural/urbanizing streams with both clayey and loamy/sandy surficial deposits have variable base flow, whereas urban streams have consistently low base flow (Figure 5D). Tinley Creek, Midlothian Creek, and Sawmill Creek are representative examples of urban streams (greater than 50% watershed urban land) with small base flows and little or no point-source contributions (Figure 7).

The scatter plot of unit-area 2-year flood peaks and urban land illustrates the complexity of the relation between percent urban land and the size of small, frequent floods (Figure 5E). From 0% to about 30% urban land, unit-area 2-year flood peaks increase linearly with percent urban land. Above 30% urban land, streams split into two groups of relatively small and large unit-area 2-year flood peaks. This change at about 30% urban land occurs near the boundary between rural/urbanizing streams and urban streams and may be caused by the extent or type of hydrologic

modifications implemented in urban streams (e.g., combined sewers and storm-water detention). Of the 10 gauged streams with greater than 30% urban land, 5 have point-source discharges (N. Br. Chicago River, Skokie River, W. Br. Du Page River, Addison Creek, and Flag Creek) and 3 are in the TARP system (Flag Creek, Addison Creek, and Midlothian Creek). Physiographic setting may play a role because the urban streams with relatively large unit-area 2-year flood peaks have higher transport indexes than the urban streams with small unit-area 2-year flood peaks (Figure 5E).

Fish IBI Scores

For all 45 streams, revised fish IBI scores had a higher correlation with watershed urban land than with any other geomorphic, habitat, or hydrologic characteristic (Table 3). High IBI scores occurred in streams with less than 25% watershed urban land, similar to Fitzpatrick et al. (2004) (Figure 5F). At 40% watershed urban land, all streams had IBI scores below 30. However, one clayey stream, Poplar Creek, had a relatively high IBI score of 40 with 38% watershed urban land.

In the revised fish IBI, 8 of the 10 metrics are expected to decrease with disturbance and 2 metrics are expected to increase. Nine of the 10 metrics responded as expected and had significant correlation coefficients with percent urban land. One metric reflecting the abundance of native sunfish did not correlate with percent urban land. The IBI had a stronger negative correlation with watershed urban land than did the individual metrics.

The fish IBI scores did not correlate with any landscape, geomorphic, habitat, or hydrologic characteristic except for a negative correlation with percent watershed clayey surficial deposits (Table 3). The total lack of correlation between fish IBI scores and watershed urban land for loamy/sandy streams compared to a relatively high (but not significant based on Bonferroni adjustments) correlation coefficient of −0.74 for clayey streams (Tables 4 and 5) suggests that fish IBI scores may respond more to urbanization in clayey streams than in loamy/sandy streams.

Redundancy Analysis

The RDA was used to examine the complex interrelations among revised fish IBI scores and geomorphic/habitat/hydrologic characteristics, as well as urban indicators and landscape characteristics. The RDA in-

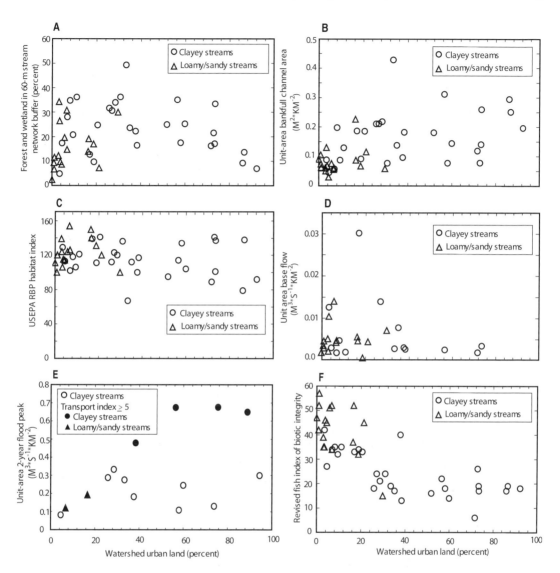

FIGURE 5. Plots of percent watershed urban land and (A) percent forest and wetland in the 60-m stream network buffer for the 45 sampled streams, (B) bank-full channel area (normalized by drainage area) for the 45 sampled streams, (C) USEPA's rapid bioassessment protocol (RBP) habitat index for the 45 sampled streams, (D) estimated base flow (normalized by drainage area) for 30 streams with less than 3% of their base flow from point-source contributions, and (E) 2-year flood peaks (normalized by drainage area) for 15 streams with streamflow-gaging stations, and (F) revised fish index of biotic integrity scores for the 45 sampled streams in the Chicago area.

cluded 40 of the 45 streams. Five large, agricultural, loamy/sandy streams (sites 42–46) with less than 5% urban land were dropped from the RDA because they exaggerated the correlation among watershed urban land and surficial deposits. The streams also are in a separate physiographic province, which added to the potential for more natural variability in landscape and geomorphic/habitat characteristics. With the five sites

removed, the Spearman correlation coefficient between watershed urban land and clayey surficial deposits dropped from 0.58 to 0.45.

As observed with the correlation results, the RDA biplot shows differing and overlapping responses of revised fish IBI and geomorphic, habitat, and hydrologic characteristics to urban indicators and landscape characteristics (Figure 8). The first two axes of the

TABLE 4. Spearman rank correlations among selected multi-scale geomorphic, habitat, and hydrologic characteristics and watershed characteristics for 15 streams with clayey surficial deposits and ≤ 33% watershed urban land in the Chicago area. Correlation coefficients shown have $P \leq 0.05$ unadjusted for multiple comparisons; bolded correlation coefficients have $P \leq 0.05$ based on Bonferroni adjustments.

	Urban indicators			Landscape characteristics										Geomorphic characteristics					Habitat characteristics								Hydrologic characteristics							Fish
	URBANLU	POPDENP	URBANDIS	DRAIN	WATCLAY	DRAINDEN	WATSLOP2	TRANSIN	SINUOS	BUFCOARS	BUFFOWE	RIPLU	CANOPY	SLOPELO	BFAREADA	POWER	EROSBF	FINES	BWDRAT	BWDRATCO	EROSION	RIFFLE	CHANSHCO	WOODDEBR	RBPHABIN	WIHABIN	BFLOWDA	FLOWXS	FLOWXSDA	FLOWVAR1	FLOWXS_P	Q2	Q2DA	FISHIBI
URBANLU	1.00																																	
POPDENP	–	1.00																																
URBANDIS	–	–	1.00																															
DRAIN	–	–	**0.87**	1.00																														
WATCLAY	–	–	–	–	1.00																													
DRAINDEN	–	–	–	–	–	1.00																												
WATSLOP2	–	–	–	–	–	0.73	1.00																											
TRANSIN	–	–	–	–	–	0.62	0.57	1.00																										
SINUOS	–	–	–	–	–	–	–	–	1.00																									
BUFCOARS	0.59	–	–	–	–	–	–	–	-0.54	1.00																								
BUFFOWE	–	–	–	–	-0.80	–	0.60	–	–	–	1.00																							
RIPLU	–	–	–	0.65	–	0.56	–	–	–	–	–	1.00																						
CANOPY	-0.51	–	–	–	–	–	–	–	–	–	–	–	1.00																					
SLOPELO	-0.60	–	–	–	–	–	–	0.66	–	–	–	–	–	1.00																				
BFAREADA	0.63	–	-0.52	-0.66	–	–	–	–	–	–	–	–	-0.83	–	1.00																			
POWER	–	–	–	–	–	–	–	–	–	–	–	–	–	**0.86**	–	1.00																		
EROSBF	–	-0.52	–	–	–	–	–	–	-0.63	–	–	–	–	–	–	-0.63	1.00																	
FINES	–	–	–	–	–	–	–	–	–	–	–	–	–	-0.77	–	-0.82	0.75	1.00																
BWDRAT	0.53	0.53	–	–	–	–	–	–	–	–	–	-0.58	–	–	-0.55	–	–	–	1.00															
BWDRATCO	–	–	–	–	–	–	–	0.56	–	–	–	–	–	–	–	–	–	-0.57	-0.63	1.00														
EROSION	–	–	–	–	–	–	–	–	–	–	–	0.62	–	–	0.52	–	–	0.52	0.74	0.74	1.00													
RIFFLE	–	–	–	–	–	–	–	–	0.63	–	–	–	–	0.68	–	–	–	-0.72	-0.79	-0.79	-0.76	1.00												
CHANSHCO	–	–	–	–	–	–	–	–	–	–	–	–	–	–	–	–	–	0.52	–	–	–	0.58	1.00											
WOODDEBR	–	-0.51	–	–	–	–	–	–	–	–	–	–	–	-0.57	–	–	–	–	–	–	–	–	–	1.00										
RBPHABIN	–	0.58	–	–	–	–	–	–	–	–	–	–	–	0.51	–	–	–	–	–	–	–	–	–	0.58	1.00									
WIHABIN	–	–	–	–	–	–	–	0.82	–	–	–	–	–	0.54	–	0.76	–	–	–	–	0.64	0.80	-0.60	–	0.52	1.00								
BFLOWDA	0.57	–	–	–	–	–	–	–	–	–	–	–	**-0.84**	–	**0.84**	0.57	–	–	–	–	–	–	–	–	–	0.56	1.00							
FLOWXS	–	–	–	0.55	–	–	–	–	–	–	–	–	–	–	–	0.59	–	–	–	–	–	–	–	–	–	–	–	1.00						
FLOWXSDA	0.57	–	–	–	–	–	–	–	–	–	–	–	–	–	0.52	–	–	–	–	–	–	–	–	–	–	–	0.52	0.76	1.00					
FLOWVAR1	–	–	–	-0.57	–	–	–	–	–	–	–	–	–	–	0.74	–	–	–	–	–	–	–	–	–	–	–	–	-0.81	-0.52	1.00				
FLOWXS_P	0.57	–	–	0.52	–	–	–	–	–	–	–	–	–	–	–	–	–	–	–	–	–	–	–	–	–	–	–	**0.97**	0.77	-0.78	1.00			
Q2	-0.80	0.60	-0.80	0.80	-0.63	–	0.80	–	–	0.63	-0.80	**-0.95**	–	**0.95**	–	–	–	-0.80	–	–	–	–	–	–	–	0.78	–	0.78	–	-0.80	0.78	1.00		
Q2DA	0.60	-0.80	0.63	-0.63	0.63	–	–	–	–	–	–	–	–	–	–	–	–	–	–	–	–	–	–	–	–	0.78	–	-0.78	–	0.77	-0.80	**-0.89**	1.00	
FISHIBI	-0.74	–	–	–	–	–	–	–	–	–	–	–	–	–	–	–	–	–	–	–	–	–	–	–	–	–	–	–	–	–	–	–	0.80	1.00

TABLE 5. Spearman rank correlations among selected multi-scale geomorphic, habitat, and hydrologic characteristics and watershed characteristics for 17 streams with loamy/sandy surficial deposits in the Chicago area. Correlation coefficients shown have $P \leq 0.05$ unadjusted for multiple comparisons; bolded correlation coefficients have $P \leq 0.05$ based on Bonferroni adjustments.

	Urban indicators			Landscape characteristics										Geomorphic characteristics													Hydrologic characteristics							Fish
	URBANLU	POPDENP	URBANDIS	DRAIN	WATCLAY	DRAINDEN	WATSLOP2	TRANSIN	SINUOS	BUFCOARS	BUFFOWE	RIPLU	CANOPY	SLOPELO	BFAREADA	POWER	EROSBF	FINES	BWDRAT	BWDRATCO	EROSION	RIFFLE	CHANSHCO	WOODDEBR	RBPHABIN	WIHABIN	BFLOWDA	FLOWXS	FLOWXSDA	FLOWVAR1	FLOWXS_P	Q2	Q2DA	FISHIBI
URBANLU	1.00																																	
POPDENP	0.63	1.00																																
URBANDIS	—	—	1.00																															
DRAIN	—	—	0.60	1.00																														
WATCLAY	—	—	—	—	1.00																													
DRAINDEN	—	—	—	—	—	1.00																												
WATSLOP2	0.52	—	—	—	—	—	1.00																											
TRANSIN	—	—	—	—	—	—	0.71	1.00																										
SINUOS	—	0.64	—	—	—	0.55	—	—	1.00																									
BUFCOARS	0.48	0.58	—	—	—	—	—	—	-0.52	1.00																								
BUFFOWE	—	—	—	—	—	—	0.74	0.74	-0.56	—	1.00																							
RIPLU	—	—	—	—	—	—	—	—	—	—	—	1.00																						
CANOPY	—	—	—	—	—	—	—	—	—	—	—	—	1.00																					
SLOPELO	—	—	—	-0.60	—	—	—	—	—	—	—	—	—	1.00																				
BFAREADA	—	—	—	—	—	—	—	—	—	—	—	—	—	—	1.00																			
POWER	—	—	—	—	—	—	—	—	—	—	—	—	—	**0.82**	0.52	1.00																		
EROSBF	—	—	—	-0.49	—	—	—	—	—	—	—	—	—	0.60	—	0.51	1.00																	
FINES	-0.68	—	—	—	—	—	—	—	—	—	—	—	—	—	—	-0.48	—	1.00																
BWDRAT	—	—	—	-0.53	—	—	—	—	—	—	—	—	—	—	—	—	—	—	1.00															
BWDRATCO	—	—	—	—	—	—	—	—	—	—	—	—	—	—	—	—	—	—	0.51	1.00														
EROSION	—	—	0.57	0.64	—	—	-0.58	0.48	—	—	-0.68	—	—	0.60	—	0.79	0.79	—	—	—	1.00													
RIFFLE	—	—	—	—	—	—	—	—	—	—	—	—	—	0.80	—	0.70	—	—	—	—	0.70	1.00												
CHANSHCO	—	—	—	—	—	0.63	—	—	—	—	—	—	—	—	—	—	—	-0.52	—	—	—	—	1.00											
WOODDEBR	-0.48	—	—	—	—	—	—	—	—	—	—	—	—	—	—	—	—	—	—	—	—	—	—	1.00										
RBPHABIN	—	0.61	—	—	—	—	—	—	—	—	—	—	-0.50	—	—	—	—	—	—	—	—	—	—	—	1.00									
WIHABIN	—	0.61	—	—	—	—	0.61	0.54	-0.54	—	—	—	—	0.51	—	—	—	-0.64	—	0.48	-0.5	—	—	—	0.55	1.00								
BFLOWDA	—	—	—	—	—	—	—	—	—	—	—	—	—	0.63	**0.86**	**0.85**	0.60	—	—	—	—	—	—	—	—	—	1.00							
FLOWXS	—	—	—	0.76	—	—	—	—	—	—	—	-0.72	—	-0.65	—	-0.49	—	—	—	—	—	-0.61	—	—	—	—	—	1.00						
FLOWXSDA	—	—	—	0.65	—	—	—	—	—	—	—	—	—	—	—	—	—	—	—	—	—	-0.53	—	—	—	—	—	0.61	1.00					
FLOWVAR1	—	—	—	—	0.65	—	—	—	—	—	—	—	—	0.69	0.52	**0.90**	—	—	—	—	—	0.58	—	—	—	—	0.79	-0.64	0.63	1.00				
FLOWXS_P	—	—	—	0.74	—	—	—	—	—	—	—	-0.70	—	-0.63	—	—	—	—	—	—	—	-0.61	—	—	—	—	—	**0.99**	-0.67	-0.62	1.00			
Q2	—	—	—	—	—	—	—	—	—	—	—	—	—	—	—	—	—	—	—	—	—	—	—	—	—	—	—	—	—	—	—	1.00		
Q2DA	—	—	—	—	—	—	—	—	—	—	—	—	—	—	—	—	—	—	—	—	—	—	—	—	—	—	—	—	—	—	—	—	1.00	
FISHIBI	—	—	—	0.59	—	—	—	—	—	—	—	—	0.48	—	—	—	—	—	—	—	—	—	—	-0.50	—	—	—	—	—	—	—	—	—	1.00

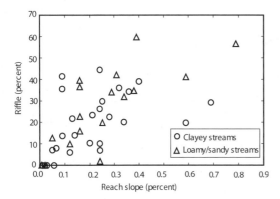

FIGURE 6. Plot of reach slope and percent riffles for clayey streams in the Chicago area.

change, watershed urban land, reach slope, clayey surficial deposits, coarse deposits in the 60-m stream network buffer, watershed slope, and transport index (correlation coefficients of 0.56, −0.53, 0.47, −0.46, 0.45, 0.41, and 0.40, respectively).

Among geomorphic and habitat characteristics, unit-area bank-full channel area was the strongest response variable and plotted closely to watershed urban land and clayey surficial deposits, whereas bank-full width/depth ratios plotted directly opposite watershed urban land and clayey surficial deposits (Figure 8). Thus, clayey urban streams had relatively large, narrow channels. Amount of fine substrate plotted closely along RDA axis 2, and opposite to the coefficient of variation of the bank-full width/depth ratio (a measurement of habitat variability), watershed and reach slope, and transport index. Thus, slope and runoff appear to be the main determinates of the amount of fine substrate and habitat variability. The RBP habitat index plotted near population density change and coarse surficial deposits in the 60-m stream network buffer and opposite erosion, indicating that these factors potentially were most influential on the habitat index.

Flow variability plotted opposite the amount of base flow (accounting for point sources) and drainage

RDA explained 68% of the variance, with the first axis explaining 55%. Monte Carlo permutation tests indicated that both axes were significant ($P = 0.002$). The first RDA axis is mainly a reflection of watershed urban land, drainage area, and clayey surficial deposits (correlation coefficients of −0.68, 0.63, and −0.46, respectively). The second RDA axis reflects a combination of features including population density

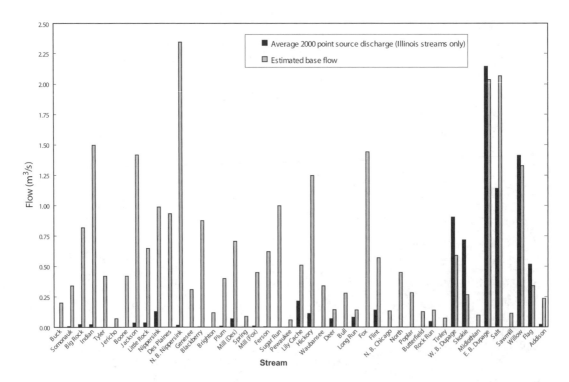

FIGURE 7. Average flow from point sources in 2000 and estimated base flow for 45 streams in the Chicago area.

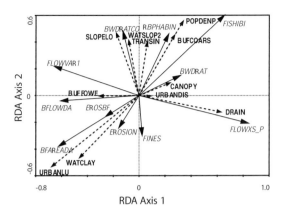

FIGURE 8. Redundancy analysis (RDA) biplot of representative landscape characteristics in relation to geomorphic, habitat, and hydrologic characteristics and revised fish IBI scores for 40 streams in the Chicago area. Refer to Table 2 for definition of abbreviations. Arrows are dashed and abbreviations are bolded for the independent variables (urban indicators and landscape characteristics).

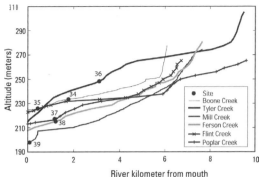

FIGURE 9. Longitudinal profiles for six tributaries to the Fox River in the Chicago area. Sampling sites with map reference numbers from Figure 1 are shown as circles on the profiles.

area. This suggests that small streams with high flow variability tended to have low base flow.

Fish IBI scores plotted opposite watershed urban land and clayey surficial deposits, indicating that IBI scores for clayey streams were negatively influenced by the amount of urbanization. Unit-area bank-full channel area plotted directly opposite fish IBI scores as well, indicating that channel enlargement may be the best reflection of physical disturbance to fish habitat associated with urbanization in clayey streams.

Longitudinal Profiles, Local Geologic Setting, and Stream Network Position

Longitudinal profiles and local geologic setting for six tributaries to the Fox River illustrate the complexity of how glacial landforms may influence geomorphic, habitat, hydrologic, and fish characteristics (Figures 2 and 9; Table 6). The six streams are located near each other (within about a 50-km radius) and represent three pairs of streams with similar percentages of watershed urban land (3%, 16–17%, and 31–38%). In general, reaches with steep slopes on the longitudinal profile are prone to incision, whereas reaches with flat slopes are prone to deposition. Reaches in a transition from steep to flat slopes may be erosional or depositional depending on upstream inputs of water and sediment. For Chicago area streams, transitions in slope and shape of longitudinal profiles mainly are caused by spatial distribution of glacial landforms such as end

moraines, outwash plains, lake plains, melt-water valleys, or bedrock outcrops.

Some of the variability in geomorphic and habitat characteristics can be explained by location of sampled reach in relation to local glacial and fluvial landforms (Figure 9). Boone and Tyler Creeks are rural streams with similar reach slopes (Table 6). However, the Boone Creek Reach (site 34) is flat and located in a sandy outwash plain, and the Tyler Creek Reach (site 36) is located in a transition zone in slope where the stream is flowing through end moraine and esker deposits. Boone Creek has finer substrate (sand included) and fewer riffles than Tyler Creek, even though overall it has less watershed clay than Tyler Creek. The eskers near Tyler Creek contribute sand and gravel that, along with the locally steep slope, promote development of riffles.

Mill (site 39) and Ferson Creek (site 38) are both rural/urbanizing streams with large changes in population density. Both have similar drainage areas, longitudinal profiles, and local glacial landforms but different reach slopes, bank-full areas, stream power, unit-area bank-full flows, and revised fish IBI scores. The Mill Creek Reach is downstream from a dam and is on the steep slope of the Fox River valley side, which consists of limestone bedrock. This local setting results in a steeper reach slope, higher power, and larger bank-full area for Mill Creek compared to Ferson Creek. The high scour potential at Mill Creek may be affecting the IBI scores. Ferson Creek's IBI scores may be elevated because of channel restoration and habitat improvements in recent years.

Flint and Poplar creeks both are clayey tributaries to the Fox River with similar drainage areas (Table 6).

TABLE 6. Values of watershed, geomorphic, habitat, hydrologic characteristics and revised fish IBI scores for six tributaries to the Fox River in the Chicago area.

Characteristic	Abbreviation	Boone Creek	Tyler Creek	Mill Cr. (Fox)	Ferson Creek	Flint Creek	Poplar Creek
Urban indicators							
Watershed urban land (%)	URBANLU	3	3	16	17	31	38
Population density change, 1980–2000 (%)	POPDENP	6	50	298	411	339	880
Landscape characteristics							
Drainage area (km²)	DRAIN	40	81	80	134	96	94
Watershed clayey surficial deposits (%)	WATCLAY	18	49	39	17	93	87
Watershed slope (%)	WATSLOP2	0.6	1.2	1.9	1.9	2.4	1.8
Transport index *1,000 (km⁻¹)	TRANSIN	7.1	5.8	7.2	8.5	5.6	4.0
Coarse deposits within 60-m stream network buffer (%)	BUFCOARS	25	0	29	39	7	4
Forest and wetland within 60-m stream network buffer (%)	BUFFOWE	26	12	14	19	36	22
Disturbed land cover in 30-m buffer (%)	RIPLU	27	9	0	9	0	68
Average open canopy angle (°)	CANOPY	75	77	25	87	82	12
Geomorphic characteristics							
Slope, low-flow water surface (%)	SLOPELO	0.24	0.25	0.59	0.34	0.36	0.28
Bank-full channel area/drainage area (m²/km²)	BFAREADA	0.13	0.06	0.23	0.09	0.08	0.10
Stream power (N/(m s))	POWER	10.6	6.7	148.8	34.9	14.7	31.1
Habitat characteristics							
Fine substrate (%)	FINES	79	24	13	6	12	3
Average bank-full channel width/depth (ratio)	BWDRAT	10	9	17	16	29	8
Average bank erosion (m)	EROSION	0.5	0.2	0.2	0.7	0.2	0.8
Amount of riffle in reach (%)	RIFFLE	2	20	41	32	34	22
Coefficient of variation of wetted channel shape index	CHANSHCO	32	64	36	63	42	29
USEPA rapid bioassessment protocol (RBP) habitat index	RBPHABIN	106	139	150	140	136	100
Hydrologic characteristics							
Bank-full flow/drainage area (m³/s/km²)	BFLOWDA	0.11	0.04	0.39	0.11	0.07	0.10
Estimated base flow at time of cross-section surveys (m³/s)	FLOWXS	0.42	0.42	0.45	0.62	0.57	0.28
Estimated base flow/drainage area (m³/s/km²)	FLOWXSDA	0.0105	0.0052	0.0056	0.0047	0.0060	0.0030
Bank-full flow/estimated low flow (ratio)	FLOWVAR1	10.1	8.4	69.2	22.7	12.4	35.0
Estimated base flow - average 2000 point source flow (m³/s)	FLOWXS_P	0.42	0.42	0.44	0.62	0.43	0.28
Fish							
Revised fish index of biotic integrity	FISHIBI	35	39	37	52	24	40

Poplar Creek (site 37) has slightly more watershed urban land and larger population density but maintains a higher revised fish IBI score than Flint Creek. In headwater areas, both flow off of a large end moraine of clayey till. Near the sampled reaches, Poplar Creek flows across an outwash plain and has a more defined valley than Flint Creek (site 35). The Poplar Creek Reach is located in a transition zone from steep to flat slope, and the Flint Creek Reach is located in a zone of relatively steep slope (Figure 9). Bank-full area, bank-full flow, and bank erosion are slightly higher, and bank-full width/depth ratio is slightly lower in Poplar Creek compared to Flint Creek. This may be caused by the slightly higher watershed urban land and population density change in Poplar Creek. It is not known what is causing the higher fish IBI scores in Poplar compared to Flint Creek. The longitudinal profile and sampling reach location for Ferson Creek is similar to that for Poplar Creek, and Ferson Creek had one of the highest revised fish IBI scores.

These example comparisons show that, in some cases, local factors of geologic setting and landforms and the boundaries and transitions between them can explain some of the variability in geomorphic and habitat characteristics and fish IBI scores. These factors are not easy to quantify, and are difficult to explore through typical multivariate statistical techniques.

Discussion and Conclusions

Clayey streams with high percent urban land had large bank-full channel areas and low fish IBI scores. Bank-full channel area (normalized by drainage area) showed the highest positive correlation to percent watershed urban land of all geomorphic, habitat, and hydrologic characteristics analyzed. There are multiple geomorphic processes by which a channel can enlarge, including incision, widening, and overbank deposition. As the magnitude of frequent floods increase with increasing imperviousness, channels with noncohesive banks, low slopes, base-level control, or armored substrates may be more likely to widen, whereas channels with cohesive banks, steep slopes, no base-level control, and erodible substrate may be more likely to incise. In our study, streams with large bank-full channel areas tended to have deeper channels (low bank-full width/depth ratios). When streams were split into two groups based on watershed surficial deposits, only clayey streams showed a positive correlation between enlarged bank-full channel areas and watershed urban land, an indication that geomorphic conditions in clayey streams may be more responsive to urbaniza-

tion than loamy/sandy streams. Booth (1990) also found that, in the Pacific Northwest, a combination of steep slopes and clayey deposits resulted in streams susceptible to incision. Our study was limited by only having loamy/sandy streams with less than or equal to 31% urban land. The potential moderating effects of watershed surficial deposits should be examined at loamy/sandy streams with higher percent urban land.

Geomorphic and habitat characteristics such as stream power, fine substrate, bank erosion, woody debris, and habitat indexes were most related to reach slope, surficial deposits, and transport index. Compared to the studies of Pacific Northwest streams (Booth 1991; Finkenbine et al. 2000), the relations in Chicago-area streams among urbanization and the amount of woody debris and bank erosion were subtle. Only clayey streams in our study had a statistically significant negative correlation between woody debris and the transport index. Bank erosion and erosivity at bank-full flow did not directly correlate with watershed urban land but the two characteristics plotted closely to percent watershed urban land and clayey deposits on the RDA biplot (Figure 8). The complexity of relations observed in these streams compared to the Pacific Northwest streams could be because the land-cover gradient used in our study ranged from agriculture to urban, and the streams potentially have had multiple historical human alterations.

Habitat index scores showed little or no response to urbanization; instead, they appeared to increase with increasing slope. Based on RDA results, high RBP habitat index scores were related to high slope, population density change, and percentage of coarse deposits in the 60-m stream network buffer; and low percentages of clayey surficial deposits and watershed urban land. In a forest-to-agricultural gradient study in eastern Wisconsin, the WDNR habitat index correlated with fish IBI scores and amount of undisturbed riparian buffer, as well as slope (Fitzpatrick et al. 2001). In the Chicago area, local geologic setting and glacial landforms determine reach slope for the most part, not modern fluvial geomorphic processes. In addition, the range of reach slopes in studied streams was relatively small, with all reaches having slopes of less than 1%. Results from our study indicate that the habitat indexes are less useful in accounting for urbanization-caused habitat degradation. This may reflect complex geomorphic processes that vary both spatially and temporally during urbanization. Habitat indexes combine characteristics from different geomorphic processes and, thus, can be insensitive to substantial changes of individual processes. Habitat indexes that have mainly been developed and used on streams impacted by agricultural practices may need refinement when used on streams impacted by urban development.

Hydrologic effects from urbanization were confounded by differences in stormwater control and sewering practices (presence of combined-sewer systems and TARP) and point-source contributions. For streams with less than 30% watershed urban land, there was a positive relation between unit-area 2-year flood peaks and percent watershed urban land. For streams with greater than 30% watershed urban land, effects from point sources, combined sewer overflows, TARP, and physiographic setting confounded the positive relation. In watersheds with a high transport index (high relief and dense drainage pattern), storm-water control efforts may be less effective at moderating small, frequent flood peaks. Effectiveness of storm-water control measures and hydrologic alterations for decreasing peak flows of small, frequent floods is variable (Finkenbine et al. 2000; Booth and Jackson 1997). Detention basins may cause more incision because they increase the duration of high flows (McCuen and Moglen 1988). Culvert placement is another important aspect influencing flood peaks and geomorphic stability (Whipple and DiLouie 1981). No information for these local factors that affect stormwater was gathered during our study.

Base flow (adjusted for point sources) in our study was consistently low in streams with more than about 33% watershed urban land (roughly equal to 10% total impervious area). Below 33% watershed urban land, base flow was variable. Near Vancouver, British Columbia, base flow was low in streams with watersheds that had more than 40% total impervious area (Finkenbine et al. 2000). Streams in the Chicago area with greater than 33% watershed urban land had low base flow, but the effects of urbanization were offset by point-source contributions.

More local information regarding stormwater practices, as well as historical stream stabilization and channelization projects, is needed to better explain the hydrologic variability for Chicago-area streams. More insight into how hydrologic conditions change for urbanizing streams could be obtained by evaluating other types of streamflow data from gauging stations in urban or urbanizing areas, such as total annual flow, seasonality of flow, base flow, flow duration, annual/seasonal flow volumes, and annual/seasonal precipitation. In addition to comparisons among gauges, historical analysis of data from a single gauging station

could be performed to identify changes in hydrologic conditions for specific historical land development, storm-water control, or sewerage practices.

Revised fish IBI scores had the highest correlation with watershed urban land of all characteristics examined. The IBI scores also were negatively correlated to watershed clayey deposits and bank-full channel area. Historical data for the Chicago area show that IBI scores most strongly relate to population density and watershed urban land cover and possibly to the amount of clayey surficial deposits (Fitzpatrick et al. 2004; no historical data were available for bank-full channel area or base flow). Correlations indicated that fish IBI scores were affected by early stages of urbanization more so in clayey streams than in loamy/sandy streams. Relations among channel enlargement and increasing urban land were more pronounced in clayey streams. However, these relations are still tentative and may be artifacts of historical alterations from agricultural land use. In addition, historical data from some clayey sites suggest that IBI scores may be dependent on fish passage issues (Fitzpatrick et al. 2004).

Geomorphic and hydrologic responses to urbanization generally were continuous among the streams; only fish IBI scores showed a possible degradation threshold, with low scores occurring in watersheds with more than 25% watershed urban land and no high scores in watersheds with greater than 40% watershed urban land. Data from other studies of aquatic communities and urbanization have not shown a threshold response, but suggest that degradation occurs as a continuum (Booth and Jackson 1997; Fitzpatrick et al. 2004). Booth and Jackson (1997) suggest that the abrupt transition (or threshold) for urban-related degradation of aquatic communities is based on human "perception of" and "tolerance for" degradation. The revised IBI used in this study may better reflect the level and scope of aquatic-community degradation tolerated and perceived as negative by humans.

Presence of stream buffers with forest and wetland did not influence geomorphic, habitat, or hydrologic characteristics, or IBI scores. Lack of correlation among forest/wetland in the stream network buffer, fish IBI scores, and base flow is in contrast to relations observed in a study of eastern Wisconsin streams along a forest-to-agriculture land-cover gradient, where the amount of forest/wetland/grassland vegetation in the stream network buffer was positively correlated with fish IBI scores and base flow (Fitzpatrick et al. 2001). This suggests that forested riparian buffers are less able to moderate the influence of urbanization on geomorphic, habitat, and hydrologic characteristics and biotic integrity of streams probably because of hydrologic alterations (such as storm sewers, detention basins, and point-source discharges) that directly bypass riparian buffers.

The range in spatial-scale of urban indicator, landscape, geomorphic, habitat, and hydrologic data used in this study helped to infer geomorphic processes in urbanizing streams and describe the response of fish biotic integrity to urbanization. However, these data were not detailed enough to confirm the geomorphic processes at work in each stream reach. Geomorphic processes at a particular reach may be influenced by present and historical upstream or downstream disturbances, such as watershed land-use and past agricultural practices, knickpoint migration, channelization, or restoration/rehabilitation projects. Longitudinal profiles were useful for distinguishing differences in local geologic settings among sampled sites. The longitudinal profiles helped to distinguish the proximity of reaches to transitions in slope that are caused by glacial landforms and gave an indication of whether erosion, transport, or deposition was dominant. Additional information on local geomorphic processes can be gained through a variety of methods, including (1) more detailed geomorphic assessments oriented toward geomorphic processes with a historical and watershed approach, such as Thorne's (1998) geomorphic reconnaissance surveys, (2) sampling at many locations within stream networks, (3) collecting temporal data (monitoring) during urban development in the watershed, and (4) collecting historical information on past land-use practices and channel alteration.

In conclusion, for Chicago-area streams, some geomorphic, habitat, and hydrologic characteristics and fish biotic integrity were affected by urbanization. However, the percent watershed slope and clayey surficial deposits influenced the effects, as did other more local factors such as reach slope, glacial landforms, and hydrologic alterations (stormwater practices and point sources), and historical and present channel alterations. Specific local-scale and temporal data on geomorphic processes are needed to distinguish the cause and effect relations between urbanization and habitat characteristics.

Acknowledgments

The authors gratefully acknowledge the assistance of USGS or former USGS colleagues involved in data collection, data analysis, and preliminary review of the manuscript. Cross-section surveys were done with assistance from Brett Esser, David Housner, Debbie Adolphson, Phillip Gaebler, and Andrea Axel. Jana Stewart, Debbie Adolphson, Krista Stensvold, Sarah Tegt, and Janice Fuller conducted habitat surveys. Barbara Scudder provided insightful technical comments and assisted with data analysis. Marie Peppler and Jennifer Bruce assisted with illustrations and tables. Steven Pescitelli of Illinois Department of Natural Resources provided insightful comments about fish assemblage data. The study was funded as part of the USGS National Water-Quality Assessment Program, Upper Illinois River Study Unit. We are also thankful for a thorough technical review of the manuscript and insightful comments by Christopher Konrad and Terry Short (both of the USGS) and the editors of this book.

References

Adolphson, D. L., T. L. Arnold, F. A. Fitzpatrick, M. A. Harris, K. D. Richards, B. C. Scudder, and J. S. Stewart. 2002. Physical, chemical, and biological methods and data from the urban land-use-gradient study, Des Plaines and Fox River basins, Illinois, 1999–2001. U.S. Geological Survey Open-File Report 01–459, Urbana, Illinois.

Allen, H. E., Jr., and R. M. Bejcek. 1979. Effects of urbanization on the magnitude and frequency of floods in northeastern Illinois. U.S. Geological Survey Water Resources Investigations 79–36, Urbana, Illinois.

American Society of Civil Engineers, Urban Hydrology Research Council. 1969. An analysis of national basic information needs in urban hydrology. American Society of Civil Engineers, New York.

Anderson, A. G., A. S. Paintal, and J. T. Davenport. 1970. Tentative design procedure for riprap-lined channels. National Academy of Sciences, National Cooperative Highway Research Program, Report 108, Washington, D.C.

Arcement, G. J., Jr., and V. R. Schneider. 1987. Roughness coefficients for densely vegetated flood plains. U.S. Geological Survey Water-Resources Investigations Report 83–4247.

Armantrout, N. B. 1998. Glossary of aquatic habitat inventory terminology. American Fisheries Society, Bethesda, Maryland.

Arnold, T. L., D. J. Sullivan, M. A. Harris, F. A. Fitzpatrick, B. C. Scudder, P. M. Ruhl, D. W. Hanchar, and J. S. Stewart. 1999. Environmental setting of the upper Illinois River basin and implications for water quality. U.S. Geological Survey Water Resources Investigations Report 98–4268, Urbana, Illinois.

Barbour, M. T., J. Gerritsen, B. D. Snyder, and J. B. Stribling. 1999. Rapid bioassessment protocols for use in streams and wadeable rivers, periphyton, benthic macroinvertebrates and fish, 2nd edition. EPA, Report 841-B-99–002, Washington, D.C.

Barnes, H. H., Jr. 1967. Roughness characteristics of natural channels. U.S. Geological Survey Water-Supply Paper 1849, Washington, D.C.

Bertrand, W. A., R. L. Hite, and D. M. Day. 1996. Biological stream characterization (BSC)–biological assessment of Illinois stream quality through 1993. Illinois Environmental Protection Agency Division of Water Pollution Control, IEPA/BOW/96–058.

Bledsoe, B. P., and C. C. Watson. 2001. Effects of urbanization on channel instability. Journal of the American Water Resources Association 37:255–270.

Booth, D. B. 1990. Stream-channel incision following drainage-basin urbanization. Water Resources Research 26:407–417.

Booth, D. B. 1991. Urbanization and the natural drainage system-impacts, solutions and prognoses. Northwest Environmental Journal 7:93–118.

Booth, D., and C. R. Jackson. 1997. Urbanization of aquatic systems: degradation thresholds, stormwater detection, and the limits of mitigation. Journal of American Water Resources Association 33:1077–1090.

Booth, D., and L. Reinelt. 1993. Consequences of urbanization on aquatic systems—measured effects, degradation thresholds, and corrective strategies. Pages 545–550 in Proceedings Watershed '93, A National Conference on Watershed Management. March 21–24, 1993, U.S. Environmental Protection Agency, Alexandria, Virginia.

Brunner, G. W. 2001. HEC-RAS, river analysis system user's manual. U.S. Army Corps of Engineers, Hydrologic Engineering Center, Davis, California.

Center for Watershed Protection. 2003. Impacts of impervious cover on aquatic systems. Center for Watershed Protection Research Monograph No. 1, Ellicott City, Maryland.

Chang, H. H. 1992. Fluvial processes in river engineering. Krieger Publishing Company, Malabar, Florida.

Colosimo, M. F. 2002. Physical and biological stream changes in an urbanizing watershed: Gwynns Falls, Maryland. Doctoral dissertation. John Hopkins University, Baltimore, Maryland.

Coon, W. F. 1998. Estimation of roughness coefficients for natural stream channels with vegetated banks. U.S. Geological Survey Water-Supply Paper 2441, Denver.

Couch, C., and P. Hamilton. 2002. Effects of urbanization on stream ecosystems. U.S. Geological Survey Fact Sheet, Reston, Virginia.

Cowan, W. L. 1956. Estimating hydraulic roughness coefficients. Agricultural Engineering 37:473–475.

Doll, B. A., D. E. Wis-Frederick, C. M. Buckner, S. D. Wilkerson, W. A. Harman, R. E. Smith, and J. Spooner. 2002. Hydraulic geometry relationships for urban streams throughout the piedmont of North Carolina. Journal of the American Water Resources Association 38:641–651.

Dreher, D. W. 1997. Watershed urbanization impacts on stream quality indicators in northeastern Illinois. Pages 129–135 in M. Murphy and R. Kirchner, editors. Assessing the cumulative impacts of watershed development on aquatic ecosystems and water quality. Northeastern Illinois Planning Commission, Chicago.

Fenneman, N. M. 1938, Physiography of the eastern United States. McGraw-Hill Book Company, New York.

Finkenbine, J. K., J. W. Atwater, and D. S. Mavinic. 2000. Stream health after urbanization. Journal of American Water Resources Association 36:1149–1160.

Fitzpatrick, F. A., M. A. Harris, T. L. Arnold, and K. D. Richards. 2004. Urbanization influences on aquatic communities in northeastern Illinois Streams. Journal of American Water Resources Association 40:461–475.

Fitzpatrick, F. A., B. C. Scudder, B. N. Lenz, and D. J. Sullivan. 2001. Effects of multi-scale environmental characteristics on agricultural stream biota in eastern Wisconsin. Journal of the American Water Resources Association 37:1489–1507.

Fitzpatrick, F.A., I. R. Waite, P. J. D'Arconte, M. R. Meador, M. A. Maupin, and M. E. Gurtz, 1998. Revised methods for characterizing stream habitat in the National Water-Quality Assessment Program. U.S. Geological Survey Water-Resources Investigations Report 98–4052, Raleigh, North Carolina.

Garie, H. L., and A. McIntosh. 1986. Distribution of benthic macroinvertebrates in a stream exposed to urban runoff. Journal of American Water Resources Association 22:447–455.

Gergel, S. E., M. G. Turner, J. R. Miller, J. M. Melack, and E. M. Stanley. 2002. Landscape indicators of human impacts to riverine systems. Aquatic Sciences 64:118–128.

Graf, W. L. 1975. The impact of suburbanization on fluvial geomorphology. Water Resources Research 11:690–692.

Gregory, K. J., R. J. Davis, and P. W. Downs. 1992. Identification of river channel change due to urbanization. Applied Geography 12:299–318.

Gregory, K. J. and J. R. Madew. 1982. Land use change, flood frequency and channel adjustments. Pages 757–781 in R. D. Hey, J. C. Bathurst, and C. R. Thorne, editors. Gravel-bed rivers. Wiley, New York.

Guy, H. P. 1970. Sediment problems in urban areas. Water in the Urban Environment, U.S. Geological Survey Circular 601-E, Washington, D.C.

Hammer, T. R. 1972. Stream channel enlargement due to urbanization. Water Resources Research 8:1530–1540.

Harrelson, C. C., C. L. Rawlins, and J. P. Potyondy. 1994. Stream channel reference sites: an illustrated guide to field technique. USDA Forest Service, General Technical Report RM-245, Fort Collins, Colorado.

Harvey, C. A., and D. A. Eash. 1996. Description, Instructions, and verification for Basinsoft, a computer program to quantify drainage-basin characteristics. U.S. Geological Survey Water-Resources Investigations Report 95–4287, Iowa City, Iowa.

Henshaw, P. C., and D. B. Booth. 2000. Natural restabilization of stream channels in urban watersheds. Journal of the American Water Resources Association 36:1219–1236.

Hicks, D. M. and P. D. Mason. 1998. Roughness characteristics of New Zealand rivers. National Institute of Water and Atmospheric Research, Christchurch, New Zealand.

Hill, M. O. 1979. DECORANA-A FORTRAN program for arranging multivariate data in an ordered two-way table by classification of the individuals and attributes. Cornell University, Ithaca, New York.

Hite, R. L., and B. A. Bertrand. 1989. Biological stream characterization (BSC): a biological assessment of Illinois stream quality. Special report # 13 of the Illinois State Water Plan Task Force. Illinois Environmental Protection Agency Division of Water Pollution Control, IEPA/WPC/89–275, Springfield.

Hollis, G. E. 1975. The effect of urbanization on floods of different recurrence interval. Water Resources Research 11:431–435.

Illinois Environmental Protection Agency. 2002. Illinois water quality report 2002, Appendix A. Illinois Environmental Protection Agency, IEPA/BOW/02–006, Springfield.

Iman, R. L., and W. J. Conover. 1983. A modern approach to statistics. Wiley, New York.

Interagency Advisory Committee on Water Data. 1982. Guidelines for determining flood flow frequency. U.S. Geological Survey, Office of Water Data Coordination, Bulletin 17B of the Hydrology Subcommittee, Reston, Virginia.

Kennen, J. G. 1999. Relation of macroinvertebrate community impairment to catchment characteristics in New Jersey streams. Journal of American Water Resources Association 35:939–955.

Knight, C. 1979. Urbanization and natural stream channel morphology: the case of two English new towns.

Pages 181–198 in G. E. Hollis, editor. Man's impact on the hydrological cycle in the United Kingdom. Geo Abstracts Ltd., Norwich, UK.

Konrad, C.P. 2003. Effects of urban development on floods. U.S. Geological Survey Fact Sheet FS-076–03, Tacoma, Washington.

Krug, W.R., and G. L. Goddard. 1986. Effects of urbanization on streamflow, sediment loads, and channel morphology in Pheasant Branch basin near Middleton, Wisconsin. U.S. Geological Survey Water-Resources Investigations Report 85–4068, Madison, Wisconsin.

LaTour, J. K. 1993. Contribution of return flows to streamflow in selected stream reaches in Illinois, 1988–89. U.S. Geological Survey Water-Resources Investigations Report 93–4089, Urbana, Illinois.

Leighton, M. M., G. E. Ekblaw, and C. L. Horberg. 1948. Physiographic divisions of Illinois. Illinois State Geological Survey Report of Investigation 129, Champaign-Urbana.

Leopold, L. B. 1968. The hydrologic effects of urban land use: hydrology for urban land planning–a guidebook of the hydrologic effects of urban land use. U.S. Geological Survey Circular 554, Denver.

Lyons, J. 1992. Using the index of biotic integrity (IBI) to measure environmental quality in warmwater streams of Wisconsin. U.S. Department of Agriculture, Forest Service, North Central Forest Experiment Station, General Technical Report NC-149, St. Paul, Minnesota.

Maxted, J., and E. Shaver. 1997. The use of retention basins to mitigate stormwater impacts on aquatic life. Pages 494–512 in L.A. Roesner, editor. Effects of watershed development and management on aquatic ecosystems, American Society of Civil Engineers, New York.

McCuen, R. H., and G. E. Moglen. 1988. Multicriterion stormwater management methods. Journal of Water Resources Planning and Management 114:414–431.

McMahon, G., and T. F. Cuffney. 2001. Quantifying urban intensity in drainage basins for assessing stream ecological conditions. Journal of American Water Resources Association 36:1247–1261.

Meador, M. R., T. F. Cuffney, and M. E. Gurtz. 1993. Methods for sampling fish communities as part of the National Water-Quality Assessment Program. U.S. Geological Survey Open-File Report 93–104, Raleigh, North Carolina.

Owens, D. W., P. Jopke, D. W. Hall, J. Balousek, and A. Roa. 2000. Soil erosion from two small construction sites, Dane County, Wisconsin. U.S. Geological Survey Fact Sheet FS-109–00, Madison, Wisconsin.

Paul, M. J., and J. L. Meyer. 2001. Streams in the urban

landscape. Annual Review of Ecological Systems 32:333–365.

Richmond, G. M. (editor), D. S. Fullerton (editor), J. A. Lineback (comp.), N. K. Bleuer (comp.), D. M. Mickelson (comp.), W. R. Farrand (comp.), and R. P. Goldthwait (comp.). 2001. Quaternary Geologic Map of the Chicago 4° x 6° Quadrangle, United States: U.S. Geological Survey Miscellaneous Investigations Series Map I-1420 (NK-16). U.S. Geological Survey, Denver.

Richards, C., L. B. Johnson, and G. E. Host. 1996. Landscape-scale influences on stream habitats and biota. Canadian Journal of Fisheries and Aquatic Sciences, Supplement 1:295–311.

Roberts, C. R. 1989. Flood frequency and urban-induced channel change: some British examples. Pages 57–82 in K. Beven and P. Carling, editors. Floods: hydrological, sedimentological and geomorphological implications. Wiley, New York.

Roesner, L. A. and B. P. Bledsoe. 2003. Physical effects of wet weather flows on aquatic habitats: present knowledge and research needs. Water Environment Research Foundation, Report 00-WSM-4, Alexandria, Virginia.

Rogers, C. E., D. J. Brabander, M. T. Barbour, and H. E. Hemond. 2002. Use of physical, chemical, and biological indices to assess impacts of contaminants and physical habitat alteration in urban streams. Environmental Toxicology and Chemistry 21:1156–1167.

Roth, N. E., J. D. Allan, and D. L. Erickson. 1996. Landscape influences on stream biotic integrity assessed at multiple scales. Landscape Ecology 11:141–156.

Schueler, T. 1994. The importance of imperviousness. Watershed Protection Techniques 1:100–111.

Simonson, T. D., J. Lyons, and P. D. Kanehl. 1994. Guidelines for evaluating fish habitat in Wisconsin streams. USDA Forest Service North Central Forest Experiment Station, General Technical Report NC-164, St. Paul, Minnesota.

Soller, D. R. and P. H. Packard. 1998. Digital representation of a map showing the thickness and character of Quaternary sediments in the glaciated United States east of the Rocky Mountains. U.S. Geological Survey Digital Data Series DDS-38, Denver.

Spieker, A. M. 1970. Water in urban planning, Salt Creek Basin, Illinois—water management as related to alternative land-use practices. U.S. Geological Survey Water-Supply Paper 2002, Washington, D.C.

Stewart, J. S., L. Wang, J. Lyons, J. A. Horwatich, and R. Bannerman. 2001. Influences of watershed, riparian-corridor, and reach-scale characteristics on aquatic biota in agricultural watersheds. Journal of the American Water Resources Association 37:1475–1487.

Ter Braak, C. J. F. 1986. Canonical correspondence analysis-a new eigenvector method for multivariate direct gradient analysis. Ecology 67:1167–1179.

Ter Braak, C. J. F., and P. Smilauer. 1998. CANOCO reference manual and user's guide to CANOCO for Windows—software for canonical community ordination, version 4. Centre for Biomet, Wageningen, Netherlands.

Terrio, P. J. 1994. Relations of changes in waste-water treatment practices to changes in stream-water quality during 1978–88 in the Chicago area, Illinois, and implications for regional and national water-quality assessments. U.S. Geological Survey Water-Resources Investigations Report 93–4188, Urbana, Illinois.

The H. John Heinz II Center for Science, Economics and the Environment. 2002. The state of the nation's ecosystems—measuring the lands, waters, and living resources of the United States. Cambridge University Press, Cambridge, UK.

Thorne, C. R. 1998. Stream reconnaissance handbook. Wiley, Chichester.

Trimble, S. W. 1997. Contribution of stream channel erosion to sediment yield from an urbanizing watershed. Science 278:1442–1444.

U.S. Bureau of the Census. 1985. Census of population (1984) and per capita income (1983) estimates—governmental units [machine readable data files on CD-ROM]. U.S. Bureau of the Census, Washington, D.C.

U.S. Bureau of the Census. 1991. Census of population and housing, 1990. Public Law 94–171 data (United States) [machine readable data files on CD-ROM]. U.S. Bureau of Census, Washington, D.C.

U.S. Bureau of the Census. 1999. 1999 TIGER/line files [machine readable data files on CD-ROM]. U.S. Bureau of the Census, Washington, D.C.

U.S. Bureau of the Census. 2001. Census of population and housing, 2000. Public Law 94–171 data (United States) [machine readable data files on CD-ROM]. U.S. Bureau of the Census, Washington, D.C.

U.S. Department of Agriculture, Soil Conservation Service. 1986. Urban hydrology for small watersheds. U.S. Department of Agriculture, Soil Conservation Service, Technical Release 55, U.S. Government Printing Office, Washington, D.C.

U.S. Geological Survey. 2001. National elevation data set, digital data. Available: http://edcnts12.cr.usgs.gov/ned/ (August 2001)

Vogelmann, J. E., S. M. Howard, L. Yang, C. R. Larson, B. K. Wylie, and N. Van Driel. 2001. Completion of the 1990s national land cover data set for the conterminous United States from Landsat thematic mapper data and ancillary data sources. Photogrammetric Engineering and Remote Sensing 67:650–662.

Wang, L., J. Lyons, P. Kanehl, and R. Bannerman. 2001. Impacts of urbanization on stream habitat and fish across multiple spatial scales. Environmental Management 28:255–266.

Wang, L., J. Lyons, P. Kanehl, R. Bannerman, and E. Emmons. 2000. Watershed urbanization and changes in fish communities in southeastern Wisconsin streams. Journal of American Water Resources Association 36:1173–1189.

Wang, L., J. Lyons, P. Kanehl, and R. Gatti. 1997. Influences of watershed land use on habitat quality and biotic integrity in Wisconsin streams. Fisheries 22(6):6–12.

Whipple, W., Jr., and J. DiLouie. 1981. Coping with increased stream erosion in urbanizing areas. Water Resources Research 17:1561–1564.

Willman, H. B. 1971. Summary of the geology of the Chicago area. Illinois State Geological Survey Circular 460, Champaign-Urbana.

Willman, H. B., E. Atherton, T. Baschback, C. Collinson, J. Frye, M. Hopkins, J. Lineback, and J. Simon. 1975. Handbook of Illinois stratigraphy. Illinois State Geological Survey Bulletin 95, Champaign-Urbana.

Wisconsin Geological and Natural History Survey. 1981. Bedrock geology of Wisconsin (revised 1995). Wisconsin Geological and Natural History Survey, Madison.

Wolman, M. G. 1967. A cycle of sedimentation and erosion in urban river channels. Geografiska Annaler 49:385–395.

Wolman, M. G., and A. P. Schick. 1967. Effects of construction on fluvial sediment, urban and suburban areas of Maryland. Water Resources Research 3:451–464.

Yoder, C. O., and E. T. Rankin. 1997. Assessing the condition and status of aquatic life designated uses in urban and suburban watersheds. Pages 201–227 *in* L. A. Roesner, editor. Effects of watershed development and management on aquatic ecosystems. American Society of Civil Engineers, New York.

American Fisheries Society Symposium 47:117–132, 2005

Physiological Stress Responses of Brown Trout to Stormwater Runoff Events in Rapid Creek, Rapid City, South Dakota

Jack W. Erickson*

South Dakota Department of Game, Fish and Parks
3305 West South Street, Rapid City, South Dakota 57702, USA

Scott J. Kenner

Department of Civil and Environmental Engineering, South Dakota School of Mines and Technology
501 East St. Patrick Street, Rapid City, South Dakota 57701, USA

Bruce A. Barton[1]

Department of Biology, University of South Dakota
Vermillion, South Dakota 57609, USA

Abstract.—Urban streams typically have increased flows, high suspended sediment concentrations, and reduced water quality during rainstorms as a result of changes within the watershed related to human activity. In the 6-month periods from May through October of 2001 and 2002, water quality was monitored continuously at five sites along Rapid Creek within Rapid City, South Dakota. Water quality samples were collected for eight base flows (nonevents) and eight storm events. Blood samples were collected from wild adult brown trout *Salmo trutta* during base flow conditions and six of eight storm events to determine if storm events could elicit physiological stress responses. Blood samples were also collected 24, 48, and 96 h after each storm event had started. Water monitoring results showed significant increases in runoff volume and peak flows during storm events. Water quality parameters exceeding South Dakota's water quality criteria for a coldwater fishery were total suspended solids and temperature. Plasma concentrations of cortisol and lactate, during and after storm events, were not significantly different than those measured during base flow conditions. Plasma glucose values were lower during storm events than during nonevent periods. These observations were compared to those predicted by a suspended sediment dose–response model developed for adult salmonids. The dose–response model overpredicted the severity of the effects of increased total suspended sediment on the brown trout during stormwater runoff events.

Introduction

Urbanization can have a negative impact on riverine systems. Direct impacts to stream morphology include straightening, channelization, installation of riprap to stabilize banks, and alteration of the riparian corridor. Changes in land-use patterns within the watershed can also impact the stream and the aquatic community. Construction of buildings, roads, parking lots,

and the resulting increase in stormwater runoff contribute to increases in suspended sediment, and other pollutants that accumulate on the watershed, as well as increase the flood frequency and runoff volume (Richards et al. 1996; Butcher 2003). Wang et al. (2003) found that even low levels of urbanization within a watershed can have a negative impact on trout populations.

Rapid Creek, South Dakota supports a brown trout *Salmo trutta* fishery within the urban area of Rapid City. Recent declines in the brown trout population (Figure 1) are of considerable concern to the responsible management agencies. The main factors

---

* Corresponding author: Jack.Erickson@state.sd.us
[1] Present address: Applied Aquatic Research Ltd., Calgary, Alberta T3C 0K3, Canada.

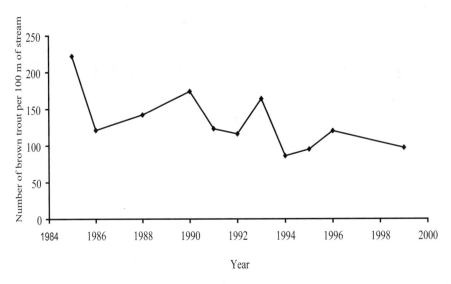

FIGURE 1. Brown trout population density estimates for Rapid Creek, near Baken Park in Rapid City, South Dakota. Population density estimates were developed from annual three-pass electrofishing surveys conducted by the South Dakota Department of Game, Fish and Parks (unpublished data).

influencing long-term maintenance of the brown trout fishery in Rapid Creek appear to be external management practices that indirectly affect the stream ecosystem. The primary external management concerns for degradation of the stream ecosystem are increased urbanization resulting in increased stormwater runoff, flow regulation, and instream and corridor management practices affecting physical habitat characteristics. We hypothesized that increased suspended sediment loads and impaired water quality during stormwater runoff events were acutely impacting brown trout.

Numerous studies have shown exposure to suspended sediments can have a sublethal impact on fish populations. Increased suspended sediment can negatively impact salmonid fishes by disrupting their behavior, impairing respiration, reducing growth rates, degrading spawning habitat, reducing feeding behavior, increasing their susceptibility to disease, and increasing stress (Redding et al. 1987; Newcombe and MacDonald 1991; Vondracek et al. 2003). Avoidance of turbid waters by fish has long been known to exist. Waters (1995) speculated avoidance of turbid water may be the most important sublethal impact of suspended sediment on fish, since it can leave long reaches of stream devoid of fish. In their experiment in artificial stream channels, Cederholm and Reid (1987) demonstrated that juvenile coho salmon *Oncorhynchus kisutch* avoided waters with total suspended sediment (TSS) concentrations above 4,000 mg/L. In a natural stream environment, however, fish populations, mainly cyprinids, avoided TSS-affected areas when levels ranged up to only 352 mg/L by simply moving downstream and returning when the disturbance had ceased (Barton 1976).

Although lethal levels of suspended sediment concentrations are rarely found in nature (Sweka and Hartman 2001), Everest et al. (1987) showed increased mortality of salmonids can occur when sediment concentrations exceed 20,000 mg/L. Using Newcombe and Jensen's (1996) impact assessment model, Bergstedt and Bergersen (1997) suggest suspended solids concentrations as high as 18,000 mg/L immediately downstream from sluicing below a lowhead dam were sufficient to cause mortality in mountain whitefish *Prosopium williamsoni*. Newcombe and MacDonald (1991) recommend researchers look at both the duration of the event as well as the concentration of the suspended sediments when quantifying the impact of suspended sediment on fish populations. We hypothesized that increased suspended sediment loads and impaired water quality during stormwater runoff events would induce a physiological stress response in the brown trout.

Changes in blood chemistry are frequently used to quantify the physiological stress response of fishes. More is probably known about the physiological stress response of salmonids than any other group of fishes (Barton and Iwama 1991). Most of this research has quantified the stress response as a result of crowding, handling, and aquaculture-related stressors in hatcheries. These physiological stress responses are similar for fish stressed from hatchery rearing practices, habitat alterations (stream morphology and water quality), or behavioral stressors such as fright, dominance hierarchies, or interspecific interactions (Wedemeyer et al. 1990). Mazeaud et al. (1977) described the rapid elevation of corticosteroids and catecholamines in the blood plasma of fish exposed to a stressor as the primary stress response. Secondary stress responses include changes in tissues and blood chemistry that may be triggered by primary stress responses or other mechanisms. Secondary stress responses include increased blood glucose (hyperglycemia) and, in freshwater fish, decreased plasma chloride (hypochloremia) concentrations (Wedemeyer et al. 1990). Secondary stress response indicators tend to take longer (minutes to hours) to manifest themselves but often remain altered for longer periods of time than primary responses (Wedemeyer et al. 1990; Barton et al. 2002).

The goal of this study was to determine if stormwater runoff in an urbanized watershed was affecting brown trout populations by imposing stress on the fish. Our objectives were to characterize the hydraulic response and water quality of Rapid Creek to determine if water quality standards for this stream were being exceeded during stormwater runoff events, test the predictions of Newcombe and Jensen's (1996) model for the effects of suspended sediments on brown trout, and determine if brown trout exhibit physiological stress responses during stormwater events that could possibly be associated with the downward trend in their population densities (Figure 1).

Study Area

Rapid Creek drains a northeastern portion of the Black Hills, approximately 960 km^2 at the upstream end of the study area (Figure 2). Rapid Creek originates from the limestone plateau in the Black Hills uplift in western South Dakota. The land cover of Rapid Creek watershed upstream of the study area is predominantly ponderosa pine *Pinus ponderosa* forest.

Upstream of the study area, Rapid Creek loses flow at an annual average rate of 0.14–0.37 m^3/s (Hortness and Driscoll 1998). Subsequently, numerous springs within the upstream portion of the study area provide a steady source of base flow to Rapid Creek and its tributaries. The most significant spring in the study area contributes an average annual flow of 0.37 m^3/s.

The climate in the study area is typical of a semiarid, temperate, continental climate. The area experiences extreme temperature fluctuations both daily and seasonally with minimal precipitation (Goddard et al. 1989). The annual rainfall over the Rapid Creek watershed is 47.2 cm. In contrast, the average annual flow in Rapid Creek in the study area represents a rainfall equivalent of about 4.6 cm, or approximately 10% of the annual rainfall. Most of the precipitation occurs during late spring and early summer (May and June) from convective thunderstorms. The precipitation pattern is reflected in the annual stream hydrograph. The typical low-flow period is from October through February, and the high-flow period is from May through July (Figure 3). Sustained high flows in July are also dependent upon releases from Pactola Reservoir located 41.8 km upstream for domestic water supply, irrigation, and maintenance of the flood storage pool.

The study area is Rapid Creek as it flows through Rapid City, a stream distance roughly 14.4 km (Figure 2). The incremental contributing drainage area within the study area is 119 km^2 and represents approximately 11% of the total drainage area of Rapid Creek at the downstream end of the study area. Through the study reach, minor amounts of irrigation water are withdrawn for lawn and garden watering (generally less than 0.057 m^3/s).

The study area was divided into four reaches (Table 1). Water quality monitoring sites were located near the upstream and downstream end of each reach (Figure 2). Two fish sampling sites were located within reaches B, C, and D. Each fish sampling site was approximately 200 m. Low fish densities in the uppermost reach (A) required sampling almost the entire reach.

Methods

Our sampling objective was to collect blood from brown trout and water quality samples during base flow conditions on a monthly basis and during eight storm events between the months of May and October of 2001 and 2002. A period of four consecutive days without measurable precipitation or stormwater runoff was selected to represent base flow conditions as well as to represent the nonstress or resting (control) state for brown trout. Similarly, a period of 4 d without measurable precipitation or stormwater runoff was selected as the minimum interevent time between rain storms to allow sufficient time for pollutants to accumulate on the watershed. Event sampling followed the guidelines established by the Environmental Protection Agency (EPA) for stormwater runoff monitoring (Smoley 1993).

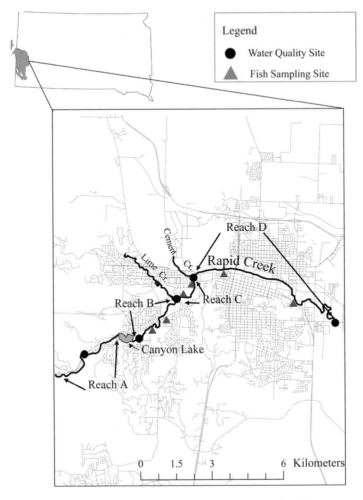

FIGURE 2. Study area and sampling locations on Rapid Creek. Rapid City, South Dakota.

A storm event was defined as a minimum of 0.25 cm of precipitation within the study area that produced a measurable response in the hydrograph. No more than one storm event was sampled each month. Blood samples were collected at each fish sampling site four times following the onset of a storm. The first sampling period began 2–4 h following the onset of a storm event. Subsequent blood samples were collected 24, 48, and 96 h following collection of the first blood samples.

Water Sampling Methods

Water quality sampling was performed using automatic samplers in steel station boxes placed within 15 m of the creek. Sites 2–5 (Table 1) were equipped with ISCO 6700 field samplers, containing 24 1-L bottles. Also installed at these sites were ISCO 720 submerged probe flow modules to allow for stage measurement. Site 1 was equipped with a Manning PST sampler that contained 24 900-mL bottles. Intake tubes were placed on concrete pads in water deep enough to allow for sampling during low-flow conditions, and at a location with sufficient turbulence and/or velocity to be representative of well-mixed instream conditions.

Each station was equipped with a multiparameter sonde to collect continuous water quality data. Sites 2–5 used YSI 6820 water quality sondes equipped with temperature, dissolved oxygen, conductivity, pH, and turbidity probes (Yellow Springs Instruments, Yellow Springs, Ohio). Site 1 used a Hydrolab III monitor equipped with temperature, dissolved oxygen, conductivity, and pH probes

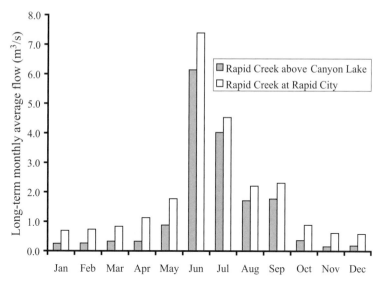

FIGURE 3. Mean monthly discharge for Rapid Creek at USGS gaging stations 06412500 (Rapid Creek above Canyon Lake 1946–2002) and 06414000 (Rapid Creek at Rapid City 1942–2002), (from USGS 2004).

(Hydrolab, Loveland, Colorado). Sondes were calibrated every 2 weeks using National Institute of Standards and Technology traceable standards to ensure accurate readings.

Flow measurements were taken at sites 2, 3, and 4 and used to develop a standard stage-discharge relationship. Discharges at sites 1 and 5 were based on stage discharge relationships for USGS streamflow gaging stations 06412500 and 06414000, respectively. Staff gauges were installed at sites 2–5 for flow module calibration.

Sampling efforts included collection of runoff event samples and base flow samples. Automated samplers were started manually to coincide with the start of runoff. Sites 1–4 were programmed to collect the first sample at activation, then 11 samples at 15-min intervals, 4 at 30-min intervals, 4 at 1-h intervals, and 4 at 3-h intervals for a 21-h duration. Sample distribution at site 5 consisted of the first sample at activation, then 11 samples at 30-min intervals, 6 at 1-h intervals, and 6 at 2-h intervals for a 24-h duration. Base flow sampling intervals ranged from 30 to 60 min for a duration of 8–12 h.

Once sampling was complete, continuous data and water samples were retrieved from each site. Continuous data from sites 2–5 were retrieved using ISCO 581 Rapid Transfer Device (RTD), and downloaded to Flowlink database software (ISCO Inc., Lincoln,

TABLE 1. Description of study reaches for Rapid Creek flowing through Rapid City, South Dakota. See Figure 2 for reach, water quality (WQ) sampling sites, and fish sampling subreach locations.

Reach	Description	Length (km)	Incremental drainage area (km²)	Percent impervious	Upstream WQ site	Downstream WQ site
A	Dark Canyon to Canyon Lake, forested with (some residential)	2.41	960	<1	–	1
B	Canyon Lake to Lime Creek, half forested, (half residential)	2.41	32.4	10–15	2	3
C	Lime Creek to Cement Creek, residential with (some commercial)	1.61	23.7	40	3	4
D	Cement Creek to Hawthorne Ditch, (residential, commercial, and some industrial)	8.00	32.5	70	4	5

Nebraska). Stage-discharge equations had been entered into Flowlink so that discharge could be estimated from stage. For site 1, discharge data were downloaded from the USGS homepage and copied into the Flowlink database. The downloaded discharge information was used to determine the beginning and end of the runoff event hydrograph. Event mean concentrations (EMCs) were computed for each site using a flow-volume method (Smoley 1993) with four sites requiring a composite volume of 5 L, and one site requiring a 9-L composite for a duplicate analysis. Although concentrations of most contaminants peak on the rising limb of the hydrograph, the product of the EMC and event duration represents exposure to the entire runoff event. A blank sample was included for each sampling effort. The composited samples were sent to an independent laboratory for analysis of 12 water quality parameters (Table 2). Based on year 1 results, zinc was the only metal analyzed in year 2.

For each of the eight storm events, the severity of ill effect (SEV) for adult salmonids was calculated at each water sampling station using a model developed by Newcombe and Jensen (1996):

$$SEV = 1.6814 + 0.4769(\log_e x) + 0.7565(\log_e y),$$

where x is the duration of the event (h) and y is the concentration of sediment (mg/L). An SEV could not be calculated for storm events at the sampling station upstream of Canyon Lake since the suspended sediment EMCs upstream of Canyon Lake were below the detection limit. Suspended sediment samples were collected approximately 4 cm off the bottom of the streambed through a pneumatic pump intake. Total suspended solids were measured with EPA Method 160.2 (USEPA 1983). These results were used in the SEV dose–response model to represent suspended sediment.

Fish and Blood Collection

For each sampling period, blood samples were collected from five adult brown trout (minimum 200 mm total length, TL) at each of seven fish sampling sites (Figure 2; Table 1). All fish were fin-clipped to ensure blood was not collected from the same fish more than once in a year. All fish were collected with Smith-Root model 12-B battery powered backpack electrofishers (Smith-Root Inc., Vancouver, Washington) operated with a pulse width of 6 ms, pulse frequency of 60 Hz, and output of 300 V. Following measurement of the weight (g) and TL (mm), blood samples were collected immediately with 1.5-mL heparinized syringes equipped with 21-G needles. Blood samples were drawn from the caudal vasculature as outlined by Houston (1990).

In order to minimize the possibility of measuring a primary acute stress response due to sampling and not an environmental stressor, the maximum amount of time allowed from the time the fish was stunned to the blood sample being drawn from the caudal vasculature was 3 min. It takes several minutes for significant hypercortisolemia to develop as a result of sampling stress (Wedemeyer et al. 1990). Preliminary laboratory studies conducted on hatchery-reared brown trout at McNenny State Fish Hatchery in Spearfish, South Dakota showed that it took more than 10 min for plasma cortisol concentrations to be elevated after initial blood samples had been drawn.

After collection of the blood from the fish, the needle was removed from the syringe and the blood transferred to heparinized 1.5-mL microcentrifuge tubes. Blood samples were separated by 5-min centrifugation at 11,500 rpm with an IEC model MB centrifuge. Plasma samples were drawn from microcentrifuge tubes with disposable transfer pipettes, transferred to clean 1.5-mL screw-top microcentrifuge tubes, and kept chilled on crushed iced for the remainder of the day. Upon return to the laboratory, plasma samples were frozen until shipment to the University of South Dakota, Depart-

TABLE 2. Selected analyses methods and reporting limits.

Analysis	Method	Reporting limit
Alkalinity	EPA 310.1	1 mg/L
Ammonia, total as N	EPA 350.1	0.1 mg/L
Phenol, total	EPA 420.2	0.01 mg/L
Total suspended solids (TSS)	EPA 160.2	5 mg/L
Total recoverable metals		
Arsenic	EPA 200.7	0.01 mg/L
Cadmium	EPA 200.7	0.01 mg/L
Chromium	EPA 200.7	0.01 mg/L
Copper	EPA 200.7	0.01 mg/L
Lead	EPA 200.7	0.01 mg/L
Nickel	EPA 200.7	0.01 mg/L
Zinc	EPA 200.7	0.01 mg/L
Mercury, total	EPA 245.1	0.0002 mg/L
Continuous parameters:		
Temperature (field)	Sonde	0.1°C
Dissolved oxygen (field)	Sonde	0.1 mg/L
pH (field)	Sonde	0.1 pH unit

ment of Biology laboratory where they were analyzed for levels of lactate, glucose, and cortisol. All samples were shipped overnight with dry ice. Chain-of-custody forms verified all samples remained frozen while in transit. Plasma samples were stored at −20°C until cortisol, glucose, and lactate were analyzed. Plasma cortisol was measured using a radioimmunoassay modified for use with unextracted plasma from salmonids (Redding et al. 1984; Barton and Schreck 1987). Plasma glucose was determined colorimetircally using Wako brand enzymatic mutarotase-glucose oxidase Autokits (Wako Chemicals USA Inc., Richmond, Virginia). Plasma lactate was determined colorimetrically with Sigma Diagnostics lactate analysis kits, procedure 735 (Sigma Chemical, St. Louis, Missouri).

Statistical Analyses

The Mann-Whitney rank sum test (U) was used to determine if there was a change in water quality parameters between nonevents and storm events. One-half the method detection limit (MDL) was used for statistical analyses when values were below the MDL (Helsel and Hirsch 1992).

The plasma cortisol, glucose, and lactate data were tested for normality using the Kolmogorov-Smirnov test. A $\log_{10}$ transformation (Zar 1999) was applied to cortisol, glucose, and lactate data to normalize the data and reduce the heterogeneity of variances. Two-way analysis of variance (ANOVA) was used to test for differences in plasma cortisol, glucose, and lactate among sampling periods (nonstorms, 0–12 h, 24–36 h, 48–60 h, and 96 h after an event) and among stream reaches. When a significant difference was identified in a plasma constituent by stream reach, a Tukey's multiple-range test was used to determine which reaches were significantly different from each other. Dunnett's posthoc two-tailed t-test was used to test for differences in plasma constituents between nonstorms (controls) and storm periods. All statistical tests were performed

TABLE 3. Composite baseflow and stormwater runoff event sampling dates.

Sample	Base flow (nonevent)	Stormwater runoff event
1	25 June 2001	30 June 2001
2	26 July 2001	30 July 2001
3	5 Sept 2001	22 Aug 2001
4	28 Sept 2001	9 Oct 2001
5	22 May 2002	16 May 2002
6	17 July 2002	8 July 2002
7	28 Aug 2002	21 Aug 2002
8	25 Sept 2002	18 Sept 2002

with SPSS version 11.5.1 for Windows (SPSS 2002) at the $\alpha = 0.01$ significance level.

Results

Water Quality Sampling

Eight stormwater runoff events and eight baseflows (nonevents) were sampled (Table 3). Runoff event durations ranged from 3 to 20 h, with an average duration of approximately 7 h (Table 4). Mean runoff volume and mean peak flow increased from upstream to downstream. The mean runoff volume at site 5 was 10.9 times greater than that at site 1.

Ammonia.—Total ammonia ($NH_3 + NH_4^+$) was detected at site 5 once in 2001 and once in 2002, at concentrations of 0.20 and 0.10 mg/L, respectively. When taking into consideration temperature and pH, calculated unionized ammonia concentrations were 0.007 and 0.003 mg/L. The allowable total and unionized ammonia concentrations based on South Dakota water quality criteria are 1.31 mg/L and 0.43 mg/L, respectively.

Alkalinity/hardness.—Alkalinity EMCs ranged from 159 to 173 mg/L for base flow conditions and from 139 to 159 mg/L for stormwater runoff events (Table 5). Alkalinity was lower during runoff events

TABLE 4. Stormwater runoff event duration, volume, and peak flow characteristics.

Site	Duration (h)			Volume (m³ × 1,000)			Peak (m³/s)		
	Minimum	Maximum	Mean	Minimum	Maximum	Mean	Minimum	Maximum	Mean
1	0	11	4	0	9	7	0	1	<1
2	3	11	5	1	28	7	1	5	2
3	2	11	6	2	30	18	1	6	3
4	4	11	8	3	45	26	2	5	3
5	8	18	11	12	302	76	3	19	7

TABLE 5. Average event sampling concentrations for alkalinity and hardness.

Site	Alkalinity (mg/L CaCO$_3$)		Hardness (mg/L CaCO$_3$)	
	Baseflow	Runoff	Baseflow	Runoff
1	159	153	194	193
2	161	159	197	195
3	165	154	201	199
4	166	155	201	202
5	173	139	210	210

than during base flow periods (Mann-Whitney U = 198.0, $P < 0.001$). The largest change occurred at site 5, where mean alkalinity decreased from 173 mg/L during nonevents to 139 mg/L during runoff events. Event mean hardness ranged from 193 to 210 mg/L, with no statistical difference between events and nonevents (Mann-Whitney U = 102.5, $P = 0.111$).

Metals.—Zinc average EMCs ranged from 0.008 to 0.027 mg/L and were found to be above MDL during base flow and runoff events (Table 6). Concentrations of zinc were higher during runoff events than nonevents (Mann-Whitney U = 407.5, $P < 0.001$). Copper was detected above the MDL in one of 40 samples in the first year. No other metals were detected above MDL during the first year and were subsequently not analyzed for during the second year.

Total phenol.—Total phenol was detected at all sites with average EMCs during base flow and runoff events ranging from 0.016 mg/L to 0.040 mg/L (Table 6). Concentrations of phenol during events were not statistically different from nonevents (Mann-Whitney U = 547, $P = 0.423$).

Total suspended solids.—Average EMCs of TSS were significantly greater during runoff events than nonevents (Mann-Whitney U = 297, $P < 0.001$). Average EMCs of TSS did not exceed MDL (5.0 mg/L) during both runoff events and nonevents at site 1 (Table 7). The average EMC during runoff events ranged from 8.3 mg/L at site 2 to 168.6 mg/L at site 5. The average EMC for TSS increased by a factor of 20.3 from upstream to downstream (site 2 to site 5). The average

EMC at site 5 exceeded the water quality criterion (53 mg/L). Maximum EMCs exceeded the water quality criterion at sites 3, 4, and 5.

Temperature and dissolved oxygen.—From 15 June 2001 to 30 September 2001, the mean temperature ranged from 15.9°C at site 1 to 18.9°C at site 5, an average increase of 3°C as Rapid Creek flows through Rapid City (Table 9). At site 5, the mean temperature of 18.9°C exceeded the state water quality criterion of 18.3°C. The percent of time the temperature criterion was exceeded increased from 16.6% to 62.8% from site 1 downstream to site 5.

Mean dissolved oxygen concentration ranged from 7.49 mg/L upstream (site 1) to 9.41 mg/L downstream (site 5) (Table 8). The mean dissolved oxygen concentration was greater than the state water quality criterion of 6 mg/L at all sites. Minimum dissolved oxygen concentrations were less than the South Dakota water quality criterion at sites 1, 3, and 5. The percent of time the dissolved oxygen concentration was less than the criterion at sites 1, 3, and 5 was 3.5%, 0.1%, and 0.5%, respectively.

Physiological Stress Responses

A total of 1,023 plasma samples were analyzed for cortisol (Table 9). Of the 1,023 samples collected, 22 had plasma cortisol concentrations greater than 50 ng/mL. There was no significant difference ($P > 0.75$) among sampling periods in the proportion of fish with plasma cortisol concentrations greater than 50 ng/mL. The two-

TABLE 6. Average event mean concentrations for zinc and phenols. Number of detections is in parentheses.

Site	Zinc (mg/L)		Phenols (mg/L)	
	Base flow	Runoff	Base flow	Runoff
1	0.008(3)	0.011(3)	0.016(5)	0.027(3)
2	0.025(1)	0.013(4)	0.020(5)	0.040(4)
3	0.010(1)	0.015(3)	0.016(5)	0.022(5)
4	0.010(1)	0.014(3)	0.038(5)	0.028(4)
5	0.010(1)	0.027(5)	0.018(3)	0.036(5)

TABLE 7. Total suspended solids event mean concentration characteristics for baseline and stormwater runoff events.

| | Total suspended solids (mg/L) | | | | | |
| | Baseflow | | | Runoff | | |
Site	Minimum	Maximum	Mean	Minimum	Maximum	Mean
1	ND[a]	ND	ND	ND	ND	ND
2	ND	ND	ND	ND	20.0	8.3
3	ND	ND	ND	ND	120.0	22.7
4	ND	8.0	3.8	14.0	140.0	45.8
5	ND	14.0	5.3	28.0	470.0	168.6

[a] ND, nondetect. The concentration was less than the method detection limit (MDL). The MDL for total suspended solids was 5 mg/L. When means were calculated, a value of one half the MDL was used for ND.

TABLE 8. Continuous (every 15 min) stream temperature and dissolved oxygen characteristics over the monitoring period (May through November 2001).

| | Temperature (°C) | | | Dissolved oxygen (mg/L) | | |
Site	Range	Mean	% > 18.3°C[a]	Range	Mean	% < 6 mg/L
1	9.6–23.1	15.9	16.6	5–11.5	7.49	3.5
2	12.6–22.0	17.3	31.6	6.4–12.8	9.12	0.0
3	12.3–24.3	17.8	46.2	5.8–13.2	8.91	0.06
4	11.9–25.2	17.9	49.3	6.4–14.3	9.19	0.0
5	10.7–25.6	18.9	62.8	4.8–15.2	9.41	0.5

[a] The % > or < represents the percent of time the parameter is greater than or less than a specified value based on the 15-min sampling intervals.

TABLE 9. Percentage of brown trout in Rapid Creek that had a plasma cortisol concentration greater than 50 ng/mL. Number of fish exhibiting this level of cortisol are given in parenthesis. Percentages were calculated by pooling samples from fish collected from six nonstorm events, and six storm events sampled between May and October of 2001 and 2002 from within the city limits of Rapid City. A chi-square test for multiple proportions found no significant difference between sampling periods ($P > 0.75$).

Sampling period (hours since storm began)	Percent of fish exhibiting cortisol level > 50 ng/mL	Number of fish sampled
Nonstorm events	1.9 (4)	206
0–12	1.9 (4)	208
24–36	4.0 (8)	198
48–60	2.4 (5)	206
96–108	2.4 (5)	205

way ANOVA showed that the stream reach ($F = 4.768$, df = 3, $P < 0.003$) was a significant factor, while sampling period ($F = 1.814$, df = 4, $P > 0.123$) and the interaction term ($F = 1.380$, df = 12, $P > 0.169$) were not. Brown trout in the upstream reach (Reach A) had higher plasma cortisol concentrations than the brown trout in the lower reaches (Figure 4). Mean plasma cortisol levels in fish among reaches B–D and among sampling periods were less than 10 ng/L (Figures 4 and 5).

Plasma glucose (Figure 5) was significantly lower during stormwater runoff events and remained lower for 96 h following storm events compared to base flow conditions ($F = 9.50$, df = 4, $P < 0.001$); mean plasma glucose levels were generally less than 80 mg/dL (Figures 4 and 5). There was no significant difference in mean plasma glucose by reach ($F = 0.171$, df = 3, $P > 0.916$). The interaction term was not significant ($F = 1.487$, df = 12, $P > 0.122$).

There was no significant difference in plasma lactate concentrations among reaches ($F = 2.428$, df = 3, P

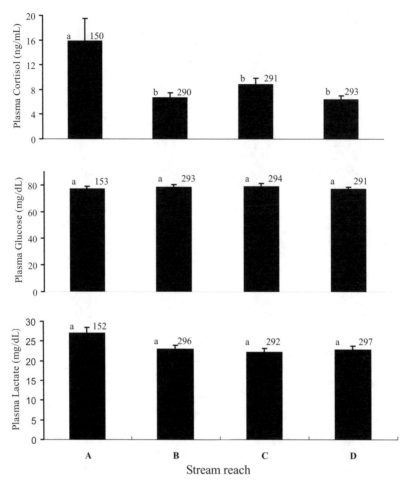

FIGURE 4. Mean concentration (±SE) of plasma constituents in samples collected from brown trout in Rapid Creek in 2001 and 2002. Bars represent samples collected from fish at separate reaches of stream. Bars within each constituent accompanied by letters in common are not significantly different ($P < 0.01$). Samples sizes are included with bars.

> 0.064) or among sampling periods ($F = 1.404$, df = 4, $P > 0.231$); mean plasma lactate remained between 20 and 30 mg/dL throughout this study (Figures 4 and 5).

Newcombe and Jensen's (1996) SEV dose–response model for adult salmonids predicted behavioral and sublethal effects for brown trout downstream of Canyon Lake (sites 2–5) for each of the eight storm events sampled (Table 10). The SEV model predicted the severity of impact would increase in a downstream manner. The highest SEV score calculated during this study was 7.8. It occurred at the downstream end of the study reach (site 5) during a rainstorm on 30 June 2002. An SEV score of 7.8 is below what the SEV dose–response model predicted for paralethal (SEV ≥ 9) and lethal effects (SEV ≥ 10).

Discussion

Water Quality

The stormwater runoff into Rapid Creek results in the degradation of water quality. Of the 17 water quality parameters measured, those of primary concern are zinc, total phenols, total suspended solids, and temperature. Copper was the only other metal detected, and it was only detected once. The highest unionized ammonia concentration measured during this study was 0.007 mg/L. This value is one-fifth the South Dakota water quality criterion (0.035 mg/L) for a permanent coldwater fishery. The maximum EMC for total phenol during base flow and runoff events was 0.04 mg/L. Total phenol concentrations were below

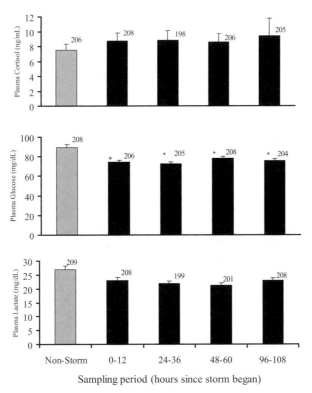

FIGURE 5. Mean concentration (±SE) of plasma constituents in samples collected from brown trout in Rapid Creek in 2001 and 2002. Bars represent samples collected from fish during six base flow periods (light bar) and six storm events at various intervals after storm began (dark bars). Bars accompanied by an asterisk are significantly different from base flow (nonstorm) values ($P < 0.01$). Sample sizes are listed above bars.

the 96-h LC50 of 10 mg/L reported by Anderson et al. (1979) for rainbow trout *O. mykiss*.

The high alkalinity and water hardness during base flow and runoff events shows that Rapid Creek has a high capacity to buffer acids and reduce the risk of acidification, acid shock, and exposure of aquatic life to high concentrations of ionic metals. During runoff events, zinc concentrations increased above base flow levels. Sources of zinc in urban stormwater runoff include tire degradation, corrosion of galvanized

TABLE 10. Severity of ill effects (SEV) for brown trout associated with excess total suspended sediment for eight storm water events in Rapid Creek (2001–2002) as predicted by a dose-response model for adult salmonids (Newcombe and Jensen 1996).

Date	Event	Site 1	Site 2	Site3	Site 4	Site 5
30 Jun 2001	1*	–	3.8	4.3	6.1	7.8
30 Jul 2001	2*	–	3.1	3.8	5.0	6.6
22 Aug 2001	3*	–	4.3	6.1	6.2	6.5
09 Oct 2001	4	–	4.2	4.9	5.5	6.5
16 May 2002	5*	–	4.2	4.6	5.0	5.3
08 Jul 2002	6*	–	2.9	3.0	4.6	6.7
21 Aug 2002	7	–	4.1	4.1	5.0	5.9
19 Sep 2002	8*	–	4.9	4.0	5.0	6.8

* -denotes storms from which blood samples were also collected.

metals, and fertilizer (ATSDR 1994). When zinc was detected, concentrations were near those at which Birge et al. (1993) reported 11% avoidance for juvenile rainbow trout (0.01 mg/L). At 0.05 mg/L, Birge et al. (1993) recorded 94.4% avoidance. Maximum zinc concentrations in Rapid Creek were well below the 96-h LC50 (0.24 mg/L) for rainbow trout in soft water at 15°C (Davies 1986). Additionally, the water hardness in Rapid Creek reduces the potential for zinc toxicity. Davies (1986) reported that as water hardness increases, zinc toxicity decreases.

The effects of total suspended solids on brown trout are a function of the magnitude and duration of exposure. During stormwater events, TSS concentrations at site 5 consistently exceeded South Dakota's standard for a coldwater fishery (53 mg/L). Estimates of LC50 values in 96-h tests range from 488 mg/L (Stober et al. 1981) for juvenile Chinook salmon *O. tshawytscha* to 19,364 mg/L (Newcombe and MacDonald 1991) for juvenile rainbow trout. Rainbow trout showed histological damage after 96-h exposures to 171 mg/L TSS (Newcombe and MacDonald 1991). The duration of runoff events represents the exposure time to the event mean concentration. The runoff event durations at site 5 ranged from 2 to 18 h with an average event duration of 10 h. Event mean concentrations during runoff events occurred at levels that the Newcombe and Jensen (1996) model predicted could result in a stress response. However, the duration of these concentrations were less than those reported in the literature for harmful levels of TSS.

Dissolved oxygen concentrations were consistently above the South Dakota water quality criterion (6 mg/L) and were not considered to be a limiting factor for the brown trout in Rapid Creek. The South Dakota temperature criterion for a permanent coldwater fishery is 18.3°C. Needham (1969) reported that 27.2°C is lethal to brown trout, but did not define the maximum temperature that would sustain a population. In a general review, Barton (1996) cited a number of studies indicating upper threshold temperature ranges for brown trout between 22.0°C and 26.7°C and optimum ranges varying between 6°C and 20°C. Mills (1971) reported the temperature tolerance range for trout to be from 0°C to 27°C. Although stream temperatures frequently exceeded the state water quality criterion, the temperatures in Rapid Creek were within the tolerance range reported by Mills (1971). The occurrence of high stream temperatures was not due to stormwater runoff but was a seasonal event, and when high during the summer months, could create conditions that limit growth.

Physiological Stress Responses

There is little evidence in this study to indicate that stormwater events in Rapid Creek of the size, duration, and water quality monitored evoke acute physiological stress responses in brown trout. After storm events, plasma cortisol concentrations did not increase above resting (control) levels. We would have expected a much higher percentage of the fish to exhibit plasma cortisol levels greater than 50 ng/mL had the storms been sufficient to invoke a primary stress response based on other studies of acute physical stressors in brown trout (Barton and Iwama 1991; Barton 2000). Plasma cortisol concentrations can become elevated in fish as a result of suspended sediment exposure. In a laboratory setting, Redding et al. (1987) demonstrated that plasma cortisol concentrations increased in rainbow trout and coho salmon exposed to suspended sediment concentrations of 2,000–3,000 mg/L for 2 d. In that study, it took 12 h for the cortisol levels to become elevated in rainbow trout and 4 h in coho salmon and concentrations remained elevated for 48 h and 96 h in the salmon and trout, respectively. Brown trout in Rapid Creek were not exposed to suspended solid concentrations as high as those nor for as long as the salmonids studied by Redding et al. (1987), the only work published to document a primary stress response in this context. Moreover, in their natural habitat, unlike a laboratory setting where fish are confined, the brown trout in this study had the ability to move out of the area or seek sheltered sites and thereby could have avoided much of the transient TSS disturbance caused by the runoff events.

Similarly, the brown trout did not exhibit characteristic secondary stress responses during stormwater events. Plasma glucose concentrations were significantly lower during and following storm events than they were during base flow. Typically, plasma glucose concentrations are elevated (hyperglycemia) after fish are subjected to an acute stressor (Barton et al. 2002). Servizi and Martens (1992) showed coho salmon plasma glucose levels were elevated in direct proportion to suspended sediment concentration following their exposure. McLeay et al. (1987) found that juvenile arctic grayling *Thymallus arcticus* had increased plasma glucose concentrations after being exposed to 1–4 d of organic sediment concentrations as low as 50 mg/L or inorganic sediment concentrations greater than 10,000 mg/L.

The failure of the brown trout in Rapid Creek to exhibit an increase in plasma glucose is consistent with the fish not showing acute responses in cortisol to the

TSS exposure. Fish exhibiting elevated cortisol levels in response to an acute stressor typically have elevated plasma glucose levels (Wedemeyer et al. 1990; Barton et al. 2002). Elevated plasma cortisol may provide a mechanism for fish to maintain high concentrations of glucose in the blood through gluconeogenesis to meet the energy requirements after initial catecholamine-stimulated hyperglycemia during a time of stress (Mommsen et al. 1999). Trout with elevated levels of plasma cortisol, however, do not necessarily exhibit elevated plasma glucose concentrations. For example, a fluctuation in flow regime was sufficient to cause an elevation in plasma cortisol levels in brown trout without elevating plasma glucose (Flodmark et al. 2002).

Environmental factors such as acclimation temperature or nutritional state are likely to have an appreciable effect on the magnitude of poststress elevations of cortisol and glucose, particularly the latter (Barton et al. 2002). During and following storm events, brown trout in Rapid Creek had lower plasma glucose levels than they exhibited during base flow conditions. Reasons for this are not evident from our data, but the decrease in plasma glucose may be a result of changes in feeding behavior rather than a physiological stress response. A resulting period of fasting may affect a drop in both resting glucose levels and stress-induced hyperglycemia (Barton et al. 1988). Foraging success of salmonids can be significantly lower in turbid waters. In laboratory stream channels, rainbow trout reactive distance (the distance from its holding position to where it took its prey) in waters with turbidities of 15 and 30 NTU were only 80% and 45%, respectively, of the controls in water with turbidities of 4–6 NTU (Barrett et al. 1992). Sigler et al. (1984) measured higher growth rates for both steelhead (anadromous rainbow trout) and coho salmon in clear water than in turbid water.

No significant difference occurred among sampling periods in plasma lactate levels of the fish. We hypothesized that plasma lactate would be elevated during the first 12 h following a storm event, as flows and velocities would be higher, and thus result in increased muscular activity for the fish to maintain its position. Apparently, brown trout were able to seek out areas of low velocity during the high flows, such as behind boulders or in backchannels, to avoid the fast current.

Newcombe and Jensen (1996) developed a risk assessment model to predict the response of fish when sediment dosage (mg/L) and duration (h) are known. Their severity of ill effect (SEV) dose–response model was developed from the meta-analysis of 80 reports.

Total suspended solids concentrations were below detection limits at site 1, which is upstream of the urbanized area of Rapid City. The SEV dose–response model predicts behavioral or sublethal effects would occur for each of the storm events we monitored (Table 10). The SEV dose–response model predicts short-term reductions in feeding rates or feeding success when SEV scores exceed 4, minor physiological stress responses when SEV scores exceed 5, and moderate physiological stress responses when SEV scores exceed 6. For the eight storm events we monitored, the SEV scores frequently exceeded 5.0 downstream of site 3. The SEV dose–response model slightly overpredicted the severity of impact that storm events had on this fish population. Other investigators have compared observed levels of effect with the predictions from the SEV dose–response model. Reid et al. (2003) found the observed level of physiological effect was consistent with the predictions of the sediment-effects dose–response when they examined differences in blood hematocrit for rainbow trout downstream from a simulated open-cut pipeline water crossing. Shaw and Richardson (2001) felt the SEV dose–response "effectively predicted a reduction in feeding rate and prey capture success for trout" when they observed decreased growth for juvenile rainbow exposed to fine sediment pulses (695–705 mg/L) of varied length (0–6 h) every other day for 19 d.

None of the physiological measures suggest that brown trout in Rapid Creek experienced significant acute stress as a result of exposure to high concentrations of total suspended solids during the monitored storm events. This does not mean that these events are not affecting the brown trout fishery. Habitat degradation may still be occurring, invertebrate populations could be negatively impacted, and reproductive success could be diminished if fine sediments are deposited onto active redds. There could be seasonal differences in how brown trout respond to storm events. The storm events monitored between May and October coincided with the time of year when food is abundant and the fish are actively growing. Brown trout may be susceptible to acute environmental stressors such as storm events during the spawning season when they are physiologically compromised, or in the early spring during snowmelt events after a winter of cold temperatures and reduced growth; however, that has yet to be determined for Rapid Creek.

The decline in brown trout population densities since 1984 (Figure 1) cannot be directly attributed to degraded water quality associated with stormwater runoff events in Rapid City. The decrease in brown trout densities is probably due to the cumulative effects of habitat degradation and increased stream temperatures associated with increased urbanization.

Quantifying acute physiological stress responses of wild fish populations to stormwater runoff events may have limited usefulness for measuring the effects of urbanization in other settings. Unlike laboratory trials, it is very difficult if not impossible to conduct replicate trials with identical flow characteristics in a natural system. Similarly, it is difficult to mimic controlled laboratory conditions in a natural setting where fish can simply avoid the noxious stimulus by migrating out of the most severely affected area or seeking more favorable microhabitat. The logistics of collecting samples from fish during storm events is difficult since one cannot control the location, timing, duration, and intensity of rainstorms. Storms with the same duration and intensity and areal pattern can generate stream hydrographs with very different water quality characteristics. The inter-event time is a major factor for determining the amount of pollutant that can accumulate on the watershed.

Acknowledgments

We are grateful to John Carriero, Ken Edel, Cory Foreman, Gene Galinat, Daniel James, Bill Miller, James Rasmussen, Tom Skoog, Greg Simpson, Eric Unkenholz, and Chad Wangen for assisting with the collection of blood samples at odd hours of the day and to Eric Krantz and Patrick Deering for their assistance with maintaining, calibrating and operating the equipment used to collect the water samples. Thanks are expressed to Erica Freeburg, Lindsey Pingel, and David Swanson at the University of South Dakota for the many hours they spent in the laboratory conducting the lactate, cortisol, and glucose analyses. We thank three anonymous reviewers and Michael Barnes at McNenny State Fish Hatchery for providing comments that improved this manuscript. Funding and support for this project were provided by the South Dakota Department of Game, Fish and Parks through the Federal Assistance in Sport Fish Restoration Program (Project F-55, Study Number 1700) in cooperation with the South Dakota School of Mines and Technology and the University of South Dakota.

References

Anderson, P., P. Spear, S. D'Apollonia, S. Perry, J. De Luca, and J. Dick. 1979. The multiple toxicity of vanadium, nickel, and phenol to fish. Alberta Oil Sands Environmental Research Program, Report # 79, Devon, Alberta, Canada.

ATSDR (Agency for Toxic Substances and Disease Registry). 1994. Toxicological profile for zinc. U.S. Department of Health and Human Services, Agency for Toxic Substances and Disease Registry, Atlanta.

Barrett, J. C., G. D. Grossman, and J. Rosenfeld. 1992. Turbidity-induced changes in reactive distance of rainbow trout. Transactions of the American Fisheries Society 121:437–443.

Barton, B. A. 1976. Short-term effects of highway construction on the limnology of a small stream in southern Ontario. Freshwater Biology 7:99–108.

Barton, B. A. 1996. General biology of salmonids. Pages 29–95 in W. Pennell and B.A. Barton, editors. Principles of salmonid culture. Elsevier B.V., Amsterdam.

Barton, B. A. 2000. Salmonid fishes differ in their cortisol and glucose responses to handling and transport stress. North American Journal of Aquaculture 62:12–18.

Barton, B. A., and G. K. Iwama. 1991. Physiological changes in fish from stress in aquaculture with emphasis on the response and effects of corticosteroids. Annual Review of Fish Diseases 1:3–26.

Barton, B. A., J. D. Morgan, and M. M. Vijayan. 2002. Physiological and condition-related indicators of environmental stress in fish. Pages 111–148 in S.M. Adams, editor. Biological indicators of aquatic ecosystems stress. American Fisheries Society, Bethesda, Maryland.

Barton, B. A., and C. B. Schreck. 1987. Metabolic cost of acute physical stress in juvenile steelhead. Transactions of the American Fisheries Society 116:257–263.

Barton, B. A., C. B. Schreck, and L. G. Fowler. 1988. Fasting and diet content affects stress-induced changes in plasma glucose and cortisol in juvenile chinook salmon. Progressive Fish-Culturist 50:16–22.

Bergstedt, L. C., and E. P. Bergersen. 1997. Health and movements of fish in response to sediment sluicing in the Wind River, Wyoming. Canadian Journal of Fisheries and Aquatic Sciences 54:312–319.

Birge, W. J., R. D. Hoyt, J. A. Black, M. D. Kercher, and W. A. Robison. 1993. Effects of chemical stresses on behavior of larval and juvenile fishes and amphibians. Pages 55–65 in L. A. Fuiman, editor. Water quality and the early life stages of fishes. American Fisheries Society, Symposium 14, Bethesda, Maryland.

Butcher, J. B. 2003. Buildup, washoff, and event mean concentrations. Journal of the American Water Resources Association 39:1521–1546.

Cederholm, C. J., and L. M. Reid. 1987. Impact of forest management on coho salmon (*Oncorhynchus kisutch*) populations of the Clearwater River, Washington: a project summary. Pages 373–398 *in* E.O. Salo and T.W. Cundy, editors. Streamside management: forestry and fisher interactions. University of Washington Institute of Forest Resources Contribution 57, Seattle.

Davies, P. H. 1986. Toxicology and chemistry of metals in urban runoff. Urban runoff quality-impact and quality enhancement technology. Pages 60–78 *in* B. Urbonas and L. A. Roesner, editors. Proceedings of an engineering foundation conference. American Society of Civil Engineers, Henniker, New Hampshire.

Everest, F. H., R. L. Beschta, J. C. Scrivener, D. V. Doski, J. R. Sedell, and C. J. Cederholm. 1987. Fine sediments and salmonid production: a paradox. Pages 98–142 *in* E.O. Salo and T.W. Cundy, editors. Streamside management: forestry and fishery interactions. University of Washington Institute of Forest Resources Contribution, Seattle.

Flodmark, L. E. W., H. A. Urke, J. H. Halleraker, J. V. Arnekleiv, L. A. Vollestad, and S. B. S. Poleo. 2002. Cortisol and glucose responses in juvenile brown trout subjected to a fluctuating flow regime in an artificial stream. Journal of Fish Biology 60:238–248.

Goddard, K. E., T. K. Lockner, L. L. Harms, and M. H. Smith. 1989. Summary of data pertaining to land use, rainfall, dryfall, stream discharge, and storm runoff collected as part of a study of the effects of urban runoff on Rapid Creek, Rapid City area, South Dakota. U.S. Geological Survey, Open-File Report 87–45, Rapid City, South Dakota.

Helsel, D. R., and Hirsch, R. M. 1992. Statistical methods in water resources. Studies in Environmental Science 49. Elsevier, New York.

Hortness, J. E., and D. G. Driscoll. 1998. Streamflow losses in the Black Hills of western South Dakota. U.S. Geological Survey Water-Resources Investigations Report 98–4116, Rapid City, South Dakota.

Houston, A. H. 1990. Blood and circulation. Pages 273–334 *in* C. B. Schreck and P. B. Moyle, editors. Methods for fish biology. American Fisheries Society, Bethesda, Maryland.

Mazeaud, M. M., F. Mazeaud, and E. M. Donaldson. 1977. Primary and secondary effects of stress in fish: some new data with a general review. Transactions of the American Fisheries Society 106:201–212.

McLeay, D. J., I. K. Birtwell, G. F. Hartman, and G. L. Ennis. 1987. Responses of arctic grayling (*Thymallus arcticus*) to acute and prolonged exposure to Yukon placer mining sediment. Canadian Journal of Fisheries and Aquatic Sciences 44:658–673.

Mills, D. 1971. Salmon and trout: a resource, its ecology, conservation and management. St. Martins Press, New York.

Mommsen, T. P., M. M. Vijayan, and T. W. Moon. 1999. Cortisol in teleosts: dynamics, mechanisms of action, and metabolic regulation. Reviews in Fish Biology and Fisheries 9:211–268.

Needham, P. R. 1969. Trout streams. Revised edition. Winchester Press, New York.

Newcombe, C. P., and J. O. T. Jensen. 1996. Channel suspended sediment and fisheries: a synthesis for quantitative assessment of risk and impact. North American Journal of Fisheries Management 16:693–727.

Newcombe, C. P., and D. D. MacDonald. 1991. Effects of suspended sediments on aquatic ecosystems. North American Journal of Fisheries Management 11:72–82.

Redding, J. M., C. B. Schreck, E. K. Birks, and R. D. Ewing. 1984. Cortisol and its effect on plasma thyroid hormone and electrolyte concentrations in fresh water and during seawater acclimation in yearling coho salmon, *Oncorhynchus kisutch*. General and Comparative Endocrinology 56:146–155.

Redding, J. M., C. B. Schreck, and F. H. Everest. 1987. Physiological effects on coho salmon and steelhead to suspended solids. Transactions of the American Fisheries Society 116:737–744.

Reid, S. M., G. Isaac, S. Metikosh, and J. Evans. 2003. Physiological response of rainbow trout to sediment released during open-cut pipeline water crossing construction. Water Quality Research Journal of Canada 38:473–481.

Richards, C., L. B. Johnson, and G. E. Host. 1996. Landscape-scale influence on stream habitats and biota. Canadian Journal of Fish and Aquatic Sciences 53(Supplement):295–311.

Servizi, J. A., and D. W. Martens. 1992. Sublethal response of coho salmon (*Oncorhynchus kisutch*) to suspended sediments. Canadian Journal of Fisheries and Aquatic Sciences 49:1389–1395.

Shaw, E. A., and J. S. Richardson. 2001. Direct and indirect effects of sediment pulse duration on stream invertebrate assemblages and rainbow trout (*Oncorhynchus mykiss*) growth and survival. Canadian Journal of Fisheries and Aquatic Sciences 58:2213–2221.

Sigler, J. W., T. C. Bjornn, and F. H. Everest. 1984. Effects of chronic turbidity on density and growth of steelheads and coho salmon. Transactions of the American Fisheries Society 113:142–150.

Smoley, C. K. 1993. NPDES storm water sampling guidance manual. U.S. Environmental Protection Agency Office of Water. CRC Press, Boca Raton, Florida.

SPSS. 2002. SPSS for Windows Version 11.5.1 for Windows Software. SPSS, Chicago.

Stober, Q. J., Ross, B. D., Melby, C. L., Dinnel, P. A., Jagielo, T. H., and Salo, E. O. 1981. Effects of suspended volcanic sediment on coho and chinook salmon in the Toutle and Cowlitz rivers. University of Washington, Fisheries Research Institute, FRI-UW-8124, Seattle.

Sweka, J. A., and K. J. Hartman. 2001. Influence of turbidity on brook trout reactive distance and foraging success. Transactions of the American Fisheries Society 130:138–146.

USEPA (U.S. Environmental Protection Agency). 1983. Methods for chemical analysis of water and wastes. U.S. Environmental Protection Agency Office of Water, EPA/600/4–79/020, Washington, D.C.

USGS (U.S. Geological Survey). 2004. Water Resource and stream flow data 1942–2001. U.S. Geological Survey. Available: http//water.usgs.gov/. (January 2004)

Vondracek, B., J. K. H. Zimmerman, and J. V. Westra. 2003. Setting an effective TMDL: sediment loading and effects of suspended sediment on fish. Journal of the American Water Resources Association 39:1005–1015.

Wang, L., J. Lyons, and P. Kanehl. 2003. Impacts of urban land cover on trout streams in Wisconsin and Minnesota. Transactions of the American Fisheries Society 132:825–839.

Waters, T. F. 1995. Sediment in streams: sources, biological effects and control. American Fisheries Society, Monograph 7, Bethesda, Maryland.

Wedemeyer, G. A., B. A. Barton, and D. J. McLeay. 1990. Stress and acclimation. Pages 451–489 *in* C.B. Schreck and P.B. Moyle, editors. Methods for fish biology. American Fisheries Society, Bethesda, Maryland.

Zar, J.H. 1999. Biostatistical analysis. 4th edition. Prentice-Hall, Inc., Upper Saddle River, New Jersey.

American Fisheries Society Symposium 47:133–156, 2005

Impacts of Land-Use Changes and Hydrologic Modification on the Lower Boise River, Idaho, USA

Dorene MacCoy*

U.S. Geological Survey, 230 Collins Road, Boise, Idaho 83702, USA

David Blew

Idaho Department of Water Resources, Box 83720, Boise, Idaho 83720-0098, USA

Abstract.—In less than two centuries, the lower Boise River below Lucky Peak Dam in southwestern Idaho has been transformed from a meandering, braided, gravel-bed river that supported large runs of salmon to a channelized, regulated, urban river that also provides irrigation water to more than 1,300 km² of land. The construction of three large dams in the upper basin dramatically altered the flow regime and sediment supply to the lower river. Flows are no longer sufficient to mobilize bed sediments and have allowed cottonwood trees and alien hardwoods to stabilize parafluvial surfaces, thereby narrowing sections of the river channel. Cadastral survey notes of 1867 and 1868 were used to recreate features associated with the lower Boise River Valley and identify characteristics of the river channel prior to dam construction and urbanization. Gravel and sand bars, historically present throughout the river, which are necessary to maintain biodiversity and productivity, are currently scarce. Sloughs were a dominant feature on the floodplain of the late 1800s, but today have been converted to irrigation canals, drains, or residential and commercial land uses. Flow alterations, water quality degradation, and habitat loss due to urbanization near the lower Boise River have resulted in macroinvertebrate and fish assemblages dominated by tolerant and alien species.

Introduction

The influence of human development on streams and rivers has been dramatic. In the United States, dams, locks, or diversions alter nearly every river in the lower 48 states (Collier et al. 1996). Human actions and their impacts on streams are well documented by numerous authors (Heede and Rinne 1990; Bayley 1991; Gilvear and Winterbottom 1992; Gilvear 1993; Baker 1994; Brookes 1996; Stanford et al. 1996; Bravard et al. 1999; Schick et al. 1999; McDowell 2000). River alterations include the acute impacts of dams, channelization, water pollution, and long-term hydrologic and sediment modifications that result from these activities. The natural disturbance regimes that maintain habitats and biological communities are lost (Stanford et al. 1996). These changes can have a dramatic impact on many aspects of aquatic ecosystems, including habitat structure and water quality. To fully comprehend and appreciate changes to aquatic eco-

systems and to develop appropriate restoration plans, the current condition of a river must be viewed as the result of a complex history of alterations and not just the result of current watershed conditions. Failure to recognize changes in natural ecosystems is due in part to the limited spatial and temporal scales with which they are measured (Sisk 1998).

The impact of urbanization on streams is not a recent phenomenon and, in some cases, can be persistent and severe. In the case of the rivers Tay and Tummel in Scotland, Gilvear (1993) and Winterbottom (2000) reported that the channels were transformed from braided to a confined, incised, single channel beginning in the late 1700s with levee construction, impoundment, decreased flood magnitude and frequency, and alterations in sediment supply. In many rivers, the impact of urbanization and development began centuries ago, and the environment prior to development is not well understood. When available, historical data are useful for understanding the ecological changes in urban watersheds.

Several authors have used data from cadastral sur-

* Corresponding author: demaccoy@usgs.gov

veys to recreate historical conditions of ecosystems. Nelson et al. (1998) described the presettlement vegetation on part of the upper Mississippi River using data from cadastral surveys of the general land office. Delcourt and Delcourt (1996) described presettlement vegetation in Michigan, also using data from cadastral surveys. In this paper, we use cadastral survey notes to explore the history of the lower Boise River and to assess changes to its structure and function since the late 1800s.

Study Area

The lower Boise River extends from the confluence with the Snake River to river kilometer 103 at Lucky Peak Dam (Figure 1). The study area is confined to the valley bottom, determined to be approximately 8 km wide, based on the 1867 and 1868 cadastral survey (Figure 2).

The lower Boise River is in the northern part of the western Snake River Plain ecoregion and has a semiarid climate with cool, wet winters and warm,

dry summers. The river lies in a broad, alluvium-filled valley with several step-like terraces, or benches, which are more pronounced and continuous on the south side of the river. The valley upstream from Lucky Peak Dam is mountainous and sparsely populated with an average gradient of 2%. Downstream from Lucky Peak Dam, the valley floor slopes northwestward at a gradient of about 0.2%. The altitude of the river near Lucky Peak Dam is about 850 m above sea level, declining to 670 m near its mouth (Thomas and Dion 1974).

Indians camped and fished along the lower Boise River prior to and during the early 1800s. There are several historical references to large groups of Indians salmon and trout fishing in the lower Boise River (Pratt et al. 2001). Trappers and traders were among the first European inhabitants of the lower Boise Valley (Bird 1971), arriving in 1813, and by 1850, many beaver had been removed. The importance of beaver in shaping the river is unknown, but they were certainly a factor influencing the hydrology and riparian zone. Parts of the upper Boise River water-

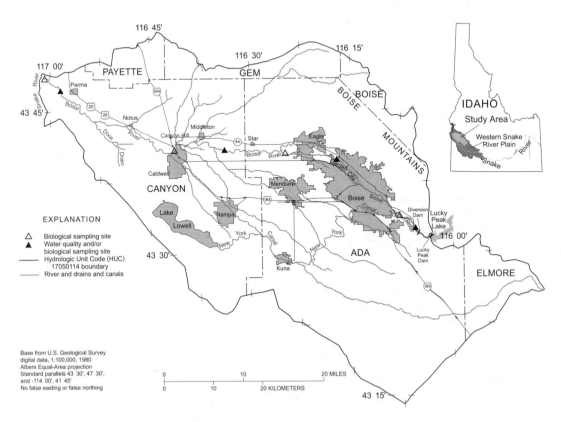

FIGURE 1. Lower Boise River Valley and USGS sampling locations, 1994–2002.

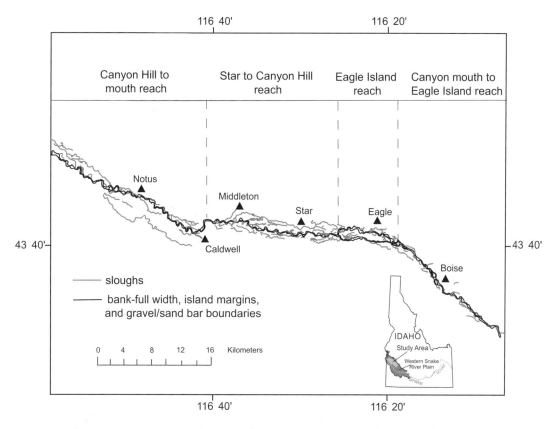

FIGURE 2. Historic map of the lower Boise River with sampling reaches recreated from cadastral survey notes of 1867 and 1868.

shed were heavily mined for gold using shaft and placer methods (Stacy 1993). Beginning in 1862, the discovery of gold in the upper basin encouraged agricultural development in the valley (Bird 1934). Early settlers also harvested timber along the river and, by 1863, were diverting water from the lower Boise River to irrigate crops. By 1867, agriculture was widespread throughout the lower Boise River Valley. Some irrigation canals and ditches had been constructed, but they were generally small. Irrigation was mainly accomplished by diverting water from the numerous sloughs already present on the floodplain. Farmers soon recognized the need for flood control and storage of irrigation water, which led to the 1902 "Boise Project," one of the earliest projects by the Reclamation Service (now known as the Bureau of Reclamation, BOR) (Stacy 1993). By 1906, the New York Canal and several small irrigation projects had been built and Arrowrock Dam was built in 1915 on the main-stem Boise River, 10.5 km upstream from Boise. The U.S. Army Corps of Engi-

neers (Corps) built Anderson Ranch Dam in 1950 on the south fork of the Boise River (Stacy 1993). In 1957, the Corps built a third dam, Lucky Peak, less than 6 km upstream from Boise (Stacy 1993).

The construction of a sewage treatment facility downstream from Boise in the early 1950s helped disinfect wastewater entering the river, but the plant was overloaded and toxic concentrations of chlorine resulted in frequent fish kills (Stacy 1993). In the late 1950s, the lower Boise River was identified as one of the three most polluted waters in Idaho (Osborne 1959; Chandler and Chapman 2001). In 1986, a second outlet was constructed for Lucky Peak Dam in order to provide additional flow during the winter, which helped dilute sewage effluent. Flows in the lower Boise River varied with allocations of water for urban and agricultural use (IDEQ 1999). Cleanup efforts have continued in the lower Boise River, such as wastewater treatment upgrades and implementation of best management practices for urban and agricultural runoff.

The Boise River provides irrigation water to more than 1,300 km² of agricultural land (Sisco 2001) in the lower Boise River valley. The lower Boise River also has a history of water quality problems related to urbanization, including raw sewage, wastewater treatment outfall, storm drainage, industrial runoff, and bacterial contamination (BOR 1977; Clark and Bauer 1983; Frenzel 1988, 1990; Stacy 1993; Mullins 1998b; Parliman and Spinazola 1998; Boyle 2001; Fox et al. 2002). Many of these urban contaminants have been eliminated through improvements to wastewater treatment and the City of Boise storm water program (Robbin Finch, City of Boise, personal communication).

In 1994, land use and land cover in the lower Boise River Valley included rangeland (50%), irrigated cropland (29%), and urban and rural areas (9%); the remaining land use is unclassified or in transition (Kramber et al. 1997). Recently, large tracts of farmland have been converted to subdivisions and commercial facilities, while older residential areas have become businesses, shopping centers, and parking lots. The major crops in the basin are alfalfa, wheat, sugar beets, barley, and potatoes. Land use in the upper Boise River basin is primarily logging and recreation. Photographs taken in 1910 and 1995 (Figure 3) show the urbanization that has occurred in the valley and the narrowing of the river channel.

In the early 1800s, the lower Boise River fishery was described as the most renowned fishing place in the country, with large numbers of salmon (Pratt et al. 2001). The Idaho Power Company (IPC) has documented evidence of Chinook salmon *Onchorhynchus tshawytscha* spawning in the lower reaches of the lower Boise River until the early 1860s, when mining and irrigation projects began (Chandler and Chapman

1910

1995

FIGURE 3. Photographs of the lower Boise Valley looking west toward the city of Boise in 1910 (Idaho State Historical Society, picture no. 81–88.3) and 1995 (dashed white lines show common location on both photographs).

2001). The IPC also reported steelhead *O. mykiss* runs in the lower Boise River, as well as the presence of Pacific lamprey *Lampetra tridentata* near Caldwell.

Within the last century, the lower reaches of the lower Boise River changed from a thriving, coldwater salmon and trout assemblage to a coolwater assemblage. Alien warmwater fish such as common carp *Cyprinus carpio*, warmouth *Lepomis gulosus* (also known as *Chaenobryttus gulosus*), crappie *Pomoxis* spp., northern pike *Esox lucius*, largemouth bass *Micropterus salmoides*, smallmouth bass *M. dolomieu*, bluegill *L. macrochirus*, pumpkinseed *L. gibbosus*, channel catfish *Ictalurus punctatus*, tadpole madtom *Noturus gyrinus*, and oriental weatherfish *Misgurnus anguillicaudatus* were introduced into the lower Boise River since the turn of the 20th century (Mullins 1999; Chandler and Chapman 2001). Hells Canyon Dam, built in 1967, prevented anadromous fish from entering the lower Boise River (Chandler and Chapman 2001). The IPC concluded that the lower Boise River is no longer suitable to support salmonid spawning due to high water temperatures in the late summer and early fall (Chandler and Chapman 2001).

Methods

We compared morphology of the lower Boise River before and after urbanization using cadastral survey notes and photo interpretation. Unfortunately, few preurbanization biological data are available. Instead, personal accounts of species in the river were compared with current water quality and biological data.

We divided the lower Boise River into four reaches with similar physical features (Figure 2): the canyon mouth to the upstream end of Eagle Island (Canyon Mouth to Eagle Island Reach), Eagle Island north and south channels (Eagle Island Reach), the downstream end of Eagle Island at Star to Canyon Hill (Star to Canyon Hill Reach), and Canyon Hill to the river mouth (Canyon Hill to Mouth Reach).

Historical Geomorphology

Land cover data from 1867 and 1868 cadastral survey notes obtained from the Bureau of Land Management (BLM) for the lower Boise Valley were used to recreate the "historical" lower Boise River. The lands were surveyed during late summer and fall when river flows were lowest. After surveyors established township boundaries, section lines were surveyed to establish section corners and quarter corners. Surveyors also noted other geographical and cultural features located on or near section lines. Meander surveys were then conducted along the river to determine the location and extent of the river margins. Bearing trees were recorded with distance and bearing of each tree to the section, quarter, or meander corner.

Data from 250 km of survey transects were entered into a database, including qualitative notes on various attributes of the lower Boise River Valley. Survey coordinates were converted to latitude and longitude and verified with recent geographic data using algorithms to convert distance in meters to directional movement in minutes. A geospatial dataset was created on the basis of the geographic coordinates created. These data were projected into the Idaho Transverse Mercator projection to correspond with other datasets being used. The data were then adjusted to the Geographic Coordinate Data Base (GCDB).

Surveyors documented slough widths and azimuths in their notes. Azimuths and back azimuths were mapped for each slough and buffered to the appropriate width; these azimuths extended 100 m from the central data point at the section line. To verify the slough location, the buffered sloughs and azimuths were layered over 1939 aerial photographs. Between 1868 and 1939, many sloughs were converted to agricultural drains or canals so their historical locations were easily determined. Many sloughs along the river corridor were obliterated due to the movement of the river. In these cases, the sloughs were only partially drawn using the meander surveys indicating the "head" or the "tail" of a slough.

Meanders of the lower Boise River were surveyed after the completion of the section line surveys in each township. Meander survey methods can be found at URL: http://www.ca.blm.gov/webmanual/id156_m.htm (accessed March 2001). Survey data were given as an azimuth and distance for each meander. Meanders were typically measured at the mean high water mark and were typically used to indicate land remaining for development or farming (Brown 1962). In this study, the surveyed meander lines are assumed to approximate bank-full width.

On the basis of azimuth and distance in the survey notes, trigonometric functions of sine and cosine were used to determine the north and west movement of each succeeding meander point. The distance was then converted to latitude and longitude as previously described and verified using the GCDB based on the original 1867 and 1868 survey notes. There were only minor deviations between the converted meander notes and the GCDB; therefore, the GCDB was adopted for the river meanders.

Current Ecological Data

Recent measurements of bank-full width were obtained from cross sections of the lower Boise River surveyed in 1997 and 1998 (Hortness and Werner 1999) and from surveys at biological sampling sites (Mullins 1999). Flow records from the water quality and biological sampling sites were obtained from the National Water Information System Web site (NWIS WEB). To compare historical and current flow conditions, discharge data were obtained from USGS gauge number 13202000. This gauge had the longest record on the lower Boise River, from 1895 to 2002 (USGS NWIS WEB: http://waterdata.usgs.gov/id/nwis/qwdata). Two metrics were used to evaluate the magnitude of change in the natural flow regime in the lower Boise River following dam construction: the magnitude and variation of mean monthly flows and the average monthly flows for December and August. For sites not equipped with continuous water stage recorders or stage-discharge ratings, instantaneous stream discharge was measured at the time of sample collection using methods described by Rantz (1982).

Water quality data were collected monthly, bimonthly, or seasonally between 1994 and 2002 by the USGS at four main-stem sites (Mullins 1998a; MacCoy 2004) (Figure 1). These sites were located at USGS gaging stations below Diversion Dam (Diversion Dam; Canyon Mouth to Eagle Island Reach), above Glenwood Bridge (Glenwood; Eagle Island Reach), above Middleton (Middleton; Star to Canyon Hill Reach), and near Parma (Parma; Canyon Hill to Mouth Reach). Biological samples associated with these sites were not always at the same location due to the lack of riffle habitat and were located upstream or downstream from the water quality sites but were within the same reach (Figure 1). Water quality data were not collected at Caldwell, but this was an important biological sampling site within the Canyon Hill to Mouth Reach.

Water quality data included instantaneous measurements of temperature, dissolved oxygen, pH, and specific conductance. Depth- and width-integrated water samples were collected, processed, and preserved according to Wilde et al. (1999) for analyses of suspended sediment and nutrients. Nutrients were analyzed by the USGS National Water-Quality Laboratory using methods described by Fishman (1993) and quality-assurance/quality-control protocols as described by Pritt and Raese (1995). Suspended sediment was analyzed by the USGS Cascades Volcano Observatory Sediment Laboratory using methods described by Guy (1969).

Water samples for bacterial analysis were collected near the center of the stream. Fecal coliform bacteria concentrations were measured using membrane-filter methods and are reported as colonies per 100 mL (Wilde et al. 1999). In 2000, the state water quality standard for bacteria changed from fecal coliform to *Escherichia coliform* (*E. coli*); beginning in 1999, the USGS began monitoring for both fecal and *E. coli*. *Escherichia coliform* concentrations were measured using the Colilert Quantitray method by Idaho Department of Health and Welfare and reported as most probable number (MPN) per 100 mL (Eaton et al. 1999). The MPN is considered equivalent to colonies per 100 mL.

Since 1995, periphyton and macroinvertebrate samples have been collected from riffle areas by the USGS (Mullins 1998b, 1999; MacCoy 2004). Periphyton samples were collected and processed using protocols developed by Porter et al. (1993). A measured sample of periphyton was collected from five areas within a riffle and composited. A subsample of the composite was passed through a glass-fiber filter, which was wrapped in foil, placed on dry ice, and delivered to the laboratory. Chlorophyll-a and ash-free dry weight were analyzed by the BOR Pacific Northwest Regional Laboratory, using spectrophotometry (standard method 10200H, Eaton et al. 1999).

Benthic macroinvertebrates were collected using protocols developed by Cuffney et al. (1993). A modified Surber sampler with a 425-mm-mesh net was used to collect a composite of invertebrates from cobble substrates near the five periphyton sampling locations. Microhabitat measures of depth, velocity, substrate, and embeddedness were measured at each macroinvertebrate sampling site. Large or rare taxa were isolated from the main sample to ensure that they were not lost or damaged during laboratory processing. Samples were fixed in 10% buffered formalin and shipped to Aquatic Biology Associates, Inc. for analysis. Periphyton chlorophyll-a, macroinvertebrate assemblage summaries, and associated habitat data were reported in Mullins (1999) and MacCoy (2004).

Fish assemblages were assessed by electrofishing a representative reach (1,700–2,100 m) using protocols developed by Meador et al. (1993). Shallow riffle areas were sampled using backpack electrofishers (700 V for an average of 10 min), and deepwater areas were sampled from a drift boat (using a 5,000-W, 240-V generator for an average of 25 min). Data collected included numbers of each species, total lengths, weights, and types and numbers of anomalies. Fish were collected annually between 1995 and 2001 (Table 1), and vouchers are located in the Orma J.

TABLE 1. Number and fish species collected at select sites in the lower Boise River between 1995 and 2001 (Mullins 1998b, 1999; MacCoy 2004). Fish attributes from Zaroban et al. (1999).

Scientific name	Common name	Origin[a]	Temperature preference	Canyon Mouth to Eagle Island Reach	Eagle Island Reach					Star to Canyon Hill Reach		Canyon Hill to Mouth Reach		
				Below diversion	Above Glenwood	Above Glenwood	Above Glenwood	South channel Eagle Island	South channel Eagle Island	Below Middleton	Below Middleton	Caldwell	Below Parma	Below Parma
				Dec-96	Feb-95	Dec-96	Sep-01	Mar-95	Dec-96	Dec-96	Aug-97	Aug-97	Dec-96	Aug-97
Salmo trutta	Brown trout	I	Cold	3	1	2	4		7					
Prosopium williamsoni	Mountain whitefish	N	Cold	94	93	68	251	125	238	110	19	5	10	4
Onchorhynchus mykiss	Wild rainbow trout	N	Cold	17	5	2	5	29	46	1				
Cottus bairdi	Mottled sculpin	N	Cold	65		2	24							
C. confusus	Shorthead sculpin	N	Cold	53		3	5							
Catostomus columbianus	Bridgelip sucker	N	Cool		36	30	18	1	7	12	99	18	59	69
C. macrocheilus	Largescale sucker	N	Cool		166	85	37	66	30	76	120	34	33	74
C. platyrhynchus	Mountain sucker	N	Cool		2	2	2	10	0	8				
Cyprinus carpio	Common carp	I	Warm							34	3	5	3	7
Acrocheilus alutaceus	Chiselmouth	N	Cool	1		1		2		2	370	20		14

TABLE 1. Continued.

Scientific name	Common name	Origin[a]	Temperature preference	Canyon Mouth to Eagle Island Reach	Eagle Island Reach					Star to Canyon Hill Reach		Canyon Hill to Mouth Reach		
				Below diversion	Above Glenwood	Above Glenwood	Above Glenwood	South channel Eagle Island	South channel Eagle Island	Below Middleton	Below Middleton	Caldwell	Below Parma	Below Parma
				Dec-96	Feb-95	Dec-96	Sep-01	Mar-95	Dec-96	Dec-96	Aug-97	Aug-97	Dec-96	Aug-97
Ptychocheilus oregonensis	Northern pikeminnow	N	Cool			2		1	2		86			13
Richardsonius balteatus	Redside shinner	N	Cool		3	16		24	9		66	120		1
Rhinichthys cataractae	Longnose dace	N	Cool		20	26	19	37	5	33	145		13	
R. osculus umatilla	Umatilla dace	N	Cool	3	60	7	5	46	10	150	61		1	
Gila bicolor	Tui chub	N	Warm											24
Lepomis macrochirus	Bluegill	I	Warm								1			
Micropterus salmoides	Largemouth bass	I	Warm				3			1	9		3	2
M. dolomieui	Smallmouth bass	I	Cool						1		1			9
Ictalurus punctatus	Channel catfish	I	Warm									1		4
	IBI score			89	46	52	68	66	60	39	27	23	11	7

[a] I = Introduced; N = Native.

Smith Museum of Natural History, Albertson College, Caldwell, Idaho.

Macroinvertebrate and fish assemblages were used to assess biotic integrity in the lower Boise River. Biological condition of the macroinvertebrate assemblages was assessed with metrics such as taxa richness, Ephemeroptera, Plecoptera, and Trichoptera (EPT) richness, percent dominant taxon, percent Elmidae, percent predators, and percent tolerant species. The biological condition of the fish assemblages was evaluated using an index of biological integrity (IBI; Mebane et al. 2003), which consists of 10 metrics: number of coldwater native species, percent sculpin (cottids), percent coldwater species, percent sensitive native individuals, percent tolerant individuals, number of alien species, CPUE of coldwater fish, percent of fish with DELT (deformities, eroded fins, lesions, or tumors) anomalies, number of trout age-classes, and percent common carp. These 10 metrics were standardized by scoring them continuously from 0 to 1 and weighted to produce a score ranging from 0 to 100. According to Mebane et al. (2003), sites with scores between 75 and 100 exhibit high biotic integrity with minimal disturbance and possess an abundant and diverse assemblage of native coldwater species; sites with scores between 50 and 74 are somewhat lower quality where alien species occur more frequently and the assemblage is dominated by coldwater, native species; and sites with scores less than 50 have poor biotic integrity where coldwater and sensitive species are rare or absent and where tolerant fish predominate.

Results and Interpretation

Canyon Mouth to Eagle Island Reach

The historical bank-full widths identified by the cadastral survey in the Canyon Mouth to Eagle Island Reach averaged 275 m and ranged between 92 and 675 m (Table 2). Historically, the river through this reach had extensive parafluvial surfaces (coarse sediments within the active channel, outside the wetted stream) with extensive gravel bars and islands. The valley gradient for this reach was approximately 0.29%. In describing a portion of this reach, the surveyor wrote, "the River is here divided by a large low gravely bar into two main channels, the bar island is entirely worthless." Based on the data in the cadastral survey the island measured 340 m wide. The surveyor goes on to say that there are "barren river bars subject to frequent inundation." At one

point, the surveyor described the river as "wide and shallow" and gravels "washed nearly clean of soil by the overflow of the river at every freshet." The meander survey notes described some gravel bars in backwater areas that contained "fine, rich alluvial soils" and "along the left bank of (the) Boise River (there are) low and generally very fertile (soils) with a dense undergrowth of willow and wildrose bushes." The river channel today contains very few gravel bars, and the bed substrate is mainly cobble embedded by fine sediments up to 50% (Mullins 1999; MacCoy 2004).

Cottonwood stands are considered essential components to large gravel-bed alluvial systems (Poff et al. 1997; Merigliano 1996) and are native to the lower Boise River. Cottonwood did occur in the canyon mouth to Eagle Island Reach prior to dam construction but were not extensive (see 1910 photo in Figure 3; Table 2). The surveyor noted, "land along the right bank of the Boise River (is) low, subject to frequent inundation (with) scattering clumps of cottonwood (and) dense undergrowth willow." The surveyor indicated that willow and wildrose were the dominant vegetation in this reach. Cottonwood stands and woody vegetation appeared to be confined to a narrow corridor at the stream margins.

Today, due to the lack of extreme flows to recruit and move instream and riparian substrate, there is a lack of parafluvial surfaces and limited recruitment of new cottonwood or willow trees. Using regression equations to determine unregulated basin flow in the lower Boise River calculated from basin characteristics (Hortness and Berenbrock 2001; USGS StreamStats at http://streamstats.usgs.gov/idstreamstats/) the annual mean flow for Diversion Dam in the Canyon Mouth to Eagle Island reach would be 53 m^3/s, while the actual regulated annual mean flow is 24 m^3/s. Presently, the average bank-full width (43 m) is less than one quarter of the historical width (Table 2; Mullins 1999). The average instantaneous temperature measured at the Diversion Dam from 1994 to 2002 was 10°C (Table 3) and ranged between 1.6°C and 19°C (MacCoy 2004). The water at the canyon mouth comes from the hypolimnion of Lucky Peak Lake and has an average temperature of 8.5°C at USGS gauge 13202000 (USGS NWIS WEB: http://waterdata.usgs.gov/id/nwis/qwdata). The river flows through the city of Boise in this reach and receives effluent from sewage treatment facilities. There is an increase in total phosphorus and bacteria between Diversion Dam and Glenwood, approximately 8 km upstream above Eagle Island, attributable to urban

TABLE 2. Features of the historic (1867–1868) and current (1994–2002) lower Boise River.

Parameter		Canyon Mouth to Eagle Island Reach	Eagle Island Reach	Star to Canyon Hill Reach	Canyon Hill to Mouth Reach
Embeddedness	Historic				
	Current	50%	75%	75%	50%
Dominant substrate	Historic				
	Current	cobble	cobble	cobble	gravel
Average bank-full width	Historic	275 m	North channel 240 m South channel 120 m	160 m	190 m
	Current	43 m	North channel 121 m South channel 47 m	87 m	76 m
Channel forms, parafluvial surfaces	Historic	Midchannel islands, gravel	gravel and sand bars	some islands, sand bars	some islands, sand bars, split channel at the mouth
	Current	run, riffle, pool	run, stabilized	run, exposed islands	deep run, few islands, no sand bars, single channel at the mouth
Sloughs	Historic	few sloughs	some development of sloughs	abundant	abundant
	Current	none		sloughs filled or converted to irrigation or drain ditches	few natural sloughs, sloughs converted to irrigation or drain ditches
Vegetation	Historic	willow and wildrose scattering of cottonwood	willows and cottonwood	cottonwood, some willow	cottonwood, some willow
	Current	some stands of native cottonwood	alien species dominate	alien species dominate	alien species dominate
Gradient	Current	0.29%	0.30%	0.02%	0.18%

sources. Total phosphorus increased slightly from Diversion Dam (median 0.04 mg/L) to Glenwood (median 0.09 mg/L), and median *E. coli* concentrations increased from 1 to 23 colonies/100 mL between these sites (Table 3; MacCoy 2004).

An average of only 22 macroinvertebrate taxa were found below Diversion Dam in the Canyon Mouth to Eagle Island Reach that included an average of 12 EPT taxa and 1 stonefly taxa (MacCoy, 2004). Coldwater native fish species, including mountain whitefish *Prosopium williamsoni*, shorthead sculpin *Cottus confusus*, and mottled sculpin *C. bairdii*, are abundant in this reach (Table 1; Mullins 1999; MacCoy 2004). Rainbow trout (nonanadromous *Onchorhynchus mykiss*) and brown trout *Salmo trutta* have been stocked in the lower Boise River. There is some salmonid spawning in tributaries of this reach, such as in Loggers Creek (Jeff Dillon, Idaho Fish and Game, personal communication). The fish IBI score calculated for this reach is 89, indicat-

Table 3. Median and range of instantaneous water quality values and select constituent concentrations from sites on the lower Boise River, 1994–2002 (MacCoy 2004).

| | Diversion | | Glenwood | | Middleton | | Parma | |
| | Mouth to Eagle Island Reach | | Eagle Island Reach | | Star to Canyon Hill Reach | | Canyon Hill to Mouth Reach | |
	median	range	median	range	median	range	median	range
Dissolved oxygen, mg/L	11.6	9.1–14.6	11.4	8.4–15.8	11.7	8.8–15.7	10.2	6.7–16.2
pH, standard units	7.6	6.6–8.5	8.0	7.8–8.9	8.0	6.7–9.1	8.0	7.3–8.9
Specific conductance, μS/cm	75	51–107	90	52–197	136	74–314	343	128–585
Temperature, °C	9.2	1.6–18.8	11.5	2.8–23.0	12	2.7–22.5	12.1	3.4–31.5
Total nitrogen, mg/L as N	0.26	0.15–0.51	0.45	0.18–1.90	0.89	0.38–3.51	2.17	0.62–5.33
Total phosphorus, mg/L as P	0.04	0.01–0.09	0.09	0.02–0.38	0.15	0.03–0.85	0.3	0.08–0.55
Suspended sediment, mg/L	4	1–38	5	1–107	6	2–211	45	8–245
Fecal coliform, colonies per 100 mL	1	1–29	43	4–1,030	73	3–3,950	440	44–3,600
*Escherichia coli*form, colonies per 100 mL	1	1–8	23	2–150	42	3–4,800	79	21–1,000
Periphyton average Chlorophyll-a, mg/m^2	6	<1–21	108	22–267	271	23–477	173	13–300

ing that it supports coldwater biota (Table 1; MacCoy 2004).

Eagle Island Reach

The Eagle Island reach gradient of 0.30% is similar to that of the Canyon Mouth to Eagle Island Reach; however, a decrease in gradient at the head of the island is evident (Hortness and Werner 1999). Historically, the north channel was dominant with an average bank-full width of 240 m, while the south channel averaged 120 m wide (Table 2). The south channel was shallow and the surveyor noted at one point no triangulations were needed to determine stream width, stating, "The stream being shallow I measured across." Several notes by the surveyor indicate that many areas along the north channel of Eagle Island were "low and subject to flooding or frequent inundation from 1 to 3 ft."

The surveyor notes indicated a change in the character of parafluvial surfaces from gravel to sand from the head of Eagle Island to its terminus. Near the head of the island, the surveyor writes "I now measure across gravel bars 7.75 chains to a slough too deep to wade." This is the last parafluvial surface

specifically described as a "gravel bar." From this point downstream, the surveyor describes the parafluvial surfaces as "beaches," "sandy beaches," or "sand bars." At one point, the surveyor described the river as "divided into a number of channels by very low sandy islands covered with willows." Current photographic evidence at the top of Eagle Island Reach near Glenwood shows that most parafluvial surfaces have been stabilized by woody vegetation or covered by residential development (Figure 4).

The Eagle Island Reach was the first section of the lower Boise River to receive extensive natural development of side channels and sloughs, according to the cadastral survey. There are numerous notes on the presence of sloughs that ranged between 4 and 56 m wide with an average width of 16 m. Sloughs had subsurface hydrologic connections with the river, and in meander survey notes, the surveyor recorded numerous surface connections between sloughs and the main channel.

The pre-dam vegetation through this reach was similar to that of the Canyon Mouth to Eagle Island Reach, with differences occurring toward the terminus of the island. The surveyor described Eagle Island as having rich soil and dense willows along the stream

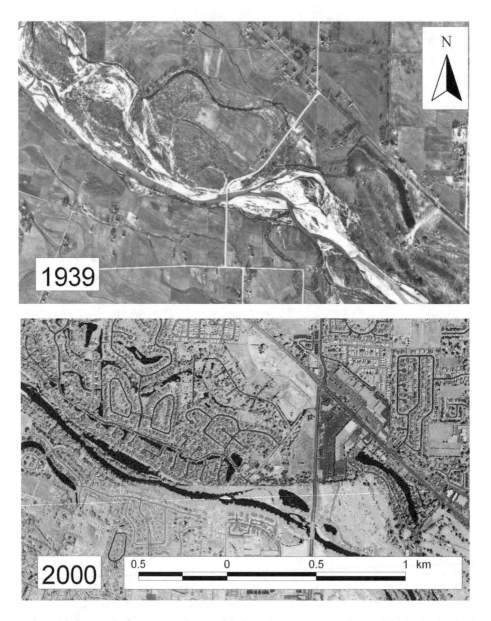

FIGURE 4. Aerial photographs from 1939 and 2000 of the lower Boise River near Glenwood Bridge (Eagle Island Reach) indicating the loss of parafluvial surfaces.

corridor with scattered cottonwoods. At the terminus of the island, the surveyor measured a cottonwood stand approximately 900 m wide. Throughout the notes, the surveyor describes the island as being populated by settlers.

Today, Eagle Island has changed both physically (Table 2) and ecologically. Many sloughs have been filled or converted to irrigation canals. The island is used mainly for residential housing with some

agriculture and gravel mining. Flows are currently managed in both channels to meet flood management objectives and ensure delivery of irrigation water. The annual mean flow at the south channel USGS gauge 13206305 in 2002 was approximately 10 m³/s with a wetted channel width of approximately 25 m (USGS NWIS WEB: http://waterdata.usgs.gov/id/nwis/qwdata). The average bank-full width from three surveyed transects in the north and south channels are 121 and 47 m, respectively (Table 2; Hortness and Werner 1999), approximately half the width of the historical river. Parafluvial surfaces are stabilized by trees and shrubs as seen in the photo of the north channel of Eagle Island near the town of Eagle (Figure 5).

At some locations in the Eagle Island Reach, embeddedness was as much as 75%, providing little opportunity for macroinvertebrate and small fish colonization (Mullins 1998a). The abundance of macroinvertebrates in this reach is similar to samples taken in the Canyon Mouth to Eagle Island Reach with few stoneflies but a higher percent tolerant species (10% compared to 3%) (Mullins 1998b). The Eagle Island Reach supports alien brown trout and rainbow trout, but no sculpins *Cottus* spp. (Table 1;

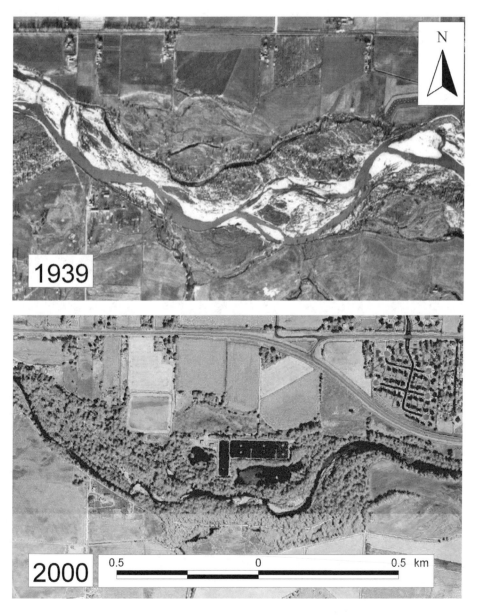

FIGURE 5. Aerial photographs from 1939 and 2000 of the south channel of the lower Boise River at Eagle Island (Eagle Island Reach) showing riparian vegetation stabilizing parafluvial surfaces.

Mullins 1999). A variety of other cold- and coolwater species were also present.

Star to Canyon Hill Reach

The historical bank-full width of the river in the Star to Canyon Hill Reach averaged 160 m (Table 2). The surveyor described the parafluvial surfaces as sand with descriptions such as beaches or sandy islands. In the spring of 1876, Judge Milton Kelly toured the lower Boise River Valley and described the river near Middleton (within the Star to Canyon Hill Reach) as "always high from springtime through July, so a ferry was a necessity. However, the sandy approaches kept washing out, the channel changing a little and the banks of the river shifting so that a ferry was not successful" (Bird 1934; p. 240). This statement suggests that nearshore deposits at Middleton were dominated by sand. There was no mention in the cadastral survey notes of multiple channels (braiding) as described in the upstream reaches. At one point, the surveyor does note "the river here is divided into two channels by a low sandy & gravelly Island about 10 chains long E & W." This is the only mid-channel island in this reach described by the survey and may be a further indication of a change in sediment characteristics. The reach gradient is 0.02%, considerably lower than that of the upstream reaches. This could be one reason for development of numerous side channels and sloughs in this reach. Through the approximately 21 km of river surveyed in this reach, the surveyors crossed sloughs 81 times with sloughs averaging 10 m wide, ranging between 3 and 60 m. Meander surveys noted that many sloughs had surface water connections with the river.

The width of the hyporheic zone through this reach is unknown, but some of the sloughs were located as far as 1.5 km from the main channel. During the September and October cadastral surveys, a period of declining flow in the basin, the surveyor indicated that sloughs were watered. Recharge of the hyporheic zone occurred during periods of high flow. Wagon roads located on the north side of the river and situated on a low ridge about 1.5 km from the river also indicate a wetted floodplain (large hyporheic zone) that would be difficult to traverse by wagon or horseback.

Cottonwood stands were well developed in the Star to Canyon Hill Reach. From surveyor notes, the cottonwood stands ranged from 500 m to 1 km and the surveyor described most of the vegetation as being "timber scattering of cottonwood." Willows were recorded in only a few areas.

Today, the Star to Canyon Hill reach contains few exposed parafluvial surfaces and there is a reduction in natural slough formation (Table 2). Aerial photographs from 1939 and 2000 of a section of the river near Middleton (Figure 6) show parafluvial surfaces colonized by woody vegetation and no longer a part of the active channel.

High flows exceeding 113 m³/s were measured at the Middleton gauge in 1993 and 1995 (USGS NWIS WEB: http://waterdata.usgs.gov/id/nwis/qwdata). Similar high flows may have caused the river to incise and increase erosion potential and riverbank sloughing. Currently, islands and backwater in this reach provide fish habitat (Mullins 1999). The average bank-full width from three surveyed transects between the terminus of Eagle Island and the Ada County line was 87 m (Table 2, Hortness and Werner 1999), almost half the historical width.

The median instantaneous temperature collected from 1994 to 2004 at the Middleton biological sampling site was 12°C with a range between 2.7°C in winter months to 22.5°C in summer months (Table 3; MacCoy 2004). The Idaho State standard temperatures of not to exceed 13°C during the salmonid spawning period between October 15 and March 15, and not to exceed 22°C to support coldwater aquatic life, were exceeded at this site (MacCoy 2004). At Middleton, total nitrogen (median 0.89 mg/L), total phosphorus (median 0.15 mg/L), and suspended sediment (median 6 mg/L) were higher than in the canyon mouth reach (Table 3).

The macroinvertebrate assemblages below Middleton between 1995 and 2000 consisted of up to 30% tolerant species such as *Tricorythodes minutus*, a sediment-tolerant mayfly, and the New Zealand mudsnail *Potamopyrgus antipodarum* (Mullins 1999; MacCoy 2004). Both species have increased since sampling began in 1995, and no stoneflies were found in the 2000 sample (MacCoy 2004). Mountain whitefish was the predominant salmonid found at Middleton, and no sculpin were found. Bridgelip sucker *Catostomus columbianus*, largescale sucker *C. macrocheilus*, chiselmouth *Acrocheilus alutaceus*, and two dace species, longnosedace *Rhinichthys cataractae* and Umatilla dace *Rhinichthys umatilla*, were the most abundant species at this site (Table 1; Mullins 1999; MacCoy 2004). These fish were collected from fast runs and are considered coolwater species (Zaroban et al. 1999). The IBI score for the Middleton fish assemblage in 1996 was less than 40, below the minimum threshold associated with coldwater biota (Table 1, MacCoy 2004).

Canyon Hill to Mouth Reach

The Canyon Hill to Mouth Reach is approximately 15 km long (Figure 2) with pre-dam average bank-full width of 190 m, ranging between 20 and 890 m (Table 2). The surveyor used "sand beach," "beach," or "sandy island" to describe the parafluvial surfaces. These sandy bars were extensive, as the surveyor described one being 74 m wide. Near the end of the reach, the surveyor described the river as divided into "a number of channels by low sandy islands and bars." The surveyor described areas "subject to frequent inundation" above the meander lines in the lower part of this reach. The valley gradient is 0.18%, which is greater than that of the Star to Canyon Hill Reach (Table 2). Judge Milton Kelly, in 1876, described the river dividing near the mouth and forming an island with the north channel approximately 5 km from the south channel (Bird 1934). This change occurred sometime between the completion of the cadastral survey in 1868 and Kelly's tour in 1876. A 1939 aerial photograph shows the north channel and the remnants of the south channel described by Kelly. The 2000 photo shows the decrease in parafluvial surfaces from 1939 (Figure 7).

Sloughs were a prominent feature in the historical Canyon Hill to Mouth Reach, averaging 15 m wide and ranging between 3 and 45 m. Some sloughs were used for irrigation and several irrigation ditches were described in the surveyor notes. One of the main sloughs, Dixie Slough, originates approximately 2 km south of the lower Boise River and runs parallel to the river for approximately 16.7 km west to its confluence with the river. The historical water source for Dixie Slough is unknown, but it is now principally fed by irrigation return flow. Sagebrush *Artemisia* sp. and greasewood *Sarcobatus* sp. were noted in the surveyor's notes between the slough and the lower Boise River. This plant association commonly grows on saline sodic-soils generally created by an accumulation of salts in the upper soil profile from evaporation of large amounts of water at the soil surface. Current soils in the area are mapped as Letha soils, which are still considered saline-sodic (USDA 1972). The cause of the saline-sodic soils between Dixie Slough and the lower Boise River is unknown.

Cottonwoods were the dominant trees in this reach. The surveyor frequently refers to the vegetation as "timber scattering of cottonwood." These stands of cottonwood were probably extensive as the surveyor provides descriptions such as "enter timber" and "leave timber" at nearly every section line. On the basis of these data, the width of the cottonwood stand was between 700 m and 1 km. These cottonwood stands do not appear to be dense, on the basis of the small number of trees marked as bearing trees. The surveyor also describes a few dispersed willow trees, not as extensive as in upstream reaches.

Today, the Canyon Hill to Mouth reach is confined to the main channel and sloughs have been converted to irrigation canals and drains (Table 2). Parafluvial surfaces are absent, and the river is mainly a deep run and the river channel is incised (Figure 7). In 1998, the average bank-full width near the mouth was 76 m (Table 3; Mullins 1999), less than half the historical width. Average instantaneous temperature measured at Parma between 1994 and 2002 was 12.1°C, ranging between 3.4°C and 31.5°C (Table 3; MacCoy 2004). Prior to urbanization, temperatures were likely colder to support the number of salmon indicated in historical documents. Nutrients, bacteria, and suspended sediment increase at Parma compared to the upstream sites, mainly from agricultural sources. Total phosphorus (median 0.3 mg/L), *E. coli* (median of 79 organisms/100 mL), and suspended sediment (median of 45 mg/L) increased from Middleton to Parma by 50%, 50%, and 30%, respectively (Table 3; MacCoy 2004). Today, there is minimal fish habitat and very few riffles for macroinvertebrate colonization (Mullins 1999). The macroinvertebrate assemblage measured below the Parma water quality site was composed mainly of the tolerant mayfly, *Tricorythodes minutus* (50%), and no stoneflies were found. The fish species that occurred in this reach were mainly coolwater suckers and minnows (Table 1; Mullins 1999; MacCoy 2004). The fish assemblage assessed near the mouth in 1996 had the lowest IBI score (under 20) of all the sites in the lower Boise River (MacCoy 2004).

General River Conditions

The magnitude and variability of seasonal flow changed on the lower Boise River following the construction of Lucky Peak Dam. Seasonal flows were similar prior to dam construction (pre-1917) at the Boise River near Boise gauge (USGS 1202000) just downstream from Lucky Peak Dam. Prior to 1917, average flows for December and August were 31 and 34 m³/s, respectively, each with a standard deviation of 13 m³/s. Average flows after dam construction (post-1957) for December and August were 10 and 114 m³/s, respectively; and standard deviations were 10 and 18 m³/s, respectively (USGS NWIS WEB: http://waterdata.usgs.gov/id/nwis/qwdata). In fact, the flow

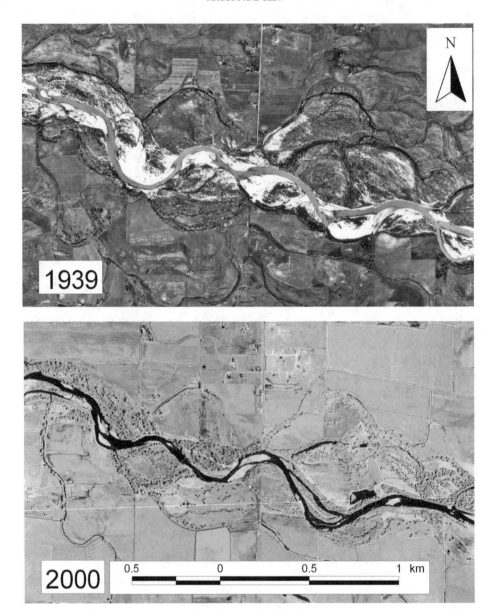

FIGURE 6. Aerial photographs from 1939 and 2000 of a section of the lower Boise River near Middleton (Star to Canyon Hill Reach) showing the stabilization of parafluvial surfaces.

regime was the opposite of pre-dam flows in December and August (Figure 8). The average December post-dam flows are significantly lower ($P < 0.001$, Wilcoxon rank sum test) than during pre-dam years, and the average August post-dam flows are significantly ($P < 0.001$) higher than during pre-dam years.

Recent water quality data revealed increases in constituent concentrations in the lower Boise River in a downstream direction (Mullins 1998b; MacCoy

2004). At four sampling locations between Diversion Dam and Parma, nitrogen, phosphorus, suspended sediment, and fecal coliform bacteria increased more than 8, 7, 11, and 400 times, respectively (Table 3). Chlorophyll-a concentrations also increased in a downstream direction and were highest at Middleton and Parma (Table 3), but there was no indication of nuisance algae (MacCoy 2004).

The state's temperature standards of 22°C and

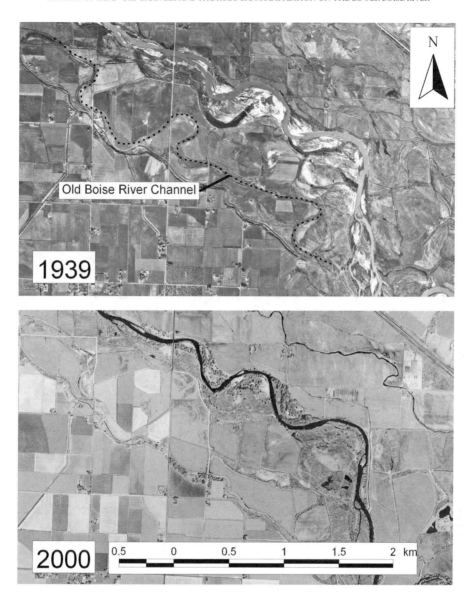

FIGURE 7. Aerial photographs from 1939 and 2000 of the lower Boise River near Parma (Canyon Hill to Mouth Reach) showing historic divided channel and stabilization of parafluvial surfaces.

13°C (IDEQ 2001) to protect coldwater biota and salmonid spawning, respectively, were exceeded most frequently at Middleton and Parma (MacCoy, 2004). The suspended sediment criterion of 80 mg/L for no more than 14 d (Rowe et al. 1999) was exceeded most frequently at Parma (Table 3). Total nitrogen concentrations at Glenwood, Middleton, and Parma exceeded national background levels of 1.0 mg/L (USGS 1999); Middleton and Parma had more than twice the median flow-adjusted total nitrogen concentrations com-pared to undeveloped basins across the country (0.26 mg/L; Clark et al. 2000). Glenwood, Middleton, and Parma also exceeded the flow-adjusted total phospho-rus concentrations for undeveloped basins (0.02 mg/L; Clark et al. 2000). The Idaho standard for *E. coli* in recreational waters (406 organisms/100 mL; IDEQ 2001) was exceeded at Middleton and Parma between 1994 and 2002.

The lower Boise River channel form and func-tion change in a downstream direction. The gradient

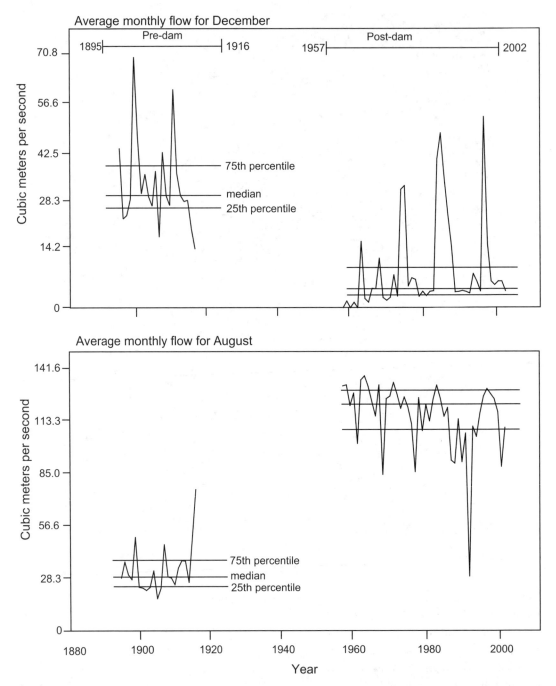

FIGURE 8. Monthly average flows for December and August pre-dam (1885–1916) and post-dam (1957–2002) in the lower Boise River at USGS gauge 13202000.

decreased from near 0.30% to 0.02% from the Canyon Mouth to Eagle Island Reach to the Star to Canyon Hill Reach (Table 2). The formation of sloughs and side channels historically dominated the Star to

Canyon Hill Reach and would have provided important habitat for fish and invertebrates. In the Canyon Hill to Mouth Reach, the gradient increased to 0.18% forming a more centralized channel but still provided slough and side channel habitat. Historically river bottom substrate above the Eagle Island Reach was dominated by cobble and gravel. Below the Eagle Island Reach, substrate was dominated by sand. Currently, there is little movement of substrate in the river due to regulated flows and embeddedness of greater than 50% is common. Throughout the river, there has been extensive loss of parafluvial surfaces, and average bankfull width, in some cases, has decreased to less than half the historical measure (Table 2).

Regulated flow, poor habitat, and water quality have affected the biological communities in the lower Boise River. Biological condition throughout the river was poor compared to other Idaho rivers not impacted by urbanization and agriculture (Maret et al. 2001; MacCoy 2004). The macroinvertebrate assemblages at each site remained similar over the 8-year USGS study; however, there were decreases in density during extremely high and low flows. The number of EPT taxa ranged between 5 and 16 and was lowest at the downstream sites (MacCoy 2004). The number of tolerant taxa increased in a downstream direction, and up to 50% of the macroinvertebrate assemblage near the mouth of the lower Boise River was composed of tolerant species (MacCoy 2004).

Discussion

Urbanization and agriculture have affected water quality and decreased aquatic habitat and parafluvial surfaces in the lower Boise River. The construction of three large dams in the upper basin dramatically altered the flow regime and sediment supply to the river. Stream regulation by dams eliminates natural variations in flow (Waters 1995). Natural seasonal patterns, timing of extreme flows, frequency of high and low flows, and droughts and floods contribute to the biodiversity of a river ecosystem (Richter et al. 1996; Stanford et al. 1996; Poff et al. 1997) and are sensitive to human impact (Olden and Poff 2003). Dams and other hydrologic alterations have decreased the natural disturbance regime and biodiversity of the lower Boise River. Phosphorus from wastewater treatment facilities and increased nutrients, bacteria, and sediment from agriculture lowered water quality. The increased abundance of tolerant and alien species has lowered the quality of natural aquatic assemblages.

Currently, alien plant species occur in all reaches of the lower Boise River. Jones (2001) reported alien hardwoods have replaced the native cottonwood stands along Eagle Island. Purple loosestrife *Lythrum*

salicaria and reed canarygrass *Phalaris arundinacea* are present along most of the lower Boise River.

The number of macroinvertebrate taxa is diminished in all reaches of the lower Boise River. There are very few stoneflies found compared to the numbers found in most rivers in Idaho (Maret et al. 2001). Most macroinvertebrates in the lower Boise River are tolerant to sediment and excess nutrients, and the percent tolerant species increases in a downstream direction. The embedded substrates restrict the colonization of macroinvertebrates and fish that require coarse sediments. Alien fish are present throughout the lower Boise River, especially in the lower reaches, and there is a lack of refuge for native species. There are no quantitative biological data prior to dam construction that would help us estimate biological conditions in the lower Boise River, but historical accounts of salmon throughout the system indicate it supported large anadromous fish populations.

Canyon Mouth to Eagle Island and the Eagle Island Reaches

The historical river channel between the canyon mouth and Eagle Island was more dynamic than the current channel. The gravel bars historically present in this reach represented part of the "shifting habitat mosaic" necessary to maintain biodiversity and productivity (Poff et al. 1997). The completion of Lucky Peak Dam exacerbated the armoring of bottom substrate by reducing sediment supply to reaches just downstream from the dam. Sediment starvation is a common occurrence on many large gravel-bed rivers (Poff et al. 1997). The maintenance of parafluvial surfaces is dependent upon an adequate supply of sediment and high flows to create sufficient shear stress to mobilize coarse streambed material. Currently, flows do not produce adequate shear stress to mobilize bed material on a regular basis. Dredging, aggregate mining, and stream channelization also reduced parafluvial surfaces in this reach. Today, with the river flowing through the city of Boise, the major land uses in this reach are urban and residential to the river's edge, necessitating channelization and bank stabilization in several sections. Regulated flows and colder than normal temperatures also affect the aquatic assemblages in these reaches.

The sloughs and side channels beginning in the Eagle Island Reach indicate an extensive hyporheic zone, a key to the functioning and productivity of gravel-bed alluvial systems (Stanford et al. 1996). The conversion of sloughs to irrigation canals and drains resulted in the loss of some of the most important habitat in the river. Stanford et al. (1996) described the importance of side channels and sloughs in maintaining fisheries and their importance for certain life stages of native salmonids.

Star to Canyon Hill Reach

The lack of extreme flows has caused the bottom substrate to be embedded as much as 75% in this reach, reducing interstitial habitat used by macroinvertebrates and fish. The apparent reduction in the size and amount of bedload through the Star to Canyon Hill Reach may have prevented the braiding and islands that were seen historically in upstream reaches. Streams and rivers with large amounts of coarse bedloads are often associated with braided or divided channels (Knighton 1998; Bravard et al. 1999). Two factors identified in the literature as affecting the width of rivers are the reduction in sediment transport and reduction of flow (Schumm 1972). We suspect that both factors are responsible for the narrowing of the channel in this reach compared to upstream reaches. The decrease in gradient aided formation of side channels and sloughs as described in the surveyor notes. At channel-forming flows, these sloughs would have reduced flow in the main channel and the capacity of the main channel to transport sediment. According to Lane (1972), reduction in flow would reduce both size and quantity of the sediment transported. This may explain why there was extensive deposition of sand in this reach. Many of the historical sloughs in the Star to Canyon Hill Reach were converted to drains or irrigation canals and no longer provide high quality aquatic habitat. Prior to construction of dams, levees, and extensive irrigation, sections of the lower Boise River had a large (up to 1.5 km wide) hyporheic zone that provided side channels for refuge and salmon spawning and rearing (Boulton et al. 1998). Many authors have described the importance of the hyporheic zone in alluvial systems (Boulton et al. 1998; Stanford and Ward 1993; Wondzell and Swanson 1999). The Boise River dams created a flow regime with higher than natural flows during the peak irrigation season (April through September) and lower than natural flows during the nonirrigation season (October through March). The change in hydraulic regime and construction of levees are associated with incision of the lower Boise River and reduction of depositional areas and wetlands associated with the hyporheic zone. A reduced hyporheic

zone along with the potential cooling effect of its groundwater discharge to the river may have increased temperature in this reach. The elevated nutrients and sediment from agricultural practices produced poor water quality conditions. These factors and the loss of important habitats for sensitive macroinvertebrates and fish aided colonization of alien and tolerant macroinvertebrates and fish in the Star to Canyon Hill reach.

Canyon Hill to Mouth Reach

The Canyon Hill to Mouth Reach had many areas described by the surveyor as being low and subject to frequent inundation, with numerous side channels and sloughs, indicating an extensive hyporheic zone. Historically, this increased the reach's susceptibity to channel avulsions and may have caused the main channel shifting north 5 km between 1867 and 1876. However, saline-resistant vegetation on parts of the floodplain indicate changes in subsurface flow patterns that resulted in the accumulation of salts in the soil profile.

Changes in flow regime and sediment supply have altered the geomorphologic characteristics of this reach; parafluvial surfaces are nearly gone, with many stabilized by woody vegetation. The lack of parafluvial surfaces necessary to maintain high quality aquatic habitat is one reason why tolerant species dominate this reach. Another reason for abundant tolerant species is the high concentrations of nutrients and sediment associated with agriculture. High stream temperatures and poor physical habitat have resulted in a poor fish assemblage near the mouth.

Conclusion

The lower Boise River needs to be viewed as the result of a complex history of alterations. The physical features of the lower Boise River in 1867 and 1868 indicate that the river was wider and more dynamic than the present river, but there were alterations prior to the cadastral surveys. Historical information helped us to identify changes within the river ecosystem, to understand the complex connectivity between the main channel and sloughs, and to identify physical processes of the river. These processes and the river's connectivity have been lost in the current urbanized system. Restoration of chemical, physical, and biological condition is dependent upon reconnecting these fragmented components.

Restoration efforts, such as agricultural best management practices to reduce sediment and nutrient runoff, and efforts to reduce urban storm water runoff have begun to improve the water quality in the lower Boise River. Sediment, nutrient and bacteria TMDLs have been or are in the process of being written to help develop additional plans to restore beneficial uses (fishable and swimable) of the river. Currently, there are no efforts to restore the coldwater fishery in the lower reaches of the river. An archeological study of fish species utilized by Native Americans might help to understand the historical distribution and the rich biodiversity that once typified the lower Boise River. Such data would provide a benchmark for efforts to restore those resources.

Acknowledgments

The authors acknowledge Peter Bell and Allen Thompson, who collected the cadastral survey data in 1867 and 1868, and Katy Koval and Mike Ciscell for help with the spatial data. A special thank you goes to Terry Maret, Bill Clark, and Bob Hughes for their extensive editorial and technical review of this chapter. There are many other individuals, too numerous to mention, who have answered questions and reviewed maps and manuscripts and whose help is greatly appreciated.

References

Baker, V. 1994. Geomorphological understanding of floods. Geomorphology 10:139–156.

Bayley, P. B. 1991. The flood pulse advantage and the restoration of river-floodplain systems. Regulated Rivers: Research and Management 6:75–86.

Bird, A. L. 1934. Boise the peace valley. Caxton Printers, Caldwell, Idaho.

Bird, A. L. 1971. Old Fort Boise. Caxton Printers, Caldwell, Idaho.

Boulton, A. J., S. Findlay, P. Marmonier, E. H. Stanley, and H. M. Valett. 1998. The functional significance of the hyporheic zone in streams and rivers. Annual Review of Ecological Systems 29:59–81.

BOR (Bureau of Reclamation). 1977. Water quality study, Boise Valley, volume 2. Boise, Idaho.

Boyle, L. 2001. Lower Boise/Canyon County nitrate degraded ground water quality summary report. Idaho Department of Environmental Quality, Boise.

Bravard, J. P., N. Landon, J. L. Peiry, and H. Piegay. 1999. Principles of engineering geomorphology for managing channel erosion and bedload transport, examples from French rivers. Geomorphology 31:291–311.

Brookes, A. 1996. River channel change. Pages 221–242 in G. Petts and P. Calow, editors. River flows and channel forms. Blackwell Scientific Publications Ltd., Oxford, UK.

Brown, C. M. 1962. Evidence and procedures for boundary location. Wiley, New York.

Chandler, J. A., and D. Chapman. 2001. Existing habitat conditions of tributaries formerly used by anadromous fish. Pages 40–48 in J. A. Chandler, editor. Feasibility of reintroduction of anadromous fish above or within the Hells Canyon Complex, Technical appendix E. 3.1–2 for Hells Canyon Complex Hydroelectric Project FERC No. 1971. Idaho Power Company, Boise.

Clark, G. M., D. K. Mueller, and M. A. Mast. 2000. Nutrient concentrations and yields in undeveloped stream basins of the United States. Journal of the American Water Resources Association 36:849–860.

Clark, W. H., and S. B. Bauer. 1983. Water quality status report, lower Boise River drains, Canyon County, Idaho. Idaho Department of Health and Welfare, Division of Environment Water Quality Series no. 50, Boise.

Collier, M., R. H. Webb, and J. C. Schmidt. 1996. Dams and rivers: a primer on the downstream effects of dams. U.S. Geological Survey circular 1126, Denver.

Cuffney, T. F., M.E. Gurtz, and M.R. Meador. 1993. Methods for collecting benthic invertebrate samples as part of the National Water-Quality Assessment Program. U.S. Geological Survey Open-file Report 93–406, Raleigh, North Carolina.

Delcourt, H. R., and P. A. Delcourt. 1996. Presettlement landscape heterogeneity: evaluating grain of resolution using General Land Office survey data. Landscape Ecology 11:363–381.

Eaton, A. D., L. S. Clesceri, and A. E. Greenberg. 1999. Standard methods for the examination of water and wastewater, 20th edition. American Public Health Association, Washington, D.C.

Fishman, M. J. 1993. Methods of analysis by the U.S. Geological Survey National Water Quality Laboratory—determination of inorganic and organic constituents in water and fluvial sediments. U.S. Geological Survey Open-File Report 93–125, Denver.

Fox, J., R. Carlson, K. Campbell, and G. Bahr. 2002. Ground and surface water interaction related to nutrients within Mason Creek agricultural drain, Canyon County, Idaho. Idaho State Department of Agriculture, Groundwater Monitoring Technical Completion Report, Boise.

Frenzel, S. A. 1988. Physical, chemical, and biological

characteristics of the Boise River from Veterans Memorial Parkway, Boise, to Star, Idaho, October 1987 to March 1988. U.S. Geological Survey Water-Resources Investigations Report 98–4206, Boise, Idaho.

Frenzel, S. A. 1990. Effects of municipal wastewater discharges on aquatic communities, Boise River, Idaho. Water Resources Bulletin 26:279–287.

Gilvear, D. J. 1993. River management and conservation issues on formerly braided river systems: the case of the River Tay, Scotland. Pages 231–240 in J. L. Best and C. S. Bristow, editors. Braided rivers. Geological Society Special Publication 75, Oxford, UK.

Gilvear, D. J., and S. J. Winterbottom. 1992. Channel change and flood events since 1783 on the regulated River Tay, Scotland: implications for flood hazard management. Regulated Rivers: Research and Management 7:247–260.

Guy, H. P. 1969. Laboratory theory and methods for sediment analysis. U.S. Geological Survey Techniques of Water Resources Investigations, book 5, chapter C1, Washington, D.C.

Heede, B. H., and J. N. Rinne. 1990. Hydrodynamic and fluvial morphologic processes: implications for fisheries management and research. North American Journal of Fisheries Management 10:249–268.

Hortness, J. E., and C. Berenbrock. 2001. Estimating monthly and annual streamflow statistics at ungaged sites in Idaho. U.S. Geological Survey Water-Resources Investigations Report 01–4093, Boise, Idaho.

Hortness, J. E., and D. C. Werner. 1999. Stream channel cross sections for a reach of the Boise River in Ada County, Idaho. U.S. Geological Survey Open-file Report 99–211, Boise, Idaho.

IDEQ (Idaho Department of Environmental Quality). 1999. Lower Boise River TMDL, sub-basin assessment, total maximum daily loads. Idaho State Department of Environmental Quality Report, Boise.

IDEQ (Idaho Department of Environmental Quality). 2001. Water quality standards and wastewater treatment requirements, Boise. Available: http://www2.state.id.us/adm/adminrules/rules/idapa58/58index.htm. (March 2003)

Jones, M. 2001. Wetland conservation strategy for the middle and western Snake River and lower reaches of its major tributaries including the Boise River and Payette River. Idaho Department of Fish and Game, Natural Resource Policy Bureau, Boise.

Knighton, D. 1998. Fluvial forms and processes. Arnold, London.

Kramber, W. J., A. Morse, B. Harmon, and H. Anderson. 1997. Mapping 80 years of change in irrigated agri-

culture. Idaho State Department of Water Resources Report, Boise.

Lane, E. W. 1972. The importance of fluvial morphology in hydraulic engineering. Pages 180–197 in S.A., Schumm, editor. Benchmark papers in geology: river morphology. Dowden, Hutchison and Ross, Inc., Stroudsburg, Pennsylvania.

MacCoy, D. E. 2004. Water-quality and biological conditions in the lower Boise River, Ada and Canyon counties, Idaho, 1994–2002. U.S. Geological Survey Scientific Investigations Report 2004–5128, Boise, Idaho.

Maret, T. R., D. E. MacCoy, K. D. Skinner, S. E. Moore, and I. O. O'Dell. 2001. Evaluation of macroinvertebrate assemblages in Idaho Rivers using multimetric and multivariate techniques, 1996–98. U.S. Geological Survey Water-Resources Investigations Report 01–4145, Boise, Idaho.

McDowell, P. F. 2000. Human impacts and river channel adjustment, northeastern Oregon: implications for restoration. Pages 257–261 in P. J. Wigington and R. L. Beschta, editors. Riparian ecology and management in multi-land use watersheds symposium proceedings. American Water Resources Association, Middleburg, Virginia.

Meador, M. R., T. F. Cuffney, and M. E. Gurtz. 1993. Methods for sampling fish communities as part of the National Water-Quality Assessment Program. U.S. Geological Survey Open-File Report 93–104, Denver.

Mebane, C. A., T. R. Maret, and R. M. Hughes. 2003. An index of biological integrity (IBI) for Pacific Northwest Rivers. Transactions of the American Fisheries Society 132:234–261.

Merigliano, M. F. 1996. Ecology and management of the south fork Snake River cottonwood forest. Idaho Bureau of Land Management Technical Bulletin 96–9, Boise.

Mullins, W. H. 1998a. Water-quality conditions of the lower Boise River, Ada and Canyon counties, Idaho, May 1994 through February 1997. U.S. Geological Survey Water Resources Investigations Report 98–4111, Boise, Idaho.

Mullins, W. H. 1998b. Biotic integrity of the Boise River upstream and downstream from two municipal wastewater treatment facilities, Boise, Idaho, 1995–96. U.S. Geological Survey Water Resources Investigations Report 98–4123, Boise, Idaho.

Mullins, W. H. 1999. Biological assessment of the lower Boise River, October 1995 through January 1998, Ada and Canyon counties, Idaho. U.S. Geological Survey Water Resources Investigations Report 99–4178, Boise, Idaho.

Nelson, J. C., L. DeHann, R. E. Sparks, and R.

Robinson. 1998. Presettlement and contemporary vegetation patterns along two navigation reaches of the Upper Mississippi River. Pages 51–60 *in* T. D., Sisk, editor. Perspectives on the land-use history of North America: a context for understanding our changing environment. U.S. Geological Survey, Biological Resources Division, Biological Science Report USGS/BRD/BSR 1998–0003, Springfield, Virginia.

Olden, J. D., and N. L. Poff. 2003. Redundancy and the choice of hydrologic indices for characterizing stream flow regimes. River Research and Applications 19:101–121.

Osborne, C. E. 1959. Federal aid in fish restoration, annual progress report, water quality investigations. State of Idaho, Department of Fish and Game, Boise.

Parliman, D. J. and J. M. Spinazola. 1998. Ground water quality in northern Ada County, lower Boise River basin, Idaho, 1985–96. U.S. Geological Survey fact sheet FS-054–98, Boise, Idaho.

Poff, N. L., J. D. Allan, M. B. Bain, J. R. Karr, K. L. Prestegaard, B. D. Richter, R. E. Sparks, and J. C. Stromberg. 1997. The natural flow regime: paradigm for river conservation and restoration. BioScience 47:769–784.

Porter, S. D., T. F. Cuffney, M. E. Gurtz, and M. R. Meador. 1993. Methods for collecting algal samples as part of the National Water-Quality Assessment Program. U.S. Geological Survey Open-File Report 93–409, Denver.

Pratt, K. L., M. Kozel, J. Mauser, L. Mauser, and R. Sarpella. 2001. Appendix I. Annotated bibliographies on the chronology of decline of anadromous fish in the Snake River basin above the Hells Canyon Dam. Pages 1–76 *in* J. A. Chandler, editor. Feasibility of reintroduction of anadromous fish above or within the Hells Canyon Complex. Technical appendices E. 3.1–2 for Hells Canyon Complex Hydroelectric Project FERC No. 1971. Idaho Power Company, Boise, Idaho.

Pritt, J. W., and J. W. Raese, editors. 1995. Quality assurance/quality control manual: National Water Quality Laboratory. U.S. Geological Survey Open-File Report 95–443, Denver.

Rantz, S. E. 1982. Measurement and computation of stream flow: volume 1. Measurement of stage and discharge. U.S. Geological Survey Water-Supply Paper 2175, Denver.

Richter, B. D., J. V. Baumgartner, J. Powell, and D. P. Braun. 1996. A method for assessing hydrologic alteration within ecosystems. Conservation Biology 10:1163–1174.

Rowe, M., D. Essig, and J. Fitzgerald. 1999. Sediment targets used or proposed for TMDLs. Idaho Department of Environmental Quality Report, Boise.

Schick, A., T. Grodeck, and M. G. Wolman. 1999. Hydraulic processes and geomorphic constraints on urbanization of alluvial flan slopes. Geomorphology 31:325–335.

Schumm, S. A. 1972. Fluvial geomorphology: channel adjustment and river metamorphosis. Pages 395–417 *in* S. A. Schumm, editor. Benchmark papers in geology: river morphology. Dowden, Hutchison and Ross, Inc., Stroudsburg, Pennsylvania.

Sisco, L. 2001. Report on canal deliveries from Boise River and different features affecting the deliveries for the irrigation season of 2001. Water District 63, Boise, Idaho.

Sisk, T. D., editor. 1998. Perspectives on the land-use history of North America: a context for understanding our changing environment. U.S. Geological Survey, Biological Resources Division, Biological Science Report USGS/BRD/BSR 1998–0003, Springfield, Virginia.

Stacy, S. 1993. When the river rises, flood control on the Boise River 1943–1985. Boise State University, College of Social Sciences and Public Affairs, Program on Environment and Behavior, Special Publication No. 27, Boise, Idaho.

Stanford, J. A., and J. V. Ward. 1993. An ecosystem perspective of alluvial rivers: connectivity and the hyporheic corridor. Journal of the North American Benthological Society 12:48–60.

Stanford, J. A., J. V. Ward, W. J. Liss, C. A. Frissell, R. N. Williams, J. A. Lichatowich, and C. C. Coulant. 1996. A general protocol for restoration of regulated rivers. Regulated Rivers: Research and Management 12:391–413.

Thomas, C. A., and N. P. Dion. 1974. Characteristics of stream flow and ground water conditions in the Boise River Valley, Idaho. U.S. Geological Survey Water Resources Investigations Report 38–74, Boise, Idaho.

USDA (U.S. Department of Agriculture). 1972. Soil survey of Canyon Area, Idaho. Soil Conservation Service, Agricultural Experiment Station, Canyon County, Idaho.

USGS (U. S. Geological Survey). 1999. The quality of our nation's water—nutrients and pesticides: U.S. Geological Survey Circular 1225, Reston, Virginia.

Waters, T. F. 1995. Sediment in streams: sources, biological effects and control. American Fisheries Society, Monograph 7, Bethesda, Maryland.

Wilde, F. D., D. B. Radtke, J. Gibs, and R. T. Iwatsubo, editors. 1999. Collection of water samples and processing of water samples in national field manual for the collection of water-quality data. U.S. Geological Survey Techniques of Water Resources Investigations, book 9, chapters A4 and A5, Denver.

Winterbottom, S. J. 2000. Medium and short-term channel planform changes on the rivers Tay and Tummel, Scotland. Geomorphology 34:195–208.

Wondzell, S. M., and F. J. Swanson. 1999. Floods, channel change, and the hyporheic zone. Water Resources Research 35:555–567.

Zaroban, D. W., M. P. Mulvey, T. R. Maret, R. M. Hughes, and G. D. Merritt. 1999. Classification of species attributes for Pacific Northwest freshwater fishes. Northwest Science 73:81–93.

American Fisheries Society Symposium 47:157–177, 2005

Hydrologic Changes in Urban Streams and Their Ecological Significance

CHRISTOPHER P. KONRAD*

U.S. Geological Survey, 1201 Pacific Avenue, Suite 600, Tacoma, Washington, 98402, USA

DEREK B. BOOTH

*Center for Water and Watershed Studies, Department of Civil and Environmental Engineering
Box 352700, University of Washington, Seattle, Washington, 98195-2700, USA*

Abstract.—Urban development modifies the production and delivery of runoff to streams and the resulting rate, volume, and timing of streamflow. Given that streamflow demonstrably influences the structure and composition of lotic communities, we have identified four hydrologic changes resulting from urban development that are potentially significant to stream ecosystems: increased frequency of high flows, redistribution of water from base flow to storm flow, increased daily variation in streamflow, and reduction in low flow. Previous investigations of streamflow patterns and biological assemblages provide a scale of ecological significance for each type of streamflow pattern. The scales establish the magnitude of changes in streamflow patterns that could be expected to produce biological responses in streams. Long-term streamflow records from eight streams in urbanizing areas of the United States and five additional reference streams, where land use has been relatively stable, were analyzed to assess if streamflow patterns were modified by urban development to an extent that a biological response could be expected and whether climate patterns could account for equivalent hydrologic variation in the reference streams. Changes in each type of streamflow pattern were evident in some but not all of the urban streams and were nearly absent in the reference streams. Given these results, hydrologic changes are likely significant to urban stream ecosystems, but the significance depends on the stream's physiographic context and spatial and temporal patterns of urban development. In urban streams with substantially altered hydrology, short-term goals for urban stream rehabilitation may be limited because of the difficulty and expense of restoring hydrologic processes in an urban landscape. The ecological benefits of improving physical habitat and water quality may be tempered by persistent effects of altered streamflow. In the end, the hydrologic effects of urban development must be addressed for restoration of urban streams.

Introduction

Streamflow is the dominant physical process distinguishing rivers and streams from other ecosystems. The structure and composition of lotic communities in fluvial ecosystems depend on source, timing, and rate of streamflow as they regulate both habitat conditions and disturbance regimes. Because of the important roles of streamflow in fluvial ecosystems, hydrologic changes in urban streams pose plausible and potentially significant ecological risks that warrant evaluation, along with other recognized changes (e.g., water chemistry, physical habitat, riparian conditions). Although previous investigations have associated degradation in the biological condition of streams with urban development (Klein 1979; Wang et al. 2000; Morley and Karr 2002; Booth et al. 2004), streamflow patterns per se are seldom implicated as a primary cause of urban stream degradation. Failure to address the significant hydrologic changes in urban areas may limit the success of restoration efforts in rivers and streams.

"Urbanization" is not a single condition; instead, it is a collection of actions that lead to recognizable landscape forms and, in turn, to changes in stream conditions. No single change defines urbanization,

* Corresponding author: cpkonrad@usgs.gov

but the cumulative effect of human activities in urban basins profoundly influences streams and their biota. Karr and Yoder (2004) provide a conceptual framework for assessing biological degradation in which the human actions that constitute urbanization modify many aspects of stream ecosystems, which elicit biological responses (Figure 1). Among the many aspects of stream ecosystems modified by urbanization, changes in hydrologic regimes (i.e., the timing and rate of streamflow) and potential biological responses are the focus of this paper. The influence of hydrologic modification, however, is likely to depend on a broader ecological context, and so the importance of hydrologic modification is likely to vary from stream to stream and region to region.

We focus on hydrology as a primary link between urban development and biological responses in urban streams because of the well-established influence of streamflow on the structure, composition, and productivity of lotic communities. In this paper, we briefly review the literature on relations between streamflow patterns and lotic communities to identify the types of streamflow patterns that have demonstrable effects on stream biota. We then extend the results of two

investigations, Poff and Allan (1995) and Clausen and Biggs (1997), that associated variation of biological assemblages with variation in a variety of streamflow statistics. Our extended analyses identify the magnitude of variation in four streamflow patterns (high flow frequency, flow distribution, daily variation, and low flow magnitude) that was associated with biological differences within their respective groups of streams. The magnitude of hydrologic variation associated with biological differences establishes the scale of ecological significance for assessing changes in each streamflow pattern. We then analyze long-term streamflow records from eight urban streams and five reference streams in the United States, where land use has been relatively stable, to identify streamflow patterns that changed in association with urban development. Finally, we discuss our results in the context of managing urban streams.

Hydrologic Effects of Urban Development

Hydrologic effects of urbanization can be characterized as the redistribution of water once intercepted by

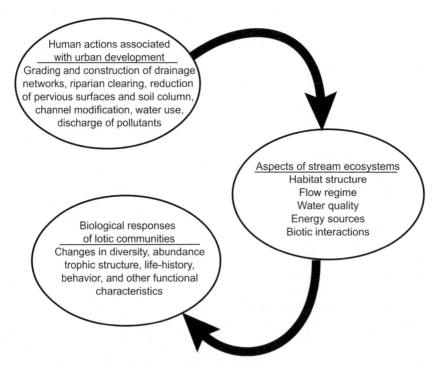

FIGURE 1. Urban development represents many distinct human actions that affect each of five major aspects of stream ecosystems. Changes in the ecosystem, in turn, elicit biological responses (modified from Karr and Yoder 2004).

vegetation or stored in the soil column, from which it drained slowly into streams or aquifers or was taken up by vegetation and transpired. Following development, this water runs off impervious surfaces or saturates thin soils and then runs off as overland flow. Drainage networks collect runoff and allow it to flow quickly as open-channel flow to receiving water bodies, greatly reducing the length of subsurface or overland flow paths. Aquifer recharge and evapotranspiration may be reduced. The hydrologic effects of urban development were evident in a comparison of runoff from two headwater catchments in western Washington (Burges et al. 1998). Novelty is a 37-ha, forested catchment. Klahanie is a 17-ha catchment with residential land use. Although much of the landscape in Klahanie is "pervious" lawn, the thin soils are quickly saturated during storms producing runoff patterns distinct from Novelty, including higher peak unit-area discharge, higher runoff volume, and more frequent peaks (Figure 2).

Changes in runoff patterns resulting from urban development manifest in streams as an increase in storm flow rates and volumes and a corresponding reduction in recessional flow and base flow rates and volumes (Leopold 1968; Konrad 2003a). There are also higher-order hydrologic effects of urban development: streamflow rises more rapidly during storms and recedes more rapidly after storms, which is typically described as "flashy" streamflow. Storm flow is more frequent and the seasonal period for storm flow may lengthen as storms produce higher streamflow in urban areas, even when antecedent conditions are dry. Because runoff is redistributed from base flow periods to storm flow periods, the total water balance and, thus, central measures of streamflow distributions such as annual mean streamflow may not change in response to urban development (Konrad and Booth 2002). The water balance for a stream basin may change when changes in vegetation alter interception of precipitation and evapotranspiration, surface or groundwater is used consumptively, or water is imported into a basin for irrigation.

Base flow changes less consistently in response to urban development. Annual base flow volume for two streams draining sewered areas of Long Island, New York was reduced from more than 60% to approximately 20% during urban development (Simmons and Reynolds 1982). Unit-area base flow during the wet season in western Washington streams clearly decreases with increasing road density, in contrast to unit-area base flow during the dry season (Figure 3). Minimum annual 7-d streamflow, however, did not change consistently in response to urban development in western Washington (Konrad and Booth 2002). Thus, urban development appears to reduce shallow subsurface flow that supports wet-season base flow but has a less evident effect on deeper groundwater recharge that supports summertime discharges.

Low flow in urban streams can increase as a result

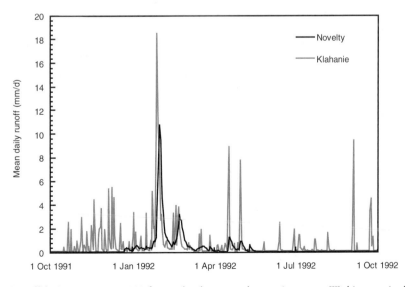

FIGURE 2. Runoff during water year 1992 for two headwater catchments in western Washington. At the time of data collection, Novelty was a fully forested 37-ha catchment; Klahanie was a fully built-out 17-ha residential catchment.

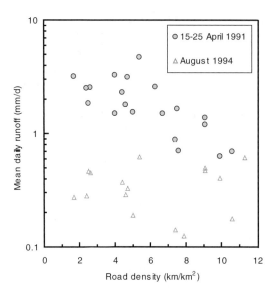

FIGURE 3. A comparison of mean unit-area base flow in the wet season and dry season for 21 streams in western Washington.

of imported water used for landscape irrigation that subsequently drains through shallow soil layers and aquifers (Harris and Rantz 1964) or used in residences with on-site septic systems. In contrast, decreases in low flow occur from increased surface drainage (storm sewers and ditches), surface water diversions, and pumping shallow groundwater. For example, annual minimum streamflow in Big Soos Creek in Washington have declined significantly in response to residential development and water use in the basin over the past few decades, while no such trends are evident in nearby rural streams (Konrad and Booth 2002).

In headwater ephemeral streams, periods of continuous flow are likely to be briefer with frequent intermittency (Figure 2). For example, during the period from water year (WY) 1991–1993, there was an average of 24 periods of flow intermittency per year in the residential Klahanie catchment, including periods of no flow during spring, compared to five times per year for the forested Novelty catchment. This difference is not reflected by the percentage of days with flow in these streams, which was 62% of the 3-year period in Klahanie compared to 54% in Novelty.

Given the magnitude of hydrologic changes resulting from urban development, urban streamflow patterns are likely to affect the biological conditions of streams, although these patterns frequently have been

quantified in ways that are not directly relevant to their ecological effects but, instead, represent only their social impacts. Few studies definitively make the link between hydrologic alteration and biological responses in urban streams, in part because urban development affects nearly all aspects of fluvial ecosystems. Orser and Shure (1972) documented lower population densities of dusky salamander *Desmognathus fuscus fuscus* with increasing levels of urban development for five streams near Atlanta, Georgia. They indicated that floods had likely transported individuals downstream, reducing salamander populations and creating unstable age structures. In 27 streams in Maryland, Klein (1979) found an association between biological conditions (macroinvertebrate diversity and fish taxa) and the percent of watershed imperviousness, which in turn was linked to unit-area base flow. Likewise, an index of the diversity and structure of macroinvertebrate assemblages was correlated with streamflow patterns in western Washington streams (Booth et al. in press). As in any study of urban streams, however, many other factors, including channel morphology, streambed material, nutrients, migration barriers, water temperature, and water chemistry, are likely to have influenced the biological conditions of these urban streams.

Biological Variation Associated with Streamflow Patterns

Although the biological effects of streamflow modification are difficult to isolate because of other changes in urban streams, many ecological investigations have documented how the rate, timing, and sources of streamflow affect the structure, composition, and productivity of lotic assemblages by regulating habitat conditions, availability of food sources, or natural disturbance regimes (Shelford and Eddy 1929; Horwitz 1978; Fisher et al. 1982; Schlosser 1985; Newbury 1988; Power et al. 1988; Resh et al. 1988; Townsend 1989; Power et al. 1999). Physical characteristics of water (e.g., velocity, depth, temperature, turbidity, and nutrient availability) and geomorphic features of the channel (e.g., width, bank height, and bed material) depend on streamflow. These characteristics and features define habitat units that compose the physical template for stream ecosystems in which distinct hydraulic conditions and substrates favor specific types of organisms or provide refugia during disturbance (Stehr and Branson 1938; Minshall 1984, 1988; Statzner and Higler 1986; Statzner et al. 1988; Townsend 1989; Townsend et al. 1997). The area, volume, and diversity of habitats generally increase with streamflow, which may account for the increasing diversity and productivity of lotic assemblages in larger streams and rivers (Harrel et al. 1967; Platts 1979; Allan 1995; Fairchild et al. 1998; Wiberg-Larsen et al. 2000). Hydrologic variability generally decreases with increasing stream size, which promotes habitat stability and may also promote increased diversity of lotic assemblages with stream size (Horwitz 1978). A relatively uniform distribution of streamflow is generally associated with relatively high groundwater inflow, which produces more stable seasonal temperatures, less ice cover in cold regions, higher dissolved oxygen during summer, and stable habitat volume (Power et al. 1999).

Disturbances in the form of high flows or hydrologic droughts (i.e., streamflow very low or absent) reduce periphyton biomass, macrophyte and fish populations, and the diversity of lotic assemblages (Stehr and Branson 1938; Douglas 1958; Anderson and Lehmkuhl 1968; Fisher et al. 1982; McAuliffe 1984; Schlosser 1985; Erman et al. 1988; McElravy et al. 1989; McCormick and Stevenson 1991; Boulton et al. 1992; Bayley and Osborne 1993; Closs and Lake 1994; Dieterich and Anderson 1995; Wootton et al. 1996). High flows, in particular, have a direct effect on stream biota by scouring streambeds, killing organisms or transporting them downstream. High flows also modify the trophic structure of streams by transporting dissolved nutrients and particulate organic material (Biggs and Close 1989; Anderson and Lehmkuhl 1968) or by selecting for benthic insects with traits (e.g., morphology) that affect their suitability as fish prey (Wootton et al. 1996; Perry et al. 2003). Lotic communities quickly recover after an individual flood or period of no flow (Shelford and Eddy 1929; Stehr and Branson 1938; Fisher et al. 1982; Power and Stewart 1987; Scrimgeour and Winter-bourn 1989; DeBrey and Lockwood 1990; Boulton et al. 1992; Bayley and Osborne 1993; Jones et al. 1995); however, rivers and streams with frequent high flows or no-flow periods have relatively simple trophic structure, low taxonomic diversity, and high dominance by a few taxa (Gorman and Karr 1978; Schlosser 1985; White and Pickett 1985; Robinson and Minshall 1986; Power and Stewart 1987; Death and Winter-bourn 1995; Rabeni and Wallace 1998). While periodic disturbance is readily accommodated in river and stream ecosystems without degrading biological productivity, diversity, or structure, frequent disturbances may have persistent biological effects.

The biological influence of disturbance is complex; it depends on the biological attribute or organism of interest and is mediated by the ecological context at a site. For example, the lack of disturbance can allow a few taxa to dominate an assemblage (Connell 1978; McAuliffe 1984; Wootton et al. 1996), as can a high frequency of disturbance. Different attributes of lotic communities do not respond consistently to disturbance. In an investigation of 11 streams in New Zealand, Death and Winterbourn (1995) found the density of invertebrate species and species richness increased with site stability, but species evenness peaked at sites with intermediate stability. The biological effects of high flows also depend on seasonal timing in relation to the life histories of aquatic organisms (Bickerton 1995; Dieterich and Anderson 1995).

The relative magnitude of streamflow is an important component of the ecological context. To account for differences in stream size in ecological investigations, high flows are often assessed with respect to the mean or median flow (Horwitz 1978; Poff and Ward 1989; Clausen and Biggs 1997). Nonhydrologic factors such as habitat diversity (Gorman and Karr 1978; Gurtz and Wallace 1984; Townsend et al. 1997) and biotic interactions (McAuliffe 1984; Feminella and Resh 1990; McCormick and Stevenson 1991; Wootton et al. 1996) also help form the broad ecological context that mediates effects of single extreme streamflow events on stream biota. Thus, the specific biological responses to changes in streamflow patterns are difficult to assess without information about the biological feature of interest and the other components of the ecosystem. Nonetheless, investigations of groups of streams representing a range of biological and physical conditions provide evidence of systematic biological responses to streamflow patterns.

Previous investigations have provided frameworks for ecological analyses of streamflow patterns. Poff and Ward (1989) developed a classification system of regional hydrologic regime. Their conceptual model included a hierarchy of four flow characteristics: duration of intermittency, high flow frequency, high flow predictability, and overall flow variability. Richter et al. (1996) assessed flow alteration of regulated rivers in terms of five characteristics of flow: magnitude, duration, frequency, timing, and rate of change. Clausen and Biggs (2000) used principal component analysis to identify four distinct categories of streamflow statistics for New Zealand streams: central tendency (stream size), flow variability, volume of high flows, and frequency of high-flow events. Clausen and Biggs (2000) did not include any statistics for the timing of flows or rate of change. Each of these frameworks include streamflow statistics that are likely to be modified by urban development. Unlike the effects of regulation by a dam or other control structure, the hydrologic consequences of urban development are incremental. Streamflow patterns are produced by runoff processes, not by controlled releases through penstocks and spillways. As a result, urban streamflow does not necessarily have clearly artificial patterns such as truncated peaks, stepped ramping of flows, or high frequency (diurnal) fluctuations. Instead, urban development causes broad changes in the rate and timing of runoff that should be evident from a limited set of streamflow statistics representing ecologically significant streamflow patterns.

Ecologically Significant Variation in Streamflow Patterns

Comparative analyses of rivers and streams provide evidence for the strongest associations between streamflow patterns and biological conditions, though not necessarily the causative mechanisms. Two studies—Poff and Allan (1995) and Clausen and Biggs (1997)—are reviewed to define ranges of streamflow variables associated with attributes of lotic assemblages. These studies did not attribute streamflow patterns to differences in land use, though it is likely that land use had an influence in some basins. Instead, they examined rivers and streams from wide geographic regions where various physiographic factors such as drainage area, climate, and geology produced different streamflow patterns.

We assume that natural physiographic factors produce differences in streamflow among the Poff and Allan (1995) and Clausen and Biggs (1997) streams comparable to the hydrologic changes resulting from urban development. Thus, these streams provide a natural correlate of an urban gradient to assess the biological response to differences in streamflow (e.g., streamflow is typically flashier in smaller streams than in large rivers). This approach avoids the covarying and, thus, confounding effects from water quality, channel form, and riparian zones that also vary with streamflow patterns across an urban gradient. Hydrologic changes in urban streams, however, may not be strictly analogous to hydrologic differences between streams. In urban streams, hydrologic changes occur over decadal time scales, so species do not have the time to evolve to modified streamflow regimes that they have had in natural systems. Thus, the biological response to changes in

streamflow patterns over decades in a stream may be greater than the biological variation between streams that have long standing natural differences in streamflow pattern.

Poff and Allan (1995) analyzed relations between four streamflow statistics and fish assemblages at 34 sites in rivers in Wisconsin and Minnesota. Streamflow statistics were calculated from records collected over various time periods spanning at least 20 years. Two functional groups of fish were identified based on species presence/absence at the sites. Canonical discriminant analysis was used to identify hydrologic characteristics of the sites associated with the two groups. A canonical variate composed of daily flow predictability, base flow stability, coefficient of variation (CV) of daily flows, and frequency of spates distinguished the two functional groups of fishes based on hydrologically variable or hydrologically stable sites. Daily flow predictability and base flow stability were significantly different ($P < 0.05$, Wilcoxon rank-sum test) between the two groups of sites, but the CV of daily flows and frequency of daily flow with a 1.67-year return interval were not (Table 1). A comparison of species traits for the two functional groups indicated that the hydrologically variable group had more trophic and habitat generalists tolerant of silt than the hydrologically stable group.

Clausen and Biggs (1997) analyzed relations between 34 streamflow statistics and benthic (periphyton and invertebrate) assemblages in 83 rivers in New Zealand. Streamflow statistics were calculated from contemporaneous records spanning 1–7-year periods. They found that periphyton biomass was inversely related to mean flow, median flow, and the frequency of high flows (daily streamflow equal to or greater than three times the median daily streamflow). Periphyton biomass was directly related to 90th-percentile flow. Periphyton species richness was inversely related to flood volume/base flow volume, frequency of high flows, and the product of frequency and duration of high flow. Periphyton species diversity was related to high flow and variation (CV) statistics but not to central-tendency or low-flow statistics. Invertebrate density and richness were inversely related to mean, median, and low flows and directly related to flow variability and the frequency of high flows. The frequency of high flows provided the single most useful measure to account for the variation in measures of benthic assemblages among the rivers.

Clausen and Biggs (1997) proposed that flood disturbance (scour, deposition, abrasion of bed mate-

TABLE 1. Median values of streamflow statistics for 34 sites in Wisconsin and Minnesotta classified by Poff and Allan (1995) as hydrologically stable or hydrologically variable based on fish assemblages.

Streamflow statistics	Sites with hydrologically stable fish assemblage	Sites with hydrologically variable fish assemblages
Frequency of daily flow with 1.67 year return interval	0.69	0.77
Daily coefficient of variation	1.3	1.9
Daily flow predictability[a]	70	46
Baseflow stability[a]	0.36	0.05
Annual frequency of flows > 10th percentile[a]	4.9	6.0
Annual frequency of flows > three times median flow[a]	3.9	6.5
T_{Qmean} (fraction of time that flow exceeds mean flow)	0.26	0.25
CV (LN transformed data)[a, b]	0.7	2.1
Median daily percent change in streamflow[a]	5%	7%
90th percentile flow/median flow[a]	0.52	0.21

[a] Values were significantly different between the two groups ($P < 0.05$, two-tailed Wilcoxon rank sum test).
[b] Coefficient of variation of natural log transformed daily flows.

rial) and relative flow stability were the dominant hydrologic mechanisms affecting the benthic assemblages. They also found that mean and median flows were negatively correlated with periphyton and invertebrate density and invertebrate richness because of decreasing bed stability and heterogeneity of bed material with stream size. Thus, the biological influence of stream size was not solely hydrologic but instead also depended on sediment supply and the size of structural features (wood, cobbles, valley width) relative to the stream channel.

Clausen and Biggs (2000) also suggested additional reasons for lower density and richness of benthic assemblages in larger rivers. These include lower velocity, lower gradient, finer bed material, reduced allochothonous inputs, and increased light availability. Inorganic nitrogen and phosphorous concentrations were also negatively correlated with specific yield (a measure of stream size) and high flow magnitude, and were likely to control autotrophic production between high flows. None of these reasons for a biological response are solely a function of streamflow patterns.

Four types of streamflow patterns examined by Poff and Allan (1995) and Clausen and Biggs (1997) were thus associated with variation of fish and benthic assemblages: high flow frequency, streamflow distribution, daily variation, and low flow magnitude (Table 2). The biological response of lotic assemblages to variation in each of these patterns has a mechanistic basis. Increased high flow frequency could result in shorter periods between disturbances and increased seasonal periods with episodic high flows. Change in high flow

frequency is particularly an issue in regions where the reproduction and growth cycles of aquatic and benthic organisms are tied to stable flow periods. The likelihood and spatial extent of bed disturbance increase with storm flow frequency (Konrad et al. 2002). The distribution of streamflow, as characterized by its central tendency (i.e., mean or median) provides a gross indication of the amount (volume and area) of habitat available to aquatic organisms. Measures of variability provide information on habitat heterogeneity over time. Stream ecosystems where storm flow, rather than base flow, constitutes much of the total distribution of streamflow will have short periods when hydraulic conditions, nutrient transport, and amount of habitat are at high levels (though not necessarily optimal) and extended periods of time when these conditions and processes are at low levels. Movement of nutrients and particulate organic material is also likely to be skewed to short periods of rapid transport and limited retention. Increased daily variation in flow may reduce the time that a given location is suitable habitat for an organism and cause the organism to expend energy moving to suitable locations. Reduced low flows can reduce the area of benthic habitat and volume of aquatic habitat, leading to lower population sizes and diversity in lotic communities.

Methods for Assessing Hydrologic Changes in Urban Streams

We examine the effects of urban development on the four types of streamflow patterns (high flow frequency,

TABLE 2. Streamflow patterns with biological responses to variation, statistics, and ranges of values for streams in each source. Statistics in italics were analyzed in this chapter for selected reference and urban streams.

Biological responses to variable:	High-flow frequency statistics	Range of values
Variation in high-flow frequency		
Dominance of trophic and habitat generalists in fish assemblages, lower periphyton density and diversity with increasing high flow frequency.	*Frequency of daily flows that exceeded three times median flow*	0 to 34 events per year[b]
		1.1 to 10 events per year[c]
	Frequency of events greater than 10th percentile flow	2.4 to 10 events per year[c]
	Frequency of daily flow corresponding to annual peak flow with 1.67 return interval	0.4 to 1.1 events per year[a]
Variation in streamflow distribution		
Dominance of trophic and habitat specialists in fish assemblages with increasing mean or median flows; lower periphyton density, richness, and diversity with increasing mean and median flows or increasing stormflow relative to baseflow; lower invertebrate density and richness with increasing mean or median flow or increasing stormflow to baseflow.	*Mean streamflow*	0.4 to 520 m^3/s[b]
		0.6 to 37 m^3/s[c]
	Median daily streamflow	0.3 to 468 m^3/s[c]
		0.1 to 30 m^3/s[c]
	T_{Qmean}	0.17 to 0.37[c]
	Flood flow index	0.03 to 2.8[b]
Variation in daily streamflow		
Dominance of trophic and habitat generalists in fish assemblages, lower periphyton diversity, lower invertebrate density and evenness with increasing daily variation.	*Coefficient of variation of logarithms of daily streamflow*	0.4 to 27[c]
	Median daily percent change	3% to 12%[c]
	Coefficient of variation	0.4 to 3.2[a]
		0.09 to 3.7[b]
Variation in low flow		
Dominance of trophic and habitat specialists in fish assemblages, higher periphyton and invertebrate density with increasing low flow	*90th percentile flow*	0 to 20.4 m^3/s[c]
	90th percentile flow/median daily flow	0.17 to 0.98[b]
		0 to 0.72[c]
	Baseflow stability	0 to 0.6[a]

Sources: [a] Poff and Allan (1995), [b] Clausen and Biggs (1997), [c] reanalysis of sites examined by Poff and Allan (1995).

streamflow distribution, daily variation, low flow/flow intermittency) in 13 streams in the United States that have streamflow records of at least 30 years (Table 3). Five streams are part of the U.S. Geological Survey (USGS) Hydrologic Benchmark Network (HBN), which represents reference streams relatively unaffected by local land uses, and eight urban streams were in counties with population densities greater than 200 people/km^2 in 2000 (Figure 4).

A host of streamflow statistics can be used to demonstrate the hydrologic effects of urbanization and their relations to stream biota, but many streamflow statistics are correlated with each other because they represent the same underlying streamflow pattern. For our analysis, we selected nine statistics representing four distinct streamflow patterns (Table 2) to assess which statistics consistently change in response to urban development while remaining stationary in reference streams. Annual values of the streamflow statistics were analyzed for changes in urban streams between WY 1957–1968 and WY 1991–2000 using the Wilcoxon rank-sum test, with rejection of the null hypothesis when $P < 0.05$. For the urban streams, the specific direction of change was hypothesized for each parameter except mean, median, and low-flow statistics. The hypotheses are described below and allow a one-tailed test (i.e., reject the null hypotheses for no change or a change in the opposite direction). Two-

TABLE 3. Selected Hydrologic Benchmark Network stations and urban streams with U.S. Geological Survey station number, county and state, and drainage area.

Stream	Station number	County and state	Drainage area
Hydrologic Benchmark Network			
Elder Creek	11475560	Mendicino, CA	17 km^2
Holiday Creek	02038850	Appomattox, VA	22 km^2
Andrews Creek	12447390	Okanogan, WA	57 km^2
Mogollon Creek	09430600	Grant, NM	177 km^2
Popple River	04063700	Florence, WI	356 km^2
Urban			
Valley Stream	01311500	Nassau, NY	12 km^2
Mercer Creek	12120000	King, WA	31 km^2
Poplar Creek	05550500	Cook, IL	90 km^2
San Francisquito Creek	11164500	Santa Clara, CA	96 km^2
Morrison Creek	11336580	Sacramento, CA	137 km^2
Northeast Branch Anacostia River	01649500	Prince George's, MD	186 km^2
Peachtree Creek	02336300	Fulton, GA	222 km^2
Salt Creek	05531500	Cook, IL	294 km^2

tailed tests were used for mean streamflow, median streamflow and the two low-flow statistics because we did not have specific hypotheses regarding the direction of change for these statistics

Streamflow records for most HBN sites began later than the urban streams, so statistics for WY 1969–1978 were compared to statistics for WY 1991–2000 for the HBN sites. For the HBN sites, periods were compared with a two-tailed Wilcoxon rank-sum test. The null hypothesis (no change over time) was rejected when $P < 0.10$ for the HBN streams to increase the power of the test to detect changes in each statistic. By reducing the likelihood of false rejection of the null hypothesis for the HBN sites, there is greater certainty for concluding that a statistic is relatively stationary despite decadal-scale variation in weather patterns.

Streamflow data available for the period of analysis include annual maxima and daily mean streamflows. Daily mean streamflow does not capture the variability of urban streamflow, which can rise and fall rapidly during an hour or two. Thus, hydrologic measures based on daily streamflow underrep-resent the hydrologic changes associated with urban development and their biological consequences. Nonetheless, these data are consistent with those used by Clausen and Biggs (1997) and Poff and Allan (1995).

Frequency of High-Flow Events

Urban development was expected to increase the volume and peak rate of runoff from storms, which re-sults in increased flood magnitude and frequency. Various approaches account for the relative magnitude of a flood in a particular stream, including scaling the flow by drainage area or channel width, converting the discharge to a depth and assessing it relative to bankfull depth, or using a reference discharge as a threshold for identifying a high flow. Clausen and Biggs (1997, 2000) selected a discharge three times the median streamflow as a threshold for defining "high" flows because of its association with variation in benthic assemblages.

In our reanalysis of streamflow data from sites examined by Poff and Allan (1995), the frequency of events greater than three times the median flow was significantly different between the hydrologically variable and hydrologically stable sites (Table 1). Poff and Allan (1995) used the daily discharge on the day when there was a peak discharge with a 1.67-year recurrence interval as the threshold for high flows because it referenced a significant, but not rare, disturbance to the fish assemblage. Although such an event may represent a disturbance, it does not provide much resolution between streams insofar as the annual frequency of a given streamflow is related to its recurrence interval. Indeed, the frequency of high flows was not significantly different between hydrologically stable and hydrologically variable sites using this frequency-based threshold (Table 1).

The cumulative exceedence distribution of streamflow (flow-duration curve) provides a mechanistic basis for selecting a geomorphically effective flow (Wolman and Miller 1960) capable of disturb-

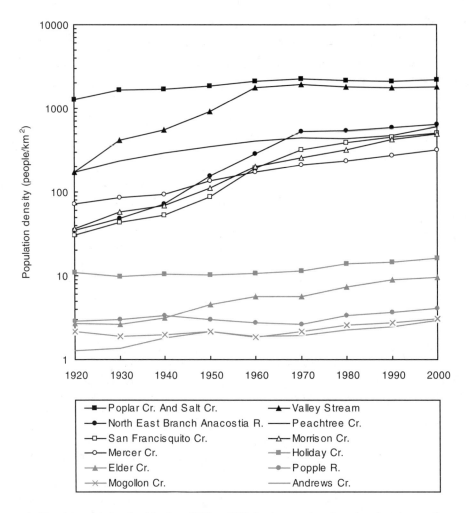

FIGURE 4. Decadal population densities from 1920 to 2000 for the counties where the selected streamflow gauges are located. Refer to Table 3 for stream locations. Data from the U.S. Census Bureau (2004).

ing a streambed. The 5th- to 10th-percentile flows represent an approximate threshold of streambed stability for many river channels (e.g., Helley 1969; Milhous 1973; Pickup and Warner 1976; Andrews 1984; Sidle 1988; Carling 1988; Konrad et al. 2002). The 5th- or 10th-percentile flows are very highly correlated; for simplicity, we use the 10th-percentile flow as the high flow threshold. When high flow frequency was reanalyzed at the sites investigated by Poff and Allan (1995), hydrologically variable sites had more frequent high-flow events than hydrologically stable sites (Table 1). Changes in the frequency of high-flow events in the urban and HBN streams were analyzed using as thresholds both the 10th-percentile streamflow and three times the median streamflow.

Flow Distribution

We did not expect central measures of streamflow distribution to change consistently in response to urban development, but both annual mean and annual median flows were tested for changes between the urban and reference streams because of the associations of these measures with characteristics of fish and benthic assemblages, and with habitat area/volume and streamflow. Streamflow was expected to be redistributed from base flow periods to storm flow periods in response to urban development. Clausen and Biggs (1997) used the ratio of flood-flow volume to base flow volume as a "flood-flow index" (FFI). However, the flood-flow index requires a stream-specific specification of base flow for each stream and reference changes in streamflow volume. These data were not available for the streams we analyzed.

As an alternative measure of the distribution of streamflow, we analyzed the fraction of time that streamflow exceeds mean streamflow (T_{Qmean}) in the urban and reference streams. T_{Qmean} provides a relative measure of the distribution of storm flow and base flow comparable to the flood-flow index, but it is based on the duration rather than the volume of streamflow. In response to urban development, T_{Qmean} is expected to decrease because there is a shorter period of the year when streamflow is greater than mean streamflow (Konrad and Booth 2002).

In the reanalysis of the Poff and Allan (1995) sites, T_{Qmean} was not significantly different between the hydrologically variable and hydrologically stable sites (Table 1). Four sites with hydrologically variable fish assemblages were associated with hydrologic stability (higher T_{Qmean}) possibly because of either low base flow stability or a short spate-free period. When these sites were excluded from the analysis, T_{Qmean} was significantly lower ($P = 0.02$, Wilcoxon rank-sum test) for the hydrologically variable group (median = 0.22), than the hydrologically stable group (median = 0.26). Annual values of T_{Qmean} were tested to assess whether there was a significant redistribution of streamflow from base flow to storm flow in urban streams and whether the distribution of streamflow between base flow and storm flow was relatively stationary year to year in the reference streams.

Daily Variation of Streamflow

Daily variation of streamflow was analyzed to represent variability, distinct from high-flow disturbances and the gross distribution of storm flow and base flow. Two statistics describing daily variation were examined: the CV of the logarithms of daily streamflow and the percentage daily change in streamflow. The values of both variability statistics were expected to increase in response to urban development. The logarithmic transformation reduced the sensitivity of CV to high flows (Stedinger et al. 1993). Because of zero values, 1 m³/s was added to each streamflow value before taking the logarithm.

Although the CV of untransformed daily streamflow was not significantly different between the hydrologically variable and hydrologically stable sites analyzed by Poff and Allan (1995), a reanalysis of these sites showed significantly higher values of CV of

log-transformed streamflow for hydrologically variable sites (median = 2.1) compared to hydrologically stable sites (median = 0.7) (Table 1). The CV of log transformed daily streamflow was included in the analysis of urban and reference streams to represent routine variation in hydraulic conditions.

The absolute value of the relative change in daily streamflow, $|Q_d - Q_{d-1}|/Q_d$, where Q_d is daily discharge for day d (expressed as the daily percent change in daily flow), was used as an alternative measure of daily flow variability. This statistic weights the relative changes in high flows and low flows equally and, thus, is less sensitive to changes in high flows than is CV. In a reanalysis of the sites in Poff and Allan (1995), the median daily percentage change in streamflow was significantly higher at hydrologically variable sites (median = 7%) compared to hydrologically stable sites (median = 5%) (Table 1).

Low Flow Magnitude

As noted earlier, low flows are not consistently affected by urban development, but we assessed changes in low flows because of their ecological significance. Two low-flow statistics were tested for significant changes over time in the HBN and urban streams: 90th-percentile flow and 90th-percentile flow divided by median streamflow. The 90th-percentile flow provides an absolute measure of streamflow during relatively common low-flow periods but does not account for extremely low flows. The 90th-percentile flow divided by the median flow, from Clausen and Biggs (1997), provides a relative measure that should be less sensitive to annual variation in low flows. In our reanalysis of the Poff and Allan (1995) sites, the values of 90th-percentile flow divided by the median flow were significantly lower at hydrologically variable sites (median = 0.21) compared to hydrologically stable sites (median = 0.52) (Table 1).

Temporal Changes in Streamflow Patterns at Urban and Reference Streams

High Flow Frequency

The frequency of high flows increased from 1958–1967 to 1991–2000 in most of the urban streams, but not in any of the HBN streams (Table 4). The frequency of events greater than the 10th-percentile flow increased in four of the urban streams, while the frequency of events greater than three times the me-

TABLE 4. Median annual frequency of high-flow events.

	Frequency of events exceeding the 10th-percentile flow (events per year)		Frequency of events exceeding the three times median (events per year)	
Stream	Period 1[a]	Period 2[b]	Period 1[a]	Period 2[b]
Hydrologic Benchmark Network				
Elder Cr.	10	9	7	9
Holiday Cr.	20	22	20	22
Andrews Cr.	3	3	2	4
Mogollon Cr.	6	10	12	15
Popple R.	5	8	7	11
Urban				
Valley Stream	26	30	25	42[c]
Mercer Cr.	18	27[c]	19	32[c]
Poplar Cr.	9	19[c]	14	26[c]
San Francisquito Cr.	7	10	15	10
Morrison Cr.	12	17	12	23[c]
Northeast Branch Anacostia R.	25	34[c]	28	41[c]
Peachtree Cr.	27	33	36	48[c]
Salt Cr.	13	19[c]	20	24

[a] Period 1 is 1969 to 1978 for Hydrologic Benchmark Network streams and 1958 to 1967 for urban streams.
[b] Period 2 is 1991 to 2000.
[c] Probability < 0.05 that frequency is the same for both periods or lower in period 2 based on a one-tailed Wilcoxon rank-sum test.

dian flow increased in six of the urban streams. Only one urban stream, San Francisquito Creek in central California, did not have a significant increase in either high-flow statistic. Streamflow in San Francisquito Creek was intermittent and the high flow regime is likely to reflect storm patterns driven by decadal-scale oscillations in ocean conditions. In this case, it appears that the frequency of events greater than the 10th-percentile flow may be less sensitive to climatic conditions than the frequency of events greater than three times the median flow.

Both of these statistics represent relatively common high-flow events with median annual values for 1991–2000 ranging from 10 to 48 events per year for urban streams and from 3 to 22 events in the HBN streams. The frequency of events greater than the 10th-percentile flow was higher in the urban streams than the streams analyzed by Poff and Allan (1995) (2.4–10.3 events per year) and, thus, all represent hydrologically variable streams by their criterion even during the earlier period from 1958 to 1967. Likewise, the change in the frequency of events exceeding three times the median flow in the urban streams was outside the range for the streams examined by Poff and Allan (1995) (1.1–10 events per

year) but spanned part of the range found by Clausen and Biggs (1997) (0–34 events per year) (Table 2).

Streamflow Distribution

The distribution of streamflow changed between 1958–1967 and 1991–2000 in many of the urban streams but not between 1969 and 1978 and 1991–2000 in the HBN streams. Mean streamflow increased significantly between 1958–1967 and 1991–2000 in two urban streams (Table 5). The increases in mean and median streamflow, however, were much less than the three to four order-of-magnitude ranges associated with responses in either fish or benthic assemblages (Table 2).

The redistribution of runoff from base flow to storm flow periods resulted in significant decreases in T_{Qmean} from 1958–1967 to 1991–2000 in three urban streams. In Valley Stream, Long Island, T_{Qmean}, decreased from 0.24 for 1958–1967 to 0.15 for 1991–2000 (Table 5). The decrease in T_{Qmean} corresponded to redistribution of annual streamflow volume from more than 60% base flow (FFI = 0.67) prior to 1960 to less than 20% base flow (FFI = 4) after 1966 (Simmons and Reynolds 1982). The urban streams without significant changes in T_{Qmean} had

TMABLE 5. Median annual values of streamflow distribution statistics.

Stream	Mean daily streamflow (m³/s)		Median daily streamflow (m³/s)		Fraction of time mean streamflow is exceeded	
	Period 1[a]	Period 2[b]	Period 1[a]	Period 2[b]	Period 1[a]	Period 2[b]
Hydrologic Benchmark Network						
Elder Cr.	0.85	0.85	0.19	0.20	0.25	0.25
Holiday Cr.	0.28	0.25	0.17	0.19	0.23	0.28
Andrews Cr.	0.91	1.07	0.15	0.18	0.20	0.22
Mogollon Cr.	0.32	0.98	0.10	0.41	0.29	0.30
Popple R.	3.30	3.07	1.95	2.05	0.28	0.31
Urban						
Valley Stream	0.07	0.04	0.04	0.01	0.24	0.15[d]
Mercer Cr.	0.57	0.64	0.37	0.40	0.33	0.26[d]
Poplar Cr.	0.57	0.83[c]	0.21	0.44[c]	0.26	0.28
San Francisquito Cr.	0.18	0.91	0.00	0.06	0.15	0.16
Morrison Cr.	0.40	0.78	0.17	0.15	0.14	0.15
Northeast Branch Anacostia R.	2.03	2.79	1.08	1.33	0.24	0.21[d]
Peachtree Cr.	3.40	4.11	1.67	1.66	0.20	0.20
Salt Cr.	2.75	5.03[c]	1.29	3.04[c]	0.27	0.28

[a] Period 1 is 1969 to 1978 for Hydrologic Benchmark Network streams and 1958 to 1967 for urban streams.
[b] Period 2 is 1991 to 2000.
[c] Probability < 0.05 that value was the same for both periods based on a two-tailed Wilcoxon rank-sum test.
[d] Probability < 0.05 that value was the same for both periods or higher for period 2 based on a one-tailed Wilcoxon rank-sum test.

low values (0.2 or lower) during the initial period of the analysis or had significant increases in base flow (Salt and Poplar Creeks). The changes in T_{Qmean} spanned much of the total range of values (0.17–0.37) from the reanalysis of streams examined by Poff and Allan (1995) (Table 3). Thus, the redistribution of runoff from base flow to storm flow in many, but not all, urban streams is likely to be ecologically significant.

Daily Flow Variability

Daily flow variability increased in many urban streams from 1958–1967 to 1991–2000. Although the CV of the logarithm of daily flows increased in five urban streams (Table 6), the changes were significant in only three of the streams because of interannual variability. No differences between 1969–1978 and 1991–2000 were significant for the HBN streams.

The median daily percentage change in streamflow appeared to be more sensitive to urban development, increasing in five urban streams between 1958–1967 and 1991–2000 and generally having higher values in urban streams than in HBN streams (Table 6). One HBN stream had a significant increase in the median daily percentage change in streamflow, and one HBN stream had a significant decrease from 1969–1978 to 1991–2000. The median daily percentage change for urban streams was more variable (10–40%), than in the HBN streams (3–12%) or the reanalyzed streams of Poff and Allan (1995) (3–12%).

Low Flow

The 90th-percentile streamflow increased significantly in four of the urban streams from 1958–1967 to 1991–2000 and increased significantly one HBN stream from 1969–1978 to 1991–2000 (Table 7). Two of the urban streams had significant increases in 90th-percentile flow normalized by median discharge, but none of the HBN streams had significant changes (Table 7). The increase in low flow may be a result of many factors, including wastewater discharges, or uses of deep groundwater or water imported from other basins that contribute to base flow (e.g., landscape irrigation or septic system effluent). These changes in low flow were small relative to the range of value reported by Clausen and Biggs (1997) and for the reanalysis of the streams examined by Poff and Allan

TABLE 6. Median annual values of streamflow-variability statistics.

Stream	Daily percentage change in streamflow		Coefficient of variation of logarithms of daily streamflow	
	Period 1[a]	Period 2[b]	Period 1[a]	Period 2[b]
Hydrologic Benchmark Network				
Elder Cr.	6%	6%	1.72	1.62
Holiday Cr.	10%	10%	0.77	0.74
Andrews Cr.	4%	3%	1.36	1.25
Mogollon Cr.	10%	12%[c]	1.17	1.43
Popple R.	5%	5%	0.78	0.76
Urban				
Valley Stream	18%	40%[d]	0.71	0.74
Mercer Cr.	11%	15%[d]	0.80	0.80
Poplar Cr.	14%	19%[d]	1.19	1.17
San Francisquito Cr.	0%	10%	1.13	2.08
Morrison Cr.	11%	11%	0.82	1.12[d]
Northeast Branch Anacostia R.	15%	19%[d]	0.91	0.93
Peachtree Cr.	15%	21%[d]	0.90	0.98[d]
Salt Cr.	13%	12%	0.97	0.80[d]

[a] Period 1 is 1969 to 1978 for Hydrologic Benchmark Network streams and 1958 to 1967 for urban streams.
[b] Period 2 is 1991 to 2000.
[c] Probability < 0.10 that value was the same for both periods based on two-tailed Wilcoxon rank-sum test.
[d] Probability < 0.05 that value was the same for both periods or lower for period 2 based on a one-tailed Wilcoxon rank-sum test.

TABLE 7. Median annual values of low-flow statistics.

Stream	90th-percentile streamflow (m³/s)		90th-percentile streamflow/ median daily streamflow	
	Period 1[a]	Period 2[b]	Period 1[a]	Period 2[b]
Hydrologic Benchmark Network				
Elder Cr.	0.03	0.03	0.20	0.17
Holiday Cr.	0.07	0.08	0.41	0.51
Andrews Cr.	0.07	0.10[c]	0.45	0.55
Mogollon Cr.	0.01	0.02	0.09	0.09
Popple R.	1.06	1.13	0.54	0.58
Urban				
Valley Stream	0.01	0.00	0.16	0.00
Mercer Cr.	0.15	0.20[d]	0.40	0.54[d]
Poplar Cr.	0.03	0.06[d]	0.20	0.14
San Francisquito Cr.	0.00	0.01[d]	0.50	0.23
Morrison Cr.	0.10	0.10	0.65	0.62
Northeast Branch Anacostia R.	0.35	0.48	0.34	0.39
Peachtree Cr.	0.69	0.72	0.41	0.46
Salt Cr.	0.48	1.58[d]	0.40	0.50[d]

[a] Period 1 is 1969 to 1978 for Hydrologic Benchmark Network streams and 1958 to 1967 for urban streams.
[b] Period 2 is 1991 to 2000.
[c] Probability < 0.10 that the value was the same for both periods based on a two-tailed Wilcoxon rank-sum test.
[d] Probability < 0.05 that value was the same for both periods based on a two-tailed Wilcoxon rank-sum test.

(1995) (Table 2). Moreover, increases in low flow would likely promote biological responses opposite from the other hydrologic effects of urban development (Table 2).

Framework for Assessing the Ecological Effects of Urban Streamflow Patterns

Urban development modifies the basic hydrologic processes generating runoff in many river basins. In our analysis of eight urban streams, changes in some streamflow patterns were comparable to hydrologic variation associated with demonstrated differences in the structure and composition of lotic communities in other streams. Hydrologic changes in urban streams are likely to affect three streamflow characteristics with ecological consequences: high-flow frequency, distribution of water between storm flow and base flow, and daily flow variability. These changes may contribute to dominance of fishes representing trophic and habitat generalists and also to lower periphyton biomass, diversity, and richness.

Biological responses to urban streamflow patterns also depend on the larger physiographic setting (climate, sediment supply, and channel/valley geomorphology) and other urban stressors (habitat alteration, changes in water chemistry). For example, even though minimum flows were not lower in the urban streams considered here, water depths during low flow may be less in an urban stream if its channel has widened in response to increased high flows.

Effects of urban development are neither uniform nor invariant—naturally "flashy" systems in arid regions may not become much more flashy after urbanization. It is likely that hydrologic changes are greatest in small to intermediate-sized streams with naturally low seasonal and storm flow variability. Large rivers may be buffered because urban development does not cover the whole basin, precipitation may not fall over the whole basin during small storms, and channel routing and overbank storage may attenuate high flows. Poff and Allan (1995) noted that large streams may function like headwater streams if they are seasonally variable. Likewise, the lotic communities in urban streams may function like those in smaller and more hydrologically variable streams because of hydrologic modification.

In streams and rivers with hydrologic changes from urban development, those changes are not necessarily outside the bounds of "natural" variation in streamflow patterns as defined by all streams spanning the range from arid to humid climates. Likewise, variation in weather patterns produces a wide range of natural variation in streamflow regardless of land use. Both types of natural hydrologic variability make it difficult to attribute specific streamflow patterns to land-use changes and to assign specific ecological consequences to streamflow patterns, because lotic species are adapted to natural hydrologic variation. Only through the systematic assessment of a long-term record is it possible to identify those changes that are persistent in hydrologic effects and ecological consequences.

Management Responses to Hydrologic Modification in Urban Streams

Two management questions arise if hydrologic modification is acknowledged as a significant factor in the biological degradation of urban streams. First, are the hydrologic influences on urban streams limited to a few, identifiable mechanisms that could become objectives (or priorities) for mitigation through stormwater management? Second, given the difficulties in accomplishing hydrologic restoration, what is the best possible condition for urban streams under an urban streamflow regime and what marginal effects might result from managing other aspects of the ecosystem (e.g., water quality treatment, stream habitat, riparian zone)?

The varied nature of urban-induced hydrologic changes and the many ways in which aquatic biota interact with flow regime suggest that there are not one or two aspects of an altered hydrologic regime that cause biological consequences. The belief in "single-issue" hydrologic changes is reminiscent of past approaches to stormwater management, namely to achieve flood control by limiting peak discharges. The single-issue focus failed to protect biological systems, because single-storm peak discharge is not a hydrologic characteristic of particular significance to biota. Ironically, that focus has even failed to provide flood protection, because most analyses have not recognized the full range of urban-induced hydrologic changes, including redistribution of streamflow, increased daily variation of streamflow, sequential peak flow events (Booth et al. 2002), and extended flow durations that result in enhanced sediment transport and deposition (Booth 1990). Inspection of comparative hydrographs (e.g., Figure 2) reveals changes in all seasons, across multiple temporal scales, and at every level of discharge. Even if hydrologic changes are limited to the types identified by the analysis of long-term streamflow patterns, mitigation would require greatly increased storage capacity of stormwater management systems. Moreover, the predevelopment patterns of many streams could not be replicated by large detention ponds with simple control structures to release the water because they cannot support gradual, sustained recessional flows after storms.

The variety of hydrologic changes is symptomatic of an underlying cause, namely the pervasive loss of water storage capacity of hillslopes that accompanies urban development where it reduces vegetation, topographic depressions, soil depths, and infiltration capacity of the land surface. Ultimately, any true solution must account for each of these hydrologic changes. The classic mitigation approach, detention ponds, fails because (1) it replaces only a scant fraction of the storage capacity of hillslopes that was lost (Booth and Jackson 1997); (2) it converts what was once spatially distributed subsurface runoff into a point discharge at a surface water outfall; and (3) it reduces the rate and changes the location of groundwater recharge and subsequent discharge because even the largest detention ponds cannot delay the production of runoff from large or long storms in the same fashion as large areas of natural landscape with intact vegetation, topography, and soils. For these reasons, objective assessments of detention-pond performance are rarely encouraging (e.g., Maxted and Shaver 1999).

Directly addressing the loss of long-term storage of storm flow is more challenging and much less widely implemented. Two other traditional engineering approaches, infiltration ponds and bypass pipelines, provide plausible opportunities for hydrologic mitigation but are each constrained by site requirements. Infiltration ponds (i.e., centralized facilities to store and reintroduce stormwater into the groundwater system) require deep infiltrative geologic strata at or near the ground surface to accommodate the large volumes of runoff collected. In many areas. such geologic conditions are ubiquitous; in others, they are widely scattered or absent altogether. Bypass systems provide partial hydrologic mitigation at best— they reduce total postdevelopment runoff volume in noninfiltrative soils and can provide nearly fail-safe reductions of peak flows and/or flow durations. However, they can leave the plethora of small and moderate discharges from paved surfaces nearly unaffected. Conversely they may eliminate all base flow once contributed from now-paved upland areas. In either case, bypass systems release all runoff as surface flow at a point discharge without any opportunity for groundwater recharge.

These considerations lead to the conclusion that hydrologic restoration requires the distributed reten-

tion of stormwater in reservoirs with a combined volume equivalent to the original soil layer and land surface. Where the land surface was steep, the soil was thin, and its infiltration capacity naturally low, the changes caused by urbanization may not be great, and achieving an equivalent degree of stormwater retention in the built environment may be relatively simple. Where predevelopment soil depths naturally approach a meter or more and porosities approach 50% and where wetlands retained much of the rainfall, simple strategies and normal land-development practices will not be successful at reestablishing streamflow patterns.

Recent efforts to achieve more comprehensive hydrologic mitigation have involved a suite of engineering and site-design approaches collectively known as "low impact development" (LID) (U.S. Environmental Protection Agency 2000). This strategy seeks to store, infiltrate, evaporate, or otherwise slowly release stormwater runoff in a close approximation of the rates and processes of the predevelop-ment hydrologic regime (Konrad and Burges 2001). To date, LID has been pursued primarily in humid, temperate regions where urban development can create the greatest alteration to the predevelopment hydrologic regime. Challenges for more widespread use of this approach include uncertainty in its application on relatively noninfiltrative soils, its effectiveness in mitigating high-intensity and (or) large-volume storms, and its construction in new or previously developed areas. Long-term performance, coupled with the uncertain level of long-term maintenance, require further study before the effectiveness of this stormwater-management approach can be advocated or its biological consequences evaluated. Until such time, we recognize no stormwater management strategy, or suite of approaches, that can achieve anything approaching full hydrologic mitigation. Some significant, measurable degree of biological decline is thus unavoidable in urban watersheds where streamflow has been altered for the foreseeable future.

Ecological Management Goals for Urban Streams

Streams nominally protected under land-use regulations have still experienced significant biological degradation. Widespread adoption of some types of development and stormwater management strategies may prevent further degradation of some streams. Yet, the full range of hydrological and ecological processes cannot be restored in urban streams, and we see no basis to expect that improvements in other aspects of stream ecosystems can mitigate the hydrologic consequences of urban development (Booth et al. 2004; Konrad 2003b). As a result, urban stream managers face the difficulty of acknowledging limits on stream ecosystem improvement imposed by the failure to restore streamflow patterns while maintaining prospects for future ecosystem recovery.

Stream restoration in the Pacific Northwest typically focuses on habitat elements in fish-bearing streams include large woody debris, pools, protective cover, gravel deposits, floodplains, and riparian vegetation. Although these elements can be imported to a site or otherwise constructed, neither the biological effectiveness (e.g., Larson et al. 2001) nor longevity (Frissell and Nawa 1992) of artificially placed elements is well documented. Over the long term, habitat elements of streams will be created and maintained only through functioning ecological processes. In recognition of the distinction between direct manipulation of stream habitat elements for an outcome and the self-regulation of habitat conditions in natural stream ecosystems, we discriminate between short-term and long-term actions for improving the biological conditions of streams. Short-term actions are generally feasible under many different management settings but are unlikely to produce long-lasting effects; long-term actions are necessary for true ecosystem enhancement but may be intractable under present-day regulatory, economic, or land-use conditions.

Short-term actions include riparian planting, water quality source control, fish-passage projects, selective instream structures, and social amenities (Bethel and Neal 2003). They address acute problems typical to stream channels in urban and urbanizing settings (e.g., denuded vegetation buffers, point source pollution, fish blockages, simplified channel structure, and dumping of solid wastes). They are not comprehensive, so their efficacy is limited by elements of the ecosystem that are missing or degraded in urban areas. Although some aspects of hydrologic modification in urban areas such as increased frequency of high flows may be addressed in part by short-term actions such as peak flow control, the range of changes in streamflow patterns resulting from urban development are unlikely to be addressed in the short term. As a consequence, hydrologic changes are likely to have persistent effects on the biological conditions of many urban streams.

Short-term actions also acknowledge the presence of people in the urban environment. Streams are affected, often irrevocably, by activities of streamside residents in pursuit of personal esthetics or low maintenance (Schauman 1998). Management actions that enhance interactions between the public and urban streams are likely to be supported, but the financial costs for such actions are commonly greater than the ecosystem benefits. Such actions are often considered desirable because they improve "quality of life" or the stream's value as a public amenity or educational resource.

Long-term, self-sustaining actions must ultimately address all of the five aspects of stream ecosystems (Figure 1). These actions might include various types of land-use planning (e.g., preserves, zoning), minimizing or redesigning road and utility crossings, upland hydrologic rehabilitation (e.g., stormwater infiltration), erosion control, riparian vegetation restoration, and reconnection of streams with floodplains. In some cases, there are fundamental conflicts between the processes that create and maintain aspects of stream ecosystems (e.g., flooding) and extensive infrastructure and human occupation around streams. Streamflow is a key habitat-forming process, and failure to reestablish streamflow patterns almost certainly precludes full restoration of the ecosystem. Over the long term, restoration of an urban stream to a predevelopment state is likely to require the exclusion of people from the immediate environment (channel and riparian areas) and, perhaps, even upland portions of the basin, even as it requires their support to ensure its implementation and success. Support and stewardship by the surrounding community would be essential to such an ambitious goal, but people's involvement would be very different from the short-term efforts that depend on human actions in and along stream channels.

Evidence to date suggests that short-term actions alone, and even some well-intentioned and well-reasoned long-term actions, do not achieve broad ecosystem protection in the urban environment. At best, biological communities in urban streams may be diverse and complex, but they will depart significantly from predevelopment conditions. These streams can be neighborhood amenities and provide nearby residents with a connection to a place not completely managed by human actions, and with a self-sustaining and self-regulating biological community. These outcomes for urban streams should be achievable even in the absence of reestablishing natural hydrologic processes, which is the likely scenario for many streams in urban and urbanizing watersheds.

Conclusions

"Urbanization" is not a single condition; it is a collection of actions that lead to recognizable landscape forms and, changes in stream conditions. Because of the broad and important roles of streamflow in fluvial ecosystems, hydrologic changes in urban streams pose significant ecological risks that warrant evaluation along with other changes (e.g., water chemistry, physical habitat, riparian conditions) long associated with urban development. Three types of hydrologic changes of ecological significance are likely to result from urban development: increased frequency of high flows; redistribution of water from periods of base flow to periods of storm flow, and increased daily variation in streamflow. These changes do not necessarily occur in all urban streams, but they are common and need to be addressed as part of any comprehensive effort to rehabilitate urban streams. Other hydrologic changes may also occur in urban streams, particularly where surface water or shallow groundwater are used for water supplies, which may also have ecological repercussions. Urban streams can provide habitat for biological communities even if the hydrologic consequences of urban development are not addressed, but the structure and composition of these communities are likely to depart from those of the predevelopment stream. Ultimately, true restoration of urban streams can only occur if hydrologic processes and the spatial distribution of the water-storage capacity is reestablished across the urban landscape.

Acknowledgments

We thank Larry Brown, Jim Karr, and Bob Gray for providing valuable suggestions to improve this paper.

References

Allan, J. D. 1995. Stream ecology. Chapman and Hall, London.

Anderson, N. H., and D. M. Lehmkuhl. 1968. Catastrophic drift of insects in a woodland stream. Ecology 49:198–206.

Andrews, E. D. 1984. Bed-material entrainment and hydraulic geometry of gravel-bed rivers in Colorado. Geological Society of America Bulletin 95:371–378.

Bayley, P. B., and L. L. Osborne. 1993. Natural rehabilitation of stream fish populations in an Illinois catchment. Freshwater Biology 29:295–300.

Bethel, J., and K. Neal. 2003. Stream enhancement projects: a King County perspective. Pages 394–421 in D. R. Montgomery, S. Bolton, D. B. Booth, and L. Wall, editors. Restoration of Puget Sound rivers. University of Washington Press, Seattle.

Bickerton, M. A. 1995. Long-term changes of macroinvertebrate communities in relation to flow variations:

the River Glen, Lincolnshire, England. Regulated Rivers 10:81–92.

Biggs, B. J. F., and M. E. Close. 1989. Periphyton biomass dynamics in gravel bed rivers: the relative effects of flow and nutrients. Freshwater Biology 22:209–231.

Booth, D. B. 1990. Stream-channel incision following drainage-basin urbanization. Water Resources Bulletin 26:407–417.

Booth, D. B., and C. J. Jackson. 1997. Urbanization of aquatic systems—degradation thresholds, stormwater detention, and the limits of mitigation. Water Resources Bulletin 33:1077–1090.

Booth, D. B., D. Hartley, and R. Jackson. 2002. Forest cover, impervious-surface area, and the mitigation of stormwater impacts. Journal of the American Water Resources Association 38:835–845.

Booth, D. B., J. R. Karr, S. Schauman, C. P. Konrad, S. A. Morley, M. G. Larson, and S. J. Burges. 2004. Reviving urban streams: land use, hydrology, biology, and human behavior. Journal of the American Water Resources Association 40:1351–1364.

Boulton, A. J., C. G. Peterson, N. B. Grimm, and S. G. Fisher. 1992. Stability of an aquatic macroinvertebrate community in a multiyear hydrologic disturbance regime. Ecology 73:2192–2207.

Burges, S. J., M. S. Wigmosta, and J. M. Meena. 1998. Hydrologic effects of land-use change in a zero-order catchment. Journal of Hydrologic Engineering 3:86–97.

Carling, P. 1988. The concept of dominant discharge applied to two gravel-bed streams in relation to channel stability thresholds. Earth Surface Processes and Landforms 13:355–367.

Clausen, B., and B. J. F. Biggs. 1997. Relationships between benthic biota and hydrologic indices in New Zealand streams. Freshwater Biology 38:327–342.

Clausen, B., and B. J. F. Biggs. 2000. Flow variables for ecological studies in temperate streams: groupings based on covariance. Journal of Hydrology 237:184–197.

Closs, G. P., and P. S. Lake. 1994. Spatial and temporal variation in the structure of an intermittent-stream food web. Ecological Monographs 64:1–21.

Connell, J. H. 1978. Diversity in tropical rain forests and coral reefs. Science 199:1302–1310.

Death, R. G., and M. J. Winterbourn. 1995. Diversity patterns in stream benthic invertebrate communities: the influence of habitat stability. Ecology 76:1446–1460.

DeBrey, L. D., and J. A. Lockwood. 1990. Effects of sediment and flow regime on the aquatic insects of a high mountain stream. Regulated Rivers 5:241–250.

Dieterich, M., and N. H. Anderson. 1995. Life cycles and food habits of mayflies and stoneflies from temporary streams in western Oregon. Freshwater Biology 34:47–60.

Douglas, B. 1958. The ecology of the attached diatoms and other algae in a small stony stream. Ecology 46:295–322.

Erman, D. C., E. D. Andrews, and M. Yoder-Williams. 1988. Effects of winter floods on fishes in the Sierra Nevada. Canadian Journal of Fisheries and Aquatic Sciences 45:2195–2200.

Fairchild, G. W., R. J. Horwitz, D. A. Nieman, M. R. Boyer, and D. F. Knorr. 1998. Spatial variation and historical change in fish communities of the Schuylkill River drainage, southeast Pennsylvania. American Midland Naturalist 139:282–295.

Feminella, J. W., and V. H. Resh. 1990. Hydrologic influences, disturbance, and intraspecific competition in a stream caddisfly population. Ecology 71:2083–2094.

Fisher, S. G., L. J. Gray, N. B. Grimm, and D. E. Busch. 1982. Temporal succession in a desert stream ecosystem following flash flooding. Ecological Monographs 52:93–110.

Frissell, C. A., and R. K. Nawa. 1992. Incidence and causes of physical failure of artificial fish habitat structures in streams of western Oregon and Washington. North American Journal of Fisheries Management 12:182–197.

Gorman, O. T., and J. R. Karr. 1978. Habitat structure and stream fish communities. Ecology 59:507–515.

Gurtz, M. E., and J. B. Wallace. 1984. Substrate-mediated response of stream invertebrates to disturbance. Ecology 65:1556–1569.

Harrel, R. C., B. J. Davis, and T. C. Dorris. 1967. Stream order and species diversity of fishes in an intermittent Oklahoma stream. American Midland Naturalist 78:428–436.

Harris, E. E., and S. E. Rantz. 1964. Effect of urban growth on streamflow regime of Permanente Creek, Santa Clara County, California. United States Geological Survey Water-Supply Paper 1591-B. Washington D.C.

Helley, E. J. 1969. Field measurement of the initiation of large particle bed motion in Blue Creek near Klamath, California. United States Geological Survey Professional Paper 562-G, Washington D.C.

Horwitz, R. J. 1978. Temporal variability patterns and the distributional patterns of fishes. Ecological Monographs 48:307–321.

Jones, J. B., Jr., S. G. Fisher; and N. B. Grimm. 1995. Vertical hydrologic exchange and ecosystem metabolism in a Sonoran desert stream. Ecology 76:942–952.

Karr, J. R., and C. O. Yoder. 2004. Biological assessment and criteria improve TMDL planning and decision making. Journal of Environmental Engineering 130:594–604.

Klein, R. D. 1979. Urbanization and stream quality impairment. Water Resources Bulletin 15:948–963.

Konrad, C. P. 2003a. Effects of urban development on floods. United States Geological Survey Fact Sheet 076–03, Tacoma, Washington

Konrad, C. P. 2003b. Opportunities and constraints for urban stream rehabilitation. Pages 292–317 in D. R. Montgomery, S. Bolton, D. B. Booth, and L. Wall, editors. Restoration of Puget Sound rivers. University of Washington Press, Seattle.

Konrad, C. P., and D. B. Booth. 2002. Hydrologic trends associated with urban development in western Washington streams, United States Geological Survey Water-Resources Investigations Report 02–4040, Tacoma, Washington.

Konrad, C. P., and S. J. Burges. 2001. Hydrologic mitigation using on-site residential stormwater detention. Journal of Water Resources Planning and Management 127:99–107.

Larson, M. L., D. B. Booth, and S. M. Morley. 2001. Effectiveness of large woody debris in stream rehabilitation projects in urban basins. Ecological Engineering 18:211–226.

Leopold, L. B. 1968. Hydrology for urban land planning—a guidebook on the hydrologic effects of urban land use. U.S. Geological Survey Circular 554, Washington D.C.

Maxted, J. R., and E. Shaver. 1999. The use of detention basins to mitigate stormwater impacts to aquatic life. Pages 6–15 in National Conference on Retrofit Opportunities for Water Resource Protection in Urban Environments. U.S. Environmental Protection Agency, Office of Research and Development EPA/625/R-99/002, Cincinnati, Ohio.

McAuliffe, J. R. 1984. Competition for space, disturbance, and the structure of a benthic stream community. Ecology 6:894–908.

McCormick, P. V., and R. J. Stevenson. 1991. Mechanisms of benthic algal succession in lotic environments. Ecology 72:1835–1848.

McElravy, E. P., G. A. Lamberti, and V. H. Resh. 1989. Year-to-year variation in the aquatic macroinvertebrate fauna of a northern California stream, Journal of the North American Benthological Society 8:51–63.

Milhous, R. T. 1973. Sediment transport in a gravel-bottom stream. Doctoral dissertation. Oregon State University, Corvallis.

Minshall, G. W. 1984. Aquatic insect-substratum relationships. Pages 358–400 in V. H. Resh and D. M. Rosenburg, editors. The ecology of aquatic insects. Praeger Scientific, New York.

Minshall, G. W. 1988. Stream ecosystem theory: a global perspective. Journal of the North American Benthological Society 7:263–288.

Morley, S. A., and J. R. Karr. 2002. Assessing and restoring the health of urban streams in the Puget Sound basin. Conservation Biology 16:1498–1509.

Newbury, R. W. 1988. Hydrologic determinants of aquatic insect habitats. Pages 323–357 *in* V. H. Resh and D. M. Rosenburg, editors. The ecology of aquatic insects. Praeger Scientific, New York.

Orser, P. N., and D. J. Shure. 1972. Effects of urbanization on the salamander *Desmognathus fuscus fuscus*. Ecology 53:1148–1154.

Perry, R. W., M. J. Bradford, and J. A. Grout. 2003. Effects of disturbance on contribution of energy sources to growth of juvenile chinook salmon (*Oncorhynchus tshawytscha*) in boreal streams. Canadian Journal of Fisheries and Aquatic Sciences 60:390–400.

Pickup, G., and R. F. Warner. 1976. Effects of hydrologic regime on magnitude and frequency of dominant discharge. Journal of Hydrology 29:51–75.

Platts, W. S. 1979. Relationships among stream order, fish populations, and aquatic geomorphology in an Idaho drainage. Fisheries 4(2):5–9.

Poff, N. L., and J. D. Allan. 1995. Functional organization of stream fish assemblages in relation to hydrologic variability. Ecology 76:606–627.

Poff, N. L., and J. V. Ward. 1989. Implications of streamflow variability and predictability for lotic community structure: a regional analysis of streamflow patterns. Canadian Journal of Fisheries and Aquatic Sciences 46:1805–1818.

Power, M. E., and A. J. Stewart. 1987. Disturbance and recovery of an algal assemblage following flooding in an Oklahoma stream. American Midland Naturalist 117:333–345.

Power, M. E., R. J. Stout, C. E. Cushing, P. P. Harper, F. R. Hauer, W. J. Matthews, P. B. Moyle, B. Statzner, and I. R. Wais de Badgen. 1988. Biotic and abiotic controls in river and stream communities. Journal of the North American Benthological Society 7:456–479.

Power, G., R. S. Brown, and J. G. Imhof. 1999. Groundwater and fish—insights from northern North America. Hydrologic Processes 13:401–422.

Rabeni, C. F., and G. S. Wallace. 1998. The influence of flow variation on the ability to evaluate the biological health of headwater streams. Pages 411–418 *in* K. Kovar, U. Tappeiner, N. E. Peters, and R. G. Craig, editors. Hydrology, water resources and ecology in headwaters. International Association of Hydrological Sciences Press, IAHS Publication 248, Wallingford, Oxfordshire, UK..

Resh, V. H., A. V. Brown, A. P. Covich, M. E. Gurtz, H. W. Li, G. W. Minshall, S. R. Reice, A. L. Sheldon, J. B. Wallace, and R. C. Wissmar. 1988. The role of disturbance in stream ecology. Journal of the North American Benthological Society 7:433–455.

Richter, B. D., J. V. Baumgartner, J. Powell, and D. P. Braun. 1996. A method for assessing hydrologic alteration within ecosystems. Conservation Biology 10:1163–1174.

Robinson, C. T., and G. W. Minshall. 1986. Effects of disturbance frequency on stream benthic community structure in relation to canopy cover and season. Journal of the North American Benthological Society 5:237–248.

Schauman, S. 1998. Gardens and red barns: the prevailing pastoral and its ecological implications. Journal of Aesthetics and Art Criticism 56(2):181–190.

Schlosser, I. J. 1985. Flow regime, juvenile abundance, and the assemblage structure of stream fishes. Ecology 66:1484–1490.

Scrimgeour, G. J., and M. J. Winterbourn. 1989. Effects of floods on epilithon and benthic macroinvertebrate populations in an unstable New Zealand river. Hydrobiologia 171:33–44.

Shelford, V. E., and S. Eddy. 1929. Methods for the study of stream communities. Ecology 10:382–391.

Sidle, R. C. 1988. Bed load transport regime of a small forest stream. Water Resources Research 24:207–218.

Simmons, D. L., and R. J. Reynolds. 1982. Effects of urbanization on base flow of selected south-shore streams, Long Island, New York. Water Resources Bulletin 18:797–805.

Statzner, B., and B. Higler. 1986. Stream hydraulics as a major determinant of benthic invertebrate zonation patterns. Freshwater Biology 16:127–139.

Statzner, B., J. A. Gore, and V. H. Resh. 1988. Hydraulic stream ecology: observed patterns and potential applications. Journal of the North American Benthological Society 7:307–360.

Stedinger, J. R., R. M. Vogel, and E. Foufoula-Georgiou. 1993. Frequency analysis of extreme events. Pages 18.1–18.66 *in* D.R. Maidment, editor. Handbook of hydrology. McGraw-Hill, New York.

Stehr, W. C., and J. W. Branson. 1938. An ecological study of an intermittent stream. Ecology 19:294–310.

Townsend, C. R., S. Doledec, and M. R. Scarsbrook. 1997. Species traits in relation to temporal and spatial heterogenity in streams: a test of habitat templet theory. Freshwater Biology 37:367–387.

Townsend, C. R. 1989. The patch dynamics concept of stream community ecology. Journal of the North American Benthological Society 8:36–50.

U.S. Census Bureau. 2004. Historical population counts.

Available: http://quickfacts.census.gov/qfd/. (January 2004)

U.S. Environmental Protection Agency. 2000. Low impact development—a literature review. U.S. Environmental Protection Agency, EPA-841-B-00–005, Washington D.C.

Wang, L., J. Lyons, P. Kanehl, R. Bannerman, and E. Emmons. 2000. Watershed urbanization and changes in fish communities in southeastern Wisconsin streams. Journal of the American Water Resources Association 36:1173–1189.

White, P. S., and S. T. A. Pickett. 1985. Natural disturbance and patch dynamics: an introduction. Pages 3–13 *in* S. T. A. Pickett and P. S. White, editors. The ecology of natural disturbance and patch dynamics. Academic Press, San Diego, California.

Wiberg-Larsen, P., K. P. Brodersen, S. Birkholm, P. N. Gron, and J. Skriver. 2000. Species richness and assemblage structure of Trichoptera in Danish streams. Freshwater Biology 43:633–647.

Wolman, M. G., and J. P. Miller. 1960. Magnitude and frequency of forces in geomorphic processes. Journal of Geology 68:54–74.

Wootton, J. T., M. S. Parker, and M. E. Power. 1996. Effects of disturbance on river food webs. Science 273:1558–1561.

American Fisheries Society Symposium 47:179–191, 2005

Setting Limits: The Development and Use of Factor-Ceiling Distributions for an Urban Assessment Using Macroinvertebrates

James L. Carter* and Steven V. Fend

U. S. Geological Survey, 345 Middlefield Road MS465, Menlo Park, California 94025, USA

Abstract.—Lotic habitats in urban settings are often more modified than in other anthropogenically influenced areas. The extent, degree, and permanency of these modifications compromise the use of traditional reference-based study designs to evaluate the level of lotic impairment and establish restoration goals. Directly relating biological responses to the combined effects of urbanization is further complicated by the nonlinear response often observed in common metrics (e.g., Ephemeroptera, Plecoptera, and Trichoptera [EPT] species richness) to measures of human influence (e.g., percentage urban land cover). A characteristic polygonal biological response often arises from the presence of a generalized limiting factor (i.e., urban land use) plus the influence of multiple additional stressors that are nonuniformly distributed throughout the urban environment. Benthic macroinvertebrates, on-site physical habitat and chemistry, and geographical information systems–derived land cover data for 85 sites were collected within the 1,600-km^2 Santa Clara Valley (SCV), California urban area. A biological indicator value was derived from EPT richness and percentage EPT. Partitioned regression was used to define reference conditions and estimate the degree of site impairment. We propose that an upper-boundary condition (factor-ceiling) modeled by partitioned regression using ordinary least squares represents an attainable upper limit for biological condition in the SCV area. Indicator values greater than the factor-ceiling, which is monotonically related to existing land use, are considered representative of reference conditions under the current habitat conditions imposed by existing land cover and land use.

Introduction

Identification of reference sites is fundamental to study designs that evaluate the composition and structure of benthic macroinvertebrate assemblages for the assessment of lotic systems. The concept underlying the use of reference sites in impact assessments is based on the use of controls in manipulative experimental designs. Reference and test sites are assumed to be sufficiently similar that, in the absence of impact, the chosen response variable(s) can be logically compared.

Green (1979) provided the principal rationale for the use of controls in field-based aquatic monitoring studies. However, most of the experimental designs were focused on geographically small-scale studies. In the last few decades, the geographic extent of assessment programs has increased substantially. Many programs are national in scope. Some examples include the River In-

vertebrate Prediction Classification system (RIVPACS; Wright 2000), Australian River Assessment System (AUSRIVAS; Davies 2000; Simpson and Norris 2000), Environmental Monitoring and Assessment Program (EMAP; USEPA 2002a), and National Water-Quality Assessment Program (NAWQA; Gilliom et al. 1995, 2001). These programs include thousands of sites located over many thousands of square kilometers. Large-scale biomonitoring programs are also integral to many state water quality programs (Carter and Resh 2001; USEPA 2002b).

Natural environmental gradients often increase as the geographic scale of a study increases (Corkum 1989; Carter et al. 1996; Fend et al. 2005, this volume). Longer environmental gradients invariably lead to higher species turnover, which can compromise the logical use of standard reference approaches. This increase in geographic scale and gradient length has influenced the methods used to identify and apply reference sites (Hughes et al. 1986; Wright 2000) and

---

* Corresponding author: jlcarter@usgs.gov

has also affected their perceived applicability (Polls 1994; Reash 1995).

Although numerous methods have been developed for identifying reference sites, the first step is to determine whether the populations of both reference and test sites possess similar nonimpact-associated physical and chemical characteristics. Similar sites are then presumed to have the same biological potential in the absence of impact; consequently, impact can be logically inferred by differences in macroinvertebrate assemblage composition and structure between the reference and test sites. This initial site classification step is overtly stated in some methods (Hughes 1995; Barbour et al. 1999), while in others it is less apparent (Wright et al. 1984). Following the initial identification of reference sites, a refinement to eliminate (Barbour et al. 1999) or account for (Wright 2000) further differences in either the physical habitat and/or the benthic assemblages among the chosen reference sites generally occurs.

Lotic habitats within urban settings are often more physically modified than in other anthropogenically influenced environmental settings (Paul and Meyer 2001). Factors influencing lotic systems include increases in the percentage of impervious surface, stream canalization, and loss of or highly modified riparian corridors. In most urban settings, these modifications often form a gradient of increasing anthropogenic effect from more distant rural areas to the core of the urban center. In many areas, particularly in the western United States, natural gradients in landform (e.g., altitude) often coincide with these anthropogenic gradients (Carter et al. 1996).

The extent and degree of modifications to lotic systems associated with urban settings often compromises the use of the reference-based study designs using benthic invertebrates. This is particularly true when assessments are relatively small-scale, such as when assessments are constrained by political boundaries but still encompass a variety of habitat conditions. Establishing justifiable expected biological conditions that can be used for evaluating lotic impairment or establishing restoration goals is difficult, and expected biological condition must be estimated or modeled.

Directly relating biological responses, such as metrics derived from the composition of macroinvertebrate assemblages, to a combination of effects, particularly those of urbanization, is further complicated by the nonlinear response often observed between commonly used biological metrics and urbanization

(Fend et al. 2005). Bivariate plots of metrics and measures of urbanization or even natural geomorphic conditions are often polygonal in form (Fausch et al. 1984; Karr and Chu 1999). These polygonal responses often arise from the presence of a generalized limiting factor plus the influence of site-specific stressors (Thomson et al. 1996).

The gradient of urbanization that increases from the outskirts to the area of maximum urban influence creates an increasingly constrained physical and chemical environmental template that sets an upper limit on potential stream quality and consequently, the lotic community. In this paper, we use the concept of polygonal distributions and factor ceilings (Thomson et al. 1996; Scharf et al. 1998) to establish a reference condition that is linearly related to and accounts for the underlying effects of this urban gradient. The reference condition identifies a potential upper limit on the condition of the benthic assemblage.

The purposes of this study were to (1) present a conceptual framework for establishing reference conditions in urban settings, (2) objectively identify reference conditions that reflect a realistic maximum biological potential that is a function of the constraints of urbanization, and (3) develop a simple bioindicator that is inexpensive to determine, has the potential to be highly comparable among programs, and reflects impairment in an urban environmental setting.

Study Area

The study location is in the Santa Clara Valley area of the San Francisco Bay region of California (Figure 1). The area is approximately 1,600 km^2. The study area is surrounded on the west, south, and east by a topographic divide and bordered on the north by San Francisco Bay. The physical setting includes upland areas that are sparsely populated and more densely populated lowland areas. Urbanization increases from the uplands to the lowlands near San Francisco Bay.

The area has a Mediterranean climate with most precipitation falling as rain during the winter and spring; almost no precipitation occurs during the summer months. Many streams are impounded, while instream withdrawals alter the natural hydrologic cycle of others. Water management is extremely complex and water is released from most impoundments for aquifer recharge, flood control, and to support sensitive species. Approximately 50% of the water used in the basin is imported.

The San Francisco Bay area contains extremely variable landforms and climates compared to many less topographically complex urban centers in the United States. Altitude ranges from sea level to more than 1,200 m and precipitation and temperature vary on a subregional basis. These variations lead to important differences in factors that influence the distribution of the local flora and fauna. Spatial differences in temperature, runoff, channel morphology, and local potential and realized vegetation create a mosaic of gradients that directly influence the habitat and resources available to lotic invertebrates throughout the area. As a result of these differences, physical habitat responses, and consequently, biotic responses to any given stressor are likely to vary both within and among regions.

Two factors confound the use of a reference site approach for determining impairment of San Francisco Bay area streams. First, humans have been significantly influencing local streams for at least 150 years; therefore, streams that could be classified as pristine or even "least-impaired" are lacking. This is particularly true for the higher order, downstream, more urbanized reaches. Second, naturally high habitat variability throughout the Bay Area leads to a diversity of potential macroinvertebrate assemblages.

Methods

Biological

Eighty-five sites located on 14 streams within the Santa Clara Valley area were sampled during May 1997 for macroinvertebrates (Figure 1). All sites were also sampled for nutrients, dissolved trace elements, and channel and riparian structure during May and June 1997. Streams included in the study were San Francisquito Creek, Corte Madera Creek, Los Trancos Creek, Stevens Creek, Saratoga Creek, Guadalupe River, Los Gatos Creek, Ross Creek, Guadalupe Creek, Alamitos Creek, Barret Creek, Arroyo Calero, Coyote Creek, and Upper Penitencia Creek.

Sampling locations were chosen to be equidistant, with sites located at approximately 2-km intervals. The most downstream site within each subbasin was located at either the point of observed or assumed intermittent flow or where a tidal influence to river flow and/or

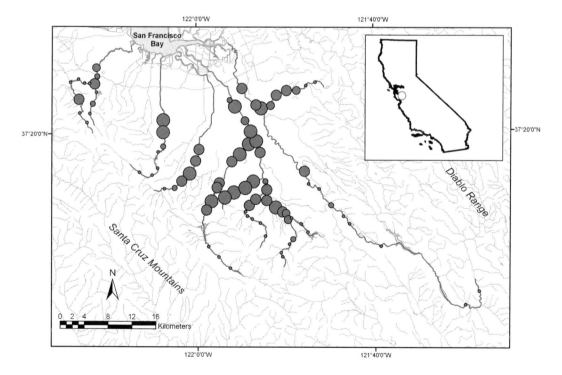

FIGURE 1. Map of study area (Santa Clara Valley, California) depicting percentage urban land cover within 200 m × 2 km buffer strips upstream of each of the 85 sites. Percentage urban land cover was derived from 30 m National Land Cover Data. Circle size increases in 10% intervals from near zero to near 100% urban land cover.

substratum type was apparent. In general, the most upstream site was at an altitude of approximately 300 m.

At each site a semiquantitative collection of macroinvertebrates was made from a single riffle. Each collection was a composite of five 0.1-m² kick samples taken with a 0.3-m-wide D-frame kicknet fitted with a 500-μm mesh. The five individual kick samples were taken systematically in each riffle in a downstream to upstream direction, crossing the stream twice along two perpendicular diagonal lines (i.e., a v-shape across the riffle's breadth). Two of the five samples were obtained in the thalweg, and the remaining three samples were taken between the thalweg and the margins. At sites containing extremely long riffles, sampling focused on the upstream portion of the riffle.

Samples were cleaned of large debris and preserved with 10% buffered formalin in the field. All samples were randomly subsampled in the laboratory using a gridded tray (Moulton et al. 2000). Approximately 500 organisms were sorted from each subsample using ~8× magnification. After each subsample was sorted a second person searched the just-sorted material for a maximum of 30 min to remove organisms that may have been overlooked during the initial sorting. All individuals sorted were placed in vials and stored in 80% ethanol prior to identification. All organisms were identified to the lowest practicable taxon.

Estimates of the combined number of taxa in the insect orders Ephemeroptera, Plecoptera, and Trichoptera (EPT) (EPT richness) and the relative abundance of individuals in the same three orders (% EPT) were used for the principal analyses. These estimates were based on the mean of 100 computer-generated, 300-organism subsamples. Samples were rarefied to a constant size to reduce the effect that variations in the number of organisms sorted has on comparing richness-based metrics among sites. Ephemeroptera, Plecoptera, and Trichoptera richness was further corrected by eliminating less-resolved higher-level taxa when at least one individual of a lower taxonomic designation was present in the sample.

An indicator value (EPT score) was constructed from EPT richness and percentage EPT. We restricted our analysis to these two metrics because the EPT are (1) the most often used taxa in biomonitoring and are generally considered intolerant of most stressors (Resh and Jackson 1993; Kerans and Karr 1994), (2) identified to species more often than any other taxa (Carter and Resh 2001), and (3) highly correlated to many other metrics (Lenat and Penrose 1996). Additionally, no assumptions regarding

higher level ecological responses are necessary when evaluating these two metrics, as there are when evaluating functional-type metrics (e.g., functional feeding-groups) because EPT richness and percentage EPT are strictly taxonomically based.

Physical

An estimate of the degree of habitat impairment near the channel due to increasing urbanization was determined for each site. Seven factors were evaluated. The first five factors were categorized on a 1–4 ordinal scale and included (1) channel form, which ranged from natural to v-shaped concrete; (2) riparian composition (including canopy cover), which ranged from all native to absent; (3) riparian width, which ranged from greater than 30 m to absent; (4) siltation, which ranged from no obvious deposited silt to a visible silt layer over the substrate; and (5) turbidity, which ranged from clear to an inability to see the bottom.

Both canopy and embeddedness were difficult to visually categorize in the field, so ordinal values (1–4) were developed from field measurements. Riparian canopy shading was measured at three mid-channel points within the sample area, using a Solar Pathfinder (Solar Pathways, Inc.) to measure the solar arc for May; the value was expressed as a percentage of the expected insolation. Sediment embeddedness was estimated as the percentage depth (the vertical axis) to which 10 randomly chosen particles were buried in sand or finer material. The mean of all seven factors was calculated and used to represent a near-site estimation of urbanization (UHA [urban habitat assessment], see Fend et al. 2005).

Land Cover

The spatial coordinates (latitude, longitude, and altitude) were determined for each site using a Global Positioning System and topographic maps. Urban land cover for a 200 m wide × 2 km long buffer strip (100 m on either side of the stream) upstream of each site was estimated using 30 m National Land Cover Data (NLCD) (Vogelmann et al. 2001). The summation of four NLCD categories (low intensity residential, high intensity residential, commercial/industrial/transportation, quarries/strip mines/gravel pits) was used to represent urban land cover.

Statistics

The relationship between individual EPT-based metrics and the total benthic assemblage was determined by correlating the first axis of a Detrended Correspondence Analysis (McCune and Mefford 1999) derived using $\log_{10}$ transformed abundance data from the entire data set. All percentage data (% EPT and land cover) were transformed using arcsine square root transformations. Rarified richness was not further transformed.

The EPT score was formed by standardizing each metric (EPT richness and % EPT) by its maximum, thereby creating values that ranged between 0 and 1. The standardized metrics were summed and the total multiplied by 5 to provide an easily interpretable multimetric that had the potential of ranging from 0 to near 10.

Partitioned regressions were used to (1) estimate an upper boundary condition (factor-ceiling) of the bivariate distribution of the EPT score and percentage urban land cover per site, and (2) define four impairment categories. The procedure was as follows. First, a primary regression by ordinary least squares (OLS) was performed using data from all sites. This separated (partitioned) the data into those EPT scores with positive residuals and those with negative residuals. Next, a secondary regression was performed using just those data identified by the primary regression to possess positive residuals. The OLS line of this secondary regression was used as the boundary condition above which EPT scores represent the proposed reference condition for any given percentage urban land cover. The boundary represents a continuously varying reference condition that accounts for the effects of urbanized land cover on the potential magnitude of EPT scores. To complete the analysis, a final regression was fit using those EPT scores identified as having negative residuals from the primary regression. This partitioned this portion of the data into two additional groups. The final two groups, along with the two groups formed from partitioning the data with positive residuals, allowed the formation of four potential categories: one category representing the reference condition and three categories representing increasing levels of impairment.

Two single factor Analysis of Variance (ANOVA) tests were used to determine whether there were significant differences in altitude and urbanization (the UHA score) among the derived impairment categories. Among-group variances were tested using Levene's test for homogeneity of variances prior to the ANOVAs, and Newman-Keuls tests were used for post hoc testing of differences among groups when appropriate. All analyses were performed using STATISTICA (StatSoft, Inc. 2004).

Results

General Description

The spring collections yielded an abundant and diverse fauna. Total number of individuals identified from the 85 sites was 65,571. Total richness (number of different taxa) across all sites was approximately 300 taxa. Mean total richness per site based on nonrarefied samples was 44 ± 8.6 (± 1 SD, $n = 85$) and ranged from 27 to 67. Although our collection methods were semiquantitative, estimated mean density per site was 9,590 individuals/m^2 and ranged from 1,386 to 29,581/m^2.

Random subsampling to provide at least 500 organisms yielded a mean of 653 ± 137 individuals and ranged from 470 to 992 individuals per subsample. This variation in the number of individuals sorted per sample necessitated rarefying the samples prior to comparing richness estimates among samples. Mean EPT richness per site, based on randomly sorted samples, was 10 ± 5.3 and ranged from 2 to 27. Mean EPT richness per site based on samples rarefied to 300 individuals was 8 ± 4.3 and ranged from 1.5 to 22.8.

Percentage EPT per site based on randomly sorted samples was 35 ± 19.0 and ranged from 1.2 to 78.2. As expected, rarefaction had little influence on percentage composition and mean percentage EPT per site based on samples rarefied to 300 individuals was 35 ± 19.1 and ranged from 1.3 to 78.3.

Urban land cover varied widely across the basin. Mean percentage of land cover per site classified as urban within the 200 m wide x 2 km long buffer strips was 41 ± 35.4 and ranged from 0 to 95.9.

The correlation between the benthic assemblage as represented by the first axis of the Detrended Correspondence Analysis (DCA) ordination and the EPT score (Figure 2) was relatively high ($r^2 = 0.44$, $P < 0.001$). Most scatter was related to the poor relationship between percentage EPT ($r^2 = 0.09$) and the first ordination axis compared to a much better relationship between EPT richness and the first axis ($r^2 = 0.69$). Both metrics were negatively correlated with percentage urban land cover and displayed considerable scatter that could best be described as polygonal in form (Figure 3A, B). The combined EPT score when plotted against percentage urban land cover also contained substantial scatter, which was polygonal in form (Figure 4A).

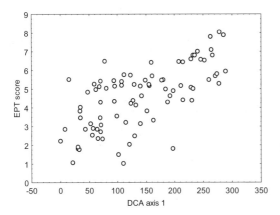

FIGURE 2. Relationship between detrended correspondence analysis (DCA) axis 1 derived from $\log_{10}$ transformed benthic data and the derived EPT score ($r^2 = 0.44$, $P < 0.001$, $n = 85$) from the Santa Clara Valley area, California.

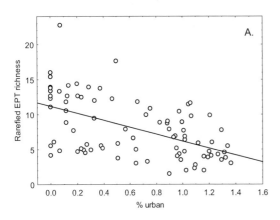

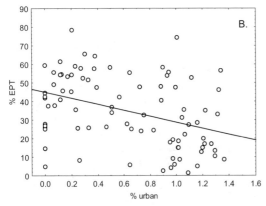

FIGURE 3. Relationship of transformed percentage urban land cover of buffer strips with (A) EPT richness rarefied to 300 individuals ($r^2 = 0.28$, $P < 0.001$, $n = 85$) and with (B) percentage EPT ($r^2 = 0.16$, $P < 0.001$, $n = 85$) for the Santa Clara Valley area, California.

Regressions

The primary OLS regression of percentage urban land cover and the EPT score partitioned the data into two near equal groups (Figure 4A). About 30% of the variation ($r^2 = 0.29$) in EPT scores was accounted for by the estimated percentage urban land cover of the site-specific buffer strips when all EPT data were used.

The OLS line formed by the secondary regression of the subset of sites with positive residuals based on the primary regression (Figure 4B) identified a conservative upper boundary condition for the EPT score (the uppermost regression line of Figure 4C, E). An EPT score above the uppermost regression line is considered to be a reference value for a given level of percentage urban land cover. The secondary regression using only those data possessing negative residuals from the primary regression (Figure 4D) provided a separation of sites into those with low EPT scores and those with even lower EPT scores over the full range of percentage urban land cover.

Assembling all three regressions results in four site-groups representing least-impaired to most-impaired conditions ($n = 20$, 23, 27, and 15, respectively) and provides a potential classification of impairment based solely on the relationship between EPT score and percentage urban land cover of the buffer strips (Figure 4E). A conservative potential value of the EPT score that represents the least-impaired condition as set by the factor-ceiling (the uppermost regression line of Figure 4E) varied from 6.8 at near zero urbanization to 4.0 at 100% urbanization.

Physical Characteristics of Site Groups

There was no significant difference in the variances among proposed impairment groups in altitude (Levene's test of homogeneity of variances; $F = 2.34$, $P = 0.079$). There also was no significant difference in mean altitude among groups ($F = 1.96$, $P = 0.126$). However, the site group that represented the most impaired sites had a mean altitude lower than the other three groups (Figure 5A).

There was no significant difference in the variances among proposed impairment groups in the UHA (Levene's test of homogeneity of variances; $F = 2.30$, $P = 0.083$). However, there was a significant difference among proposed impairment groups in the mean UHA ($F = 3.16$, $P = 0.029$). The most highly urbanized site group (group 4) was significantly different from the two least urbanized site groups. Although no other site groups differed, there was an apparent near-linear decrease in UHA across the four groups (Figure 5B).

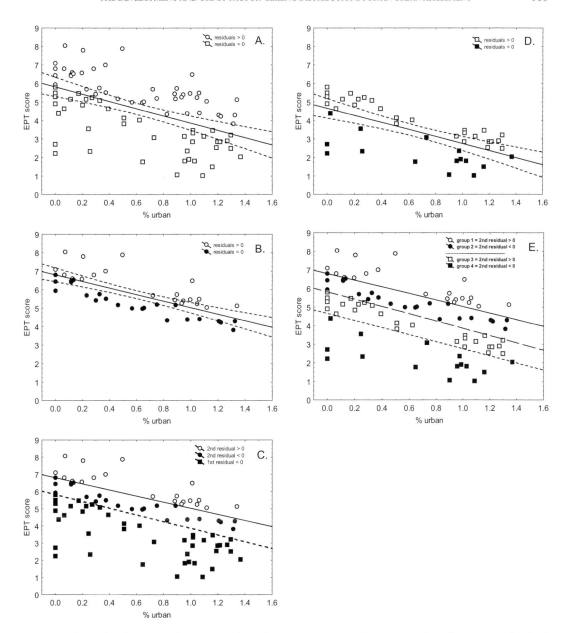

FIGURE 4. Results of primary and secondary ordinary least squares regression between transformed percentage urban land cover of buffer strips and EPT score from the Santa Clara Valley area, California: (A) primary regression ($r^2 = 0.29$, $P < 0.001$, $n = 85$), (B) secondary regression of positive residuals, (C) Solid line indicates the proposed factor-ceiling with EPT scores greater than the boundary representative of reference conditions, (D) secondary regression of negative residuals, and (E) formation of potential percentage urban-specific-impairment categories from least impaired most impaired.

Discussion

Current bioassessment methods are based on comparing test sites to reference sites or a reference condition. Whether these comparisons use the benthic assemblage directly as in RIVPACS-type models, or indirectly when metrics and multimetrics derived from the benthic assemblage (e.g., richness, percentage composition) are used, a reference condition is necessary to evaluate the biological condition of a test site. Reference conditions can be represented by a single site on a stream, as in upstream-to-down-

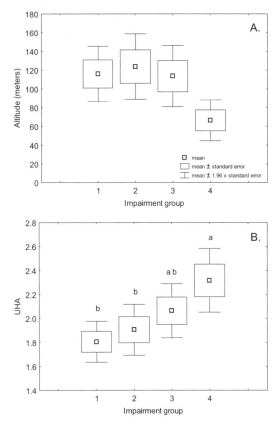

FIGURE 5. Values of (A) altitude, and (B) study-specific urban habitat assessment (UHA) for potential impairment groups as determined by single factor ANOVAs for data from the Santa Clara Valley area, California. Means with different letters are significantly different (Newman-Keuls test).

stream designs often used to identify the influence of point source impacts, although arguments have been presented against this approach (Underwood 1997; Downes et al. 2002; Bailey et al. 2004). Alternatively, reference conditions can be represented by the average biological condition among numerous sites and indicate an expected condition for a region as in larger-scale studies of impairment (Reynoldson et al. 1997; Bailey et al. 2004). Reference sites can also be used to model the expected species composition of a test site given a database of species occurrences and a limited suite of environmental variables (Wright 2000).

Large-scale studies have used various criteria for establishing reference conditions. Wright et al. (1984) initially stratified by stream size, excluding both low and high order streams. Large U.S. programs that are state specific or regional have also stratified prior to establishing reference conditions. These programs have used various methods and criteria to geographically partition study areas in an effort to control for environmental variability. Examples include the use of physiographic provinces (Lenat 1993), general landform (Yoder and Rankin 1995), and ecoregions (Barbour et al. 1999). Stratifying based on ecoregion is often a first step in the stratification process (Omernik and Bailey 1997). Whittier et al. (1988) were among the first to detail the similarities and differences in assemblage composition and structure of macroinvertebrates and other taxa within and among ecoregions of the northwestern United States.

Unfortunately, some studies showed that within-ecoregion variability in physical habitat, and consequently the potential biota, is often too high to establish logical comparisons (Hawkins et al. 2000; Fend et al. 2005). Thus, it is often necessary to subdivide ecoregions into subecoregions or stratify study areas and/or sites based on other physical characteristics such as basin size, stream order, or local conditions. Barbour et al. (1996), in an assessment of Florida streams, found that partitioning into subecoregions was necessary to adequately represent expected faunal composition and structure.

Hawkins et al. (2000) summarized numerous studies concerned with the applicability of ecoregions as a stratifying factor in water quality studies. These studies were worldwide in scope and evaluated responses of a variety of taxa. In general, ecoregions were considered too coarse a structure (species turnover was too high) to be applicable for most lotic assessments. Coincidentally, USEPA Science Advisory Board lists the "state of the science in defining ecoregions and reference areas" as one limitation in the use of biocriteria in water quality studies (SAB 1993).

A basic assumption of bioassessment designs is that reference conditions that are sufficiently comparable to test sites exist and that reference sites and test sites have a similar biological potential. The widespread degradation of surface waters (Karr and Chu 1999) has led to a dearth of pristine or pre-Columbian conditions that can be used as reference sites. Consequently, the standard of pristine conditions has been supplanted by the acceptance of least-impaired conditions for defining both reference conditions and restoration goals (Barbour et al. 1999; Karr and Chu 1999). This strategy allows assessments to be designed when least-impaired conditions can be identified. Acceptance and use of least-impaired conditions establishes a precedent for using a factor-ceiling approach to identify reference-type conditions across environmental gradients, as shown in the present study.

Urban environmental settings often display a continuum of potential stream function from near-natural potential at near-zero urbanization to extremely limited potential at the urban core (Paul and Meyer 2001). There are many well-known and obvious factors that create this gradient in potential stream function and are detailed throughout this volume. Although the fluvial hydrologic effects of some factors can be mitigated (e.g., impacts on stream chemistry), others will likely not change under most restoration scenarios. These latter factors (e.g., road corridors, canalization, high imperviousness) form a complex gradient of increasing effect that starts at the rural–urban interface and progresses to the urban core and set limits to stream function and probable restoration goals (Booth and Jackson 1997).

These limits to stream function influence the biotic potential of lotic systems along a rural–urban gradient (Allan and Flecker 1993; Morley and Karr 2002). In our study, biological condition ranged from near-zero to a higher, maximum value across the full range of urban land cover. The objectively modeled factor-ceiling represents an attainable biological potential given current urban land cover. Therefore, sites displaying an EPT score below the potential can be nominally ranked into impairment categories, while accounting for the constraints existing because of background urban land cover.

Altitude is a significant constraint on the distribution of benthic macroinvertebrates (Ward 1986) and often confounds detecting impairment in streams (Carter et al. 1996; Cuffney et al. 2005, this volume; Fend et al. 2005). Our analyses indicated that altitude was not significantly different among the impairment groups, and given the relatively large within-group sample size, similarity among groups in mean altitude was likely attributable to a large range in altitude within each impairment group. However, estimated differences in mean UHA of each group displayed an almost linear relationship among impairment groups. This indicates at least a partial decoupling of estimated urban impairment from altitude and a partial controlling of the confounding effect of altitude on interpreting impairment based on macroinvertebrate distributions in the Santa Clara Valley basin.

High species turnover along the extensive environmental gradients present in large-scale studies limits logical comparisons among sites (Hawkins and Vinson 2000). One of these gradients in lotic studies is longitudinal change (Ward 1986; Carter et al. 1996) and is predicted by the River Continuum Concept (Vannote et al. 1980). In urban studies, a second gradient in stream structure and function results from the background template of urban land use cover. This second gradient also leads to excessive species turnover, which further confounds comparing assemblages for evaluating water quality impacts. Even though this latter gradient is anthropogenic, both of these gradients are continuous in nature, which strongly argues against partitioning (stratifying) geographical areas even as small as our study basin (Hawkins et al. 2000). The coincidence of these gradients is particularly common in areas that are environmentally diverse, such as the topographically complex western United States. (see Cuffney et al. 2005).

If a continuous gradient in potential condition is not used, but a method which partitions a basin is chosen, the boundaries between partitions should be viewed as somewhat artificial. Use of rigid partitions places the onus on those who develop monitoring strategies to make the boundaries at least fuzzy if not probabilistic relative to expected response values (biological potential), such as in RIVPACS-type models (Wright et al. 2000). Conceptually, establishing a reference system by incorporating the effects of either a natural gradient or, in the case of an urban setting, an immutable anthropogenic gradient, functionally integrates, instead of ignores, the influence of environmental setting on stream structure and function. This reference condition can be represented by a modeled factor-ceiling in urban environmental settings.

We consider the urban environment part of the overall template within which bioassessments must be designed. Although some mitigation of the influence of the urban setting is possible and desirable from a cultural standpoint, there are other aspects that society probably will not change. The method we present to estimate the biological potential acknowledges many of these limitations; it seems only pragmatic to include this urban portion of the template in our assessment designs and development of potential indicators (Palmer et al. 2004).

One of our goals was to develop a simple, but effective bioindicator. The majority of bioassessment programs attempt to identify all taxa that are sorted from benthic samples collected for biomonitoring (Carter and Resh 2001). Even with this level of effort—or possibly because of it—variability exists among programs. This leads not only to poor comparability among programs (Houston et al. 2002), but also, in general, a less tractable biological response. We based our bioindicator on two metrics derived from the EPTs because we desired an indicator that was more tractable, inexpensive to determine, had a high probability of among-program comparability, and adequately responded to anthropogenic stressors. Wallace et al. (1996) showed that the EPT and the total benthic assemblage responded similarly when evaluating impairment. Our data also indicate a high correlation between the entire benthic assemblage and the derived EPT score.

Although rare in biomonitoring studies, basing the biological response on fewer taxa likely contributes to a clearer understanding of the effects of both anthropogenic and natural factors on individual metrics. Basing an indicator on fewer taxa also allows more effort to be spent on species-level identifications, which leads to a better understanding of each taxon's contribution to the chosen metric (Resh and Unzicker 1975). Most importantly, this knowledge can lead to a more mechanistic understanding of the specific indicator response (Lenat and Resh 1999). Our failure to understand these responses is currently one of the fundamental limitations to incorporating biocriteria in water quality standards (SAB 1993).

We estimated a potential indicator value using partitioned OLS regression using percentage urban land cover derived from NLCD database. Other measures of urbanization (or even other land cover types or natural gradients) as well as other bioindicators could be used in these analyses. Also, other methods of defining the upper limits of polygonal distributions such as quantile regression (Scharf et al. 1998; Cade et al. 1999) are available and may even be more appropriate in some situations. However, the method presented here can be objectively implemented with relatively little effort using readily available statistical packages.

The advantages of assessing water quality using the biota have been repeatedly stated (Rosenberg and Resh 1993; Barbour et al. 1999; Karr and Chu 1999). However, numeric criteria based on the composition and structure of lotic benthic macroinvertebrate assemblages currently exist for only a few state water quality programs (USEPA 2002b). Concerns still surround the nonimpact related effects of specific natural and anthropogenic factors, as well as the identification of reference conditions (SAB 1993; Polls 1994; Reash 1995). Clearly, a more thorough understanding of these factors is necessary. In the interim, incorporation of the effects of known limiting factors, which are often represented by continuous gradients, seems an important component of establishing practical and broadly acceptable limits for biomonitoring lotic systems. For the foreseeable future, humans will continue to impact natural systems (Palmer et al. 2004);

acknowledging these influences seems a necessary component when modeling optimal ecosystem structure and function within urban systems.

Acknowledgments

This research was partially funded by the Santa Clara Valley Urban Runoff Pollution Prevention Program (project SC22.6.0) and the NAWQA program of the U.S. Geological Survey.

References

Allan, J. D., and A. S. Flecker. 1993. Biodiversity conservation in running waters: identifying the major factors that threaten destruction of riverine species and ecosystems. BioScience 43:32–43.

Bailey, R. C., R. H. Norris, and T. B. Reynoldson. 2004. Bioassessment of freshwater ecosystems: using the reference condition approach. Kluwer Academic Publishers, Boston.

Barbour, M. T., J. Gerritsen, G. E. Griffith, R. Frydenborg, E. McCarron, J. S. White, and M. L. Bastian. 1996. A framework for biological criteria for Florida streams using benthic macroinvertebrates. Journal of the North American Benthological Society 15:185–211.

Barbour, M. T., J. Gerritsen, B. D. Snyder, and J. B. Stribling. 1999. Rapid bioassessment protocols for use in streams and wadeable rivers: periphyton, benthic macroinvertebrates and fish, 2nd edition. U.S. Environmental Protection Agency, Office of Water, Washington, D.C.

Booth, D. B., and C. R. Jackson. 1997. Urbanization of aquatic systems: degradation, thresholds, storm-water detection, and the limits of mitigation. Journal of the American Water Resources Association 33:1077–1090.

Cade, B. S., J. W. Terrell, and R. L. Schroeder. 1999. Estimating effects of limiting factors with regression quantiles. Ecology 80:311–323.

Carter, J. L., S. V. Fend, and S. S. Kennelly. 1996. The relationships among three habitat scales and stream benthic invertebrate community structure. Freshwater Biology 35:109–124.

Carter, J. L., and V. H. Resh. 2001. After site selection and before data analysis: sampling, sorting, and laboratory procedures used in stream benthic macroinvertebrate monitoring programs by USA state agencies. Journal of the North American Benthological Society 20:658–682.

Corkum, L. D. 1989. Patterns of benthic invertebrate assemblages in rivers of northwestern North America. Freshwater Biology 21:191–205.

Cuffney, T., H. Zappia, E. Giddings, and J. Cole. 2005.

Effects of urbanization on benthic macroinvertebrate assemblages in contrasting environmental settings: Boston, Massachusetts; Birmingham, Alabama; and Salt Lake City, Utah. Pages 361–407 *in* L. R. Brown, R. Gray, R. M. Hughes, and M. R. Meador, editors. Effects of urbanization on stream ecosystems. American Fisheries Society, Symposium 47, Bethesda, Maryland.

Davies, P. E. 2000. Development of a national river bioassessment system (AUSRIVAS) in Australia. Pages 1–24 *in* J. F. Wright, D. W. Sutcliffe, and M. T. Furse, editors. Assessing the biological quality of fresh waters: RIVPACS and other techniques. Freshwater Biological Association, Ableside, Cumbria, UK.

Downes, B. J., L. A. Barmuta, P. G. Fairweather, D. P. Faith, M. J. Keough, P. S. Lake, B. D. Mapstone, and G. P. Quinn. 2002. Monitoring ecological impacts: concepts and practice in flowing waters. Cambridge University Press, Cambridge, UK.

Fausch, K. D., J. R. Karr, and P. R. Yant. 1984. Regional application of an index of biotic integrity based on stream fish communities. Transactions of the American Fisheries Society 113:39–55.

Fend, S. V., J. L. Carter, and F. R. Kearns. 2005. Relationships of field habitat measurements, visual habitat indices, and land cover to benthic macroinvertebrates in the urbanized streams of the Santa Clara Valley, California. Pages 193–212 *in* L. R. Brown, R. H. Gray, R. M. Hughes, and M. R. Meador, editors. Effects of urbanization on stream ecosystems. American Fisheries Society, Symposium 47, Bethesda, Maryland.

Gilliom, R. J., W. M. Alley, and M. E. Gurtz. 1995. Design of the National Water-Quality Assessment Program: occurrence and distribution of water-quality conditions. U.S. Geological Survey Circular 1112. Sacramento, California.

Gilliom, R. J., P. A. Hamilton, and T. L. Miller. 2001. The National Water-Quality Assessment Program – entering a new decade of investigations. U.S. Geological Fact Sheet 071–01, Reston, Virginia.

Green, R. H. 1979. Sampling design and statistical methods for environmental biologists. Wiley, New York.

Hawkins, C. P., R. H. Norris, J. Gerritsen, R. M. Hughes, S. K. Jackson, R. K. Johnson, and R. J. Stevenson. 2000. Evaluation of the use of landscape classifications for the prediction of freshwater biota: synthesis and recommendations. Journal of the North American Benthological Society 19:541–556.

Hawkins, C. P., and M. R. Vinson. 2000. Weak correspondence between landscape classifications and stream invertebrate assemblages: implications for bioassessment. Journal of the North American Benthological Society 19:501–517.

Houston, L., M. T. Barbour, D. Lenat, and D. Penrose. 2002. A multi-agency comparison of aquatic macroinvertebrate-based stream bioassessment methodologies. Ecological Indicators 1:279–292.

Hughes, R. M. 1995. Defining acceptable biological status by comparing with reference conditions. Pages 31–47 *in* W. S. Davis and T. P. Simon, editors. Biological assessment and criteria: tools for water resource planning and decision making. Lewis Publishers, Washington, D.C.

Hughes, R. M., D. P. Larsen, and J. M. Omernik. 1986. Regional reference sites: a method for assessing stream potentials. Environmental Management 10:629–635.

Karr, J. R. and E. W. Chu. 1999. Restoring life in running waters: better biological monitoring. Island Press, Washington, D.C.

Kerans, B. L., and J. R. Karr. 1994. A benthic index of biotic integrity (B-IBI) for rivers of the Tennessee Valley. Ecological Applications 4:768–785.

Lenat, D. R. 1993. A biotic index for the southeastern United States: derivation and list of tolerance values, with criteria for assigning water-quality ratings. Journal of the North American Benthological Society 12:279–290.

Lenat, D. R., and D. L. Penrose. 1996. History of the EPT taxa richness metric. Bulletin of the North American Benthological Society 13:305–307.

Lenat, D. R., and V. H. Resh. 1999. Taxonomy and stream ecology - the benefits of genus - and species-level identifications. Journal of the North American Benthological Society 20:287–298.

McCune, B., and M. J. Mefford. 1999. PC-ORD. Multivariate analysis of ecological data, Version 4. MjM Software Design, Gleneden Beach, Oregon.

Morley, S. A., and J. R. Karr. 2002. Assessing and restoring the health of urban streams in the Puget Sound basin. Conservation Biology 16:1498–1509.

Moulton S. R., II, J. L. Carter, S. A. Grotheer, T. F. Cuffney, and T. M. Short. 2000. Methods of analysis by the U.S. Geological Survey National Water Quality Laboratory - processing, taxonomy, and quality control of benthic macroinvertebrate samples. U.S. Geological Survey, Open-File Report 00–212, Denver.

Omernik, J. M., and R. G. Bailey. 1997. Distinguishing between watersheds and ecoregions. Journal of the American Water Resources Association 33:935–949.

Palmer, M., E. Bernhardt, E. Chornesky, S. Collins, A. Dobson, C. Duke, B. Gold, R. Jacobson, S. Kingsland, R. Kranz, M. Mappin, M. Martinez, F. Micheli, J. Morse, M. Pace, M. Pascual, S. Palumbi, O. J. Reichman, A. Townsend, and M. Turner. 2004. Ecology for a crowded planet. Ecological science and sustainability for a crowded planet: 21st century vision and action plan for the Ecological Society of America. Available: www.esa.org/ecovisions (September 2004).

Paul, M. J., and J. L. Meyer. 2001. Streams in the urban landscape. Annual Review of Ecology and Systematics 32:333–365.

Polls, I. 1994. How people in the regulated community view biological integrity. Journal of the North American Benthological Society 13:598–604.

Reash, R. J. 1995. Biocriteria: a regulated industry perspective. Pages 153–166 in W. S. Davis and T. P. Simon, editors. Biological assessment and criteria: tools for water resource planning and decision making. Lewis Publishers, Washington, D.C.

Resh, V. H., and J. K. Jackson. 1993. Rapid assessment approaches to biomonitoring using benthic macroinvertebrates. Pages 195–233 in D. M. Rosenberg and V. H. Resh, editors. Freshwater biomonitoring and benthic macroinvertebrates. Routledge Chapman and Hall Inc, New York.

Resh, V. H., and J. D. Unzicker. 1975. Water quality monitoring and aquatic organisms: the importance of species identification. Journal of the Water Pollution Control Federation 47:9–19.

Reynoldson, T. B., R. H. Norris, V. H. Resh, K. E. Day, and D. M. Rosenberg. 1997. The reference condition: a comparison of multimetric and multivariate approaches to assess water-quality impairment using benthic macroinvertebrates. Journal of the North American Benthological Society 16:833–852.

Rosenberg, D. M., and V. H. Resh. 1993. Introduction to freshwater biomonitoring and benthic macroinvertebrates. Pages 1–9 in D. M. Rosenberg and V. H. Resh, editors. Freshwater biomonitoring and benthic macroinvertebrates. Chapman and Hall, New York.

SAB (Science Advisory Board). 1993. An SAB report: evaluation of draft technical guidance on biological criteria for streams and small rivers. Biological Criteria Subcommittee of the Ecological Processes and Effects Committee. 1993. EPA-SAB-EPEC-94–003 Science Advisory Board, Washington, D.C.

Scharf, F. S., F. Juanes, and M. Sutherland. 1998. Inferring ecological relationships from the edges of scatter diagrams: comparison of regression techniques. Ecology 79:448–460.

Simpson, J. C., and R. H. Norris. 2000. Biological assessment of river quality: development of AUSRIVAS models and outputs. Pages 125–142 in J. F. Wright, D. W. Sutcliffe, and M. T. Furse, editors. Assessing the biological quality of fresh waters: RIVPACS and other techniques. Freshwater Biological Association, Ableside, Cumbria, UK.

StatSoft, Inc. 2004. STATISTICA (data analysis software system), Version 6. Available: www.statsoft.com (September 2004).

Thomson, J. D., G. Weiblen, B. A. Thomson, S. Alfaro, and P. Legendre. 1996. Untangling multiple factors in spatial distributions: lilies, gophers, and rocks. Ecology 77:1698–1715.

Underwood, A. J. 1997. Experiments in ecology: their logical design and interpretation using analysis of variance Cambridge University Press, Cambridge, UK.

USEPA (U.S. Environmental Protection Agency). 2002a. Research strategy: environmental monitoring and assessment program. U.S. Environmental Protection Agency, EPA-620/R-02/002, Washington, D.C.

USEPA (U.S. Environmental Protection Agency). 2002b. Summary of biological assessment programs and biocriteria development for states, tribes, territories, and interstate commissions: streams and wadeable rivers. U.S. Environmental Protection Agency, EPA-822-R-02–048, Washington, D.C.

Vannote, R. L., G. W. Minshall, K. W. Cummins, J. R. Sedell, and C. E. Cushing. 1980. The river continuum concept. Canadian Journal of Fisheries and Aquatic Sciences 37:130–137.

Vogelmann, J. E., S. M. Howard, L. Yang, C. R. Larson, B. K. Wylie, and N. Van Driel. 2001. Completion of the 1990s National Land Cover Data Set for the conterminous United States from Landsat Thematic Mapper data and ancillary data sources. Photogrammetric Engineering & Remote Sensing 67:650–662.

Wallace, J. B., J. W. Grubaugh, and M. R. Whiles. 1996. Biotic indices and stream ecosystem processes: results from an experimental study. Ecological Applications 6:140–151.

Ward, J. 1986. Altitudinal zonation in a Rocky Mountain stream. Archiv fur Hydrobiologie Supplement 74:133–199.

Whittier, T. T., R. M. Hughes, and D. P. Larsen. 1988. Correspondence between ecoregions and spatial patterns in stream ecosystems in Oregon. Canadian Journal of Fisheries and Aquatic Sciences 45:1264–1278.

Wright, J. F., D. Moss, P. D. Armitage, and M. T. Furse. 1984. A preliminary classification of running water sites in Great Britain based on macroinvertebrate species and prediction of community type using environmental data. Freshwater Biology 14:221–256.

Wright, J. F. 2000. An introduction to RIVPACS. Pages 1–24 in J. F. Wright, D. W. Sutcliffe, and M. T. Furse, editors. Assessing the biological quality of fresh waters: RIVPACS and other techniques. Freshwater Biological Association, Ableside, Cumbria, UK.

Wright, J. F., D. W. Sutcliffe, and M. T. Furse. 2000. Assessing the biological quality of fresh waters:

RIVPACS and other techniques. Freshwater Biological Association, Ableside, Cumbria, UK.

Yoder, C. O. and E. T. Rankin. 1995. Biological criteria program development and implementation in Ohio. Pages 109–144 *in* W. S. Davis and T. P. Simon, editors. Biological assessment and criteria: tools for water resource planning and decision making. Lewis Publishers, Washington, D.C.

American Fisheries Society Symposium 47:193–212, 2005

Relationships of Field Habitat Measurements, Visual Habitat Indices, and Land Cover to Benthic Macroinvertebrates in Urbanized Streams of the Santa Clara Valley, California

STEVEN V. FEND*, JAMES L. CARTER

U.S. Geological Survey, 345 Middlefield Road, Mail Stop 465, Menlo Park, California 94025, USA

FAITH R. KEARNS

Environmental Science, Policy, and Management, University of California, Berkeley 94720, USA

Abstract.—We evaluated several approaches for measuring natural and anthropogenic habitat characteristics to predict benthic macroinvertebrate assemblages over a range of urban intensity at 85 stream sites in the Santa Clara Valley, California. Land cover was summarized as percentage urban land cover and impervious area within upstream buffers and the upstream subwatersheds. Field measurements characterized water chemistry, channel slope, sediment, and riparian canopy. In addition to applying the visual-based habitat assessment in U.S. Environmental Protection Agency's rapid bioassessment protocol, we developed a simplified urban habitat assessment index based on turbidity, fine sediment deposition, riparian condition, and channel modification. Natural and anthropogenic habitat variables covaried along longitudinal stream gradients and were highly correlated with elevation. At the scale of the entire watershed, benthic macroinvertebrate measures were equally correlated with variables expressing natural gradients and urbanization effects. When natural gradients were reduced by partitioning sites into ecoregion subsection groupings, habitat variables most highly correlated with macroinvertebrate measures differed between upland and valley floor site groups. Among the valley floor sites, channel slope and physical modification of channel and riparian habitats appeared more important than upstream land cover or water quality in determining macroinvertebrate richness and ordination scores. Among upland sites, effects of upstream reservoir releases on habitat quality appeared important. Rapid habitat evaluation methods appeared to be an effective method for describing habitat features important to benthic macroinvertebrates when adapted for the region and the disturbance of interest.

Introduction

Biological sampling protocols for water quality assessment usually include habitat measurements. Habitat information is commonly used to predict an expected (unimpaired) condition that can be used for comparison with potentially impaired sites. One approach is to designate reference (unimpaired) sites (e.g., Hughes et al. 1986) based in part on the quality of local habitat conditions. At a large spatial scale, programs may use habitat measurements from many reference sites to develop models that predict biota on the basis of habitat characteristics (e.g., Wright 1995). Habitat measurements such as amount of urban land cover

(e.g., Kennen 1999; Morley and Karr 2002) or local habitat structure (e.g., Robinson and Minshall 1998; Barbour et al. 1999; Beavan et al. 2001) may also be used as a direct measure of anthropogenic disturbance.

Habitat variables used in bioassessment protocols usually include a combination of landscape measurements and field observations (Fitzpatrick et al. 1998; Barbour et al. 1999). Landscape variables such as land cover and watershed morphology are typically calculated using maps, photographs, and geographical information systems data. Field observations can be direct measurements, visual estimates or expert evaluation. Field measurements can be standardized and often have good statistical properties, but have the disadvantage of being relatively time-consuming to acquire at the appropriate spatial/temporal scale. To

---

* Corresponding author: svfend@usgs.gov

reduce costs, alternative habitat scoring approaches have been developed, such as the visual-based habitat assessment (VBHA) in the U.S. Environmental Protection Agency's rapid bioassessment protocol (Barbour et al. 1999). The VBHA and similar approaches are usually standardized using ordinal scores based on explicitly defined categories.

The list of potential habitat effects on aquatic biota is extensive, and cost constraints make selection of habitat measurements an important component of bioassessment study design. Selection of appropriate measurements may be particularly difficult in urbanized stream systems, which are characterized by novel habitat modifications that may differ greatly among watersheds or regions. Recent approaches to regional prediction of biota using habitat characteristics often have emphasized habitats with minimal anthropogenic modifications (Wright 1995; Hawkins et al. 2000; Weigel et al. 2003). Nevertheless, many areas have become so extensively modified that it has become difficult to identify unimpaired sites (Hughes 1995; Yoder and Rankin 1995; Alba-Tercedor and Pujante 2000).

Our purpose was to determine which habitat features and measurement techniques were most useful

in predicting the biological condition of stream reaches in an urbanized watershed. We evaluated data from a survey of streams in the Santa Clara Valley, California, by correlating a wide range of habitat variables with benthic macroinvertebrate scores. Much of the valley is urbanized; therefore, both natural and anthropogenic factors were assumed to be important. Rather than using predetermined categories (e.g., test versus reference) based on either habitat quality or macroinvertebrate measures, we considered both to be continuous. We sampled the area at a high density to account for both large-scale patterns and the possibility of local habitat effects on macroinvertebrates.

Study Area

Streams within the Santa Clara Valley (SCV) drain northward into south San Francisco Bay in central California, USA (Figure 1). The SCV is located between the northwest-trending Santa Cruz Mountains to the west and the Diablo Range to the east. The total watershed area is approximately 1,600 km^2, and maximum elevations are about 1,000 m. The climate is Mediterranean, with almost no rainfall from May to October. Historically, many of the streams in the SCV

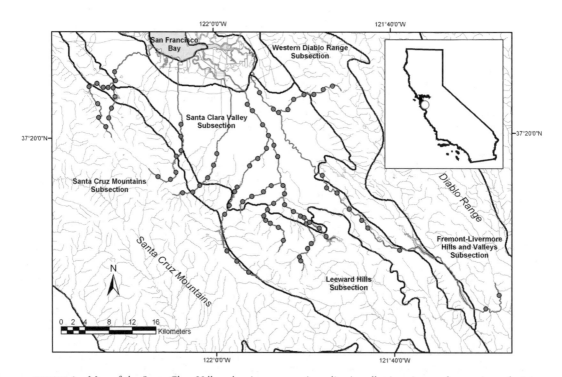

FIGURE 1. Map of the Santa Clara Valley, showing streams (gray lines), collection sites, and ecoregion subsection boundaries (dark lines). Inset shows location on California map.

were dry during the summer (Santa Clara Basin Watershed Management Initiative 2001), but now most mid to lower reaches are intensively managed by storage reservoirs and are augmented by water imported from outside the watershed. Consequently, flow regime in the SCV is highly modified, and many formerly intermittent reaches are now perennial.

Santa Clara Valley watersheds occupy portions of two ecoregions (provinces), which are divided into sections and subsections by Miles and Goudey (1997). The valley floor corresponds to the Santa Clara Valley subsection of the California Coastal Chaparral Forest and Shrub Province and is mostly located on gently sloping floodplain and alluvial fans of Late Quaternary origin. Predisturbance vegetation was mostly grasslands and oaks, but much of this subsection is now dominated by urban and more limited agricultural land cover. The western slopes include portions of two subsections, both of which are largely forested: the Santa Cruz Mountains and the Leeward Hills. The Leeward Hills subsection is underlain primarily by metamorphosed sediments and volcanics of the Franciscan Complex, and the Santa Cruz Mountains subsection is primarily a mix of Mesozoic and Tertiary marine sedimentary rock (Miles and Goudey 1997). The eastern slopes include portions of the Fremont-Livermore Hills and Valleys subsection and the Western Diablo Range subsection, which are at the northwestern edge of the California Coastal Range Shrub-Forest-Meadow Province. This part of the watershed is more xeric, dominated by grasslands, chaparral, and oak-savanna, and the sampled areas are dominated by Franciscan Complex rocks. Upland areas of both the eastern and western slopes are mostly nonurban.

Methods

Study Design

We sampled near-perennial reaches of 14 streams throughout the watershed at 2-km intervals, within constraints of accessibility, available riffle habitat, and an approximately 300-m upper elevation limit. Reach length was variable (30–175 m, median = 70 m) and generally included at least two riffle-pool sequences.

The relationship between macroinvertebrates and habitat was evaluated by correlation. Two spatial scales were considered: the watershed scale (entire data set of 85 sites), and the ecoregion subsection scale. Because five upland sites on the east slope are in a different ecoregion province, they were used only in the water-

shed-scale analyses and were omitted from the ecoregion subsection analyses ($N = 80$). The subsection analyses were done separately for valley sites (the valley floor; within the Santa Clara Valley subsection; $N = 46$) and upland sites (the western slope; combined Santa Cruz Mountain and Leeward Hills subsections; $N = 34$). Although there was substantial overlap, the division between valley and upland site groups corresponds approximately to the 100 m elevation contour.

Macroinvertebrate Samples

Benthic macroinvertebrates were collected in riffle habitat at 85 sites during May 1997 (Carter and Fend 2000), which was a period of declining flow in natural streams. Each collection was a composite of 5–0.1-m^2 kick samples taken with a 0.3-m-wide D-frame kicknet fitted with a 500-mm mesh. The five individual kick samples were collected systematically in each riffle in a downstream to upstream direction, crossing the stream twice along two diagonal lines (i.e., a V-shape across the riffle's breadth). Two of the five samples were obtained in the thalweg, and the remaining three samples were taken between the thalweg and the margins. At sites containing long riffles, sampling focused on the upstream portion of the riffle. The composited collection was preserved in the field with 10% buffered formalin. Each composited collection was subsampled to a target of 500 organisms (Moulton et al. 2000), sorted at 8× magnification, and invertebrate counts scaled to the estimated 0.5-m^2 total. The remainder of the sample was sorted without magnification for large, rare organisms that may have been missed during the subsampling process (Moulton et al. 2000), and these were added to the total. All macroinvertebrates were identified to the lowest practical taxonomic level (Moulton et al. 2000); in most cases, to species or genus.

Habitat Measurements

A wide range of habitat data were obtained for each macroinvertebrate collection site. Habitat measures were limited to those requiring minimal field time or readily available from other sources. These were grouped according to spatial measurement scale and general approach: landscape measurements, field measurements, and field visual estimates (Table 1).

Landscape measurements.—Following determination of spatial coordinates in the field using a Global Positioning System receiver, a stream segment was identified for each site on a 1:24,000-scale U.S. Geological

TABLE 1. Definitions and abbreviations of habitat variables used in the analyses. Medians and ranges of values for the entire Santa Clara Valley watershed (all sites) and for the two site groups defined by ecoregion subsections (see text). VBHA scores refer to the visual-based habitat assessment protocol (Barbour 1999).

Abbreviation	Variable definition	All sites (N = 85)		Valley sites (N = 46)		Upland sites (west slope) (N = 34)	
		Median	Range	Median	Range	Median	Range
Landscape variables							
ELEV	Site elevation (m)	82	8–341	56	8–110	134	55–299
AREA	Subwatershed area upstream of site (km^2)	49	5–824	105	8–824	25	5–102
DFM	Distance to mouth of stream at SF Bay (km)	25.0	7.1–79.8	23.7	7.1–53.1	25.8	13.8–41.7
DAMDIST	Distance to nearest upstream dam (km) (undammed = 50 km)	10.4	0.3–50	11.0	0.6–50	6.0	0.3–50
SLOPEMAP	Slope (%), derived from map contours	0.6	0.2–12	0.50	0.2–3.5	2.0	0.4–6
BUFURB	% urban land cover in 200 m × 2 km, upstream buffer	36	0–96	71	4–96	4	0–77
BUFNURB	% nonurban, nonagricultural land cover in upstream buffer	34	3–100	13	3–82	86	23–100
BUFPIA	% impervious area in upstream buffer	25	1–74	42	4–74	3	1–44
AREAURB	% urban land cover in subwatershed	5	0–70	11	1–70	2	0–19
AREANURB	% nonurban, nonagricultural land cover in subwatershed	92	26–100	84	26–98	97	79–100
AREAPIA	% impervious area in subwatershed	4	1–40	8	2–40	2.1	1–12
RDDENS	Road density in subwatershed, m/ha	26	9–96	30	13–96	25	9–46
Field measurements							
SLOPERIF	Slope (%), field measurement of sampled riffle	1.70	0.04–6.27	1.27	0.11–4.17	2.35	0.04–6.08
SLOPERCH	Slope (%), field measurement of sampled reach	0.83	0.11–4.70	0.64	0.11–1.34	1.35	0.34–3.62
WWIDTH	Riffle wetted width (m) (mean of 3)	4.3	1.2–12.2	4.6	1.5–12.2	3.8	1.8–9.8
RDEPTH	Riffle depth (cm) (mean of 5)	12.8	4.6–24.4	14.3	4.6–24.4	12.2	5.5–20.7
RVELOC	Riffle velocity (m/s) (mean of 5)	0.43	0.15–0.98	0.44	0.15–0.98	0.41	0.2–0.68
EMBED	Sediment embeddedness, mean % depth of 10 rocks	26	0–60	27	9–47	22	0–60
16%PS	16th percentile particle size (mm), riffle sediment	21	1–71	18	9–48	20	1–60
50%PS	50th percentile particle size (mm), riffle sediment	57	12–130	50	19–130	66	12–120
84%PS	84th percentile particle size (mm), riffle sediment	120	22–270	104	31–270	138	22–240
SEDSORT	Sediment sorting coefficient	2.1	1.5–6.9	2.1	1.5–4.3	2.4	1.5–6.9
CANOPY	% open canopy (mean of 3)	30	3–100	60	5–100	11	3–92
DO	Dissolved oxygen, percent saturation	101	50–178	109	50–178	98	66–116
COND	Specific conductance (µS)	546	272–1277	554	296–1,277	458	272–853
PH	pH	8.2	7.2–9.3	8.3	7.5–9.3	8.1	7.2–8.5
TEMP	Water temperature, °C	18.5	10.7–30.3	20.2	14.1–30.3	15.5	10.7–21.6
NO3	Nitrate + nitrite nitrogen (µg/L)	175	0–5,884	268	0–5,884	136	2–3,557
PO4	Phosphate phosphorus (µg/L)	28.9	0.2–289	28.4	0.6–289	30.0	0.5–210
NH4	Ammonia (µg/L)	0.50	0–616	0.58	0–200	0.34	0–616

TABLE 1. Continued.

Abbreviation	Variable definition	All sites (N = 85) Median	Range	Valley sites (N = 46) Median	Range	Upland sites (west slope) (N = 34) Median	Range
Al	Aluminum (µg/L)	1.36	0.30–12.80	1.49	0.43–5.86	1.13	0.30–12.80
V	Vanadium (µg/L)	1.60	0.28–4.10	2.12	0.56–4.10	1.32	0.28–3.82
Cr	Chromium (µg/L)	0.5	0–53.2	0.6	0.1–53.2	0.4	0–42.9
Mn	Manganese (µg/L)	3.6	0.2–2,868	3.0	0.3–69.8	4.8	0.2–2868
Fe	Iron (µg/L)	95	15–221	85	15–221	132	23–208
Co	Cobalt (µg/L)	0.09	0.03–0.56	0.09	0.03–0.26	0.10	0.03–0.56
Ni	Nickel (µg/L)	2.5	0.03–13.5	2.7	0.48–5.0	2.3	0.03–13.5
Zn	Zinc (µg/L)	22.8	3.9–45.2	22.2	5.1–32.5	22.6	3.9–45.2
Cu	Copper (µg/L)	0.87	0.23–4.29	1.15	0.28–3.05	0.71	0.23–4.29
Cd	Cadmium (µg/L)	0.006	0.001–0.021	0.006	0.001–0.020	0.005	0.001–0.021
Pb	Lead (µg/L)	0.027	0.009–0.166	0.026	0.010–0.166	0.027	0.009–0.074
	Field visual observations						
VBBSTAB	VBHA bank stability score[b]	12	5–18	14	5–18	11	5–16
VBBVEG	VBHA bank vegetative protection score[b]	13	4–18	13	4–17	14	6–18
VBCHFLO	VBHA channel flow score[b]	13	4–18	15	8–18	11	4–18
VBCHALT	VBHA channel alteration score[b]	13	4–18	12	4–18	13	5–17
VBEMBED	VBHA embeddedness score[b]	14	7–18	13	7–17	14	8–18
VBEPSUB	VBHA epifaunal substrate score[b]	15	6–19	15	8–18	15	6–19
VBRIFFQ	VBHA riffle frequency score[b]	11	4–18	10	6–17	13	5–17
VBRIPZW	VBHA riparian zone width score[b]	12	2–18	10	2–17	15	6–18
VBSEDDP	VBHA sediment deposition score[b]	12	5–17	11	5–17	13	5–17
VBVELDP	VBHA velocity-depth regime score[b]	14	4–18	13	4–18	15	4–18
VBTOT	VBHA combined index score	130	69–161	129	69–161	132	103–151
ALGCOVR	Algal cover score (0–4 scale)	1	0–4	2	0–4	0	0–4
SILT	Benthic silt cover score (riffle sediment)[a]	2	1–4	2	1–3.5	1.5	1–3
TURB	Turbidity score (1–3 scale)	1	1–3	2	1–3	1	1–3
CHANMODF	Channel modification score[a]	2	1–4	3	1–4	1.5	1–3.5
RIPVEG	Riparian vegetation composition score[a]	2	1–4	3	1.5–4	1	1–3.5
RIPW	Riparian vegetation width score[a]	3	1–4	3	1.5–4	2	1–4
UHA	Urban habitat assessment	2.0	1.1–3.0	2.4	1.5–3.0	1.4	1.1–2.4

[a] 1–4 scale.
[b] 1–20 scale.

Survey topographic map. Stream segments were defined as sections between major tributaries that had relatively constant slope and valley form (Frissell et al. 1986). Segment slope and distance from mouth were determined from map measurements, using a map wheel. Stream order was determined from solid blue map lines according to Strahler (1957).

Watershed boundaries were obtained from the Santa Clara Valley Water District. Topographically defined "subwatersheds" (defined here as the watershed upstream of each sampling site) were hand-digitized using 1:24,000 scale maps to reflect the influence of major stormwater drain systems. National Land Cover Data (NLCD; Vogelmann et al. 2001) at 30-m resolution were used to generate land cover estimates at two spatial measurement scales: (1) 200-m buffer strips (100 m wide on each side), extending 2 km upstream; and (2) the total subwatershed upstream of each site. Land cover was summarized as percentage urban, percentage nonurban/nonagricultural, and percentage impervious area (PIA). The percentage urban area was the sum of NLCD categories "Low Intensity Residential," "High Intensity Residential," "Commercial/Industrial/Transportation," and "Quarries/Strip Mines/Gravel Pits."

Imperviousness is a common means of weighting the influence of urban land cover on aquatic habitats (Walsh 2000), but sources of data relating it to land cover in the SCV are limited. The NLCD assigns a median total PIA of 90% to high intensity residential and industrial land cover categories and 55% to low intensity residential. Imperviousness for other NLCD land cover categories was estimated as 1% for natural habitats, 2% for agricultural land, and 3% for "Urban/Recreational Grasses" (Appendix 4A-1 in Santa Clara Basin Watershed Management Initiative 2001). As the categories were coarse, our calculated PIA values were assumed to be imprecise and were used in a relative sense. Density (length/area) of paved roads was derived for upstream subwatersheds using data from the California Department of Fish and Game (2002); calculations were based on road length only, due to inconsistencies in width information.

Field measurements.—Temperature, conductivity, pH, and dissolved oxygen were measured at the time of macroinvertebrate sampling (May 1997) and once again during the following month, using handheld meters. Nitrate+nitrite nitrogen was sampled in June 1997 and again in September 1998. Phosphate, ammonia, and selected trace elements were sampled once, in September 1998. Nutrients (nitrate, ammonia, and phosphate) were analyzed by automated spectropho-

tometry. Dissolved trace elements were determined by direct-injection inductively coupled plasma mass spectrometry using both external and internal standardization. Elements analyzed included aluminum, vanadium, chromium, manganese, iron, cobalt, nickel, zinc, copper, cadmium, and lead.

Physical measurements were made on site, at either the scale of the sample reach or the sampled riffle. Depth and velocity were measured at each macroinvertebrate sample point at the time of macroinvertebrate sampling. Sediment particle size (d) was measured as the length of the second-longest axis and based on a random selection of 100 particles from throughout the riffle sample area (Wolman 1954). Particle size was summarized as the 16th percentile ($d16$), the median ($d50$), and the 84th percentile ($d84$) of the second axis widths. As a measure of sediment heterogeneity, a sorting index (Andrews 1983) was calculated: $1/2(d84/d50+d50/d16)$. Sediment embeddedness was measured as the percentage depth (along the vertical axis) a particle was buried in sand or finer material, and the mean value was based on 10 randomly chosen particles. Water surface slope was measured at low flow over the sampled riffle and for the entire reach, using an auto-level. Riparian canopy shading was measured at three mid-channel points within the sample area, using a Solar Pathfinder (Solar Pathways, Inc.) to measure the solar arc for May; the value was expressed as a percentage of the expected insolation.

Field visual observations.—Visual habitat scoring approaches are used in most state bioassessment protocols in the United States (USEPA 2002a). The VBHA in the U.S. Environmental Protection Agency's rapid bioassessment protocol (Barbour et al. 1999) is commonly used and is currently recommended for use in California bioassessments (California Department of Fish and Game 2003). The VBHA scores 10 reach-scale channel features on a 1–20 scale with respect to habitat. The individual scores are summed to calculate the total index score, which can range from 10 (extremely poor) to 200. The VBHA was conducted by a single observer (F. R. Kearns) during June–July 1999 and again in summer 2000 (Kearns 2003), after prior calibration exercises with one of the developers of the protocol (Dr. M. T. Barbour, Tetra-Tech, Inc.). For consistency, all observations were based on the protocol for high gradient streams.

A study-specific Urban Habitat Assessment index (UHA) was devised from descriptive field notes taken during the macroinvertebrate sampling trip.

Categorical observations (Table 2) on a simplified, 1–4 scale were ordered to increase with urban disturbance. The categorical observations were made about one month after the macroinvertebrate collection and postcalibrated with photos. Mean values were assigned for riparian scores when the two stream banks differed and for sediment scores where the value varied over the macroinvertebrate sample reach. Visual estimates of canopy shading and sediment embeddedness were difficult to standardize, so data from the field measurements were converted to a 1–4 linear scale and used in the final calculation. Turbidity was recorded at three levels because of difficulty in standardizing observations at higher turbidity levels; the values were rescaled to a range of 1–4 (i.e., 1, 2.5, 4) for the UHA calculation. The total UHA index score was calculated as the average of these values.

In contrast to the VBHA, values of the UHA increase with urbanization. Cover by filamentous algae in riffle sediments was estimated as an additional, 1–5 visual score, but was not included in the UHA or VBHA.

Analysis Methods

We summarized macroinvertebrate data by calculating two conceptually different scores or metrics. The first, "EPT richness," is the number of species of three orders of insects that are considered sensitive to pollution: Ephemeroptera, Plecoptera, and Trichoptera (EPT). Ephemeroptera, Plecoptera, and Trichoptera richness is used in most macroinvertebrate bioassessments in the United States and almost invariably shows a negative correlation with measures of urban intensity (Kerans and Karr 1994). Because variation in the number of macroinvertebrates sorted has a major effect on estimated richness values, all samples were standardized by randomly resampling the scaled data to 470 organisms (the size of the actual minimum sample). Calculated EPT richness was based on the mean of 100 resamplings. The second biological score was derived from the first axis of a detrended correspondence analysis (DCA) ordination of the macroinvertebrate data, using log-transformed abundance data and the "detrending by segments" option in the PC-ORD software package (McCune and Mefford 1999). Detrended correspondence analysis derives a dominant trend from patterns in macroinvertebrate assemblages, and the resulting site scores are not based on prior assumptions of pollution tolerance. Detrended correspondence analysis ordination was done for the entire watershed and also separately for valley and upland site groups.

Habitat data were initially summarized by principal components analysis (PCA) to show general trends and interrelationships among the variables. For

TABLE 2. Habitat categories used in calculating the urban habitat assessment index (UHA) in Santa Clara Valley streams. Observations were scored 1–4, except for turbidity, which was collapsed to three levels.

Variable	Score value			
	1	2	3	4
Embeddedness, mean % depth of 10 rocks	<25%	25–50%	51–75%	>75%
% open canopy, mean of three measurements	<25%	25–50%	51–75%	>75%
Benthic silt cover (riffle sediment)	no obvious deposits of silt	deposits along stream margins	interstitial silt visible from surface	tops of rocks with visible silt layer
Turbidity	clear	turbid, bottom visible in about 0.3 m depth	turbid, bottom not visible	–
Channel modification	approximately natural channel	small structures: riprap, check dams	dirt or setback levees	v-shaped concrete
Riparian vegetation composition	native plants, nearly natural structure	nonnative, structure similar to natural	nonnative, structure different	very sparse
Riparian vegetation width	>30 m	15–30 m	<15 m	mostly absent

the PCA, percentage data were arcsine square root transformed (Zar 1974) and chemical measurements were $\log_{10}$ transformed. Spearman rank correlation coefficients (r_s) were used to compare the strength of relationships between environmental variables and benthic macroinvertebrate scores. Because of multicolinearity among habitat variables, the correlation coefficients were used as a descriptive measure of relative explanatory value, rather than a measure of significance. Principal components analysis and correlation analyses were performed using STATISTICA 6.0 (StatSoft, Inc. 2004).

Results

Habitat Data

Stream order ranged from 2 to 5 among the 85 sites. Dissolved oxygen was near or above saturation (Table 1); only six below-dam or downstream sites were at or below 80% saturation on the May and June 1997 sampling dates. All sites were circumneutral to slightly alkaline. Daytime water temperatures during May ranged from 11–30°C, but only four sites were greater than 25°C. Similar temperature ranges were observed in June. Concentrations of trace elements (Table 1) were below continuous aquatic life criteria (USEPA 2002b), and only one ammonia measurement was near the criterion. Although ranges of most values overlapped between valley and upland sites (Table 1), median values for nitrate, urban land cover, and variables expressing modification of channel and riparian habitats were higher at valley sites.

The first PCA axis of habitat data for the entire watershed (Table 3) suggested a typical, up- to downstream longitudinal gradient (e.g., Hawkes 1975). Variables such as channel slope (SLOPEMAP, SLOPERCH), sediment particle size (84%PS), and nonurban land use (BUFNURB, AREANURB) were associated with higher site elevation (ELEV). Lower elevation sites were associated with increased temperature (TEMP), canopy opening (CANOPY), urban land use (e.g., AREAURB, BUFPIA, RDDENS), and local habitat modification (CHANMODF, RIPVEG, RIPW). Consequently, it did not appear possible to separate effects of urbanization from natural, longitudinal/elevation gradients when evaluating the entire watershed.

Several water chemistry variables, including phosphate, conductivity, and trace elements (Fe, Co, Cd, and Pb), were negatively associated with the second PCA axis, suggesting that they were not entirely a function of our measures of land cover or the dominant up- to downstream habitat gradient. Distance to the nearest upstream dam (DAMDIST) also was negatively associated with the second axis, but some visual measures of habitat quality (VBBSTAB, VBCHFLO) had positive loadings.

Principal components analysis results for the valley and upland site groups differed somewhat from those for the entire watershed (Table 3). Axis 1 of the valley site group PCA indicated an association between urban land cover and categorical observations of habitat modification (positive loadings for VBBVEG, VBCHALT, VBEPSUB, VBRIPZW, and VBVELDP; negative for CHANMODF and RIPW). Axis 2 showed a negative relationship between elevation and most dissolved constituents. In the upland site group, axis 1 associated subwatershed urban land cover (AREAURB) with most of the dissolved constituents (all had negative loadings). Axis 2 negatively associated upland sites not influenced by upstream dams (ELEV, DAMDIST) with ammonia, manganese, algal cover, silt, turbidity, and decreased pH.

Macroinvertebrate Data

The median total richness (number of taxa in a 470-count subsample) per site was 48.5 (range = 30.2–72); median EPT richness was 10.5 (2.7–26.5). Widespread EPT taxa present in over half of the samples included the ephemeropterans *Baetis tricaudatus* and *Tricorythodes minutus*, the plecopteran *Malenka californica*, and the trichopterans *Hydropsyche californica* and *Hydroptila*. The median percentage of individuals per site that were EPT taxa was 34.8% (range = 1.3–78.4). Ephemeroptera, Plecoptera, and Trichoptera abundance was dominated by two families considered relatively tolerant to pollutants (California Department of Fish and Game 2003), the Baetidae (Ephemeroptera) and Hydropsychidae (Trichoptera). The median percentage abundance represented by Baetidae was 15.7% (0–60.8%); that of the filter feeding Hydropsychidae was 3.4% (0–46.7%). For the entire data set, numerically dominant (greater than 1% of the total abundance) EPT taxa were the ephemeropterans *B. tricaudatus*, *Fallceon quilleri* and *Diphetor hageni*, the plecopteran *M. californica*, and the trichopterans *H. californica* and *Cheumatopsyche mickeli*. Other numerically dominant taxa included members of the dipteran families Simuliidae (four *Simulium* species) and Chironomidae (seven species), and the oligochaete family Naididae (five species).

TABLE 3. Factor loadings of original variables on the first two axes from principal components analysis of habitat variables measured in Santa Clara Valley streams. Separate analyses were done for the entire data set and for the two site groups. Only variables with at least one loading ≥ |0.5| are shown; loadings ≥ |0.5| are in bold. The total VBHA and UHA scores were not included, as they are linear combinations of other variables. Abbreviations for variables as in Table 1.

Habitat variable	All sites (N = 85)		Valley sites (N = 46)		Upland sites (west slope) (N = 34)	
	Factor 1	Factor 2	Factor 1	Factor 2	Factor 1	Factor 2
Landscape variables						
ELEV	**0.79**	−0.19	0.31	**−0.66**	0.40	**0.73**
AREA	−0.29	0.23	0.41	**0.53**	−0.16	**−0.55**
DFM	0.46	0.45	**0.50**	**−0.51**	**0.77**	0.01
DAMDIST	−0.06	**−0.52**	**−0.67**	0.29	−0.27	**0.80**
SLOPEMAP	**0.60**	−0.37	0.16	−0.14	0.19	**0.65**
BUFURB	**−0.80**	0.04	**−0.61**	0.04	−0.29	−0.31
BUFNURB	**0.86**	−0.12	**0.63**	−0.13	0.39	**0.68**
BUFPIA	**−0.82**	0.04	**−0.56**	0.21	−0.31	−0.29
AREAURB	**−0.85**	−0.29	**−0.90**	0.18	**−0.89**	−0.22
AREANURB	**0.88**	0.20	**0.86**	−0.20	**0.86**	0.38
AREAPIA	**−0.85**	−0.30	**−0.89**	0.22	**−0.89**	−0.21
RDDENS	**−0.69**	−0.44	**−0.90**	0.11	**−0.87**	0.04
Field measurements						
SLOPERCH	**0.63**	−0.42	0.29	−0.16	0.06	**0.70**
RDEPTH	−0.16	0.45	0.24	0.10	**0.52**	−0.20
CANOPY	**−0.57**	0.43	−0.23	−0.27	0.07	−0.37
COND	−0.25	**−0.55**	−0.05	**0.70**	**−0.91**	0.19
pH	−0.41	−0.01	**−0.64**	−0.43	−0.11	**0.53**
TEMP	**−0.67**	0.05	**−0.54**	0.00	**−0.56**	−0.19
NO3	−0.25	−0.32	0.06	**0.65**	−0.40	0.03
PO4	−0.26	**−0.69**	−0.49	0.29	**−0.69**	0.20
NH4	−0.11	−0.19	−0.27	0.27	−0.18	**−0.57**
V	**−0.56**	−0.33	−0.23	**0.62**	−0.45	0.21
Mn	0.03	−0.22	0.35	**0.77**	−0.45	**−0.59**
Fe	0.17	**−0.62**	0.37	**0.73**	**−0.72**	0.25
Co	−0.07	**−0.51**	0.37	**0.86**	**−0.77**	−0.14
Ni	0.01	0.03	**0.64**	**0.51**	−0.19	−0.40
Cu	−0.30	−0.38	0.05	**0.62**	**−0.58**	0.13
Cd	−0.34	**−0.68**	−0.33	**0.69**	**−0.80**	0.20
Pb	−0.30	**−0.56**	−0.11	**0.82**	**−0.62**	0.50
Field visual observations						
VBBSTAB	0.08	**0.51**	0.49	0.02	0.49	−0.08
VBBVEG	0.34	0.43	**0.73**	0.17	0.30	−0.28
VBCHFLO	−0.29	**0.52**	0.36	−0.04	0.49	−0.34
VBCHALT	0.41	0.26	**0.74**	−0.03	0.03	−0.03
VBEPSUB	0.40	0.14	**0.59**	0.09	0.05	0.19
VBRIFFQ	0.42	−0.26	0.25	−0.22	0.02	**0.59**
VBRIPZW	**0.69**	−0.10	**0.70**	0.25	0.00	0.14
VBVELDP	0.42	0.07	**0.64**	−0.17	−0.04	0.08
ALGCOVR	−0.39	0.38	−0.08	−0.25	0.11	**−0.62**
SILT	−0.32	0.07	−0.03	0.11	−0.13	**−0.68**
TURB	−0.12	0.40	0.31	0.41	**0.56**	**−0.66**
CHANMODF	**−0.73**	0.14	**−0.52**	0.11	−0.08	−0.12
RIPVEG	**−0.79**	0.22	−0.46	0.08	−0.02	−0.41
RIPW	**−0.75**	0.13	**−0.64**	0.16	−0.01	−0.39

The first DCA axis of the macroinvertebrate data for all 85 sites was clearly dominant (eigenvalue = 0.354 versus 0.090 and 0.071 for axes 2 and 3, respectively). In terms of the taxonomic assemblage, axis 1 was consistent with a gradient of increasing impairment: nearly half (34 of 70) of the EPT taxa had ordination scores in the upper quartile, whereas only three EPT taxa were in the lowest quartile. Relative to other ephemeropterans, the latter taxa (*F. quilleri*, *Callibaetis* sp., and *Caenis* sp.) have been associated with warmer, more polluted, or less erosional conditions (Edmunds et al. 1976; Leland and Fend 1998). Most of the abundant or widespread EPT taxa had intermediate DCA taxon scores.

Macroinvertebrate Scores versus Habitat Data

Landscape data.—At the watershed scale (all 85 sites), EPT richness and DCA axis 1 were highly correlated with elevation (Table 4). This relationship appeared continuous, although not entirely linear (Figures 2A, B). The reduced, but still significant correlation between elevation and macroinvertebrate scores within both upland and valley site groups (Table 4; Figures 3A, B) indicated the importance of natural environmental gradients even over a small elevation range. Segment slope, which was also related to longitudinal stream gradient ($r_s = 0.73$ for SLOPEMAP

TABLE 4. Correlation coefficients (Spearman r_s) for habitat variables versus EPT S (number of Ephemeroptera, Plecoptera, and Trichoptera taxa) and DCA 1 (axis 1 of detrended correspondence analysis of macroinvertebrate data), from Santa Clara Valley streams. Separate results are given for the entire data set and the two site groups. Only values where $P \le 0.05$ are shown; r_s values $\ge |0.5|$ are in bold. For consistency, polarity of DCA axis 1 scores was reversed for the valley and upland sites. Abbreviations for variables as in Table 1.

Habitat variable	All sites (N = 85) EPT S	All sites (N = 85) DCA 1	Valley sites (N = 46) EPT S	Valley sites (N = 46) DCA 1	Upland sites (west slope) (N = 34) EPT S	Upland sites (west slope) (N = 34) DCA 1
Landscape variables						
ELEV	**0.66**	**0.75**	0.30	0.49	0.39	**0.66**
AREA	**−0.53**	**−0.61**	−0.33	−0.45	−0.34	−0.46
DAMDIST	–	–	−0.40	−0.42	**0.65**	**0.77**
SLOPEMAP	**0.71**	**0.82**	**0.53**	**0.66**	0.42	**0.65**
BUFURB	**−0.50**	**−0.51**	–	–	–	–
BUFNURB	**0.66**	**0.68**	–	–	**0.58**	**0.66**
BUFPIA	**−0.53**	**−0.56**	–	–	–	–
AREAURB	**−0.52**	−0.46	−0.39	−0.34	–	–
AREANURB	**0.65**	**0.62**	0.43	0.38	**0.52**	0.40
AREAPIA	**−0.55**	**−0.50**	−0.39	−0.34	−0.36	
RDDENS	−0.31	–	−0.33	–	–	–
Field measurements						
SLOPERIF	0.36	0.46	–	–	–	–
SLOPERCH	**0.57**	**0.69**	–	0.47	–	–
WWIDTH	–	−0.27	–	–	–	–
RDEPTH	−0.27	−0.34	–	–	–	–
RVELOC	−0.25	−0.30	–	−0.42	–	–
EMBED	–	–	–	–	–	0.34
16%PS	0.25	–	0.38	–	–	–
50%PS	0.44	0.40	**0.55**	0.49	–	–
84%PS	**0.50**	**0.50**	**0.54**	**0.56**	–	–
SEDSORT	0.24	0.25	0.29	0.38	–	–
CANOPY	**−0.55**	**−0.64**	−0.34	−0.45	–	–
DO	−0.33	−0.37	–	–	–	–
pH	–	–	–	–	**0.66**	**0.57**
TEMP	**−0.52**	**−0.62**	–	**−0.52**	–	–
NO3	−0.23	–	−0.32		–	

TABLE 4. Continued.

Habitat variable	All sites (N = 85)		Valley sites (N = 46)		Upland sites (west slope) (N = 34)	
	EPT S	DCA 1	EPT S	DCA 1	EPT S	DCA 1
NH4	−0.29	−	−	−	**−0.60**	**−0.60**
Al	−	−	−	−	−	0.43
V	**−0.50**	−0.47	−	−	−	−
Mn	−	−	−	−	**−0.69**	**−0.57**
Fe	−	0.25	−	−	−	−
Co	−	−	−	−	**−0.56**	−0.37
Field visual observations						
VBCHFLO	−0.41	**−0.52**	−	−		
VBCHALT	−	−	0.32	−	−	−
VBEMBED	0.24	−	−	−	−	−
VBRIFFQ	0.35	0.48	−	−	−	0.43
VBRIPZW	0.45	0.48	−	−	−	−
VBSEDDP	0.38	0.30	−	−	**0.54**	0.36
VBVELDP	0.27	0.25	−	−	−	−
VBTOT	0.22	−	−	−	−	−
ALGCOVR	−0.47	**−0.56**	−	−	**−0.57**	**−0.75**
SILT	−0.38	−0.46	−	−	−0.42	**−0.75**
TURB	−0.35	−0.42	−	−0.32	−0.40	**−0.58**
CHANMODF	**−0.58**	**−0.62**	−0.36	**−0.55**	−	−
RIPVEG	**−0.66**	**−0.79**	−0.32	**−0.63**	−	−
RIPW	**−0.58**	**−0.67**	−0.31	**−0.50**	−0.37	−0.46
UHA	**−0.73**	**−0.86**	−0.48	**−0.78**	**−0.53**	**−0.57**

versus ELEV), was also correlated with macroinvertebrate scores at the watershed scale and within the two site groups (Table 4).

Distance to the nearest upstream dam (DAMDIST) was highly correlated with macroinvertebrate measures within the upland site group, where most of the dams occurred (Table 4). In contrast, DAMDIST was negatively correlated with the same measures within the valley site group. In the upland site group, the exclusion of sites within 2 km of an upstream dam increased the correlations (r) between elevation and EPT richness from 0.39 to 0.52, and DCA axis 1 from 0.66 to 0.84 (Figures 4A, B).

Buffer and subwatershed land cover variables were highly correlated with macroinvertebrate measures over the entire SCV watershed, but less so within the valley and upland site groups (Table 4). In the entire watershed and within the upland site group, percentage nonurban/nonagricultural land (BUFNURB, AREANURB) was more highly correlated with

macroinvertebrates than were percentage urban land cover (BUFURB, AREAURB), PIA or road density (RDDENS) (Table 4; Figures 2C, D, 3C, D). Correlations based on land cover in buffer strips were similar to those based on upstream subwatersheds (Table 4), except in the valley site group, where macroinvertebrate measures were more highly correlated with subwatershed land cover.

Field measurements.—Most water chemistry measurements were weakly correlated with biological variables (Table 4). Exceptions were mostly in the upland site group, suggesting that decreased pH and/or high levels of some trace elements had some effect on biota at below-dam sites. Ammonia concentrations were high (greater than 100 µg/L) at four sites immediately below dams. Temperature, although derived from a single field measurement, was correlated with macroinvertebrates at the watershed scale (Table 4), due to the long elevation gradient.

Channel slope measured over the sample reach

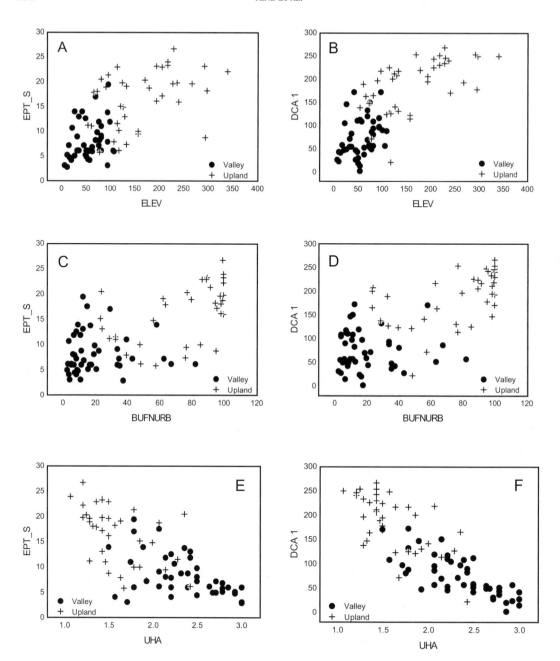

FIGURE 2. Plots of macroinvertebrate variables against habitat variables for all Santa Clara Valley streams. Definitions of variables: EPT S (number of Ephemeroptera, Plecoptera, and Trichoptera taxa), DCA 1 (axis 1 from a detrended correspondence analysis of macroinvertebrate data × 100), ELEV (site elevation in meters), BUFNURB (percent nonurban, nonagricultural land cover in 200 m by 2 km upstream buffers), and UHA (urban habitat index, see Table 2).

(SLOPERCH) was more highly correlated with macroinvertebrate scores than was the slope of the sample riffle (SLOPERIF), but not as highly as the map-derived segment slope (SLOPEMAP) (Table 4). Most other on-site, physical measurements were weakly correlated with macroinvertebrate scores. Riffle sediment measurements were only moderately correlated with the macroinvertebrate variables. Among sediment variables, the 84th percentile particle size (84%PS) usually had higher correlations than the

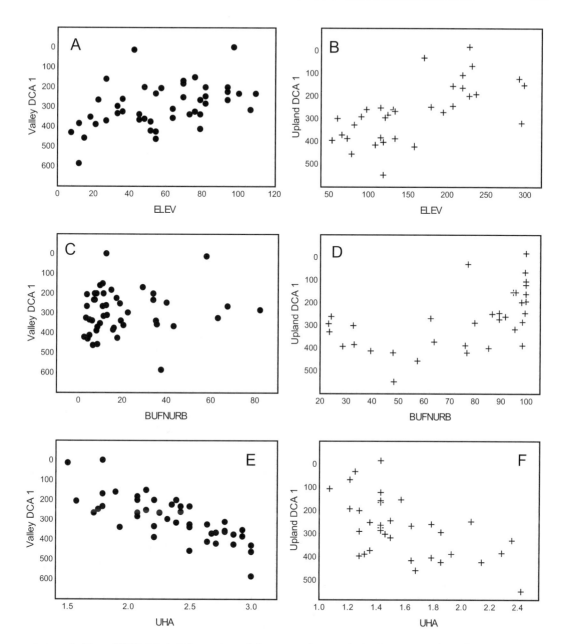

FIGURE 3. Plots of DCA 1 (axis 1 from a detrended correspondence analysis of macroinvertebrate data × 100) against habitat variables for valley (A, C, E) and upland (B, D, F) Santa Clara Valley site groups. Definitions of habitat variables: ELEV (site elevation in meters), BUFNURB (percent nonurban, nonagricultural land cover in 200 m by 2 km upstream buffers), and UHA (urban habitat index, see Table 2).

16th percentile (16%PS) or embeddedness (EMBED).

Field visual scores.—The combined VBHA index (VBTOT) was weakly correlated with macroinvertebrate scores, although some component metrics had higher correlations within one or more site groups

(Table 4). Channel flow (VBCHFLO) was negatively correlated with site elevation, due to augmented flow below reservoirs during the low-flow sampling period. Consequently, this variable tended to increase with urbanization, and higher flow values were associated with poorer macroinvertebrate scores. Values for

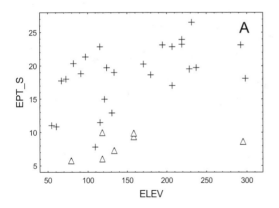

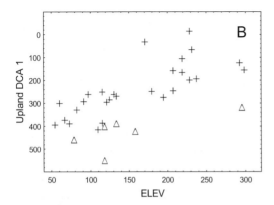

FFGURE 4. Plots of macroinvertebrate variables against ELEV (site elevation in meters) for the Santa Clara Valley upland sites. Sites within 2 km of an upstream dam are indicated by triangles. Exclusion of sites within 2 km of an upstream dam increased the correlations (r) between elevation and EPT richness from 0.39 to 0.52, and DCA axis 1 from 0.66 to 0.84. Definitions of macroinvertebrate variables: EPT S (number of Ephemeroptera, Plecoptera, and Trichoptera taxa) and DCA 1 (axis 1 from a detrended correspondence analysis of macroinvertebrate data × 100).

riffle frequency (VBRIFFQ), riparian zone width VBRIPZW), and sediment deposition (VBSEDDP) were positively associated with macroinvertebrate scores.

The combined UHA index had relatively high correlations with the biological variables at the watershed scale and within the separate upland and valley site groups (Figures 2E, F, 3E, F). All component metrics (which increased with urbanization) were negatively correlated with macroinvertebrate measures. Habitat metrics related to channel modification (CHANMODF) and riparian condition and extent (RIPVEG, RIPW) were correlated with macroinver-

tebrates at the watershed scale and within the valley site group, where channels were most highly modified. Benthic silt (SILT) and turbidity (TURB) appeared more important within the upland site group. This presumably related to the downstream effects of dams, most of which were in the upland site group. The visual score for algal cover (ALGCOVR) was not included in the UHA, but was positively correlated with macroinvertebrate measures in the upland sites.

Discussion

Distribution of Macroinvertebrates in the SCV

The general responses of aquatic invertebrates to urban land use have been consistently documented in many regions and at different spatial scales. Even in the absence of obvious point sources or exceedances of water quality criteria, there is a general reduction in sensitive species such as EPT taxa, and increased dominance by a few widespread taxa, particularly Oligochaeta and Chironomidae (Klein 1979; Pratt et al. 1981; Duda et al. 1982; Pedersen and Perkins 1986; Jones and Clark 1988; Lenat and Crawford 1994; Kennen 1999; Walsh et al. 2001; Roy et al. 2003). Our results from the SCV are consistent with these expectations. Number of EPT taxa decreased with increasing urban land cover and habitat modification. The primary DCA axis, which could be interpreted as a trend from numerical dominance by EPT taxa to dominance by more tolerant taxa, was also correlated with measures of urbanization.

For the entire SCV watershed, benthic macroinvertebrate measures were equally associated with variables expressing natural gradients (elevation, slope, temperature) and urbanization effects (land cover and reach habitat quality). As in many other urbanizing watersheds, development is concentrated in lowland areas of the SCV and is inversely related to elevation and slope. Longitudinal patterns in stream biota have long been recognized (e.g., Hawkes 1975) and tend to dominate macroinvertebrate spatial distributions (e.g., Marchant et al. 1999). Thus, longitudinal patterns can be expected to have a confounding effect in many urbanization studies. Habitat variables related to longitudinal stream gradients (e.g., elevation, slope, temperature) often covary with measures of habitat impairment in macroinvertebrate surveys (Bargos et al. 1990; Tate and Heiny 1995; Carter et al. 1996; Robinson and Minshall 1998; Roy et al. 2003). Morley and Karr (2002) also noted an interaction between elevation and urban land use, even though their study was limited to a 5–140-m elevation range. Although they were able to partially control the problem by comparing two streams with different patterns of land use with respect to elevation, this amount of local variation in land use may not always be available. Cuffney et al. (2005, this volume) controlled known environmental factors such as elevation, while emphasizing a range of urbanization, but the process is complex, requires prior knowledge of natural gradients, and may severely limit spatial coverage in study areas with strong physical gradients.

The uniform arrangement of sample sites in our survey identified continuous relationships between biota and habitat characteristics from upper reaches through the valley floor in the SCV. However, although distinct strata were lacking, partitioning the watershed into upland and valley subsections indicated different habitat–macroinvertebrate relationships in different parts of the watershed. Reservoirs were a major anthropogenic effect on patterns within the upland site group. Downstream effects of reservoirs vary widely, depending on the relative modifications to flow regime, sediment supply, temperature regime, and/or trophic conditions (e.g., Stanford and Ward 1979; Ligon et al. 1995). Our categorical field observations and subsequent measurements of benthic fine sediments (Choy 2004) indicated an increase in fine sediment in the stream bed below the hypolimnetic-release reservoirs in the SCV. Increased fine sediment below dams has generally been attributed to the loss of seasonal flushing flows (Waters 1995), but our categorical observations of turbidity below dams in the SCV also suggested increased fine sediment supply under low-flow conditions. Reservoir effects may have been too localized to appear important in correlations at the scale of the entire watershed. The negative correlation of macroinvertebrate variables with DAMDIST in the valley site group can be attributed to the location of most dams in the upland part of the watershed; hence, DAMDIST is a surrogate for longitudinal position.

Because all of the valley sites (Santa Clara Valley subsection) were downstream of dams or experienced other forms of flow modification, effects of other habitat modifications were more apparent on the valley floor. Most valley sites had noticeably turbid water under low-flow conditions, most likely a result of combined effects of reservoir operation and urban land use (Jones and Clark 1988; Waters 1995). Because valley sites had a generally depauperate EPT assemblage compared with upland sites, macroinvertebrate response to measured habitat variables would likely be differ-ent. Within this setting, local channel and riparian habitat modification appeared to have a major effect on macroinvertebrate assemblages.

Evaluation of Habitat Variables

Landscape measurements.—Land cover determinations would appear the most direct and objective measures of urbanization, although even these measures include subjective elements, particularly when summarized as variables. Some land cover measures can indicate processes, such as the effect of watershed imperviousness on hydrology (Booth and Jackson 1997) and contaminant loads (Klein 1979; Jones and Clark 1988). Land-cover measures were more highly correlated with macroinvertebrates when the entire SCV watershed was analyzed than when the upland and valley site groups were analyzed separately, possibly because of the combined effects of interacting land use and natural gradients.

Landscape-scale processes are widely considered to constrain local habitat features (Frissell et al. 1986; Richards et al. 1997). Although it appears that aquatic macroinvertebrates can be reasonably well predicted by both large- and small-scale habitat observations (Carter et al. 1996; Roy et al. 2003; Townsend et al. 2003; Weigel et al. 2003), there is little consensus regarding the spatial scale at which aquatic systems respond to land cover. Studies in different settings have implicated measurements of reach conditions (Richards et al. 1997; Dovciak and Perry 2002; Townsend et al. 2003), upstream buffer strips (Sponseller et al. 2001; Morley and Karr 2002), and upstream subwatersheds (Wang et al. 1998; Kennen 1999), although Allan et al. (1997) suggested that results of such studies may depend on their spatial extent. In small, forested streams Sponseller et al. (2001) found that land cover was a better predictor of macroinvertebrate assemblages and water temperature when measured at a local scale (200 m corridor length) than when measured at larger spatial scales and cited other studies showing highly localized effects of riparian habitat on stream temperature and organic matter processing. Nevertheless, land cover measurements based on upstream buffer strips and subwatersheds were similarly correlated with macroinvertebrates in the SCV, except in the valley subregion. The better correlation with subwatershed measurements in the valley subregion should be interpreted with caution because headwaters of almost all streams were forested, and the gradually increasing percentage urban land cover in lower reaches may simply have been a surrogate for position in the drainage.

Differences in the association of land cover variables with macroinvertebrate measures in the SCV may relate more to imprecision of the available data than to differences in effects. The weaker association of PIA compared to percentage nonurban land cover may reflect imprecision in assigning imperviousness coefficients using NLCD. Road density was less highly correlated with macroinvertebrate scores, possibly because a large range of road types was given equal weighting. An additional problem in considering watershed effects is the lack of connectivity of urban streams to their topographically-defined watersheds (Short et al. 2005; this volume). Hydrologic modifications such as reservoir operation, interbasin transfers, storm drains, and withdrawals, combined with channelization, create difficulties in linking watershed processes to instream biotic responses in the SCV.

Booth and Jackson (1997) suggest that effects of imperviousness on lotic systems in urban areas are irreversible, and it is unlikely that large-scale changes in land use will be used to mitigate these effects. The most important questions may not relate to documentation of biotic responses to urbanization in general, but rather to identifying deviations due to local effects such as point sources, local habitat modifications, and runoff management. In this context, it may be useful to consider land cover as a background (predictive) variable rather than an "impairment" (Carter and Fend 2005, this volume). An alternative approach is to set lower criteria for sites in urbanized watersheds (Yoder and Rankin 1995).

Field measurements.—Field measurements were time-consuming relative to visual estimates of condition and, except for channel slope, had limited predictive value. In typical streams, dissolved constituents, particularly nutrients, should increase in a downstream direction (Hawkes 1975); dissolved constituents such as nutrients and metals also tend to increase with urbanization (Paul and Meyer 2001; Walsh et al. 2001). This general pattern occurred in the SCV, but correlations of these constituents with geomorphic, land use, and biological variables were low, most likely due to high variability in local sources. Principal components analysis results indicated that hypolimnetic water releases from reservoirs influenced longitudinal patterns in some constituents, and correlations of some chemical variables with macroinvertebrates within the upland site group suggested a macroinvertebrate response. Decreased pH and dissolved oxygen and high values of manganese and ammonia associated with some below-dam sites were presumably a consequence of al-

tered redox conditions in the reservoir hypolimnion (Hannan 1979).

Sediment particle size and other microhabitat measurements had little predictive value, despite their importance in determining macroinvertebrate assemblage composition at smaller spatial scales (e.g., Minshall 1984). Some microhabitat effects (depth, velocity) were probably reduced by sampling only in riffle habitat. The better correlations with the largest particle size (d84) suggests that stability and/or local hydraulic habitat complexity may be more important than other sediment properties.

As in some other urban systems having impaired fauna (Duda et al. 1982; Walsh et al. 2001), chemical constituents in our limited samples generally did not approach concentrations expected to limit aquatic life. Low correlations of these and some other field measurements with biota could also imply that single measurements poorly represented rapidly changing discharge and water chemistry in these highly seasonal streams (Duda et al. 1982). However, most field measurements express components of a complex gradient, and the higher correlation of biota with elevation and land cover is presumably due to the combined effects of predictably covarying habitat characteristics, such as temperature regime and large-scale hydraulic environment (e.g., Hawkes 1975).

Field visual scores.—The macroinvertebrate variables were in some cases more highly correlated with field visual estimates than with land cover in the SCV, suggesting that rapid assessments are useful in accounting for local variation in biota caused by anthropogenic habitat modifications.

Components of the two habitat scoring systems were similar. However, the UHA was more highly correlated with biological variables than was the generic VBHA, indicating the value of adaptation to local conditions. On a smaller scale, differences in correlations between macroinvertebrate metrics and components of the UHA in the valley versus upland habitats of the SCV suggest that habitat assessments may need to be modified to account for particular influences.

Despite common use of macroinvertebrates in aquatic bioassessments, more of the literature on rapid habitat evaluation methods relates to fish habitat assessment. Results have been mixed, and studies have indicated regional variation in fish responses to habitat indices. Rankin (1995), working in Ohio, had greater success predicting fish metrics with a locally derived habitat index than with the VBHA and argued for regional adaptation of habitat evaluation methods. Wang et al. (1998) found observations of channelization, instream cover, and riparian habitat to be most useful in predicting fish index of biotic integrity scores in a statewide survey of low gradient streams in Wisconsin. In contrast, Hall et al. (2002) found that hydraulic complexity and sediment embeddedness distinguished reference from impaired sites in Maryland streams. Channel alteration and riparian buffer width did not appear important. In a Wisconsin study, Fitzpatrick et al. (2001) found that a Wisconsin habitat index was a better predictor of both fish and macroinvertebrate metrics than was a Michigan index. They attributed this to differences in the component habitat metrics, rather than to regional differences. The Michigan index emphasized local (instream) effects, whereas the Wisconsin index better represented riparian condition and was more highly correlated with other habitat measures, including land cover. Stauffer and Goldstein (1997) found that three rapid habitat approaches developed in other regions were of little use in predicting fish assemblages in prairie streams. Nevertheless, they proposed that careful selection of habitat metrics appropriate to the region could improve their predictive value.

Regional considerations may be important even if a habitat evaluation procedure is specifically developed for urbanization. For example, some processes commonly associated with urbanization, such as channel widening and downcutting, or increased runoff and sediment transport (Klein 1979), are greatly modified by flood-control engineering (channel enlargement and reservoir operations) in the SCV. The VBHA's emphasis on fluvial processes (erosion, sedimentation, and channel formation) may account for its poor performance in the highly controlled SCV streams. Visual-Based Habitat Assessment habitat metrics related to bank/channel stability were difficult to apply at sites with anthropogenically stabilized stream channels. Additionally, because decreased base flow may be expected in streams within impervious watersheds (Klein 1979), the metric "Channel Flow Status" positively weighted higher stream discharge. However, increased discharge may reflect anthropogenic modifications to the natural hydrograph of the SCV, a region with many intermittent streams having supplemented flows in their lower reaches. It is important to note that although the UHA provided information useful in interpreting macroinvertebrate distributions in the SCV, there is room for improvement. In addition to improving category definitions and optimizing scaling, further development of rapid habitat protocols for the SCV and urban systems in general might be gained by developing inexpensive measures

for other stream attributes influenced by urbanization, such as habitat complexity and flow regime.

Because habitat effects on biota are location-dependent, it is difficult to make an a priori choice among potentially important habitat attributes. Consequently, habitat evaluations in biomonitoring protocols need to be comprehensive and express the range of conditions and modifications characteristic of the type of system in question; however, protocols must also be cost-effective. Petersen (1992) reported 20 min average time to complete a rapid habitat assessment protocol, which had many of the components of the VBHA. Our UHA procedure was a comparable effort, even with the limited measurements of embeddedness and canopy cover. Rapid habitat assessment protocols may be as efficient as more rigorous measurements in summarizing the complex channel information needed to describe some stream processes, and may be easier to apply at the scale of interest (reach, rather than a point or transect). For example, the category "channelized" may provide information equivalent to many measurements of bank angle, substrate, and riparian condition. At an exploratory or general monitoring stage, coarse observations of relevant environmental constraints are likely to be more useful than costly, precise measures of less-important habitat characteristics.

Acknowledgments

This research was partially funded by the Santa Clara Valley Urban Runoff Pollution Prevention Program (project SC22.6.0) and the NAWQA program of the U.S. Geological Survey. Leila Gass (USGS) did much of the data acquisition and spatial summarization of land cover data. Ron Avanzino and Steve Hager (USGS) ran the nutrient analyses, and Brent Topping (USGS) analyzed the trace element samples. Graduate students Brent Spencer (San Jose State University), Kateri Harrison (San Francisco State University), and Paul Weissich (Hayward State University) assisted with field work and laboratory processing of macroinvertebrate samples. Chris Fischer and Charles Pruess of the Coyote Creek Riparian Station provided access information and assisted with site selection. John Shay provided information and access to sites administered by the Santa Clara Valley Water District.

References

Allan, J. D., D. L. Erickson, and J. Fay. 1997. The influence of catchment land use on stream integrity across multiple spatial scales. Freshwater Biology 37:149–161.

Alba-Tercedor, J., and A. Pujante. 2000. Running- water biomonitoring in Spain: opportunities for a predictive approach. Pages 207–216 in J. F. Wright, D. W. Sutcliffe, and M. T. Furse, editors. Assessing the biological quality of fresh waters: RIVPACS and other techniques. Freshwater Biological Association, Ambleside, Cumbria, UK.

Andrews, D. F. 1983. Entrainment of gravel from naturally sorted riverbed material. Geological Society of America Bulletin 94:1225–1231.

Barbour, M. T., J. Gerritsen, B. D. Snyder, and J. B. Stribling. 1999. Rapid bioassessment protocols for use in streams and wadeable rivers: periphyton, benthic macroinvertebrates and fish, 2nd edition. U.S. Environmental Protection Agency, Office of Water, EPA 841-B-99–002, Washington, D.C.

Bargos, T., J. M. Mesanza, A. Basaguren, and E. Orive. 1990. Assessing river water quality by means of multifactorial methods using macroinvertebrates. A comparative study of main water courses of Biscay. Water Research 24:1–10.

Beavan, L., J. Sadler, and C. Pinder. 2001. The invertebrate fauna of a physically modified river. Hydrobiologia 445:97–108.

Booth, D. B., and C. R. Jackson. 1997. Urbanization of aquatic systems: degradation thresholds, stormwater detection, and the limits of mitigation. Journal of the American Water Resources Association 33:1077–1091.

California Department of Fish and Game. 2002. The California environmental information catalog. Roads. Available: http://gis.ca.gov/catalog/BrowseRecord.epl?id=269. (June 2003)

California Department of Fish and Game. 2003. California stream bioassessment procedure. Revision, December, 2003. California Department of Fish and Game, Water Pollution Control Laboratory, Sacramento, California. Available: www.dfg.ca.gov/cabw/csbp_2003.pdf . (March 2004)

Carter, J. L., and S. V. Fend. 2000. The distribution and abundance of lotic macroinvertebrates during spring 1997 in seven streams of the Santa Clara Valley area, California. U.S. Geological Survey Open-File Report 00–68, Menlo Park, California.

Carter, J. L., and S. V. Fend. 2005. Setting limits: the development and use of factor-ceiling distributions for an urban assessment using macroinvertebrates. Pages 179–191 in L. R. Brown, R. H. Gray, R. M. Hughes, and M. R. Meador, editors. Effects of urbanization on stream ecosystems. American Fisheries Society, Symposium 47, Bethesda, Maryland.

Carter, J. L., S. V. Fend, and S. S. Kennelly. 1996. The

relationships among three habitat scales and stream benthic invertebrate community structure. Freshwater Biology 35:281–299.

Choy, M. L. 2004. A comparison of the effects of regulated and non-regulated hydrologic regimes on fine sediment deposition and benthic macroinvertebrate distributions. Senior thesis. University of California, Berkeley.

Cuffney, T. F., H. Zappia, E. M. P. Giddings, and J. F. Coles. 2005. Effects of urbanization on benthic macroinvertebrate assemblages in contrasting environmental settings: Boston, Massachusetts; Birmingham, Alabama; and Salt Lake City, Utah. Pages 361–407 in L. R. Brown, R. M. Hughes, R. Gray, and M. R. Meador, editors. Effects of urbanization on stream ecosystems. American Fisheries Society, Symposium 47, Bethesda, Maryland.

Dovciak, A. L., and J. A. Perry. 2002. In search of effective scales for stream management: does agroecoregion, watershed, or their intersection best explain the variance in stream macroinvertebrate communities? Environmental Management 30:365–377.

Duda, A. M., D. R. Lenat, and D. L. Penrose. 1982. Water quality in urban streams – what we can expect. Journal of the Water Pollution Control Federation 54:1139–1147.

Edmunds, G. F., S. L. Jensen, and L. Berner. 1976. The mayflies of North and Central America. University of Minnesota Press, Minneapolis.

Fitzpatrick, F. A., I. R. Waite, P. J. D'Arconte, M. R. Meador, M. A. Maupin, and M. E. Gurtz. 1998. Revised methods for characterizing stream habitat in the National Water-Quality Assessment Program. U.S. Geological Survey Water-Resources Investigations Report 98–4052, Raleigh, North Carolina.

Fitzpatrick, F. A., B. C. Scudder, B. N. Lenz, and D. L. Sullivan. 2001. Effects of multi-scale environmental characteristics on agricultural stream biota in eastern Wisconsin. Journal of the American Water Resources Association 37:1489–1507.

Frissell, C. A., W. J. Liss, C. E. Warren, and M. D. Hurley. 1986. A hierarchical framework for stream habitat classification: viewing streams in a watershed context. Environmental Management 10:199–214.

Hall, L. W., R. P. Morgan, I. I., E. S. Perry, and A. Waltz. 2002. Development of a provisional physical habitat index for Maryland freshwater streams. Environmental Monitoring and Assessment 77:265–291.

Hannan, H. H. 1979. Chemical modifications in reservoir-regulated streams. Pages 75–94 in J. V. Ward and J. A. Stanford, editors. The ecology of regulated streams. Plenum, New York.

Hawkes, H. A. 1975. Chapter 5. River zonation and

classification. Pages 312–374 *in* B. A. Whitton., editor. River ecology. University of California Press, Berkeley.

Hawkins, C. P., R. H. Norris, J. N. Hogue, and J. W. Feminella. 2000. Development and evaluation of predictive models for measuring the biological integrity of streams. Ecological Applications 10:1456–1477.

Hughes, R. M. 1995. Defining acceptable biological status by comparing with reference conditions. Pages 31–47 *in* W. S. Davis and T. P. Simon, editors. Biological assessment and criteria: tools for water resource planning and decision making. Lewis Publishers, Boca Raton, Florida.

Hughes, R. M., D. P. Larsen, and J. M. Omernik. 1986. Regional reference sites: a method for assessing stream potentials. Environmental Management 10:629–635.

Jones, R. C. and C. C. Clark. 1988. Impact of watershed urbanization on stream insect communities. Water Resources Bulletin 23:1047–1055.

Kearns, F. R. 2003. The relationship between physical habitat and biology in freshwater ecosystems. Doctoral dissertation. University of California, Berkeley.

Kennen, J. G. 1999. Relation of macroinvertebrate community impairment to catchment characteristics in New Jersey streams. Journal of the American Water Resources Association 35:939–955.

Kerans, B. L., and J. R. Karr. 1994. A benthic index of biotic integrity (B-IBI) for rivers of the Tennessee Valley. Ecological Applications 4:768–785.

Klein, R. D. 1979. Urbanization and stream quality impairment. Water Resources Bulletin 15:948–963.

Leland, H. V., and S. V. Fend. 1998. Benthic invertebrate distributions in the San Joaquin River, California, in relation to physical and chemical factors. Canadian Journal of Fisheries and Aquatic Sciences 55:1051–1067.

Lenat, D. R., and J. K. Crawford. 1994. Effects of land use on water quality and aquatic biota of three North Carolina piedmont streams. Hydrobiologia 294:185–199.

Ligon, F. K., W. E. Dietrich, and W. J. Trush. 1995. Downstream ecological effects of dams: a geomorphic perspective. BioScience 45(3):183–192.

Marchant, R., A. Hirst, R. Norris, and L. Metzeling. 1999. Classification of macroinvertebrate communities across drainage basins in Victoria, Australia: consequences of sampling on a broad spatial scale for predictive modeling. Freshwater Biology 41:253–268.

McCune, B., and M. J. Mefford. 1999. Multivariate analysis of ecological data version 4.20. MjM Software, Gleneden Beach, Oregon.

Miles, S. R. and C. B. Goudey. 1997. Ecological subregions of California. Section and subsection descriptions. U.S. Department of Agriculture, Forest Service, Pacific Southwest Region, R5-EM-TP-005, San Francisco.

Minshall, G. W. 1984. Aquatic insect-substratum relationships. Pages 358–400 *in* V. H. Resh, and D. M. Rosenberg, editors. The ecology of aquatic insects. Praeger Publishers, New York.

Morley, S. A., and J. R. Karr. 2002. Assessing and restoring the health of urban streams in the Puget Sound basin. Conservation Biology 16:1498–1509.

Moulton, S. R., II, J. L. Carter, S. A. Grotheer, T. F. Cuffney, and T. M. Short. 2000. Methods of analysis by the U.S. Geological Survey National Water Quality Laboratory—processing, taxonomy, and quality control of benthic macroinvertebrate samples. U.S. Geological Survey Open-File Report 00–212, Denver.

Paul, M. J., and J. L. Meyer. 2001. Streams in the urban landscape. Annual Review of Ecology and Systematics 32:333–365.

Pedersen, E. R., and M. A. Perkins. 1986. The use of benthic invertebrate data for evaluating impacts of urban runoff. Hydrobiology 139:13–22.

Petersen, R. C. Jr. 1992. The RCE: a riparian, channel, and environmental inventory for small streams in the agricultural landscape. Freshwater Biology 27:295–306.

Pratt, J. M., R. A. Coler, and P. J. Godfrey. 1981. Ecological effects of urban stormwater runoff on benthic macroinvertebrates inhabiting the Green River, Massachusetts. Hydrobiologia 83:29–42.

Rankin, E.T. 1995. Habitat indices in water resource quality assessments. Pages 181–208 *in* W. S. Davis, and T. P. Simon, editors. Biological assessment and criteria: tools for water resource planning and decision making. Lewis Publishers, Boca Raton, Florida.

Richards, C., R. J. Haro, L. B. Johnson, and G. E. Host. 1997. Catchment and reach-scale properties as indicators of macroinvertebrate species traits. Freshwater Biology 37:219–230.

Robinson, C. T., and G. W. Minshall. 1998. Regional assessment of wadable streams in Idaho, USA. Great Basin Naturalist 58:54–65.

Roy, A. H., A. D. Rosemond, M. J. Paul, D. S. Leigh, and J. B. Wallace. 2003. Stream macroinvertebrate response to catchment urbanization (Georgia, U.S.A.) Freshwater Biology 48:329–346.

Santa Clara Basin Watershed Management Initiative. 2001. Watershed Management Plan, volume 1 unabridged. Watershed Characteristics Report. Available: www.scbwmi.org.

Short, T. M., E. M. P. Giddings, H. Zappia, and J. F. Coles. 2005. Urbanization effects on stream habitat characteristics in Boston, Massachusetts; Birmingham, Alabama; and Salt Lake City, Utah. Pages 317–332 *in* L. R. Brown, R. H. Gray, R. M. Hughes, and M. R. Meador, editors. Effects of urbanization on stream ecosystems. American Fisheries Society, Symposium 47, Bethesda, Maryland.

Sponseller, R. A., E. F. Benfield, and H. M. Valett. 2001. Relationships between land use, spatial scale and stream macroinvertebrate communities. Freshwater Biology 46:1409–1424.

StatSoft, Inc. 2004. STATISTICA (data analysis software system), version 6. Tulsa, Oklahoma.

Stanford, J. A., and J. V. Ward. 1979. Stream regulation in North America. Pages 215–236 *in* J. V. Ward and J. A. Stanford, editors. The ecology of regulated streams. Plenum, New York.

Stauffer, J. C., and R. M. Goldstein. 1997. Comparison of three qualitative habitat indices and their applicability to prairie streams. North American Journal of Fisheries Management 17:348–361.

Strahler, A. N. 1957. Quantitative analysis of watershed geomorphology. American Geophysical Union Transactions 38:913–920.

Tate, C. M., and J. S. Heiny. 1995. The ordination of benthic invertebrate communities in the South Platte River basin in relation to environmental factors. Freshwater Biology 33:439–454.

Townsend, C. R., S. Dolédec, R. Norris, K. Peacock, and C. Arbuckle. 2003. The influence of scale and geography on relationships between stream community composition and landscape variables: description and prediction. Freshwater Biology 48:768–785.

USEPA (U.S. Environmental Protection Agency). 2002a. Summary of biological assessment programs and biocriteria development for states, tribes, territories, and interstate commissions: streams and wadeable rivers. U.S. Environmental Protection Agency, EPA-822-R-02-048, Washington, D.C.

USEPA (U.S. Environmental Protection Agency). 2002b. National recommended water quality criteria: 2002. U.S. Environmental Protection Agency, EPA-822-R-02-047, Washington, D.C.

Vogelmann, J. E., S. M. Howard, L. Yang, C. R. Larson, B. K. Wylie, and N. Van Driel. 2001. Completion of the 1990s National Land Cover Data Set for the conterminous United States from Landsat Thematic Mapper data and ancillary data sources. Photogrammetric Engineering and Remote Sensing 67:650–662.

Walsh, C. J. 2000. Urban impacts on the ecology of receiving waters: a framework for assessment, conservation and restoration. Hydrobiologia 431:107–114.

Walsh, C. J., A. K. Sharpe, P. F. Breen, and J. A. Sonneman. 2001. Effects of urbanization on streams of the Melbourne region, Victoria, Australia. I. Benthic macroinvertebrate communities. Freshwater Biology 46:535–551.

Wang, L., J. Lyons, and P. Kanehl. 1998. Development and evaluation of a habitat rating system for low-gradient Wisconsin streams. North American Journal of Fisheries management 18:775–785.

Waters, T. F. 1995. Sediment in streams: sources, biological effects, and control. American Fisheries Society, Monograph 7, Bethesda, Maryland.

Weigel, B. M., L. Wang, P. W. Rasmussen, J. T. Butcher, P. M. Stewart, T. P. Simon, and M. T. Wiley. 2003. Relative influence of variables at multiple spatial scales on stream macroinvertebrates in the Northern Lakes and Forest ecoregion, U.S.A. Freshwater Biology 48:1440–1461.

Wolman, M. G. 1954. A method of sampling coarse riverbed material. Transactions of the American Geophysical Union 35:951–956.

Wright, J. F. 1995. Development and use of a system for predicting the macroinvertebrate fauna in flowing waters. Australian Journal of Ecology 20:181–197.

Yoder, C. O. and E. T. Rankin. 1995. Biological criteria program development and implementation in Ohio. Pages 109–144 *in* W. S. Davis and T. P. Simon, editors. Biological assessment and criteria: tools for water resource planning and decision making. Lewis Publishers, Boca Raton, Florida.

Zar, J. H. 1974. Biostatistical analysis. Prentice-Hall Inc., Englewood Cliffs, New Jersey.

American Fisheries Society Symposium 47:213–227, 2005
© 2005 by the American Fisheries Society

Managing Conflicts on the Lower American River—Can Urban and Agricultural Demands Be Met while Maintaining Healthy Fisheries?

Leo Winternitz* and Elizabeth Holtz

*Sacramento Water Forum/Metropolitan Water Planning
660 J Street, Suite 260, Sacramento, California 95814, USA*

Abstract.—The lower American River, located in Sacramento County, California, provides important habitat, a high-quality water source, a critical floodway, and a spectacular regional recreational parkway. It is also a key water source for the Central Valley Project, which provides irrigation water to 3 million acres of the country's most productive agricultural lands. The river supports 43 species of native and nonnative fish, including fall-run Chinook salmon *Oncorhynchus tshawytscha* and steelhead *O. mykiss*. In the last decade, one quarter of all fall-run Chinook salmon produced in California's Central Valley have come from the American River. The Sacramento region's population is expected to double to more than 2 million people in the next 30 years. Water demand to meet population growth will cause additional stress on a river system that currently experiences low flow and high temperatures during critical salmonid spawning and rearing life stages. Increased demand for American River water outside the region will contribute to higher fall river water temperatures and more frequent fluctuating flows that result in stranding and/or isolation of fish. In 1993, regional stakeholders decided that new methods were needed to avoid water shortages, environmental degradation, groundwater contamination, and limits to economic prosperity. Consequently, they created the Water Forum. After 6 years of intense, interest-based negotiations, 40 stakeholder organizations approved the comprehensive Water Forum Agreement in 2000. The agreement allows the region to meet its needs in a balanced way through implementation of a comprehensive package of linked actions.

Introduction

More than 75% of the U.S. population lives in urban areas (Paul and Meyer 2001). As a result of this concentration of people, urban streams and rivers are increasingly vulnerable to degradation. More than 130,000 km of urban stream habitat were considered impaired as of 2000 (USEPA 2000). Degradation may occur as a result of a number of factors, including increased water diversion to meet increasing urban demand or increased pollution due to nearby human activities. Urban runoff containing common urban chemicals can contribute to declines in the species richness of the biota inhabiting urban waterways, including fish populations (Paul and Meyer 2001). Maintaining the ecological and esthetic values of streams as urbanization occurs is a growing and difficult challenge for managers.

The lower American River (LAR) runs through the heart of Sacramento County—a metropolitan area with a population of 2 million people (Figure 1). Growth projections estimate that about 2.5 million people will inhabitant the region by 2025 (SACOG 2003). This population growth is expected to result in increased diversions from the LAR for water supply. From Nimbus Dam to the confluence with the Sacramento River, a 37-km, 20-km² nature preserve and recreation area provides public access to the American River and supports 5 million visitor days per year. In addition, the LAR contributed about 17% of the Chinook salmon *Oncorhynchus tshawytscha* produced in the Central Valley during the period 1952–2003 (ranging from a low about 4% to a high of about 35% based on Central Valley Chinook salmon escapement estimates) (Rob Titus, California Department of Fish and Game, personal communication), supporting both recreational and commercial fisheries. It seems likely that the increased water diversions projected to result from growing ur-

---

* Corresponding author: lwinternitz@waterforum.org

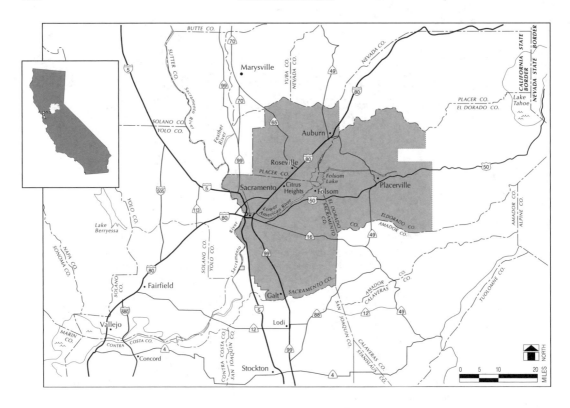

FIGURE 1. Map of region—shaded areas indicate Water Forum area of interest.

ban demand could have a large impact on the recreational and fishery uses of the river (The Lower American River Task Force 2002). The objective of this paper is to describe how local agencies came together to address these problems cooperatively after a long period of conflict. We first provide the historical context for the resources and the litigation, which eventually led to cooperation. We then describe how the agencies came together and reached consensus and the terms of the present agreement. Finally, we describe recent accomplishments and future steps and challenges.

Study Area

The LAR is located in Sacramento County, California and is the second-largest tributary to the Sacramento River, the largest river in the state (Lower American River Task Force 2002). The American River originates at an elevation of 3,048 m in the Sierra Nevada mountain range (Figure 2). Average annual runoff from the 3,017 km² watershed is 3,329 million m³ (SWRI 2001a). The area, like much of California, has a Mediterranean climate of warm, dry summers and cool, wet winters. Most precipitation falls from October through May. Annual average precipitation in the mountains is about 91 cm and about 46 cm in the vicinity of Sacramento (Domagalski et al. 2000). The majority of the watershed is located in Placer and El Dorado counties both having much lower population densities (250,000 and 156,000 people, respectively) than Sacramento County (greater than 1.2 million people) (SACOG 2003). Consequently, American River water is of excellent quality and is in high demand for both in-basin and out-of-basin use.

Historical Context for Resources

Before the arrival of nonindigenous settlers, three native American tribes resided on the floodplain of the LAR, relying on the abundant resources of the LAR and changing few of the natural processes of the river (Lower American River Task Force 2002). Although there are few historical data, the fish communities of the watershed likely included at least 18 species (Table 1), with at least three recognizable assemblages (Moyle 2002). The anadromous salmonids were likely particu-

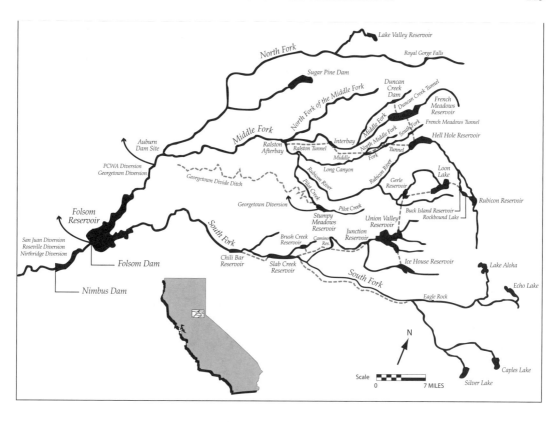

FIGURE 2. The watershed of the American River. Located on the western face of the Sierra Nevada, the watershed includes numerous reservoirs, tunnels, and irrigation diversion projects.

larly important to the tribes. The most abundant species were likely spring-run and fall-run Chinook salmon and summer-run, fall-run, and winter-run steelhead *Oncorhynchus mykiss*. These species spawned and reared in the lower 210 km of the drainage (SWRI 2001b).

With the discovery of gold on John Sutter's property in 1848, the American River and its surroundings drastically changed. Gold brought many thousands of people to the region eventually leading to statehood in 1850. Hydraulic gold mining using high powered water cannons to mine gravels in the banks and floodplains of the river, was employed in the middle and lower reaches of the river, turning one of the best salmon rivers in the state into a shallow, muddy stream (Williams 2001). An estimated total of 196 million m³ of sand and silt were deposited downstream, raising the riverbed and floodplain. In addition, the dams constructed to supply water to the water cannons likely acted as barriers to many anadromous fishes (Brown and Moyle, in press). From the late 1800s to the middle of the 1900s, dredge mining

was employed in the lower reaches of the river, southwest of the modern city of Folsom (Lower American River Task Force 2002). This further degraded the banks of the river and destroyed any remnants of the original riverbed by scooping out active gravel bars and hillsides for both gold mining and cement production. The loosened material accumulated in other parts of the system, changing channel dynamics and making the entire river more flood-prone.

In 1895, Old Folsom Dam was constructed to create power for the surrounding community (Snider 2002). The dam, located about 43 km upstream from the confluence of the Sacramento River, prevented access to the upper reaches of the American River by anadromous salmonids. An ineffective fish ladder was built in 1919 and was subsequently replaced by a more effective one in 1931 (Gerstung 1971). Another dam was built just upstream of the confluence of the middle and north forks of the American River in 1939, effectively barring salmonid access to the north fork American River. The fish ladder built in

TABLE 1. Fish species occurring in the American River watershed. Species not regularly encountered in the lower American River are indicated by an asterisk.

Scientific name (**family**, species)	Common name	Status[a]
Petromyzontidae		
Lampetra tridentata	Pacific lamprey	N
Acipenseridae		
Acipenser transmontanus	white sturgeon	N
Clupeidae		
Alosa sapidissima	American shad	I
Dorosoma petenense	threadfin shad	I
Cyprinidae		
Carassius auratus	goldfish	I
Cyprinus carpio	common carp	I
*Gila crassicauda**	thicktail chub	NE
*Hesperoleucus symmetricus**	California roach	N
Lavinia exilicauda	hitch	N
Mylopharodon conocephalus	hardhead	N
Notemigonus crysoleucas	golden shiner	I
Orthodon microlepidotus	Sacramento blackfish	N
Pimephales promelas	fathead minnow	I
Pogonichthys macrolepidotus	splittail	N
Ptychocheilus grandis	Sacramento pikeminnow	N
Rhinichthys osculus sp.*	Speckled dace	N
Catostomidae		
Catostomus occidentalis	Sacramento sucker	N
Ictaluridae		
Ameiurus catus	white catfish	I
A. nebulosus	brown bullhead	I
A.melas	black bullhead	I
Ictalurus punctatus	channel catfish	I
Osmeridae		
Hypomesus nipponensis	wakasagi	I
Salmonidae		
*Oncorhynchus gorbuscha**	pink salmon	N
*O. keta**	chum salmon	N
*O. kisutch**	coho salmon	N
O. mykiss[b]	steelhead	N
*O. nerka**	kokanee	I
O. tshawytscha [c]	Chinook salmon	N
*Salmo trutta**	brown trout	I
Atherinidae		
Menidia beryllina	inland silverside	I
Poeciliidae		
Gambusia affinis	western mosquitofish	I
Gasterosteidae		
Gasterosteus aculeatus	threespine stickleback	N
Cottidae		
Cottus asper	prickly sculpin	N
C. gulosus	riffle sculpin	N
Moronidae		
Morone saxatilis	striped bass	I
Centrarchidae		
Archoplites interruptus	Sacramento perch	NL

TABLE 1. Continued.

Scientific name (**family**, species)	Common name	Status[a]
Lepomis cyanellus	green sunfish	I
L. macrochirus	bluegill	I
L. microlophus	redear sunfish	I
Micropterus dolomieui	smallmouth bass	I
M. salmoides	largemouth bass	I
Pomoxis annularis	white crappie	I
Embiotocidae		
Hysterocarpus traskii	tule perch	N

[a] N, native species; NE, native species now extinct; NL, native species but locally extirpated; I, alien species.

[b] The anadromous form (steelhead) dominates the lower river with resident populations above the dams. Historically, there were summer-run, fall-run, and winter-run steelhead. Only winter-run steelhead are still found in the river.

[c] Historically, the river supported spring-run and fall-run Chinook salmon. Only fall-run Chinook salmon are still found in the river.

1931 was washed out by floodwaters in 1950 and was not replaced (Gerstung 1971). Five years later, both Folsom and Nimbus dams were constructed on the main stem of the American River, 45 and 37 km upstream from the confluence with the Sacramento River, respectively. Nimbus Dam restricted anadromous fishes to the lower 37 km of the river (CDFG 2003). This condition persists in the present-day system. The two remaining species of anadromous salmonids are fall-run Chinook salmon and steelhead. After the construction of Nimbus Dam, the Nimbus Hatchery was established just downstream to mitigate for the impacts on fall-run Chinook salmon and steelhead of Folsom Dam.

The dams shift the timing of peak river flow from the historic snowmelt flows in April and May to February and March, as dictated by flood control needs (SWRI 2001a). The historic peak flows usually occurred during smolt out-migration, whereas the present peak flows occur before fry emergence, increasing the risk of stranding redds. Because of water quality and water use demands, and the recreation requirements on the LAR, summer flows are now higher and cooler than historical measurements.

Before the construction of the dams, the summertime temperature of the LAR approached 26°C (Gerstung 1985). The creation of Folsom dam did not, at first, change this. Water was released from the top of the reservoir through radial gates or the spillway. This water was low in nutrients and warm due to thermal stratification in the reservoir. These releases resulted in low salmonid production and survival, as well as an increase in disease occurrence among the population because the fish could not access their cooler, upstream historic spawning grounds. With increased attention given to the importance of aquatic resources in the1960s, a temperature control device was installed at Folsom Dam, enabling reservoir managers to release colder water from the deeper levels of the reservoir[1]. Current June–August river temperatures below Folsom Dam rarely rise above 18°C (SWRI 2001a).

In addition to changes in flow, the river channel itself has been highly modified. Prone to flooding, the Sacramento area has been protected with construction of a complicated levee system surrounding the LAR. This system has created a more channelized, scoured riverbed, resulting in less habitat diversity and complexity (SWRI 2001b). Despite these physical changes, the LAR supports about 35 of the 43 native and alien fish species likely inhabiting the watershed (Brown et al. 1992) (Table 1). Over the last 10 years, the LAR has produced 23% of all fall-run Chinook salmon produced in California's Central Valley (Figure 3). The exact proportion of hatchery to wild production is unknown, but the hatchery contribution is likely large.

Of course, the development of water resources in the watershed was not intended to damage fisheries, but to provide beneficial uses to the human popula-

---

[1] A new temperature control shutter device was recently installed (2002) and has resulted in more precise temperature control. However, of concern is the depletion of a limited coldwater pool over the season. Reservoir managers continuously monitor the volume of coldwater in the reservoir, especially as the summer progresses.

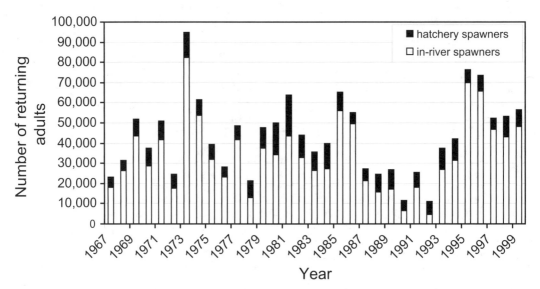

FIGURE 3. Annual Chinook salmon returns on the lower American River from 1967 to 1999 (from SWRI 2001a).

tion. As noted, Old Folsom Dam was built to provide hydroelectric power. The rapidly expanding urban areas in California's Central Valley and southern coastal region, the need to maintain water quality in the Sacramento/San Joaquin Delta Estuary, and agricultural interests in southern San Joaquin Valley all contribute to the great demand already placed on the LAR by the growing Sacramento region. In 1955, Folsom Dam was constructed to store a maximum capacity of 1,202 million m³ to satisfy this demand as well as for flood protection. In addition to Folsom Dam, an afterbay was formed by the construction of Nimbus Dam, 11 km downstream. This structure was completed to store and reregulate releases from Folsom Dam, which can vary greatly due to changing water and power demands (CSP 2004). Both structures were constructed by the U.S. Bureau of Reclamation (USBR) as part of the Central Valley Project (CVP). Water from the federal storage facility of Folsom Reservoir is committed first to urban, in-basin users and second to agricultural contractors of the federal CVP south of the Delta (Winternitz and White 2001). Agriculture is an important industry in California, contributing nearly $28 billion to the state's economy in 2001 (CDFA 2002). Revision of the CVP in 1993 made fishery protection and enhancement an equal goal of the project. The importance of this legislation (the CVP Improvement Act, or CVPIA) has been demonstrated by use of water for environmental purposes as well as agricultural needs.

The commitment of Folsom Reservoir water to south Central Valley users can create problems when water deliveries are required during Chinook salmon and steelhead migration, spawning, and rearing periods. Unnatural flow and temperature fluctuations caused by these deliveries create adverse conditions for the fishes, resulting in significant incidences of prespawn mortality for adult, fall-run Chinook salmon and lower survival for oversummering juvenile steelhead.

Urban demand on the river is significant and growing. In 2002, 293 million m³ was diverted from the LAR for urban supply, up from 244 million m³ in 2001 (Water Forum 2001). Assuming total buildout of the Sacramento area in 2030 according to the County's General Plan, diversions for urban supply will peak in wet and/or average years at 519 million m³. Meeting this demand is vital to the area's future economy and necessary to fulfill various legal agreements and contracts. At the same time, this demand must be met while maintaining a viable fishery and protecting the resources of the LAR. Community water needs are generally met through conjunctive use. Conjunctive use means that supply comes both from surface water of the American River and groundwater pumping, with the ratio varying from dry to wet or normal years.

The groundwater contamination caused by various military and rocket engine production activities in the Sacramento area has put an additional strain on the groundwater supply of several water agencies. Additional diversions from the American River are considered a possible substitute for the supply of those agencies. Greater take of water from the river will result in an imbalanced supply ratio, conceivably putting greater strain on the LAR fishery.

Demand for flood protection along the LAR is a controversial issue. From river km 22 to its confluence with the Sacramento River, the American River is bound on north and south sides by levees, protecting more than 400,000 people and $37 billion in property (Jones and Stokes Associates 1998). Rip-rap is intermittently placed along the banks, enhancing bank stability, though inhibiting vegetation growth and natural stream functions. In comparison, on the Sacramento River, floodwater is passed through weirs and bypasses that guide floodwaters out into larger areas—often farmland (Sommer et al. 2001). On the LAR, the demand for flood protection is sometimes in conflict with the management of the river. The Sacramento Area Flood Control Agency (SAFCA) is trying to minimize ecological harm by building projects of varying size using "softer" technologies (Jones and Stokes Associates 1998) such as use of vegetation to stabilize stream banks. Bank erosion along LAR threatens the integrity of the levee system, while at the same time degrading habitat. The SAFCA worked with the Lower American River Task Force in 1994 and 1995 to stabilize the banks and restore valuable riverine habitat (SAFCA 2004).

As part of the CVP, the LAR plays a crucial role in the management of water quality in the Sacramento-San Joaquin Delta (Delta), the heart of California's water system. The Delta is formed by the confluence of California's two largest river systems, the Sacramento River and the San Joaquin River. Water from the Delta is exported south through federal and state pumping facilities to augment Southern California's urban and agricultural water needs. Pulses of freshwater are often needed to control salinity encroachment from Suisun Bay into the Delta that can affect the quality of exported water. Folsom Reservoir is the closest source of stored water to the Delta. Water from Lake Shasta, a federal project facility located to the north at the headwaters of the Sacramento River, takes about 5 d to arrive in the Delta. Water from Lake Oroville, a facility of the State Water Project (SWP) located on the Feather River in the northern Sacramento Valley, takes 3–4 d to reach the Delta. As travel time increases for the water, more is lost due to evaporation and seepage. Consequently, the preferred alternative for Delta managers is to wait until the need for water is certain and then to take it from Folsom Reservoir. Releases from Folsom Reservoir arrive in 1 d with less loss. As the water is released from Folsom Reservoir, depletion of the coldwater pool becomes a concern. High usage can quickly deplete both the coldwater pool and total volume of the reservoir. Con-

sequently, there is little coldwater and often inadequate flow to support salmonid spawning and incubation in the late fall/early winter period.

Finally, the LAR provides extensive recreational opportunities for urban residents. Recreational use of the LAR is protected by law under the national Wild and Scenic Rivers Act (Wild and Scenic Rivers Act 1968). Legitimate use of the American River Parkway is encouraged by Sacramento County, which provides various access points and recreational facilities (Lower American River Task Force 2002). However, increased public access means increased Parkway use and additional stress on natural resources, in particular, the fauna and flora (Lower American River Task Force 2002). Anglers, boaters, swimmers, scuba divers, hikers, equestrians, and other recreants use the river and LAR Parkway, but also strain river resources, native biota, and habitat. For example, animal waste from horses and dogs contributes to higher nitrate levels; high levels of human visitation leads to the accumulation of garbage in the stream and riparian zone; and equestrian and hiking activities are associated with bank trampling, a factor in degrading bank stability and losses of riverine and riparian habitat.

Historical Context for Regulation and Litigation

Given the wide variety of natural and human needs the LAR is expected to fulfill, it is not surprising that the history of regulation and litigation is complex. Recent history begins with authorization to construct Folsom and Nimbus dams. The USBR was granted authorization to proceed with the Folsom Dam projects (known as D-893) by the California State Water Resources Control Board (SWRBC) (Somach 1990). Permission for water storage was granted subject to a minimum flow requirement as follows:

- 1 January through 14 September: 7 m³/s (250 ft³/s); and
- 15 September through 31 December: 14 m³/s (500 ft³/s).

Water rights permits for the USBR to operate the planned, but never built Auburn Dam came with new requirements. In 1972, Decision 1400 (D-1400) stated that minimum flows for the LAR needed to be at least

- 15 October through 14 July: 35 m³/s (1,250 ft³/s); and
- 15 July through 14 October: 23 m³/s (800 ft³/s).

Minimum recreation flows were set at 42 m³/s (1,500 ft³/s) and could be exempted, along with a reduction in fishery flow requirements, in the event of a dry year. These requirements were dependent on the construction of Auburn Dam. Because the dam has not been built, they are not legally binding on USBR. This leaves only the D-893 flows as a legal requirement.

In 1972, at the same time the D-1400 flows were produced, the USBR contracted with the East Bay Municipal Utilities District (EBMUD) for dry-year deliveries of 185 million m³ (150,000 acre-feet) of water from Folsom Reservoir through a proposed Folsom South Canal. The litigation following this contract defines the water scene, prior to the formation of the Water Forum. Partly as a result of the unrest regarding management of the American River during this time, and questions that D-1400 had raised over the flows, the Environmental Defense Fund (EDF) and Save the American River Association filed complaint on hearing of the EBMUD contract, citing the California Constitution and the California Water Code. Sacramento County sided with the plaintiffs, alleging that scenic and recreational values of the river would be threatened or lost if the contract were to be fulfilled and that D-1400 flows were not sufficient to provide optimum conditions on the river.

The California Supreme Court first ruled in favor of EBMUD in 1977. On appeal, the U.S. Supreme Court did not uphold that ruling and remanded the case to the California Supreme Court for review in 1978. The earlier decision was reversed, and in the second decision, the courts took the side of the plaintiff. Following this decision, additional complaints were filed on the side of the plaintiff, all alleging damage to the LAR. In 1984 all 21 specific issues—legal and factual—went to the SWRCB to referee. The SWRCB produced a report, and the case transferred to the Alameda County Superior Court.

The Superior Court found that EBMUD could divert its full contractual amount, but must provide minimum flows with the goal of protecting LAR resources. Judge Richard A. Hodge, presiding over the case in the Alameda County Superior Court, attempted to balance in-stream values and water as a contracted resource. The final decision was a "physical solution" requiring EBMUD to ensure in-stream flows if the contracted water was to be taken from Folsom Reservoir through Folsom South Canal. EBMUD was allowed to take its contracted 185 million m³ (150,000 acre-feet) if it ensured that minimum flows were always

- October 15 through February: 57 m³/s (2,000 ft³/s);
- March through June: 85 m³/s (3,000 ft³/s); and
- July through October 15th: 50 m³/s (1,750 ft³/s).

This judgment was entered in May of 1990.

As a result of this decision, EBMUD never diverted its contracted water and, consequently, never has had to provide for these flows. Since USBR was not a party to the case, the decision does not affect its actions. The issue of an adequate LAR minimum flow standard, the same problem that started the case, remains. This is one of the main issues that led to the formation of the Water Forum (Somach 1990).

In addition to the EDF versus EBMUD cases, two other conflicts also set the stage for a region-wide forum for water issues. The first was a proposal by the city of Sacramento to expand one of its existing water treatment plants. There was so much opposition directed at the project that the city dropped its plans. The second conflict was a water management plan developed by the city and county of Sacramento. Both environmentalists and regional water purveyors were outraged by this action because they were not informed of the plan nor consulted in its formulation. They worried that other region-wide water needs would not be met. This was the final conflict, creating enough discord that a region-wide round table became the only apparent answer (Lamb 2004).

The Water Forum Agreement

As outlined above, by the early 1990s, competing interests and unyielding stakeholders had kept the Sacramento region in water litigation for decades. The LAR was in jeopardy because of rapid urban growth and groundwater contamination leading to an increasing need for surface water from the LAR. The Water Forum was created to deal with these challenges.

The formation of the Water Forum had its genesis in the formation of the Sacramento City-County Office of Metropolitan Water Planning (CCOMWP). This office was created to discuss regional solutions to Sacramento's water challenges. The CCOMWP released a 5-year water plan, but local water purveyors and environmentalists rejected it because they had not been involved during its development. Realizing a broader effort was needed, city and county officials established the Water Forum in 1993. Early members included water agencies in Sacramento County, environmental groups, other citizen groups such as the League of Women Voters, and business leaders. In

1995, water purveyors from Placer and El Dorado counties joined, creating the Water Forum, as it exists today.

Guided by a professional paid facilitator/mediator, 6 years of negotiations and discussions ensued. Ground rules were quickly established, and the first year was spent not in negotiations but on building trust among participants by fact-finding and educating each other on various viewpoints. The services of several biologists were employed to supply scientific background and status on the LAR. There were also many federal agencies present, representing interests affected by regional decisions such as USBR and U.S. Fish and Wildlife Service (USFWS).

The negotiation of the Water Forum Agreement (WFA) went forward in five distinct stages. Planning and assessment came first. This stage involved the identification of issues and the determination of parties' intentions—whether they had interest in collaboration. The second stage was organization, which involved the hiring and training of mediators and the establishment of ground rules that remain in place today. The third stage involved educating all stakeholders on specific technical issues by selected experts in the field. All sides of the issue including science and policy viewpoints were presented. With the fourth stage, stakeholders were asked to set aside their positions and, instead, identify and express only their interests, which then would be the focus of negotiations. Implementation is the fifth stage and continues today (Water Forum 1995).

Ultimately, participants were forced to move beyond their demands and historic positions. They instead focused on the underlying reasons (interests) behind both their own and their antagonist's concerns, a process known as interest-based negotiations. Stakeholders were advised that no one organization would get everything it wanted, but that all should achieve goals that were truly needed (Water Forum 1995). This approach to decision-making allowed participants to define areas for agreement, determine issues for trade-offs, and draft language that assured each of gain in return for another member's profit.

At first, many small agreements were achieved, which led up to the large WFA at the Forum's climax (Connick and Innes 2003). For example, water purveyors wanted increased surface water diversions. In exchange, environmentalists got surface water for the American River in dry years, an improved lower American River flow standard, and water conservation programs and habitat projects. Assurances were built into the WFA guaranteeing that all aspects of the WFA would be implemented.

In April 2000, 6 years after its formation and after tens of thousands of hours of research and negotiations, including a draft and final environmental impact report, the WFA was created and signed by 40 stakeholder organizations representing public interests, environmental interests, business interests, and water interests (Table 2). Creation of the WFA allowed the Sacramento region, for the first time, to share a common vision on the use and protection of the region's water supply, including the American River.

The signatures of the representatives of participating agencies on the WFA testifies to their support through 2030 for the two coequal objectives of the Water Forum: to provide a reliable and safe water supply for the region's economic health and planned development to the year 2030 *and* to preserve the fishery, wildlife, recreational, and esthetic values of the lower American River. These objectives are supported by seven elements, which are described below. In order to achieve the coequal objectives, the WFA clearly states these elements must move forward together (Water Forum 2000).

The first element, increased surface water diversions, provides for meeting the Water Forum's coequal objective of reliable water supply. The growing population of the Sacramento region demands that more water be available, and this element allows for a significant increase in surface water diversions from a current 293 million m^3 to 519 million m^3 by the year 2030.

The second element, to reduce diversion impacts on the LAR in drier years while maintaining service to customer needs, provides for protecting aquatic resources during dry years, while maintaining water supply reliability. In dry years, water purveyors have agreed to reduce their LAR surface water diversions. Instead, they will increase efforts at conservation and reclamation and use groundwater.

The third element, improvement of flow releases from Folsom Reservoir, is an important consideration for the health of the LAR fishery. The current LAR flow standard was adopted by the SWRCB in 1958 (Decision 893, the same decision that gave USBR the right to construct and operate Folsom Dam). In 1990, the SWRCB recognized the standard as insufficient to protect beneficial uses. An updated flow standard based on models constructed by Water Forum stakeholders, staff, and consultants will protect aquatic resources even as surface water diversions increase.

TABLE 2. The Water Forum Stakeholder groups.

Group	Group
Business	Water
Associated General Contractors	Arden-Cordova Water District
AKT Development	California-American Water Company
Building Industry Association	Carmichael Water District
Sacramento Association of Realtors	Citrus Heights Water District
Sacramento Metropolitan Chamber of Commerce	City of Folsom
Sacramento Sierra Bldg/Construction Trade Council	City of Roseville
	Clay Water District
Environment	Del Paso Manor County Water District
Environmental Council of Sacramento	El Dorado County Water District
Friends of the River	El Dorado Irrigation District
Save the American River	Fair Oaks Water District
Sierra Club Motherlode Chapter	Florin County Water District
	Galt Irrigation District
Public	Georgetown Divide P.U.D.
City of Sacramento	Natomas Mutual Water Company
County of Sacramento	Omochumne-Hartnell Water District
League of Women Voters	Orange Vale Water Company
Sacramento County Taxpayers League	Placer County Water Agency
Sacramento County Alliance of Neighborhoods	Rancho Murieta C.S.D.
Sacramento Municipal Utility District	Regional Water Authority
	Rio Linda/Elverta Water District
	Sacramento Suburban Water District
	Sacramento County Farm Bureau
	San Juan Water District

The fourth element, the Habitat Management Element (HME), is important for the preservation of the LAR as an ecological resource and is necessary for compliance of the WFA with the California Environmental Quality Act (CEQA) (WFA 2000). Five programmatic factors are designed to address the various parts of the LAR as a working ecosystem. The Lower American River Habitat Management Plan, developed by a consortium of federal, state, and local agencies as well as community groups, details reasonable and feasible projects that could be implemented to offset and/or avoid impacts due to increased diversions. Some of these projects have already been approved for funding by a variety of sources. Monitoring and evaluation play a part in the HME to establish baseline conditions for future reference and provide the basis for adaptive management. Project specific mitigation is required of each purveyor on a site-specific basis to maintain these baseline conditions. Recreation on the LAR will be somewhat affected by mitigation and monitoring activities, but efforts will be made to choose and locate projects to minimize recreation consequences.

The fifth element is water conservation. Conservation plays a major role in the future by extending the supply of water for the growing Sacramento area community. Achieving the WFA regional conservation programs are expected to result in a 25% reduction in water use, meaning that about 25% less water will be taken from the LAR and groundwater basins at ultimate buildout, in 2030. Conservation also means less runoff contaminated by street and landscaping pollutants. A 4-year ramp-up program was initiated in 2000 to help achieve the water conservation programs. Agricultural water conservation goals will be negotiated in the future.

The sixth element, groundwater management, is important for supply stability because groundwater accounts for more than half of the total water used in the region. Conjunctive use is encouraged both for the integrity of surface supply and for the stability of groundwater levels (MWH 2003). During their negotiations, Water Forum stakeholders developed sustainable yield quantities for the region's three groundwater subbasins (Figure 4). Sustainable yield accounts for inputs from wet years, water extraction as

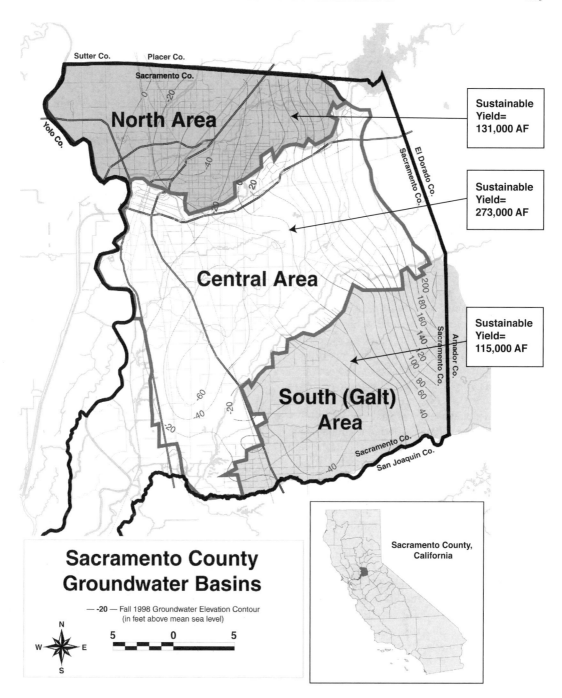

FIGURE 4. Three subbasins of the Sacramento Groundwater basin with negotiated sustainable yields in thousands of acre-feet.

reported by purveyors, and withdrawals by private pumpers. Development of governance structures to implement groundwater management plans are a Water Forum Successor Effort (the seventh element) responsibility. A groundwater management plan has been developed for the north basin, and a second is being developed for the central basin. There are also plans for the management of the south basin. Land use in the south area is more heavily agricultural than in other areas of the county.

The seventh element, the Water Forum Successor Effort (WFSE), is the most far-sighted action of the Water Forum stakeholders. Water Forum Successor Effort membership includes every signatory stakeholder to the WFA. It requires each stakeholder to continue in collaborative problem solving, open discussions and agendas, and fulfillment of past commitments (WFA 2000). Just as the WFA is not a legally binding document, the WFSE has no governing or regulatory authority. However, its membership is comprised of the stakeholder organizations to the Water Forum, who, with the assistance of an impartial staff, are charged with overseeing, monitoring, and reporting on the implementation of the WFA.

Accomplishments and Future Challenges

Accomplishments since the signing of the agreement include expansion of water treatment plants in the cities of Sacramento, Folsom, and Roseville in preparation for increased demand in those areas; development of the Sacramento Groundwater Authority to manage the groundwater resources in the north area; the development and implementation of an American River Corridor Management Plan; implementation of regional water conservation programs; and construction of a temperature control device at Folsom Dam. The most critical milestone, an updated flow standard for the LAR, is currently being developed. It will incorporate regulatory criteria for minimum flow, water temperature and fluctuating flows, a river management element comprised of a working group of biologists and water managers, and a monitoring and reporting program.

Significant effort and resources have been expended over the last 4 years by the Water Forum to develop an improved flow standard for the LAR. While many parties, including the state and federal water contractors and state and federal agencies, agree that the current flow standard is outdated, a number of technical and institutional barriers have added significantly to efforts expended. The following paragraphs represent a summary on the development of a draft flow standard. Much of the material in this section is from a report prepared by Surface Water Resources, Inc. for the Water Forum, describing the development of and providing for the presentation of an improved flow standard for the LAR (SWRI 2004).

The USBR operates Folsom Dam and Reservoir under a state water right permit, including fish protection requirements that was adopted in 1958 as SWRCB D-893 (see Historical Context section for further explanation). Under this decision, fish protection flows are allowed to fall as low as 4.2 m³/s (250 ft³/s) from January through mid-September, with a minimum of 14.2 m³/s (500 ft³/s) required between 15 September and 31 December. In comparison, a recent instream flow study conducted by the USFWS using the Instream Flow Incremental Methodology (IFIM) for steelhead and fall-run Chinook salmon spawning in the American River suggests optimal flows in the range of 56.6 m³/s (2,000 ft³/s) (USFWS 2003).

In 1988 the SWRCB, acting in its role as a referee in the water rights case *Environmental Defense Fund versus East Bay Municipal Utilities District*, conducted an extensive investigation and prepared a Report of Referee concluding that the existing flow requirements do not provide an adequate level of protection to the uses in the LAR. In 1990, the SWRCB prepared a workplan to review water rights on the American River and to determine the appropriate flows for an improved flow standard. The SWRCB anticipated adopting a final order on improved flows in the river by November 1992 (SWRCB 1990). This work has never been completed.

The primary purpose of the flow standard being developed by the Water Forum is to maximize the annual production and survival of the anadromous fall-run Chinook salmon and steelhead in the LAR, within water availability constraints and in consideration of USBR's obligation for multipurpose beneficial uses of Folsom Dam. An improved flow standard will include

- Water flows, temperature, ramping flow rate, and flow fluctuation criteria;
- The establishment of a river management group consisting of water resource managers, biologists, and interested stakeholders for Folsom Reservoir and LAR operations; and
- A monitoring and evaluation program to report the resultant hydrologic and biological conditions.

Thus, the proposed flow standard consists of three separate elements: required flows and water temperatures, river management, and monitoring and evaluation. Major tools being used to develop an improved flow standard for the LAR include

- USBR and the California Department of Water Resources' CALSIM II model—This model is the primary operations and planning model for the CVP and SWP operations. The model simulates SWP and CVP system operations and the hydrologic effects of those operations within the geo-

graphical area affected by the CVP and SWP facilities on a monthly timestep.

- USBR Water Temperature models—These models are the primary water temperature models for
the major northern California rivers. The models
simulate reservoir releases and instream water tem-
peratures on a monthly basis for the Sacramento,
Feather, and American rivers.
- USBR Chinook Salmon Mortality models—
These models produce a single estimate of each
Chinook salmon run's early life stage mortality
for each year of the simulation based on output
from USBR water temperature models. These
models have been developed for the Sacramento,
Feather, and American rivers.
- USFWS 2003 IFIM for Steelhead and Fall-Run
Chinook Salmon in the Lower American River—
The IFIM was developed by the USFWS to help
natural resource managers and their constituen-
cies determine the benefits or consequences of
different water management alternatives. The
IFIM is composed of a library of linked analytical
procedures that describe the spatial and temporal
features of habitat resulting from a given river
regulation management alternative.

As of this writing, Water Forum staff and consultants are working with the state and federal resource
managers and water agencies, as well as interested stakeholders, to refine the draft flow standard, which was
presented to the public in January 2004. A final flow
standard should be completed by September 2005
and then presented to the SWRCB.

Challenges faced by the WFSE include groundwater issues and conflicts over the linkage of land use
and water supply. Groundwater contamination is
prevalent in the Sacramento region and has put stress
on the water supply of a few area purveyors. New
challenges in water supply availability and water quality are testing the tenacity of the WFA as well as the
creativity of the WFSE in its application of adaptive
management to changing conditions. Land-use issues
in a region growing as quickly as Sacramento generate
substantial controversy. For the Water Forum to remain relevant, it must be able to maintain its objectiv-
ity regarding these issues, as called for in the WFA,
and retain its primary function as a forum for the
discussion of water.

A related challenge that has not been totally defined is the scope of the Water Forum as a regional
clearinghouse for water issues. The Water Forum is a
group of Sacramento-area stakeholders brought together through mutual concerns about the quantity
and quality of water supply as they relate to environmental and anthropogenic use. Water use and watershed management upstream of Folsom Reservoir both
have direct effects on these elements of water supply
but are largely unmonitored and unrepresented by
and in the forum.

Federal management of water for environmental
purposes is another topic of concern in the basin. The
new LAR flow standard may affect the ability of
USFWS to use environmental water to aid threatened
and endangered species in other Central Valley rivers
and the Delta. Specifically, under CVPIA, the USFWS
is annually allocated 988 million m^3 (800,000 acre-
feet) of CVP water to be used for protection of fish
and wildlife resources in federally managed rivers and
streams in California. A permanent flow standard for a
particular river operated by the CVP, such as the LAR,
may require a permanent allocation of that water, reducing the flexibility of the USFWS to use the water
in other aquatic systems. This conflict is now the largest issue facing development of an improved LAR flow
standard. State and federally listed steelhead in the
American River should not have to compete with federally and state listed delta smelt in the Delta for water
to maintain habitat for critical life stages; yet under
our current water governance system, that is precisely
what is happening.

Conclusion

Despite the challenges, the WFSE is successfully implementing the WFA and is dealing well with changing
conditions and challenges. Establishing an organization like the Water Forum in another area is likely if
some prerequisites are fulfilled. There must be the
political will to establish the organization, and in most
cases, alternative methods to problem solving, such as
litigation, must be exhausted. The time commitment
is great, and a member of each organization must be
willing to make that commitment. All members must
fully participate for decisions to be valid. Participants
must be convinced that other, apparently simpler alternatives will not work. Such a committed group,
willing to work together, is more likely to stay at the
table, work through new challenges, and find alternative solutions (Connick and Innes 2003). A good
mediation team is also important for moving discussions forward, for focusing stakeholder positions, and
for making decisions in a timely manner.

The process of creating the Water Forum involved
a huge amount of time and money, and the WFSE

continues to demand these resources. The city and county of Sacramento are instrumental in the financial sustainability of the forum. The contributions of all the cost-sharing partners are augmented by grants from federal and state agencies. The WFA has assured protection for the LAR that could not have been provided by any court battle. Opening communications between stakeholders lead to greater, faster, more cooperative, and more flexible decision-making power for the region.

Acknowledgments

I would like to thank Eme Iturralde and Sarah Foley with the Water Forum Office for their patient reviews and excellent editorial suggestions. Eme also worked hard on the graphics and other aspects of the paper. I am also very grateful to my coauthor for the long hours and hard work she devoted to this effort. And finally, a heartfelt thanks to Larry Brown with the U.S. Geological Survey for his encouragement, advice, review, and edits, which have finally resulted in this paper.

References

Brown, L. R., P. B. Moyle, and C. D. Vanicek. 1992. American River studies: intensive fish surveys, March–June 1991. University of California, Department of Wildlife, Davis and California State University, Department of Biology, Sacramento.

CDFG (California Department of Fish and Game). www.delta.dfg.ca.gov/camp/ (September 2003)

CSP (California State Parks). www.parks.ca.gov/ (January 2004)

Connick, S., and J. E. Innes. 2003. Outcomes of collaborative water policy making: applying complexity thinking to evaluation. Journal of Environmental Planning and Management 46:177–197.

Domagalski, J. L., D. L. Knifong, P. D. Dileanis, L. R. Brown, May, J. T., Connor, V., and C. N. Alpers. 2000. Water quality in the Sacramento River basin, California,1994–98: U.S. Geological Survey Circular 1215. Available: http://pubs.water.usgs.gov/circ1215/. (October 2003)

Gerstung, E. 1971. Fish and wildlife resources of the American River to be affected by the Auburn Dam and Reservoir and the Folsom South Canal, and measures proposed to maintain these resources. California Department of Fish and Game, Sacramento.

Gerstung, E. 1985. The fish and wildlife resources of the American River and proposed measures to maintain these resources. State of California Department of Fish and Game, Environmental Services Branch, Sacramento.

Jones and Stokes Associates. 1998. Floodway management plan for the Lower American River. Prepared for the Sacramento Area Flood Control Agency, Sacramento, California.

Lamb, C. 2004. Enviros: West Roseville deal violates water treaty. Sacramento Business Journal 21(1):1–37.

Lower American River Task Force. 2002. Lower American River: river corridor management plan. Jones and Stokes Associates, Sacramento, California.

Moyle, P. B. 2002. Inland fishes of California, 2nd edition. University of California Press, Berkeley.

MWH (Montgomery-Watson-Harza). 2003. Central Sacramento County Groundwater Forum: groundwater digest. Prepared for the Water Forum. Funded by the Water Forum and the California Department of Water Resources, Sacramento.

Paul, M. J., and J. L. Meyer. 2001. Streams in the urban landscape. Annual Review of Ecological Systems 32:333–365.

SACOG (Sacramento Area Council of Governments). www.sacog.org (October 2003)

SAFCA (Sacramento Area Flood Control Agency). www.safca.com (January 2004)

Sommer, T., B. Harrell, M. Nobriga, R. Brown, P. Moyle, W. Kimmerer, and L. Schemel. 2001. California's Yolo Bypass: evidence that flood control can be compatible with fisheries, wetlands, wildlife, and agriculture. Fisheries 26:6–16.

Snider, B. 2002. DRAFT lower American River flow fluctuation study. California Department of Fish and Game, Sacramento.

Somach, S. L. 1990. The American River decision: balancing instream protection with other competing beneficial uses. Rivers 1:251–263.

SWRCB (State Water Resources Control Board). 1990. Workplan: review of water rights on the American River. State Water Resources Control Board, Sacramento, California.

SWRI (Surface Water Resources, Inc.). 2001a. Aquatic resources of the lower American River: baseline report. Draft report prepared for the Lower American River Fisheries and Instream Habitat (FISH) Working Group, Sacramento, California.

SWRI (Surface Water Resources, Inc.). 2001b. Initial fisheries and in-stream habitat management and restoration plan for the lower American River. Prepared for the Lower American River Fisheries and Instream Habitat (FISH) Working Group, Sacramento, California.

SWRI (Surface Water Resources, Inc.). 2004. Draft policy

document: lower American River flow management standard. Prepared for the Water Forum, Sacramento, California.

USEPA (U.S. Environmental Protection Agency). 2000. The quality of our nation's waters. U.S. Environmental Protection Agency, EPA 841-S-00–001, Washington, D.C.

USFWS (U.S. Fish and Wildlife Service). 2003. Comparison of PHABSIM and 2-D modeling of habitat for steelhead and fall-run Chinook salmon spawning in the lower American River. Prepared by The Energy Planning and Instream Flow Branch, Sacramento Fish and Wildlife Office, Sacramento, California.

Water Forum. 1995. Water Forum: early review and authorization to proceed. Water Forum, Sacramento, California

Water Forum. 2001. Water Forum 2001 annual report. Water Forum, Sacramento, California.

Water Forum. 2000. Water Forum Agreement (WFA). Water Forum, Sacramento, California.

Wild and Scenic Rivers Act. 1968. U.S. Code, volume 16, sections 1271–1287. Public Law 90–542 as amended.

Williams, J. G. 2001. Chinook Salmon in the lower American River, California's largest urban stream. Pages 1–38 *in* Randall L. Brown, editor. Fish Bulletin 179: contributions to the biology of the Central Valley salmonids. Volume 2. California Department of Fish and Game, Sacramento.

Winternitz, L., and J. White. 2001. Implementing the CALFED Bay-Delta Program's Environmental Water Account—California. Pages 71–85 *in* J. Schaack and S. S. Anderson, editors. Transbasin water transfers. Proceedings of the 2001 Water Management Conference. U.S. Committee of Irrigation and Drainage, Denver, Colorado.

American Fisheries Society Symposium 47:229–238, 2005

Relations between Fish Assemblages and Urbanization in Southern California Coastal Streams[1]

CINDY J. LIN[*]

U.S. EPA Region IX, 600 Wilshire Boulevard, Suite 1460, Los Angeles, California 90017, USA

RICHARD F. AMBROSE

Environmental Science & Engineering Program, School of Public Health, University of California,
Los Angeles, California 90095, USA

Abstract.—Data collected as part of two studies to examine the influences of landscape modification on the ecology of three coastal Southern California river systems—the Calleguas Creek, Malibu Creek, and Santa Clara River watersheds—provided the opportunity to examine relations between urbanization and fish assemblages in Southern California coastal streams. Fish were collected at 63 sites from 1999 to 2001. Watershed land use was determined and classified into three land use types: agriculture, developed, and open space. Seven fish assemblage metrics were examined, including species richness, number of native and alien species, total fish abundance, percent abundance of native and alien species, and percent abundance of arroyo chub *Gila orcuttii*. Ten fish species were collected, and arroyo chub was the only species collected in all three watersheds. Native species included arroyo chub, threespine stickleback *Gasterosteus aculeatus*, steelhead *Oncorhynchus mykiss*, and Pacific staghorn sculpin *Leptocottus armatus*. There were no significant differences in fish assemblage metrics among the three land-use types. Both wetted stream width and depth were significantly related to native fish abundance. Results from this study suggest that the relatively species poor fish assemblages of Southern California may not be sensitive to watershed land use disturbance, but may be sensitive to local hydrologic conditions.

Introduction

The natural landscape of Southern California has been altered dramatically by human activities. Construction and expansion of cities, big and small, have changed the way watersheds look and function. Stream networks, floodplains, and hill slopes have been reshaped, causing heavy erosion, sedimentation, and aquatic resource degradation (Natural Resources Conservation Service 1995). In Southern California, metropolitan Los Angeles has grown rapidly, leading to suburban sprawl, development of industrial parks, and the shrinking of traditionally agricultural areas.

In light of increasing human modification of the landscape, the U.S. Environmental Protection Agency (EPA) and states need comprehensive water quality monitoring and assessment information on environmental conditions to provide critical information for water resource planning and decision making. Recommended elements of a state water monitoring and assessment program include identification of appropriate biological metrics or water quality indicators and data collection based on the integration of more than one sampling design (U.S. EPA 2003)

Barbour et al. (1995) suggest that the multiple biological metric approach is the most suitable tool for assessing a broad range of human impacts. Indices of biotic integrity (IBIs) are based on a multimetric concept that has been developed to assess the overall condition of aquatic ecosystems. In practice, IBIs have tended to be based primarily on measures of fish assemblages including total species richness and measures of alien and native fish abundance (Karr 1981, 1991; Fausch et al. 1984). Whereas IBIs have been widely used in the eastern United States, they have been difficult to develop in the western United States

* Corresponding author: lin.cindy@epa.gov
[1] The views expressed in this paper are those of the authors and do not necessarily reflect the view or policies of the U.S. Environmental Protection Agency.

because of a number of factors, including the fact that total fish species richness is relatively low whereas introduced species richness is often relatively high, even in relatively undisturbed waters (Moyle and Marchetti 1999). Miller et al. (1988) provided a skeptical assessment that IBI approaches could be applied to California streams. Moyle and Marchetti (1999) suggested that although an IBI concept might be applicable to some relatively high biodiversity streams in California, such an IBI might be most beneficial if it incorporated amphibians and invertebrate metrics. Recently, the California Department of Fish and Game has begun the development of invertebrate indices to assess stream condition (Harrington and Born 2000). Thus, despite the spread of urbanization, relatively few assessments of fish assemblages have been conducted in Southern California coastal streams.

An accurate assessment of relations between anthropogenic influences such as urbanization and stream biota is dependent upon a sampling and monitoring design appropriate to these objectives. Ideally, an integrated study design for assessing urban influences on water quality incorporates multiple tools in a tiered approach to address management decisions at multiple scales. These tools include probabilistic designs and targeted site-specific monitoring. When developing designs to meet specific objectives, the EPA encourages states to consider a combination of designs that include probabilistic site selection using simple random, stratified, or nested approaches as well as targeted site selection based on land use, geological setting, and other natural and human influences.

Data collected as part of two studies to examine the influences of landscape modification on the ecology of three coastal Southern California river systems—the Calleguas Creek, Malibu Creek, and Santa Clara River watersheds—provided the opportunity to examine relations between urbanization and fish assemblages in Southern California streams using two different monitoring designs. In 1999 and 2000, data on fish assemblages in the Calleguas Creek watershed were collected as part of the Calleguas Regional Environmental Monitoring and Assessment Program (REMAP) (Lin 2002). The REMAP study design was based on a probabilistic sampling approach, in which sites were randomly distributed within a described area of interest. In 2001–2002, data on fish assemblages in the Calleguas Creek, Malibu Creek, and Santa Clara River watersheds were collected as part of the Los Angeles Regional Water Quality Control Board (RWQCB) stream bioassessment (Ambrose et al. 2003). In the RWQCB study, sites were selected nonrandomly.

By examining fish assemblage data collected using two different sampling designs, we can provide a comprehensive assessment of relations between fish assemblages and urbanization in semiarid coastal streams in Southern California.

Study Areas

Southern California experiences a Mediterranean-type climate, with dry, warm summers, and mild, wet winters. Vegetation in all three watersheds was typical of Southern California chaparral.

Calleguas Creek Watershed

The Calleguas Creek watershed is located in the southern part of Ventura County, California, approximately 97 km northwest of Los Angeles (Figure 1). The watershed drains an area of 878 km² (Natural Resources Conservation Service 1995) and extends from the Los Angeles County line in the east to Mugu Lagoon and the Pacific Ocean in the west (Bookmand-Edmonston Engineering and Associates 1997). Mountains up to 1,100 m in elevation surround the watershed (Natural Resources Conservation Service 1995). Roughly 85% of rainfall in the Calleguas Creek watershed occurs between November and March. Mean annual precipitation in the valleys is 550 mm, compared with 790 mm in the higher elevations (Natural Resources Conservation Service 1995; Birosik 1996).

The Calleguas Creek watershed included all streams flowing westward from the ridge of the mountains to the coastline. All streams and tributaries empty into Mugu Lagoon, which is one of the largest remaining salt marshes in southern California. The main tributaries to Mugu Lagoon are Calleguas Creek and the Beardsley Wash/Revolon Slough. A historically intermittent watershed, Calleguas Creek and other main tributaries now experience continuous flow due primarily to six public-owned wastewater treatment works. Groundwater seepage into the surface water in the upper reaches of the watershed provides some flow.

Malibu Creek Watershed

The Malibu Creek watershed covers 270 km² at the southwestern end of Los Angeles County and the southern end of Ventura County (Figure 1). The second largest watershed to drain into Santa Monica Bay, the Malibu Creek watershed includes the city of Malibu and portions of Los Angeles and Ventura counties. Much of the watershed is open space and in-

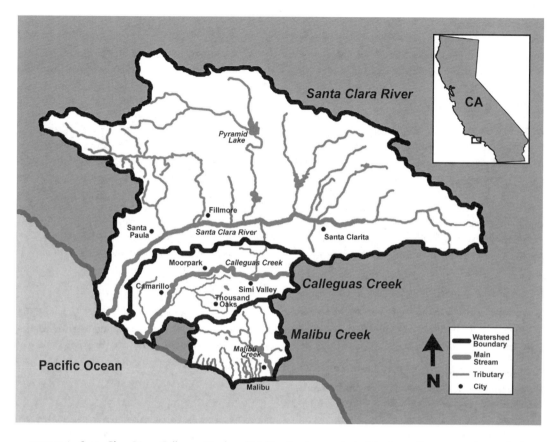

FIGURE 1. Santa Clara River, Calleguas Creek and Malibu Creek watersheds. The three adjacent coastal watersheds are located within the Los Angeles and Ventura counties and discharge into the Pacific Ocean.

cludes the Malibu Creek State Park and portions of the Santa Monica Mountains National Recreation Area. Most of the rainfall in the Malibu Creek watershed occurs between November and March. Rainfall in the Malibu Creek watershed varies widely, with some 330 mm annually falling over the coast and 635 mm falling over the mountains.

Malibu Creek cuts through the steep-sided Malibu Canyon gorge and drains through Malibu Lagoon into Santa Monica Bay. Malibu Creek provides freshwater, sediments, nutrients, detritus, and anthropogenically generated inputs to Malibu Lagoon, a small (5.2 ha) shallow water embayment. Freshwater input into Malibu Lagoon is naturally seasonal, with low natural flows during the dry summer months. Like many Southern California estuaries, Malibu Lagoon has been modified significantly by human activities. Sources of nonnatural water include the Tapia Reclamation Water District, which releases tertiary-treated water into Malibu Creek from November to

May, and urban run-off from the surrounding commercial and residential areas. Nonnatural water inputs during the summer are higher than the natural background inputs.

Santa Clara River Watershed

The Santa Clara watershed covers about 4,200 km^2 and drains from the east (Figure 1). Natural flow in all the major streams and tributaries in the basin is intermittent or ephemeral, with most of the stream flow related to flood flows. At certain times of the year, the river is continuous from the headwaters to the discharge at the estuary. The release of treated wastewater and imported water has resulted in an additional flow in the Santa Clara River across the Los Angeles–Ventura County line. The flow of the Santa Clara River has been modified by partial drawdown of some regional aquifers from decades of pumping, release of treated effluent, and releases of imported water. Discharges from waste water treatment plants and nonpoint source discharges in the watershed have changed the flow and concentrations of nutrients and other contaminants in receiving waters. Almost all precipitation in the Santa Clara River watershed occurs between November and April. Mean annual precipitation in the Santa Clara River watershed ranges from 360 mm along the coast to 630 mm near the surrounding mountains.

The Santa Clara River is the largest river system in the Los Angeles region remaining in a relatively natural state. Like most areas in Southern California, the watershed of the Santa Clara River has been subjected to significant land use and flow modifications due to urban development and agricultural practices. However, the Santa Clara River still retains many forested areas and relatively undisturbed tributaries.

Methods

A total of 51 sites was sampled as part of the REMAP study, including 24 sites in 1999 and 31 sites in 2000. Four sites were sampled in both years. Limited sampling was conducted at three selected reference sites in the Santa Clara River (two sites) and Malibu Creek (one site) watersheds to provide a qualitative evaluation of more pristine sites. In 2001–2002, a total of 12 sites was sampled as part of the RWQCB study, including 5 sites in the Malibu Creek watershed, 3 sites in the Santa Clara River watershed, and 4 sites in the Calleguas Creek watershed.

Watershed boundaries were delineated for each of the three watersheds using a digital elevation model. Stream order (Strahler 1964) was determined from examination of stream networks represented on 1:100,000-scale U.S. Geological Survey topographic maps. Stream order was grouped into four categories (1, 2, 3, and >3).

Land use data for each of the watersheds were derived from digital land cover information obtained using the Southern California Association of Governments (SCAG) Land Use and Land Cover database (SCAG 2001). The SCAG database contains 105 land-use categories based on a modified Anderson Level III/IV classification (Anderson and Sedell 1979). All land use categories were collapsed into three principal land use types: open space, developed, and agriculture. The open space classification contained undeveloped lands, parks, conservation, and pasture areas. The developed land use category included all areas with industrial, residential, commercial, and urban activities. Agriculture lands covered both row crops and orchards.

The REMAP study used a stratified-randomized sampling design to select sites (U.S. EPA 1990; Stevens 1993). Candidate stream reaches within the watershed were stratified by land-use type (open space, developed, and agriculture) and stream order, and sites were randomly selected within those strata. For the RWQCB study, sites were specifically selected within each watershed to represent the three land-use types (open space, developed, and agricultural). RWQCB site selection followed a series of reconnaissance surveys during which certain selection criteria were assessed, including land-use type, stream order, seasonal flow characteristics, substrate type, and degree of habitat alteration. For detailed description of the site selection, see Lin (2002) and Ambrose et al. (2003).

A sampling reach was identified at each site. Reach lengths were determined based on a distance of 40 times the wetted channel width to ensure representation of all habitats within the reach. A minimum reach length of 150 m and a maximum reach length of 300 m were established prior to sampling in order to prevent unessential sampling and crew fatigue (Fitzpatrick et al. 1998).

Fish Sampling

For both studies, fish sampling was conducted between March and August. Backpack electrofishing was the principal sampling method. Sampling effort in each reach focused on a single electrofishing pass along one stream bank, including all available habitats. The stream bank chosen for sampling was determined randomly. Sampling proceeded upstream through the reach and took between 45 min and 3 h. Block nets and seining were used in habitats where flow and substrate affected electrofishing efficiency. Fish were identified to species and counted. Species were classified as native or alien based on Swift et al. (1993) and the Nonindigenous Aquatic Species database (U.S. Geological Survey 2000).

Stream Habitat

Stream habitat assessments were conducted during both studies based on the EPA's Environmental Monitoring and Assessment Program field operations protocol and a transect-point data collection framework (Lazorchak and Klemm 1997). However, approaches used in applying the habitat assessment protocol varied between studies. Thus, the data analyzed for this investigation included only stream wetted width and depth. Wetted stream width and depth were measured at 21 equally spaced transects within the longitudinal boundaries of each reach. Stream depth was measured at the thalweg. Mean wetted width and depth were determined for each reach.

Data Analysis

Seven fish assemblage metrics were examined for both studies: species richness (total number of fish species), total fish abundance, number of native species, number of alien species, percent abundance of native species, percent abundance of alien species, and percent abundance of arroyo chub *Gila orcuttii*. An analysis of variance (ANOVA) with Tukey's comparisons was used to assess differences in metrics among the three land use types. Data normality was assessed by examination of probability plots prior to statistical analysis. Percent abundance data were arcsine-square root transformed prior to ANOVA. Simple linear regression was used to assess relations between fish metrics and stream width and depth. Statistical comparisons were considered significant when P was less than 0.05.

Results

Ten fish species were collected in the three coastal watersheds, both studies combined (Tables 1 and 2). Arroyo chub was the only species collected in all three watersheds. Pacific staghorn sculpin *Leptocottus armatus*, and common carp *Cyprinus carpio*, were collected only in the Calleguas Creek watershed, whereas largemouth bass *Micropterus salmoides* was collected only in the Malibu Creek watershed. The Santa Ana sucker *Catostomus santaanae* was collected only in the Santa Clara River watershed, where it is an alien species (Swift et al. 1993). Steelhead *Oncorhynchus mykiss* was only collected in the Santa Clara River watershed at the REMAP qualitative reference sites (Table 1). Native species included arroyo chub, threespine stickleback *Gasterosteus aculeatus*, steelhead, and Pacific staghorn sculpin.

REMAP

Seven fish species were collected in the Calleguas Creek watershed over both years of the REMAP study (Table 1). In addition, threespine stickleback and steelhead were observed in the Santa Clara River watershed qualitative reference sites (these collections are not included in any of the following statistics). In 1999, five fish species were collected. Of the 21 sites (not including 3 reference sites) sampled in 1999, fish were collected at only 17 sites. The average number of species collected per site across all land-use types was 1.6. Arroyo chub was collected at 12 of the 21 sites (57%). Western mosquitofish *Gambusia affinis* were collected at 43% of sites, whereas fathead minnow *Pimephales promelas* was collected at 38% of sites. No other single species was collected at greater than 25% of the sites. The average number of species collected at developed, agriculture and open space sites was 1.2, 2.5, and 1.6, respectively. For developed sites, the average number of alien species was 0.8 compared with 0.4 for native species. For agricultural sites, the average number of alien species was 2.0 compared with 0.5 native species. For open space sites, the average number of alien species was 0.9 compared with 0.8 native species. Among land use types, there were no significant differences in total species richness, alien species richness, percent abundance of arroyo chub, total fish abun-

TABLE 1. Fish species collected in the Calleguas Creek watershed during the Regional Environmental Monitoring and Assessment Program 1999 and 2000 study.

Common name	Scientific name	Status	Year collected
Arroyo chub	*Gila orcuttii*	Native	1999, 2000
Black bullhead	*Ictalurus melas*	Alien	1999, 2000
Common carp	*Cyprinus carpio*	Alien	2000
Fathead minnow	*Pimephales promelas*	Alien	1999, 2000
Green sunfish	*Lepomis cyanellus*	Alien	1999, 2000
Pacific staghorn sculpin	*Leptocottus armatus*	Native	2000
Rainbow trout[a]	*Oncorhynchus mykiss*	Native	2000
Threespine stickleback[a]	*Gasterosteus aculeatus*	Native	1999, 2000
Western mosquitofish	*Gambusia affinis*	Alien	1999, 2000

[a] Fish species was not collected in the Calleguas Creek watershed and observed only in the Santa Clara River watershed reference sites.

TABLE 2. Fish species collected in the Calleguas Creek (CC), Malibu Creek (MC), and Santa Clara River (SCR) watersheds during the Los Angeles Regional Water Quality Control Board 2001–2002 study.

Common name	Scientific name	Status	Watershed
Arroyo chub	*Gila orcutti*	Native	CC, MC, SCR
Black bullhead	*Ictalurus melas*	Alien	CC, MC
Fathead minnow	*Pimephales promelas*	Alien	CC, SCR
Green sunfish	*Lepomis cyanellus*	Alien	CC, MC
Largemouth bass	*Micropterus salmoides*	Alien	MC
Santa Ana sucker	*Catostomus santaanae*	Alien	SCR
Threespine stickleback	*Gasterosteus aculeatus*	Native	CC, SCR
Western mosquitofish	*Gambusia affinis*	Alien	CC, MC

dance, alien fish abundance, or native fish abundance (ANOVA, all $P > 0.05$).

In 2000, seven fish species were collected. Of the 28 sites (not including 3 reference sites) sampled, fish were collected at only 24 sites. The average number of species collected per site across all land use types was 2.9. Western mosquitofish were collected at 19 of the 28 sites (68%). Other species collected at greater than 25% of the sites included arroyo chub (57%), fathead minnow (43%), common carp (43%), green sunfish *Lepomis cyanellus* (32%), and black bullhead *Ameiurus melas* (32%). The average number of species collected at developed, agriculture and open space sites was 1.6, 3.3, and 3.0, respectively. For developed sites, the average number of alien species was 1.2 compared with 0.4 for native species. For agricultural sites the average number of alien species was 2.7 compared with 0.6 for native species. For open space sites, the average number of alien species was 2.2 compared with 0.8 for native species. Among land-use types, there were no significant differences in total species richness, alien species richness, native species richness, percent abundance of arroyo chub, total fish abundance, alien fish abundance, or native fish abundance (ANOVA, all $P > 0.05$).

Wetted stream width and depth were significantly related to several fish assemblage metrics. Total fish species richness and native fish abundance increased with increasing stream wetted width in both years, but only the 2000 relationship was statistically significant (Figure 2). In 2000, wetted width explained 38% of the variability in species richness ($r^2 = 0.38$, $P = 0.001$), about three times greater than proportion of the total variation explained in 1999 ($r^2 = 0.13$, $P = 0.09$). Arroyo chub abundance decreased with increasing mean water depth in the stream channel ($r^2 = 0.36$, $P = 0.01$), but fish species richness increased with increasing mean water depth ($r^2 = 0.23$, $P = 0.02$) (Figure 3).

RWQCB

Eight fish species were collected in the three coastal watersheds (Table 2). Arroyo chub was collected at 9 of the 12 sites (75%). No other single species was collected at greater than 25% of the sites. The average number of species collected at developed sites was 1.3 (range = 1–3), whereas the average number of species collected at agricultural sites was 3.5 (range = 1–5). Fish were not collected at any of the open space sites due to low water levels or absence of water in the streams; these open space sites were located in the upper reaches of the watersheds and were highly ephemeral. For developed sites, the average number of alien species was 0.6, whereas the average number of native species was 0.7. For agricultural sites, the average number of alien species was 2.3, whereas the average number of native species was 1.3. The percent abundance of alien individuals was significantly greater at developed sites than at agricultural sites ($P = 0.012$). There was no significant difference in the percent abundance of native individuals between the two land-use types (ANOVA, $P > 0.05$). There was also no significant difference in the percent abundance of arroyo chub between the two land-use types (ANOVA, $P > 0.05$). Stream wetted width was significantly related to native fish abundance ($r^2 = 0.55$, $P = 0.001$) (Figure 2).

Discussion

The fish assemblage metrics we tested did not appear to discriminate among agricultural, developed and open watershed land uses in coastal Southern California streams. The ichthyofauna of California is characterized by many endemic species (Moyle and Williams 1990), but the small coastal streams we studied typically had an average of less than three species per site. The number of alien species collected was higher than the number of native species, and the number of spe-

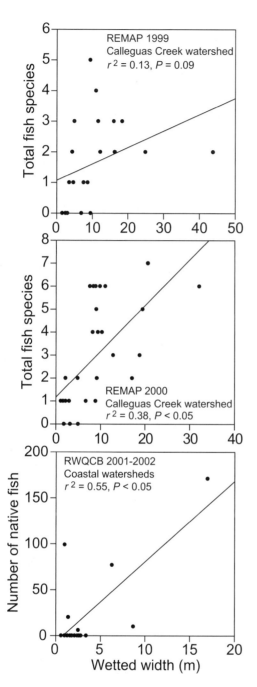

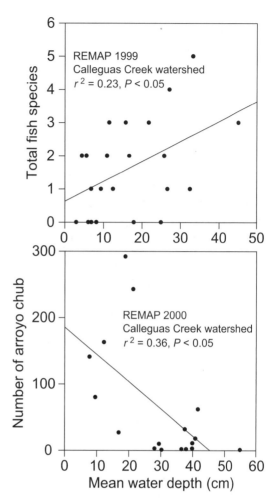

FIGURE 3. Arroyo chub abundance and total fish species richness plotted with mean water depth (cm) for the Regional Environmental Monitoring Assessment Program (REMAP) study in 1999 and 2000.

FIGURE 2. Total fish species richness and native fish abundance plotted with wetted width (m) for the Regional Environmental Monitoring and Assessment Program (REMAP) study of Calleguas Creek watershed, and the Los Angeles Regional Water Quality Control Board (RWQCB) study of Calleguas Creek, Santa Clara River and Malibu Creek watersheds.

cies collected for each study amounted to no greater than eight species. Human modification of Southern California watersheds may be so widespread that there is relatively little variation among fish assemblages attributable to watershed land use. In this case, it is not surprising that we found so few differences in fish metrics among land-use categories.

Clearly, the presence and quantity of flow was a major factor impacting fish assemblages. Wetted width, a measure of stream size, explained a significant portion of the variation for number of fish species and native fish abundance. The relationship between water depth and native (arroyo chub) fish in the Calleguas Creek watershed suggests that native species are sensitive to water levels. Similarly, Brown et al. (2005, this volume) found that native fishes were most abundant at sites of intermediate depth, with western mosquito-fish dominant in shallow concrete channels and other alien fishes dominant in deep, more natural channels. Thus, alteration of stream flow may be of greater direct importance to native fish species than watershed-scale land use.

We found arroyo chub, a California State Species of Special Concern (CDFG 1995), in all three watersheds and land-use types. Arroyo chubs are native to the Los Angeles, San Gabriel, San Luis Rey, Santa Ana, and Santa Margarita rivers and to Malibu and San Juan creeks (Wells and Diana 1975). However, their historical distribution does not include the Calleguas Creek or Santa Clara River watersheds (Swift et al. 1993). Arroyo chubs are found in slow-moving or backwater sections of warm to cool (10–24°C) streams with mud or sand substrates (CDFG 1995). Their native range, like that of the sympatric Santa Ana sucker, is largely coincident with the Los Angeles metropolitan area where most streams are degraded and populations reduced and fragmented, especially the low-gradient stream reaches, which formerly contained optimal habitat (Swift et al. 1993). In the Calleguas Creek watershed, arroyo chub was found primarily in effluent dominated tributaries, suggesting that it may benefit from continuous flow in such channels.

Other native species have been less successful at adapting to human modifications to the environment. The Ventura River along the California coast historically supported annual steelhead runs of approximately 5,000 fish before the construction of the Matilija Dam in 1948. Recent runs have dipped to alarming levels of approximately 50–100 steelhead, and the southern steelhead was listed as endangered in 1997. Numerous flood control projects, construction encroachment, erosion, exotic species, and nonpoint source pollution have all contributed to the decline of the Ventura River steelhead population (CDWR 2001). All three watersheds in this study supported steelhead in the past (NMFS 2005), but current populations are very low. Currently, there are local efforts to create a fish passage facility and remove the Matilija Dam on the Ventura River. Habitat restoration coupled with reintroduction of steelhead to local watersheds may aid population recovery in smaller watersheds like those in our study (CDWR 2001). Similarly, Ono and Williams (1983) document the impact of urbanization on local populations of unarmored threespine stickleback, *G. aculeatus williamsoni*. Populations were once abundant and widespread in coastal streams in and around Los Angeles, but now, only relict populations exist, which are still threatened by continued urbanization spread and introduction of exotic species. Similarly around the world, many habitats originally occupied by threespine stickleback have disappeared or decreased significantly in size as a consequence of water diversion and depletion (Foster et al. 2003). The examples of the arroyo chub, steelhead, and threespine stickleback exemplify the threats facing all native fish species in the Southern California region.

Although fish may not be effective bioindicators of habitat condition on a watershed scale, they nonetheless reflect condition on a regional scale and can be a useful bioindicator. The low number of native fish species at a given site, poor discrimination among land uses, and dominance of nonnative species at many sites demonstrate clearly the decline in native fish assemblages that has occurred throughout Southern California. In these highly altered coastal watersheds, fish assemblages may no longer be sensitive to watershed disturbance but may only be responsive to immediate local environmental changes such as water quantity and quality. In Southern California, studies of fish assemblages have concentrated primarily on coastal bays and estuaries. Thus, there is a relatively poor understanding of freshwater fish assemblages in the midst of widespread urbanization. The ongoing developmental pressures in this region have directed landscape and stream alterations further inland as the coastline has been developed, causing greater impact to critical fish habitat in the headwaters. Although stream bioassessment in Southern California may require examination of macroinvertebrate or amphibian assemblages (Lin 2002), increased coastal and inland stream monitoring of fish assemblages, in concert with assessments of physical and chemical conditions, are essential to assessing the extent of impacts on fish ecology in semiarid and urbanizing environments. Such comprehensive assessments will aid federal and state agencies and stakeholder groups in the management and restoration of aquatic resources in Southern California streams.

Acknowledgments

The U.S. Environmental Protection Agency, Office of Research and Development funded the research for the Calleguas Creek watershed REMAP study. The Los Angeles Regional Water Quality Control Board (RWQCB) funded the Coastal Watersheds RWQCB study. We deeply appreciate all the reviewers for their constructive suggestions. We are indebted to Steve Lee for his expertise in the field. We are grateful to

Mike Meador for his invaluable contribution that substantially improved the manuscript.

References

Ambrose, R. A., S. Lee, and S. Bergquist. 2003. Environmental monitoring and bioassessment of coastal watersheds in Ventura and Los Angeles counties. Final Report to Los Angeles Regional Water Quality Control Board, Los Angeles.

Anderson, N. H., and J. R. Sedell. 1979. Detritus processing by macroinvertebrates in stream ecosystems. Annual Review of Entomology 23:351–377.

Barbour, M. T., J. B. Stribling, and J. R. Karr. 1995. Multimetric approach for establishing biocriteria and measuring biological condition. Pages 63–77 *in* W. S. Davis and T. P. Simon, editors. Biological assessment and criteria. Tools for water resource planning and decision making. Lewis Publishers, Boca Raton, Florida.

Birosik, S. 1996. Calleguas Creek watershed, preliminary report: water quality. Ventura County, California Regional Water Quality Control Board, Los Angeles.

Bookmand-Edmonston Engineering and Associates. 1997. Workplan: Calleguas Creek characterization study. Ventura County, Calleguas Creek Characterization Study Committee, Thousand Oaks, California.

Brown, L. R., C. A. Burton, and K. Belitz. 2005. Aquatic assemblages of the highly urbanized Santa Ana River basin, California. Pages 263–287 *in* L. R. Brown, R. H. Gray, R. M. Hughes, and M. R. Meador, editors. Effects of urbanization on stream ecosystems. American Fisheries Society, Symposium 47, Bethesda, Maryland.

CDFG (California Department of Fish and Game). 1995. Fish species of special concern in California, arroyo chub. California Department of Fish and Game, Sacramento.

CDWR (California Department of Water Resources). 2001. Fish passage improvement: first annual report. California Department of Water Resources, Division of Planning and Local Assistance, Bulletin 250–2001, Sacramento.

Fausch, K. D., J. R. Karr, and P. R. Yant. 1984. Regional application of an index of biotic integrity based on stream fish communities. Transactions of the American Fisheries Society 113:39–55.

Fitzpatrick, F. A., I. R. Waite, P. J. D'Arconte, M. R. Meador, M. A. Maupin, and M. E. Gurtz. 1998. Revised methods for characterizing stream habitat—National Water-Quality Assessment Program. U.S. Geological Survey Water-Resources Investigations Report 98–4052, Raleigh, North Carolina.

Foster, S. A., J. A. Baker, and M. A. Bell. 2003. The case for conserving threespine stickleback populations: protecting an adaptive radiation. Fisheries 28(5):10–17.

Harrington, J., and M. Born. 2000. Measuring the health of California streams and rivers. Sustainable Land Stewardship International Institute, Sacramento, California.

Karr, J. R. 1981. Assessment of biotic integrity using fish communities. Fisheries 6(6):21–27.

Karr, J. R. 1991. Biological integrity - a long-neglected aspect of water resource management. Ecological Applications 1:66–84.

Lazorchak, J. M., and D. J. Klemm. 1997. EMAP surface water: field operations and methods for measuring the ecological condition of wadeable streams. U.S. Environmental Protection Agency, Office of Research and Development, EPA/620/R-94/004, Cincinnati, Ohio.

Lin, C. J. 2002. Effects of landscape modification on stream ecology and structure in a mixed-use watershed in mediterranean Southern California. Doctoral dissertation. University of California, Los Angeles.

Miller, D. L., P. M. Leonard, R. M. Hughes, J. R. Karr, P. B. Moyle, L. H. Schrader, B. A. Thompson, R. A. Daniels, K. D. Fausch, G. A. Fitzhugh, J. R. Gammon, D. B. Halliwell, P. L. Angermeier, and D. J. Orth. 1988. Regional applications of an index of biotic integrity for use in water resource management. Fisheries 13(5):12–20.

Moyle, P. B., and J. E. Williams. 1990. Biodiversity loss in the temperate zone: decline of the native fish fauna of California. Conservation Biology 4:275–284.

Moyle, P. B., and M. P. Marchetti. 1999. Application of indices of biotic integrity to California streams and watersheds. Pages 367–380 *in* T. P. Simon, editor. Assessing the sustainability and biological integrity of water resources using fish communities. CRC Press, Boca Raton, Florida.

National Marine Fisheries Service (NMFS). 2005. California anadromous fish distribution, Southern California steelhead ESU, Santa Maria to Malibu Creek, historic stream habitat distribution. Available: http://swr.nmfs.noaa.gov/hcd/soCalHistoric.htm (March 2005).

Natural Resources Conservation Service. 1995. Calleguas Creek Watershed erosion and sediment control plan for Mugu Lagoon. Natural Resources Conservation Service, Davis, California.

Ono, R. D., and J. D. Williams. 1983. Vanishing fishes of North America. Stonewall, Washington, D.C.

SCAG (Southern California Associated Government). 2001. Land use – Southern California Associated

Government (SCAG). Available: http://gis.ca.gov/catalog/BrowseRecord.epl?id=4109 (January 2001).

Stevens, D. L. J. 1993. Implementation of a national monitoring program. U.S. Environmental Protection Agency, Office of Research and Development, Corvallis, Oregon.

Strahler, A. N. 1964. Quantitative geomorphology of drainage basins and channel networks. Handbook of applied hydrology. McGraw-Hill, New York.

Swift, C. C., T. R. Haglund, M. Ruiz, and R. N. Fisher. 1993. The status and distribution of the freshwater fishes of Southern California. Bulletin of Southern California Academy of Science 92:101–167.

U.S. EPA. 1990. Design report for EMAP. U.S. Environ-mental Protection Agency, Office of Research and Development, Washington, D.C.

U.S. EPA. 2003. Elements of a state water monitoring and assessment program. U.S. Environmental Protection Agency, Oceans and Watershed, Assessment and Watershed Protection Division, Office of Wetlands, EPA 841-B-03–003, Washington, D.C.

U.S. Geological Survey. 2000. Nonindigenous fish distribution information. Available: http://nas.er.usgs.gov/fishes/ (March 2005).

Wells, A. W., and J. S. Diana. 1975. Survey of the freshwater fishes and their habitats in the coastal drainages of Southern California. California Fish and Game, Inland Fisheries Branch, Final Report, Sacramento.

American Fisheries Society Symposium 47:239–262, 2005

Assessing Water Source and Channel Type as Factors Affecting Benthic Macroinvertebrate and Periphyton Assemblages in the Highly Urbanized Santa Ana River Basin, California

Carmen A. Burton *

U.S. Geological Survey, 5735 Kearny Villa Road, Suite O, San Diego, California 92123, USA

Larry R. Brown

U.S. Geological Survey, Placer Hall, 6000 J Street, Sacramento, California 95819-6129, USA

Kenneth Belitz

U.S. Geological Survey, 5735 Kearny Villa Road, Suite O, San Diego, California 92123, USA

Abstract.—The Santa Ana River basin is the largest stream system in Southern California and includes a densely populated coastal area. Extensive urbanization has altered the geomorphology and hydrology of the streams, adversely affecting aquatic communities. We studied macroinvertebrate and periphyton assemblages in relation to two categorical features of the highly engineered hydrologic system—water source and channel type. Four water sources were identified—natural, urban-impacted groundwater, urban runoff, and treated wastewater. Three channel types were identified—natural, channelized with natural bottom, and concrete-lined. Nineteen sites, covering the range of these two categorical features, were sampled in summer 2000. To minimize the effects of different substrate types among sites, artificial substrates were used for assessing macroinvertebrate and periphyton assemblages. Physical and chemical variables and metrics calculated from macroinvertebrate and periphyton assemblage data were compared among water sources and channel types using analysis of variance and multiple comparison tests. Macroinvertebrate metrics exhibiting significant ($P < 0.05$) differences between water sources included taxa and Ephemeroptera-Plecoptera-Trichoptera richness, relative richness and abundance of nonchironomid dipterans, orthoclads, oligochaetes, and some functional-feeding groups such as parasites and shredders. Periphyton metrics showing significant differences between water sources included blue-green algae biovolume and relative abundance of nitrogen heterotrophic, eutrophic, motile, and pollution-sensitive diatoms. The relative abundance of trichopterans, tanytarsini chironomids, noninsects, and filter feeders, as well as the relative richness and abundance of diatoms, were significantly different between channel types. Most physical variables were related to channel type, whereas chemical variables and some physical variables (e.g., discharge, velocity, and channel width) were related to water source. These associations were reflected in correlations between metrics, chemical variables, and physical variables. Significant improvements in the aquatic ecosystem of the Santa Ana River basin are possible with management actions such as conversion of concrete-lined channels to channelized streams with natural bottoms that can still maintain flood control to protect life and property.

Introduction

Human influence on the environment has been extensive for thousands of years. The introduction of

agriculture changed human–environmental relations in virtually all parts of the world (Grimm et al. 2000). However, some of the more severe human-induced environmental impacts are those associated with urbanization. Even in ancient cities, dense human populations caused extreme regional degradation, resulting

---

* Corresponding author: caburton@usgs.gov

in abandoned cities and reductions in agricultural productivity leading to the collapse of entire civilizations (Grimm et al. 2000).

Currently, urbanization is second only to agriculture as the main cause of stream impairment (Paul and Meyer 2001). Urbanization alters the geomorphic and hydrologic characteristics of streams that drain urban catchments. Drainage basin boundaries are made meaningless by imports and exports of water and construction of drainage and flood control structures. Flow regimes are altered by diversions of water to and from natural channels, water storage and release activities, and changes in surrounding land use that alter runoff patterns (Leopold 1968; Klein 1979; Booth 1991). In addition, flow may be augmented by discharges from wastewater treatment plants. These changes in stream geomorphology, hydrology, and landscape affect water quality. Urban catchments typically have elevated concentrations of phosphorus and other nutrients (U.S. Geological Survey 1999; Winter and Duthie 2000); inorganic ions such as chloride, sodium, and potassium (Paul and Meyer 2001); metals (Paul and Meyer 2001); pesticides (U.S. Geological Survey 1999); and other organic contaminants (Moring and Rose 1997; Frick et al. 1998; Burton 2002).

Changes in landscape and water quality also alter aquatic biotic communities. Taxa richness (number of taxa) declines and communities shift to more tolerant species in association with measures of urbanization including increased population density, increased impervious surface area, and changes in streambed substrate and water quality (Garie and McIntosh 1986; Winter and Duthie 1998; Ourso 2001; Kennen and Ayers 2002). Tolerant species increase in abundance and often dominate the biological community (Barbour et al. 1999; Paul and Meyer 2001).

The Santa Ana River basin is the largest stream system in Southern California, encompassing about 6,900 km² of the densely populated coastal area (Figure 1). The river begins in the San Bernardino Mountains (which reach altitudes exceeding 3,000 m) and flows more than 160 km to the Pacific Ocean. The watershed is home to almost 5 million people, and the population is expected to reach almost 7 million by the year 2025 (Santa Ana Watershed Project Authority 2003).

The hydrologic system is highly engineered. Flow from most headwater tributaries is diverted to groundwater-recharge facilities (Figure 1), public supply, and, on the Santa Ana River, to hydroelectric plants. Because of diversions and hot, dry summers, the Santa Ana River and almost all its tributaries lose surface flow once they reach the alluvium-filled basin. Groundwater is withdrawn and supplemented with imported water for public use. Some of the water used by the public returns to the ground through infiltration from lawns, some is lost through evapotranspiration from ornamental plants, some becomes urban runoff, and most is sent to wastewater treatment plants. Farther downstream, flow is reestablished in some channels due to inputs from wastewater treatment plants (Figure 1). In a few small streams, urban runoff or groundwater forced upward by faulting or by bedrock outcrops restores surface flow. Imported water is occasionally discharged to a stream and then diverted for groundwater recharge farther downstream. Most water in streams is from sources impacted by human activities. Treated wastewater and urban runoff maintain perennial flow in some streams that historically were ephemeral. Flow in these streams is 70–100% treated wastewater (Mendez and Belitz 2002). Moreover, the volume of treated wastewater is increasing every year (Burton et al. 1998). In addition to changes in source water, the tributary network on the basin floor has been greatly altered. Natural stream courses are typically channelized and, in many cases, concrete-lined.

Ecological conditions in the Santa Ana River basin have also been significantly altered. Watersheds have been converted from natural habitats to urban land uses and riparian vegetation has been removed. Many streams have been channelized and concrete-lined for the protection of life and property. Human activities have introduced many toxic compounds to surface- and groundwater, rerouted the distribution of streamflow, and changed the timing of these flows. Changes to the landscape and streams imposed by urbanization cannot be fully corrected (Booth and Reinelt 1993); however, that does not mean ecosystem conditions cannot be improved. The problem is identifying differences in biological conditions related to anthropogenic factors that may be mitigated.

Many urban studies focus on an urbanization gradient either within one catchment or among several catchments. Other studies compare reference conditions to urban condition. Because of the engineered hydrologic system, the arid climate, and the high percentage of urban land use in the basin, gradient studies are not feasible in the Santa Ana River basin. However, some aspects of the hydrologic system in the Santa Ana River basin are well constrained. It is possible to identify the source of water as well as the channel modification or type for many streams. This provides an opportunity for assessing the effects of these two anthropogenic factors. Objectives of this

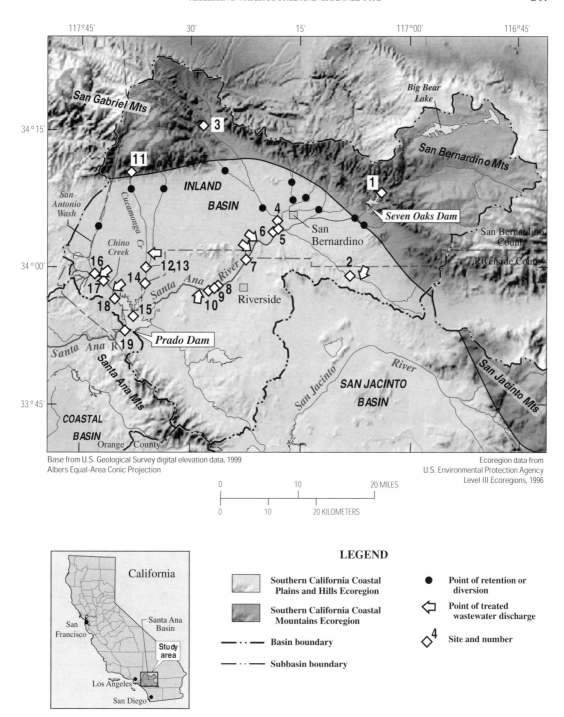

FIGURE 1. Location of stream sites, retention basins, and points of treated-wastewater discharge in the Santa Ana River basin, California.

paper are to relate condition of the benthic macroinvertebrate and periphyton (attached algae) assemblages to water source and channel type. We also address

some challenges of studying and understanding highly urbanized streams. In a companion paper (Brown et al. 2005, this volume), we use multivariate ordination techniques to better understand the ecological processes affecting aquatic communities in the Santa Ana River basin and generating the patterns observed in this study.

Methods

Study Area

Urban and agricultural land uses occur primarily in the alluvium-filled valleys and coastal plain, which are located in the Southern California Plains and Hills ecoregion (Omernik 1987) (Figure 1). The uplands, which include the San Gabriel, San Bernardino, and San Jacinto Mountains, lie within the Southern California Coastal Mountain ecoregion and are generally steep and undeveloped. Land use in the entire basin is about 35% urban; 10% agricultural; and 55% open space, primarily steep, mountain slopes. The alluvium-filled valleys and coastal plain are more than 70% urban. Population density in the entire basin is about 580 people/km^2; population density in the alluvium-filled valleys and coastal plains is about 1,160 people/km^2. The climate is Mediterranean and characterized by hot, dry summers and cool, wet winters. Average annual precipitation ranges from 25 to 60 cm in the coastal plains and inland valleys, and from 60 to 122 cm in the San Gabriel and San Bernardino Mountains (U.S. Army Corps of Engineers 1994).

Site Selection

Preliminary assessments identified four categories of water source (natural, human-impacted groundwater, urban runoff, and treated wastewater) and three categories of channel type (natural, channelized with natural bottom, and concrete-lined). Conceptually, this represents a 4 × 3 categorical design, but perennial stream reaches that represented all combinations were not available (Table 1). At least one study reach was selected to represent all combinations available in the basin for a total of 19 sites (Table 2).

TABLE 1. Number of sites in each combination of water source and channel type, Santa Ana River basin, California.

Water source	Channel type		
	Natural	Channelized	Concrete
Natural	3	0	0
Groundwater	0	1	3
Urban runoff	0	2	1
Treated wastewater	4	2	3

Natural landscape variability was minimized by locating reaches within one ecoregion, the Southern California Plains and Hills (Omernik 1987), with one exception. Sites with little to no urban land use could not be found within the ecoregion. Therefore, three sites (1, 3, and 11) located near the interface with the Southern California Mountain ecoregion were selected to represent least-impacted conditions (Table 2; Figure 1). These mountain-runoff sites are supplied with natural water, have a natural channel type, and represent conditions as streams enter the valley floor.

Four sites are primarily supplied with human-impacted groundwater. Of these, one is channelized (9) and the remaining three are concrete-lined (4, 6, and 8). Three sites are primarily supplied with urban runoff. Two of these sites are channelized (5 and 16), and the third is concrete lined (12). Nine sites are dominated by discharge from wastewater treatment plants. Four of these sites are located in natural channels (2, 10, 15, and 19), two in channelized streams (7 and 18), and three in concrete-lined channels (13, 14, and 17).

Basin area and percentage of urban land use were calculated for all sites for the natural, topographical drainage basin. The actual contributing drainage area also was calculated based on information about retention basins, storm drains, and treated wastewater discharge locations (Table 2). Drainage areas behind retention basins were subtracted from the topographical drainage basin, and basin boundaries were adjusted to account for storm drains and treated wastewater discharge locations. The contributing area was usually a subset of the topographical drainage area that is separated from mountain runoff by retention basins. In the case of the three least-impacted sites, the topographical drainage basin area and contributing basin area are the same. Percentage of urban land use also was calculated using the contributing basin area. In the case of a stream receiving 100% treated wastewater, the contributing basin area has no meaning because the flow emerges from a pipe and all of the water is from urban uses (100%).

Data Collection

Water samples for major ions, nutrients, pesticides, and field parameters (specific conductance, pH, water temperature, dissolved oxygen, and discharge) were collected using standard U.S. Geological Survey (USGS) protocols (Shelton 1994). Water samples were collected in Teflon bottles using either the equal-width-incremental method or the multiple-vertical method,

TABLE 2. Site number, site name, drainage area, land use, population density, major source of water, and channel type for study sites, Santa Ana River basin, California.

Site no.	Station name	Drainage area (topographical, km²)	Drainage area (contributing, km²)	Urban land use (topographical, %)	Urban land use (contributing, %)	Population density (contributing, people per km²)	Major contributing water source[a]	Channel type[b]
1	Santa Ana River (SAR) at upper powerhouse	398	398	5	5	20	N	N
2	San Timoteo Creek near Eastside Ranch	141	NA[c]	20	100[d]	NA[c]	W	N
3	Cajon Creek below Lone Pine	145	145	4	4	10	N	N
4	Warm Creek above Orangeshow	4	4	90	90	1,990	G	C
5	Warm Creek above E Street	30	30	93	93	1,890	U	Ch
6	Warm Creek near San Bernardino	32	32	94	94	1,890	G	C
7	SAR above Riverside Road	1,918	743	21	46	690	W	Ch
8	Sunnyslope channel near Rubidoux Nature Center	19	19	52	52	870	G	C
9	Sunnyslope channel in SAR Regional Park	19.4	19.4	53	53	870	G	Ch
10	SAR at MWD Crossing	2,136	960	25	49	730	W	N
11	Cucamonga Creek near Upland	26	26	0	0	2	N	N
12	Cucamonga Creek at Chino Ave, main channel	180	132	58	80	1,460	U	C
13	Cucamonga Creek at Chino Ave, wastewater channel	180	NA[c]	65	100[d]	NA[c]	W	C
14	Cucamonga Creek near Mira Loma	208	160	56	72	1,280	W	C
15	Mill Creek near Slatter S Duck ponds	234	186	52	63	1,120	W	N
16	Little Chino Creek above Pipeline	16	16	46	46	560	U	Ch
17	Chino Creek above Central Ave	234	155	55	78	1,680	W	C
18	Chino Creek below Pine Road	259	191	51	69	1,520	W	Ch
19	SAR below Prado Dam	3,726	2,394	32	45	690	W	N

[a] N, natural; W, treated wastewater; G, urban ground water; U, urban runoff.
[b] C, concrete-lined channel; Ch, channelized; N, natural channel.
[c] Contributing area is not applicable (NA) because all flow in the channel comes from a wastewater treatment plant.
[d] Urban land use is 100% because all flow in the channel comes from wastewater treatment plant.

depending on site conditions. Water samples for determination of dissolved nutrients and major ions were filtered through a 0.45-µm Gelman capsule filter. Water samples for determination of cations were preserved with nitric acid. Water samples collected for pesticides were filtered through a baked glass-fiber filter. Water samples for major ions, nutrients, and pesticides were chilled to 4°C and shipped to the USGS National Water-Quality Laboratory (NWQL), Denver, Colorado, for analysis. Samples for major ions, nutrients, and pesticides were collected once, when the algae samples were collected. Field parameters were collected during each site visit.

Habitat variables were measured at each of 11 transects within each sampling reach (Fitzpatrick et al. 1998). Reaches ranged from 150 m for small streams and concrete-lined channels to 900 m for larger streams. Basin area, urban land use, and population densities were determined using geographic information system databases. Land-use information was obtained from the Southern California Association of Governments (1997), and population density information is from the 1990 U.S. Census (Hitt 1994).

Periphyton, benthic macroinvertebrate, and water quality samples were collected and the habitat was characterized at the 19 sites from July to September

2000. Artificial substrates were used for periphyton and benthic macroinvertebrates to decrease the effect of radically different substrate types among sites (cobbles, sand, concrete), facilitating comparisons among sites (Aloi 1990; Lowe and Pan 1996).

Unglazed clay tiles (approximately 7.5 × 7.5 cm) attached to concrete paving blocks were used to collect periphyton. Four paving blocks with two tiles each were placed at each site. Water depth and velocity were measured at each paving block when the substrates were deployed and when they were collected. After a 2-week colonization period, the clay tiles were removed from the paving blocks. Periphyton was collected and processed using the top-rock scrape method (Moulton et al. 2002). Samples were preserved in 4% formalin. Periphyton taxa were identified and enumerated at the Philadelphia National Academy of Science following the methods of Charles et al. (2002).

Artificial substrates for benthic macroinvertebrates consisted of a section of bristled plastic doormat (approximately 15 × 15 cm) and an 18-cm length of 3.2-cm polyvinyl chloride (PVC) pipe wrapped three times with plastic fencing (1.9-cm mesh) attached to a concrete paving block (Figure 2). Four substrates were placed at each site. Water depth and velocity were measured at each paving block when the substrates

FIGURE 2. Artificial substrate used to collect macroinvertebrate samples from the Santa Ana River basin, California.

were deployed and when they were collected. Up to three substrates were removed after a 6-week colonization period. The doormat and PVC pipe were removed from the paving block, and placed in a bucket. A 500-μm-mesh net was placed downstream from the substrate to collect any macroinvertebrates that were dislodged in the removal process. The doormat, PVC pipe, and fencing were scrubbed and inspected to remove macroinvertebrates. The sample was sieved (500 μm) and preserved in 10% formalin (Moulton et al. 2002). Macroinvertebrates were identified and enumerated at the NWQL following protocols for a 100-organism fixed-count (Moulton et al. 2000).

Data Analysis

More than 80 chemical and 30 physical variables were measured, including concentrations of dissolved nutrients, concentrations of dissolved major ions, concentrations of dissolved pesticides, and habitat characteristics. Analysis of variance (ANOVA) was used on ranked chemical and physical variables to identify those that were significantly different ($P < 0.05$) between water sources or channel types. These selected chemical and physical variables were used in all further analyses. Principal components analysis (PCA) was used to explore overall patterns among the final set of environmental variables.

Benthic macroinvertebrates were generally identified to genus. Ambiguous individuals identified at a higher taxonomic level (usually family) were distributed among the lower taxa (usually genera) in accordance with the relative abundance of each genus when most of the individuals were identified at the lower level. Otherwise, data were aggregated at the higher level of taxonomy. Species lists and counts are not presented in this paper but are available from the corresponding author (Carmen Burton). The taxa data were summarized as biological metrics using the Invertebrate Data Analysis System program (Cuffney 2003).

Periphyton was identified to species in most cases. As with the macroinvertebrates, species lists and counts are not presented in this paper. Metrics were calculated using autecological and tolerance information described by Van Dam et al. (1994), Bahls (1993), and Lange-Bertalot (1979).

More than 120 macroinvertebrate metrics and 40 periphyton metrics were calculated. Macroinvertebrate metrics included taxa richness, relative taxa richness, taxa abundance (density), and relative taxa abundance, functional-feeding group (taxa having similar adaptations for feeding) richness and abundance, and relative richness and abundance. Periphyton metrics include taxa richness, relative richness, abundance, relative abundance, biovolume, and percentage of biovolume of periphyton classes, as well as relative abundance of taxa according to autecological characteristics such as motility and pollution tolerance. Only those metrics that were statistically different among water sources or channel types are discussed further.

Biological metric values were compared among water sources or channel types using ANOVA. The data were transformed by ranking before using the general linear model procedure in SAS. Tukey's multiple comparisons tests (Helsel and Hirsch 1992) were conducted for biological metrics showing significant differences among water sources or channel types. The test was modified using the harmonic mean to account for unequal sample sizes (Helsel and Hirsch 1992). Significant metrics ($P < 0.05$) were correlated (Spearman's correlation) with the selected chemical and physical variables. The significant macroinvertebrate metrics and the significant periphyton metrics also were analyzed by PCA to determine patterns of correlation among metrics within each taxa group and facilitate interpretation of general patterns. The number of important axes was determined by Kaiser's rule, which states that the minimum eigenvalue for an axis should be greater than the average of the eigenvalues for all axes.

Results

Chemical and Physical Variables

Nineteen chemical and physical variables were significantly different between sources of water or channel type (ANOVA, $P < 0.05$). Fifteen chemical and physical variables showed significant differences between sources of water, and nine physical variables showed significant differences between channel types (Tables 3 and 4). Concentrations of dissolved chemicals were highest in streams with treated wastewater and lowest in streams with natural water (Table 3). Inorganic ions such as chloride (Cl), potassium (K), and sodium (Na) were significantly different among water sources, but specific conductance was not. Of the physical variables, discharge, water velocity, and wetted channel width were highest in streams supplied with treated wastewater and usually lowest in natural streams (Table 3). Streams supplied with water from natural sources had the highest values for the remaining physical variables. Streams supplied with urban runoff and groundwater had the highest percentages of urban land use.

BURTON ET AL.

TABLE 3. Median values for chemical and physical variables that were significantly different among water-source categories (ANOVA, $P < 0.05$). For each variable, water sources with different letters were significantly different (Tukey tests, $P < 0.05$).

	Water source			
Variable	Natural	Groundwater	Urban runoff	Treated wastewater
Cl (mg/L)	6 A	7 A	61 AB	94 B
K (mg/L)	2 A	3 A	4 A	11 B
Na (mg/L)	19 A	71 AB	64 AB	82 B
Ammonia (mg/L as N)	0.01 A	0.02 AB	0.04 AB	0.09 B
PO_4 (mg/L as P)	0.005 A	0.005 A	0.087 B	1.05 C
Discharge (m³/s)	0.03 A	0.07 A	0.06 A	0.88 B
cv[a] bank-full width	33 A	5 B	14 AB	14 B
Channel width, wetted (m)	3.8 AB	4.4 A	5.7 AB	14.1 B
cv depth	61 A	52 B	49 AB	36 B
% riffle	53 A	0 B	0 B	0 B
Streambed substrate size[b]	7.0 A	1.7 B	2.5 B	3.1 AB
Velocity (m/s)	0.18 A	0.12 A	0.21 AB	0.47 B
cv velocity	101 AB	98 AB	102 A	44 B
% urban land use (contributing)	4 A	71 B	80 B	69 AB
Water temperature (°C)	20.0 A	29.8 B	30.5 B	28.0 B

[a] cv, coefficient of variation.

[b] The streambed substrate size was characterized as 1, concrete; 2, silt, mud, or detritus; 3, sand (>0.063–2 mm); 4, fine/medium gravel (>2–16 mm); 5, coarse gravel (>16–32 mm); 6, very coarse gravel (>32–64 mm); 7, small cobble (>64–128 mm); 8, large cobble (>128–256 mm); 9, small boulder (>256–512 mm); 10, large boulder, irregular bedrock, irregular hardpan, or irregular artificial surface (Fitzpatrick et al. 1998).

Water temperature, open canopy, and percentage of urban land use were highest in concrete-lined channels and lowest in natural channels (Table 4). Bank shading, coefficient of variation (cv) of bank-full width, cv of open canopy, presence of riffles, and streambed substrate size were lowest in concrete-lined channels and highest in natural channels. Values for channelized streams fell between the values for concrete-lined and

TABLE 4. Median values for chemical and physical variables that were significantly different among channel-type categories (ANOVA, $P < 0.05$). For each variable, channel types with different letters were significantly different (Tukey tests, $P < 0.05$).

	Channel type		
	Natural	Channelized	Concrete
% bank shading	87 A	69 A	9 B
cv[a] of bank-full width	24 A	21 A	0 B
Depth (m)	0.19 A	0.23 A	0.10 B
Open canopy (degrees)	61 A	122 AB	153 B
cv open canopy	47 A	24 AB	9 B
% riffle	17 A	7 AB	0 B
Streambed substrate size[b]	4.9 A	4.1 A	1.0 B
% urban land use (contributing)	45 A	53 B	79 B
Water temperature (°C)	23.5 A	26.0 B	30.3 B

[a] cv, coefficient of variation.

[b] The streambed substrate size was characterized as 1, concrete; 2, silt, mud, or detritus; 3, sand (>0.063–2 mm); 4, fine/medium gravel (>2–16 mm); 5, coarse gravel (>16–32 mm); 6, very coarse gravel (>32–64 mm); 7, small cobble (>64–128 mm); 8, large cobble (>128–256 mm); 9, small boulder (>256–512 mm); 10, large boulder, irregular bedrock, irregular hardpan, or irregular artificial surface (Fitzpatrick et al. 1998).

natural streams; however, they were usually more similar to values for natural streams.

Principal components analysis of chemical and physical variables resulted in four PCA axes accounting for more than 80% of the variance in the data (Table 5). The first two PCA axes accounted for most of the variance (65%). Principal components analysis axis 1 explains about 39% of the variation among sites and is composed of variables associated with water source (Figure 3). Loadings for the chemical variables of chloride, potassium, sodium, phosphate, and ammonia increase in the positive direction toward the sites supplied

TABLE 5. Loadings of ranked chemical and physical variables and biological metrics derived from principal component analysis.

Variable	Loadings					
	Axis 1	Axis 2	Axis 3	Axis 4	Axis 5	Axis 6
Chemical and physical variables:						
Cl	0.28	—[a]	—	0.42	NA[b]	NA
K	0.31	—	—	—	NA	NA
Na	0.28	—	—	0.30	NA	NA
Ammonia	0.26	—	—	0.32	NA	NA
PO$_4$	0.31	—	—	—	NA	NA
Discharge	0.26	—	—	—	NA	NA
cv[c] bank-full width	—	—	0.25	—	NA	NA
Bank shading	—	0.31	−0.28	—	NA	NA
Channel width, wetted	—	—	0.43	—	NA	NA
Depth	—	0.36	—	0.29	NA	NA
cv depth	—	—	—	—	NA	NA
Open canopy	—	−0.26	0.39	—	NA	NA
cv open canopy	—	0.32	−0.33	—	NA	NA
% riffle	−0.24	—	—	—	NA	NA
Streambed substrate size	—	0.35	—	—	NA	NA
% urban land use (contributing)	—	—	−0.46	—	NA	NA
Velocity	0.26	—	—	−0.35	NA	NA
cv velocity	−0.25	—	—	0.47	NA	NA
Water temperature	—	−0.31	—	—	NA	NA
Cumulative variance explained:	39	65	75	83	NA	NA
Macroinvertebrate taxa metrics:						
Richness	—	0.22	—	0.22	0.24	—
EPT richness	0.21	—	0.24	—	—	—
Trichoptera richness	—	—	0.23	—	—	—
% nonchironomid dipteran richness	—	0.28	—	−0.24	—	—
% nonchironomid abundance	—	0.28	—	—	—	—
% Orthoclad richness	—	−0.23	−0.21	−0.30	—	—
% Orthoclad abundance	—	—	—	−0.24	0.21	0.31
% Oligochaete richness	—	−0.22	—	—	—	—
% Oligochaete abundance	—	—	—	—	—	—
EPA tolerance, based on richness	−0.22	—	−0.20	—	—	0.21
% parasite richness	—	—	−0.23	—	—	—
% parasite abundance	—	—	−0.23	—	—	—
Scraper richness	—	—	0.38	—	—	—
% shredder richness	—	−0.25	—	—	—	0.46
% shredder abundance	—	—	0.22	—	—	0.28
% predator richness	—	—	—	0.32	—	0.37
% gatherer richness	—	—	−0.25	—	—	0.31
% Trichoptera abundance	0.25	—	—	—	—	—

TABLE 5. Continued.

Variable	Loadings					
	Axis 1	Axis 2	Axis 3	Axis 4	Axis 5	Axis 6%
%Tanytarsini abundance	0.20	—	—	0.22	0.23	—
% Tanytarsini abundance/Chironomid abundance	—	—	–0.20	—	0.25	—
% noninsect abundance	–0.23	—	—	—	—	—
Nonmidge diptera plus noninsect abundance	–0.23	—	—	—	—	—
% filterer richness	—	—	—	–0.26	—	—
% filterer abundance	0.24	—	—	—	—	—
Cumulative variance explained:	38	65	75	83	88	92
Periphyton taxa metrics:						
% diatom richness	—	0.56	—	NA	NA	NA
% diatom abundance	—	0.52	0.27	NA	NA	NA
Green algae biovolume	–0.29	—	–0.55	NA	NA	NA
Blue-green algae biovolume	–0.44	—	0.33	NA	NA	NA
% blue-green algae biovolume	–0.36	—	0.53	NA	NA	NA
% Nitrogen-heterotrophic diatom abundance	–0.38	0.33	–0.34	NA	NA	NA
% eutrophic diatom abundance	–0.35	0.37	–0.28	NA	NA	NA
% motile diatom abundance	–0.33	0.31	—	NA	NA	NA
% Pollution-sensitive diatom abundance	0.39	—	—	NA	NA	NA
Cumulative variance explained:	43	69	84	NA	NA	NA

[a] —, loading < 0.20 for macroinvertebrate metrics; loading < 0.24 for periphyton metrics and chemical and physical variables.
[b] NA, not applicable.
[c] cv, coefficient of variation.

with treated wastewater. Physical variables of discharge and velocity also increase in the positive direction. Physical variables of percentage of riffles and cv of velocity increase in the negative direction toward the sites supplied with natural water (Table 5; Figure 3).

Principal components analysis axis 2 explains 26% of the variation among sites and includes primarily variables associated with channel type (Table 5; Figure 3). Loadings for the physical variables of bank shading, depth, streambed substrate size, and cv of open canopy increase in the positive direction toward sites that are channelized or have natural channels. Open canopy and water temperature increase in the negative direction toward sites that are concrete-lined.

Biological Metrics and Water Source

Twenty-four benthic macroinvertebrate and six periphyton metrics were significantly different among water sources (ANOVA, $P < 0.05$). Eight benthic macroinvertebrate metrics are measures of taxa richness, 6 are measures of taxa abundance, and 10 are measures of functional-feeding groups. Several macroinvertebrate metrics based on slightly different measures of the same taxa (e.g., oligochaetes) gave similar results, suggesting that they were redundant. In these cases, only results for relative richness and abundance are given (Tables 6 and 7). Macroinvertebrate metrics varying with water source included taxa richness, Ephemeroptera-Plecoptera-Trichoptera (EPT) richness, nonchironomid dipterans, orthoclad chironomids, oligochaetes, richness of tolerant taxa, parasites, shredders, predators, scrapers, and gatherers.

Streams supplied by natural water and streams supplied by treated wastewater were significantly different from other sources for more biological metrics than were streams supplied by either human-impacted groundwater or urban runoff (Table 6). Streams supplied by natural water sources generally had higher values for total richness, EPT richness, trichopteran

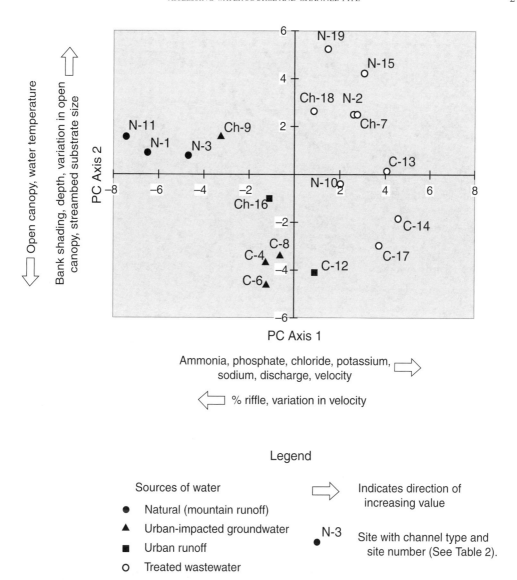

FIGURE 3. Principal component analysis (PCA) site scores based on chemical and physical data from the Santa Ana River basin, California. Principal component analysis axis 1 is controlled by water-source variables. Principal component analysis axis 2 is controlled by channel-type variables.

richness, and measures of nonchironomid dipteran abundance (predominantly Simuliidae and *Caloparyphus* sp.) than did streams dominated by treated wastewater (Table 6). Urban runoff and treated wastewater generally had higher values than those of natural water or groundwater sources for measures of orthoclad chironomids (dominated by *Cricotopus* sp.) and oligochaetes.

The importance of functional-feeding groups varied among water sources (Table 6). Measures of parasites (Nematoda) and predators (Turbellaria) were greatest at urban groundwater sites. Measures of shredders (predominantly *Cricotopus* sp.) were greatest at urban runoff and treated wastewater sites. Scraper richness (dominated by *Physella* sp., *Petrophila* sp., and *Helicopsyche* sp.) was significantly greater in natural waters and urban runoff compared with treated wastewater and urban groundwater. Percentage gatherer richness (predominantly Naididae, *Fallceon* sp., and *Baetis* sp.) was lowest in natural waters compared with urban runoff or groundwater.

Thirteen of the 19 selected chemical and physical

TABLE 6. Median values for biological metrics that were significantly different among water-source categories (ANOVA, p < 0.05). For each variable, medians with different letters were significantly different (Tukey tests, P < 0.05).

| Metric | Water source | | | |
	Natural	Groundwater	Urban runoff	Treated wastewater
Macroinvertebrate taxa metrics:				
Taxa richness	19 A[b]	17 AB	14 AB	9 B
EPT[a] richness	6 A	5 B	1.5 B	2 B
Trichoptera richness	4 A	3 AB	1.5 AB	1 B
% nonchironomid dipteran richness	11 AB	23 A	11 AB	0 B
% nonchironomid dipteran abundance	9 A	11 A	1 B	0 B
% Orthoclad richness	0 A	10 AB	9 AB	14 B
% Orthoclad abundance	0 A	<1 A	35 B	4 B
% Oligochaete richness	0 A	0 A	14 B	14 B
% Oligochaete abundance	0 A	0 A	28 B	17 B
EPA[b] tolerance, based on richness	4.9 A	6 B	7.2 B	5.5 AB
Macroinvertebrate functional-feeding group metrics:				
% parasite richness	0 A	7 B	0 A	0 A
% parasite abundance	0 A	<1 B	0 A	0 A
% shredder richness	8 A	7 A	19 B	17 AB
% shredder abundance	1 AB	<1 A	36 B	5 B
% predator richness	23 AB	42 A	33 AB	20 B
Scraper richness	4 A	2 B	3 A	1 B
% gatherer richness	30 A	42 B	48 B	33 AB
Periphyton taxa metrics:				
Blue-green algae biovolume	0 A	0.004 B	0 AB	0.1 B
% blue-green algae biovolume	0 AB	<1 AB	<1 A	5 B
% Nitrogen heterotrophic diatom abundance	11 A	16 A	86 B	94 B
% eutrophic diatom abundance	57 AB	22 A	87 BC	97 C
% motile diatom abundance	33 A	53 A	81 AB	76 B
% pollution-sensitive diatom abundance	46 A	2 AB	3 A	<1 B

[a] EPT, Ephemeroptera-Plecoptera-Trichoptera.
[b] EPA, U.S. Environmental Protection Agency.

variables were correlated with more than 2 of the 24 benthic macroinvertebrate metrics associated with water source. Measures of taxa richness, EPT richness, and nonchironomid dipterans were commonly negatively correlated with concentrations of dissolved chemicals (Table 7). These metrics tended to be positively correlated with cv of bank-full width, presence of riffles, and streambed substrate size. That is, these metrics were higher at sites that had lower concentrations of Cl, K, Na, orthophosphate (PO_4), ammonia, and lower percentages of urban land use and more heterogeneous habitat. Measures of orthoclad chironomids, oligochaetes, and U.S. Environmental Protection Agency's (EPA) tolerance tended to show the opposite patterns. Correlations of functional-feeding groups with chemical and physical variables were more limited, and there were no strong general patterns (Table 7).

Two of six periphyton metrics associated with water source are measures of blue-green algal biovolume, and four metrics are autecological measures (Table 6). Streams with natural waters were lower in blue-green algal biovolume and relative abundance of nitrogen heterotrophic, eutrophic, and motile diatoms (predominantly *Nitzschia amphibia*, *N. palea*, and *Diadesmis confervacea*) than were streams with treated wastewater (Table 6). The relative abundance of pollution-sensitive diatom species (predominantly *Cymbella affinis*) was greater in natural waters than in treated wastewater (Table 6). The relationships of sites with urban runoff and groundwater were mixed.

All fifteen chemical and physical variables differing among sources of water were correlated with at least one of six periphyton metrics. The periphyton metrics associated with water source, except pollution-

TABLE 7. Results of Spearmans' correlations for chemical and physical variables with invertebrate metrics that were associated with water-source categories.

Metric	Cl	K	Na	Ammonia	PO$_4$	Discharge	cv[a] bankfull width	cv depth	% riffle	Streambed substrate size	Velocity	% urban land use (contributing)	Water temperature
Macroinvertebrate taxa metrics:													
Taxa richness	—[b]	—	—	—	—	—	+	NS	NS	NS	—	—	NS
EPT[c] richness	—	NS	—	—	—	NS	++	NS	+	+	NS	—	NS
Trichoptera richness	—	NS	—	—	—	NS	++	NS	+	+	NS	—	NS
% nonchironomid dipteran richness	—	—	NS	NS	—	NS	NS	NS	NS	NS	NS	NS	++
% nonchironomid dipteran abundance	—	—	—	—	—	—	NS	NS	NS	NS	NS	NS	NS
% Orthoclad richness	++	+	++	+	++	+	NS	NS	NS	NS	+	NS	NS
% Orthoclad abundance	+	NS	+	++	+	NS	NS	NS	NS	NS	NS	+	NS
% Oligochaete richness	NS	++	++	++	++	NS	NS	NS	NS	NS	—	+	—
% Oligochaete abundance	NS	NS	NS	++	+	NS	NS	NS	NS	NS	NS	NS	NS
EPA tolerance, based on richness	NS	NS	NS	NS	NS	NS	—	—	—	—	NS	+	NS
Macroinvertebrate functional-feeding group metrics:													
% parasite richness	NS	—	NS	NS	NS	NS	NS	NS	NS	NS	NS	NS	+
% parasite abundance	NS	—	NS	NS	NS	NS	NS	NS	NS	NS	NS	NS	++
Scraper richness	—	NS	—	NS	—	—	NS	NS	+	NS	NS	—	NS
% shredder richness	NS	++	NS	+	+	+	NS	NS	NS	NS	+	NS	NS
% shredder abundance	NS	NS	NS	NS	NS	NS	NS	NS	NS	NS	NS	NS	NS
% predator richness	NS	NS	NS	NS	NS	NS	NS	NS	NS	NS	NS	NS	NS
% gatherer richness	NS	NS	NS	NS	NS	NS	-	-	—	—	NS	+	NS

[a] cv, coefficient of variation.

[b] +, positive correlation at $P < 0.05$; —, negative correlation at $P < 0.05$; ++, positive correlation at $P < 0.01$; —, negative correlation at $P < 0.01$.

[c] EPT, Ephemeroptera-Plecoptera-Trichoptera.

TABLE 8. Results of Spearmans' correlations for chemical and physical variables with periphyton metrics that were associated with water-source categories.

Metric	Cl	K	Na	Ammonia	PO$_4$	Discharge	cv^a bankfull width	Channel width, wetted	cv depth	% riffle	Stream bed substrate size	Velocity	cv velocity	% urban land use (contributing)	Water temperature
Blue-green algae biovolume	++^{b}	NS	++	NS	NS	+	NS	++	NS	NS	NS	NS	NS	NS	NS
% blue-green algae biovolume	NS	NS	+	NS	NS	+	NS	++	NS	NS	NS	NS	NS	NS	NS
% Nitrogen-heterotrophic diatom abundance	+	++	+	+	++	+	NS	++	NS	−	NS	++	−	NS	−
% eutrophic diatom abundance	+	++	+	+	++	++	NS	++	NS	NS	NS	++	−	NS	−
% motile diatom abundance	+	+	++	+	+	NS	NS	+	NS	NS	NS	NS	−	NS	−
% pollution-sensitive diatom abundance	−	−	−	−	−	NS	++	NS	+	++	++	NS	NS	−	NS

^{a} cv, coefficient of variation.

^{b} +, positive correlation at $P < 0.05$; −, negative correlation at $P < 0.05$; ++, positive correlation at $P < 0.01$, —, negative correlation at $P < 0.01$.

TABLE 9. Median values for biological metrics that were significantly different among channel types (ANOVA, $P < 0.05$). For each variable, medians with different letters were significantly different (Tukey tests, $P < 0.05$).

Metric	Channel type		
	Natural	Channelized	Concrete
Macroinvertebrate taxa metrics:			
% Trichoptera abundance	29 A	57 A	0.3 B
% Tanytarsini abundance	1 A	2.9 AB	0 B
% Tanytarsini/Chironomid abundance	0.2 A	0.4 AB	0 B
% noninsect abundance	9.2 AB	6.7 A	49 B
Nonmidge diptera plus noninsect abundance	5,346 A	9,863 A	44,878 B
Macroinvertebrate functional-feeding group metrics:			
% filterer richness	25 A	22 AB	0 B
% filterer abundance	50 A	57 A	0 B
Periphyton taxa metrics:			
% diatom richness	20 A	21 A	13 B
% diatom abundance	86 A	90 A	45 B
Green algae biovolume	0.003 A	0 A	1.5 B

sensitive diatom abundance, tended to be positively correlated with chemical variables and with most physical variables but had negative correlations with cv of stream velocity, water temperature, and presence of riffles (Table 8). Therefore, these metrics were higher at sites with higher Cl, K, Na, PO_4, and ammonia concentrations but cooler water temperatures. Pollution-sensitive diatom abundance tended to be negatively correlated with these chemical variables and urban land use and positively correlated with most physical variables (Table 8).

Biological Metrics and Channel Type

Thirteen benthic macroinvertebrate and three periphyton metrics were significantly different among channel types (ANOVA, $P < 0.05$). Nine macroinvertebrate metrics are measures of taxa abundance. Four macroinvertebrate metrics are measures of functional-feeding groups. Similar to water source results, several macroinvertebrate metrics based on slightly different measures of the same taxa gave similar results suggesting redundancy. Therefore, only results for relative abundance are given (Tables 9 and 10). Macroinvertebrate metrics differing with channel type included measures of abundance of trichopterans, tanytarsini chironomids, noninsects, and filterers.

Concrete-lined channels had significantly lower abundances of trichoptera, tanytarsini chironomids, and filterers (predominantly *Hydropsyche* sp. and *Rheotanytarsus* sp.) in comparison with natural and channelized channels (Table 9). Concrete-lined chan-

nels were highest in noninsect abundance (predominantly Naididae, Turbellaria, *Hyalella* sp., and *Physella* sp.). No significant differences in macroinvertebrate metrics were observed between natural and channelized sites (Table 9).

Nine physical variables showing significant differences between channel types were correlated with at least 1 of the 13 benthic macroinvertebrate metrics associated with channel type (Table 10). Several strong patterns were evident in macroinvertebrate correlations. Metrics for trichopterans and tanytarsini chironomids were positively correlated with percentage of bank shading, depth, and streambed substrate size and negatively correlated with open canopy, water temperature, and urban land use (Table 10). This was generally reflected in results for filterers because the two taxonomic groups were dominated by filtering genera, *Hydropsyche* sp. and *Rheotanytarsus* sp., respectively. Hence, trichopterans and tanytarsini chironomids were found in higher abundance at sites with more shading, larger streambed substrate, cooler water temperatures, and less urban land use. Noninsects showed reverse patterns with negative correlations to percentage of bank shading, depth, streambed substrate size, and urban land use. Noninsect metrics also showed negative correlations with cv of bank-full width and presence of riffles indicating higher abundance of noninsects in concrete-lined channels.

Relative diatom richness and abundance were lowest in concrete-lined channels (Table 9). Biovolume of green algae was greater in concrete-lined channels than in channelized and natural streams (Table

TABLE 10. Results of Spearman's correlations for physical and chemical variables with invertebrate metrics that were associated with channel type.

Metric	% bank shading	cv[a] of bank-full width	Depth	Open canopy	cv open canopy	% riffle	Streambed substrate size	% urban land use (contributing)	Water temperature
Macroinvertebrate taxa metrics:									
% Trichoptera abundance	+[b]	+	+	NS	NS	+	++	–	NS
% Tanytarsini abundance	++	NS	+	–	+	NS	+	–	NS
% Tanytarsini/Chironomid abundance	++	+	+	–	+	NS	+	–	–
% noninsect abundance	–	NS	NS	NS	NS	NS	–	NS	NS
Nonmidge diptera plus noninsect abundance	NS	–	–	NS	NS	–	—	++	NS
Macroinvertebrate functional-feeding group metrics:									
% filterer richness	++	NS	++	–	++	NS	+	NS	NS
% filterer abundance	++	NS	++	–	+	NS	++	NS	NS

[a] cv, coefficient of variation.

[b] +, positive correlation at $P < 0.05$; ++, positive correlation at $P < 0.01$; –, negative correlation at $P < 0.05$; —, negative correlation at $P < 0.01$.

TABLE 11. Results of Spearman's correlations of physical variables with periphyton metrics that were associated with channel type.

Metric	cv[a] bank-full width	Streambed substrate size	Water temper- ature
% diatom richness	++[b]	+	–
% diatom abundance	++	+	–
Green algae biovolume	–	–	NS

[a] cv, coefficient of variation
[b] +, positive correlation at $P < 0.05$; –, negative correlation at $P < 0.05$; ++, positive correlation at $P < 0.01$.

9).Three variables were correlated with at least one of three periphyton metrics (Table 11). Relative richness and the abundance of diatoms were positively correlated with cv of bank-full width and streambed substrate size but negatively correlated with water temperature (Table 11). Therefore, more diatoms were found in higher abundances in natural and channelized streams than in concrete channels. Biovolume of green algae showed a reverse pattern and was negatively correlated to both cv of bank-full width and streambed substrate size (Table 11).

Principal Components Analysis

Principal components analysis effectively summarized the relations between macroinvertebrate and periphyton metrics. Principle components analysis of the macroinvertebrate metrics resulted in six PCA axes that accounted for more than 90% of the variance in the macroinvertebrate metrics among sites (Table 5). The first axis explained 38% of the variance among sites. Most of the metrics dominating this axis were associated with channel type; however, three metrics associated with water source—EPT richness, EPA tolerance, and shredder abundance—were also important (Table 5; Figure 4). The second axis explained 27% of the variation among sites and was dominated by macroinvertebrate metrics associated with water source. Loadings for orthoclads, oligochaetes and shredders increase in the negative direction toward the sites supplied with treated wastewater. Taxa richness and nonchironomid dipteran metrics increase in the positive direction toward sites supplied by natural water or groundwater.

Principal component analysis of periphyton metrics resulted in three PCA axes that accounted for 84% of the variance among sites (Table 5). The first axis accounted for 42% of the variance among sites

and is dominated by metrics associated with water source (Figure 5). The second axis accounts for 26% of the variance and is also dominated by metrics associated with water source; however, metrics associated with channel type also contribute to the second axis. In general, sites with treated wastewater are in the upper left portion of the graph, whereas sites with natural sources of water are more toward the right of the graph; sites with urban runoff and groundwater are between the two (Figure 5).

Discussion

The categorical study design successfully characterized associations of biological assemblages with water source and channel type. Many macroinvertebrate and periphyton metrics showed significant differences among the four sources of water or the three types of channels (Tables 6 and 9). In addition, many chemical and physical variables that correlated to these biological metrics also showed significant differences between sources of water and channel types (Tables 3 and 4). Although water source and channel type were treated largely as independent factors for analysis, organisms are responding to physical and chemical conditions generated jointly by these two factors and others not explicitly considered in the study (such as annual patterns in hydrology). For example, PCA axis 1 from the analysis of chemical and physical variables (Figure 3) clearly separates sites with natural and wastewater sources, but the gradient includes chemical and physical variables related to differences among streams with natural channels and streams in concrete-lined channels. Brown et al. (2005) address these issues more fully.

Artificial substrates were used to mitigate some effects caused by different channel types; however, it is likely that the macroinvertebrate and periphyton assemblages sampled from the artificial substrates were somewhat different from the natural assemblages. Lamberti and Resh (1985) found that clay tiles were similar to natural substrates for algae and macroinvertebrates after colonizing for 28 d. Other studies showed artificial substrates had different compositions and abundances of invertebrates in comparison with natural substrates (Garie and McIntosh 1986; Casey and Kendall 1996). Colonization rates and replacement of colonizing periphyton by more persistent species can be affected by environmental conditions, including current velocity, nutrient concentrations, water temperature, and light (Oemke and Burton 1986). Although assemblages on artificial substrates are likely different from assemblages in the stream,

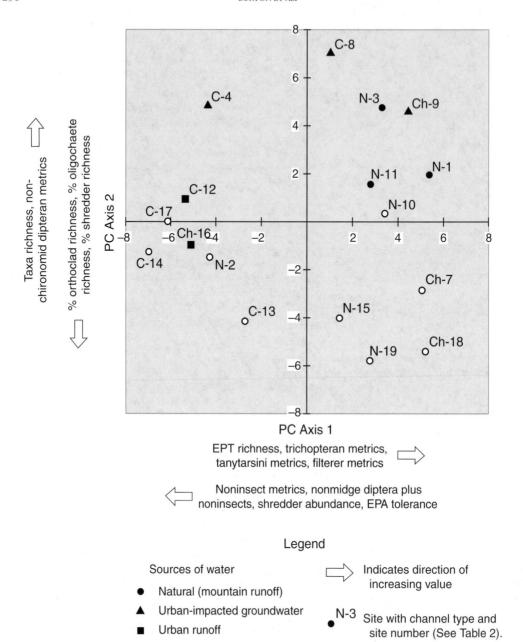

FIGURE 4. Principal component analysis (PCA) site scores based on macroinvertebrate metrics from the Santa Ana River basin, California. Principal component analysis axis 1 is controlled principally by metrics associated with channel type. Principal component analysis axis 2 is controlled principally by metrics associated with water source.

artificial substrates should represent a similar sub-assemblage, including the taxa best at colonizing and exploiting new habitats. Therefore, assemblages on artificial substrates likely reflect differences between sites.

Macroinvertebrate Response

Macroinvertebrate metrics appeared most responsive to habitat alteration. The first PCA axis (Figure 4) emphasizes tanytarsini, trichoptera, noninsect, and filterer metrics that differed among channel types.

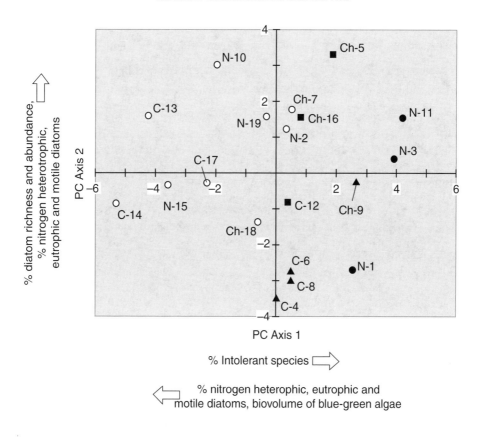

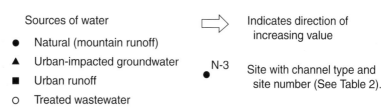

FIGURE 5. Principal component analysis (PCA) site scores based on periphyton metrics from the Santa Ana River basin, California. Principal component analysis axis 1 is controlled principally by metrics associated with water source. Principal component analysis axis 2 is controlled by metrics associated with both water source and channel type.

Concrete-lined channels always differed from one or both of the other channel types (Table 9). Although channelized sites appeared to be intermediate between concrete-lined and natural sites, differences between channelized sites and natural sites were not statistically significant. This suggests that channelized sites are able to support the same assemblages as natural channels. Most habitat measures were similar between these two channel types (Table 4). In particular, some riparian vegetation was present at most channelized sites, ranging from grasses and cat-

tails to trees. There was less riparian vegetation in channelized streams compared with natural channels, but channelized streams were not as bare as concrete channels.

Several metrics related to water source—EPT richness, trichoptera richness, EPA tolerance, and shredder abundance—mainly reflect differences among the natural, least-impacted sites and the other sites with a variety of water sources (Table 6). Natural-water source sites were chemically and physically different from other sites (Figure 3; Table 3). These sites are at the interface of the mountains and valley and have little urban land use in their drainage areas (Figure 1; Table 3).

Specific conductance and other surrogates for salinity are commonly related to macroinvertebrate assemblages (Leland and Fend 1998; Brown and May 2000), but they were not correlated in this study. The lack of such correlation, despite correlations of metrics with ionic species, could be due to the relatively narrow range of specific conductance (286–1,250 µS/cm) and one of the least-impacted sites having a fairly high value (804 µS/cm at site 3). In addition, the least-impacted site was high in calcium, magnesium, and sulfate instead of Na, Cl, or K. There were differences in ionic composition among water sources (Table 3); however, it is unknown if differences of this relatively small magnitude can affect macroinvertebrate taxa.

The macroinvertebrate metric responses observed in this study are generally consistent with results of other studies. The least-impacted streams had the highest macroinvertebrate taxa richness, EPT richness, and trichopteran richness in comparison with urban streams. Barbour et al. (1999) observed that increases in tolerance and relative abundance of oligochaetes were expected responses to stream degradation. The proportion of oligochaetes is expected to be higher in urban areas (Winter and Duthie 1998; Ourso 2001; Paul and Meyer 2001; Kennen and Ayers 2002) and to increase with stream degradation (Karr and Kerans 1992; Fore et al. 1996).

A number of other macroinvertebrate metrics suggest differences among the urban water sources (Table 6). For example, macroinvertebrate metrics at urban-impacted groundwater sites appear to be different from those for other water sources as indicated by the dominance of nematodes (parasite metrics), turbellarians (predator metric), and nonchironomid dipterans and relatively low values for oligochaete metrics (Table 6). These metrics were responsive to environmental stresses including urbanization in other studies (Garie and McIntosh 1986; Karr and Kerans 1992; Barbour et al. 1996; Fore et al. 1996). However, those studies were conducted in less altered streams across a relatively wide range of urbanization. It is unclear what such differences mean ecologically in the context of highly altered streams all within a highly urbanized area.

Several functional-feeding group metrics were responsive to water source or channel type and warrant discussion because of implications for ecological functions within highly urbanized areas. With respect to water source, the most interesting relationships involved shredders and scrapers. Shredder metrics tended to be higher at sites affected by urban runoff and

treated wastewater (Table 6), mainly because of the abundance of *Crictopus* sp., a pollution tolerant genus of chironomids that has been associated with highly urbanized sites (Jones and Clark 1987; Kennen and Ayers 2002). Cummins et al. (1989) and Kerans and Karr (1994) suggested that the presence of shredders may be more indicative of local riparian habitat rather than more general indicators of urbanization. Although a number of these sites have riparian vegetation present, the highest abundance of this genus occurred at an urban-runoff site (site 12) with no riparian vegetation and high urbanization. Shredders could be feeding on macroalgae present at the site.

Scraper richness was higher at sites supplied with natural water or urban runoff compared to sites supplied with groundwater or treated wastewater. Decreasing scraper richness has been considered an indicator of environmental degradation, although Fore et al. (1996) suggested that the response of scrapers can be variable. Scraper taxa at urban-runoff sites and at groundwater sites consisted of both highly pollution-tolerant genera (i.e., *Physella* sp.) and pollution-sensitive genera (i.e., *Petrophila* sp. and *Helicopsyche* sp.). However, the pollution-tolerant *Physella* sp. was significantly more abundant at sites with urban runoff than at sites with groundwater.

Filterer metrics were strongly affected by channel type (Table 9), with concrete-lined channels having the lowest abundances. Primary filtering taxa in this study were the trichopteran *Hydropsyche* sp. and the chironomid *Rheotanytarsini* sp. These taxa were also most responsible for responses of trichoptera and tanytarsini metrics to channel type. Previously reported responses of filterers to environmental degradation are variable (Karr and Kerans 1992; Barbour et al. 1996; Fore et al. 1996; Winter and Duthie 1998). *Hydropsyche* sp. and *Rheotanytarsini* sp. are generally considered pollution sensitive (DeShon 1995; Barbour et al. 1999); however, in this study, water chemistry of concrete channels was variable (Figure 4). A simple physical explanation might be applicable. Both of these filterer taxa are net builders (*Rheotanytarsini* sp. can also build tubes) (Merritt and Cummins 1984). The relatively two-dimensional nature of the concrete substrate may limit the number of locations appropriate for net and tube construction, therefore limiting the population.

Periphyton Response

Periphyton metrics were most responsive to water source. Principal component analysis axis 1 included only metrics responsive to water source. Principal component analysis axis 2 included metrics responsive to water source and those responsive to channel type (Figure 3; Table 5). Sites with treated wastewater generally had the highest values for the periphyton metrics, except for percentage pollution-sensitive diatoms, which had the lowest value (Table 6). Other water sources were more variable, with each being at the other extreme from treated wastewater for at least one metric. Clearly, treated wastewater has a strong effect on periphyton assemblages.

Three periphyton metrics highest in treated wastewater—nitrogen-heterotrophic diatom abundance, eutrophic diatom abundance, and motile diatom abundance—were dominated by *Nitzchia palea*, a species most abundant in the most disturbed streams in a New Jersey urban study (Kennen and Ayers 2002). All three metrics show a positive relationship with inorganic salts, ammonia, phosphate, and wetted channel width and a negative relationship with cv of velocity. Treated wastewater has the highest concentrations of these chemical constituents and sites with treated wastewater had the widest channels and the most uniform velocities. Similar relationships between periphyton metrics and physical and chemical variables were found in the mid-Appalachian region (Hill et al. 2000).

Two periphyton metrics—relative diatom richness and abundance—were lowest in concrete-lined channels, whereas green algae biovolume was highest in concrete-lined channels (Table 9). Response of the diatom metrics is indicative of higher environmental stress in concrete channels (Barbour et al. 1999). Diatom metrics have a positive correlation to streambed substrate and cv of bank-full width, indicating that diatoms prefer more complex aquatic habitat than is available in concrete-lined channels. Also, diatom metrics had a negative correlation with water temperature. Previous studies showed that diatom richness decreases when water temperature is greater than 30°C and diatoms are often replaced with green or blue-green algae (DeNicola 1996). In our study, fewer diatoms and a higher biovolume of green algae were present in concrete channels, which were warmer than the other channel types. Median water temperature at sites with concrete channels was 30°C compared to 23°C at sites with natural channels and 26°C in channelized streams.

Challenges of Studying Highly Urbanized Areas

A general approach to urban aquatic studies is to examine hydrologic, geomorphic, chemical, habitat, and biological characteristics of streams over a gradient of urban land use intensities in specific environmental settings (e.g., Tate et al. 2005, this volume). The basic requirements for these studies include (1) consistent definition of the land-use gradient; (2) consistent environmental setting to minimize natural gradients (e.g., temperature, stream size, hydrologic variability, soil type, and precipitation); (3) collection of sufficient physical, chemical, and biological data to characterize stream response to land use; and (4) sufficient distribution and number of sites to accurately represent a response over the range of the land-use gradient. Conditions in the Santa Ana River basin did not support this approach.

The traditional view of precipitation falling on the landscape and flowing toward stream channels through various land uses does not apply in the Santa Ana River basin and in other basins in the arid and semiarid Southwest. Some streams are ephemeral in nature. Other streams are diverted for public supply or into retention basins for groundwater recharge. As a result, many streams lose surface flow shortly after reaching the valley floor. Flow is reestablished in some stream channels from anthropogenic sources (e.g., treated wastewater, urban runoff). Therefore, the traditional view that water quality in a stream channel reflects the proportions of land uses in a basin also does not apply. Alternatively stated, land use is not a surrogate for the source of water in the Santa Ana River basin, and land use and basin area are not surrogates for the volume of water in the streams. These discontinuities in the hydrologic cycle owing to the semiarid climate and human engineering in combination with extreme urbanization made it impossible to find least-impacted sites in the valley. The rapid change from undeveloped mountains to the highly urbanized valley made it impossible to define an urbanization gradient because there were few streams with low to intermediate levels of urbanization (Table 2). This also precludes another common approach to urban studies, comparing reference or least-impacted conditions with conditions in urbanized areas.

An alternative model is to explicitly identify aspects of highly urbanized streams, such as impervious area, and determine the associations of the chosen factor with some of the effects this has on habitat quality, water quality, or aquatic communities. However, it is difficult to study just one or two aspects of urbanization because the observed effect may also be caused by other factors not included in the study. In the Santa Ana River basin, some aspects of the hydrologic system are well constrained despite the complexities of human involvement. Therefore, it was possible to identify the source of water and channel type for many of the streams. This provided an opportunity for assessing the effects of these two anthropogenic factors; however, even in this highly constrained system, the effects of the two factors could not be separated completely.

Conclusions

Based on analysis of macroinvertebrate and periphyton metrics and their correlations with chemical and physical variables, water source and channel type had significant associations with ecosystem condition. The source of water affected not only chemical variables such as Cl and K, but also some physical variables such as velocity and water temperature, whereas channel type affected only physical variables such as streambed substrate size. Macroinvertebrate assemblages appeared to be most sensitive to physical variables, particularly those associated with differences between concrete-lined channels and streams with natural channels or channelized streams with natural bottoms. In contrast, periphyton metrics mainly reflected associations with aspects of water quality related to water source.

Our results suggest that significant improvements in aquatic ecological condition are possible in streams of the highly urbanized Santa Ana River basin even though conditions will not be returned to full ecological function. These results are likely to be similar for other urban streams in arid or semiarid areas. Given appropriate design criteria, converting concrete-lined channels to channelized streams with stabilized sides and natural bottoms could support aquatic ecosystems more similar to those of less degraded sites and still maintain flood control to protect life and property. Reducing chloride, sodium, potassium, ammonia, and phosphate concentrations in treated wastewater could also contribute to such changes.

Acknowledgments

This work was funded by the U.S. Geological Survey's National Water-Quality Assessment Program. We thank Cathy Tate and Anne Brasher (USGS) for reviews of the manuscript that significantly improved the final product.

References

Aloi, J. E. 1990. A critical review of recent freshwater periphyton field methods. Canadian Journal of Fisheries and Aquatic Sciences 47:656–670.

Bahls, L.L. 1993. Periphyton bioassessment methods for Montana streams (Revised January 1993). Department of Health and Environmental Sciences, Water Quality Bureau, Helena, Montana.

Barbour, M. T., J. Gerritsen, G. E. Griffith, R. Frydenborg, E. McCarron, J. S. White, and M. L. Bastian. 1996. A framework for biological criteria for Florida streams using benthic macroinvertebrates. Journal of the North American Benthological Society 15:185–211.

Barbour, M. T., J. Gerritsen, B. D. Snyder, and J. B. Stribling. 1999. Rapid bioassessment protocols for use in streams and wadeable rivers: periphyton, benthic macroinvertebrates and fish, 2nd edition. U.S. Environmental Protection Agency Report 841-B-99–02, Washington, D.C.

Booth, D. B. 1991. Urbanization and the natural drainage system—impacts, solutions, and prognoses. Northwest Environmental Journal 7:93–118.

Booth, D. B., and L. E. Reinelt. 1993. Consequences of urbanization on aquatic systems—measured effects, degradation thresholds, and corrective strategies. Pages 545–550 in Proceedings of Watershed '93, a national conference on watershed management, March 12–24, 1993, Alexandria, Virginia.

Brown, L. R., and J. T. May. 2000. Macroinvertebrate assemblages on woody debris and their relations with environmental variables in the lower Sacramento and San Joaquin River drainages, California. Environmental Monitoring and Assessment 64:311–329.

Brown, L. R., C. A. Burton, and K. Belitz. 2005. Aquatic assemblages of the highly urbanized Santa Ana River basin, California. Pages 263–287 in L. R. Brown, R. H. Gray, R. M. Hughes, and M. R. Meador, editors. Effects of urbanization on stream ecosystems. American Fisheries Society, Symposium 47, Bethesda, Maryland.

Burton, C. A. 2002. Effects of urbanization and long-term rainfall on the occurrence of organic compounds and trace elements in reservoir sediment cores, streambed sediment, and fish tissue from the Santa Ana River basin, California, 1998. U.S. Geological Survey Water-Resources Investigations Report 02–4175, Sacramento, California.

Burton, C. A., J. A. Izbicki, and K. S. Paybins. 1998. Water-quality trends in the Santa Ana River at MWD Crossing and below Prado Dam, Riverside County, California. U.S. Geological Survey Water-Resources Investigations Report 97–4173, Sacramento, California.

Casey, R. J., and S. A. Kendall. 1996. Comparisons among colonization of artificial substratum types and natural substratum by benthic macroinvertebrates. Hydrobiologia 341:57–64.

Charles, D. F., C. Knowles, and R. S. Davis, editors.

2002. Protocols for the analysis of algal samples collected as part of the U.S. Geological Survey National Water-Quality Assessment Program. Patrick Center for Environmental Research Report No. 02–06, Academy of Natural Sciences, Philadelphia.

Cuffney, T. F. 2003. User's manual for the National Water-Quality Assessment program invertebrate data analysis system (IDAS) software: Version 3. U.S. Geological Survey Open-File Report 03–172, Raleigh, North Carolina.

Cummins, K. W., D. M. Wilzbach, D. M. Gates, J. B. Perry, and W. B. Taliaferro. 1989. Shredders and riparian vegetation. Bioscience 39:24–30.

DeNicola, D. M. 1996. Periphyton responses to temperature at different ecological levels. Pages 149–181 in R. J. Stevenson, M. L. Bothwell, and R. L. Lowe, editors. Algal ecology: freshwater benthic ecosystems. Academic Press, San Diego, California.

DeShon, J. E. 1995. Development and application of the invertebrate community index. Pages 217–243 in W. S. Davis and T. P. Simon, editors. Biological assessment and criteria: tools for water resource planning and decision making. Lewis Publishers, Boca Raton, Florida.

Fitzpatrick, F. A., I. A. Waite, P. J. D'Arconte, M. R. Meador, M. A. Maupin, and M. E. Gurtz. 1998. Revised methods for characterizing stream habitat in the National Water-Quality Assessment Program. U.S. Geological Survey Water-Resources Investigations Report 98–4052, Raleigh, North Carolina.

Fore, L. S., J. R. Karr, and R. W. Wisseman. 1996. Assessing invertebrate responses to human activities: Evaluating alternative approaches. Journal of the North American Benthological Society 15:212–231.

Frick, E. A., D. J. Hippe, G. R. Buell, C. A. Crouch, and E. E. Hopkins. 1998. Water quality in the Apalachicola-Chattahoochee-Flint River basin, Georgia, Alabama, and Florida, 1992–1995. U.S. Geological Survey Circular 1164, Reston, Virginia.

Garie, H. L., and A. McIntosh. 1986. Distribution of benthic macroinvertebrates in a stream exposed to urban runoff. Water Resources Bulletin 22:447–455.

Grimm, N. B., J. M. Grove, S. T. A. Pickett, and C. L. Redman. 2000. Integrated approaches to long-term studies of urban ecological systems. BioScience 50:571–584.

Helsel, D. R., and R. M. Hirsch. 1992. Statistical methods in water resources. Elsevier, New York.

Hill, B. H., A. T. Herlihy, P. R. Kaufmann, R. J. Stevenson, F. H. McCormick, and C. B. Johnson. 2000. Use of periphyton data as an index of biotic integrity. Journal of North American Benthological Society 19:50–67.

Hitt, K. J. 1994. Refining 1970's land-use data with 1990 population data to indicate new residential development. U.S. Geological Survey Water-Resources Investigations Report 94–4250, Reston, Virginia.

Jones, R. C., and C. C. Clark. 1987. Impact of watershed urbanization on stream insect communities. Water Resources Bulletin 23:1047–1055.

Karr, J. R., and B. L. Kerans. 1992. Components of biological integrity: Their definition and use in developments of an invertebrate IBI. Pages 1–16 in W. S. Davis and T. P. Simon, editors. Proceedings of the 1991 Midwest Pollution Control Biologists Meeting, March 19–22, 1991, Lincolnwood, Illinois. U.S. Environmental Protection Agency 905/R-92/002, Chicago.

Kennen, J. G., and M. A. Ayers. 2002. Relation of environmental characteristics to the composition of aquatic assemblages along a gradient of urban land use in New Jersey, 1996–98. U.S. Geological Survey Water-Resources Investigations Report 02–4069, West Trenton, New Jersey.

Kerans, B. L., and J. R. Karr. 1994. A benthic index of biotic integrity (B-IBI) for rivers of the Tennessee Valley. Ecological Applications 4:768–785.

Klein, R. D. 1979. Urbanization and stream quality impairment. Water Resources Bulletin 15:948–963.

Lamberti, G. A., and V. H. Resh. 1985. Comparability of introduced tiles and natural substrates for sampling lotic bacteria, algae and macroinvertebrates. Freshwater Biology 15:21–30.

Lange-Bertalot, H. 1979. Pollution tolerance of diatoms as a criterion for water quality estimation. Nova Hedwigia 64:285–304.

Leland, H. V., and S. V. Fend. 1998. Benthic invertebrate distributions in the San Joaquin River, California, in relation to physical and chemical factors. Canadian Journal of Fisheries and Aquatic Sciences 55:1051–1067.

Leopold, L. B. 1968. Hydrology for urban land planning—a guidebook on the hydrologic effects of urban land uses. U.S. Geological Survey Circular 554, Washington, D.C.

Lowe, R. L., and Y. Pan. 1996. Benthic algal communities as biological monitors. Pages 705–739 in R. J. Stevenson, M. L. Bothwell, and R. L. Lowe, editors. Algal ecology: freshwater benthic ecosystems. Academic Press, San Diego, California.

Mendez, G. O., and K. Belitz. 2002. Identifying sources of baseflow in the Santa Ana River, California. Pages 567–572 in J. F. Kenny, editor. Ground water/surface water interactions. Proceedings American Water Resources Association 2002 Summer Specialty Conference, TPS-02-2, Keystone, Colorado.

Merritt, R. W., and K. W. Cummins. 1984. An introduction to the aquatic insects, 2nd edition. Kendall/Hunt Publishing Company, Dubuque, Iowa.

Moring, J. B., and D. R. Rose. 1997. Occurrence and concentrations of polycyclic aromatic hydrocarbons in semipermeable membrane devices and clams in three urban streams of the Dallas-Fort Worth Metropolitan Area, Texas. Chemosphere 34:551–566.

Moulton, S. R. II, J. G. Kennen, R. M. Goldstein, and J. A. Hambrook. 2002. Revised protocols for sampling algal, invertebrate, and fish communities as part of the National Water-Quality Assessment Program. U.S. Geological Survey Open-File Report 02–150, Reston, Virginia.

Moulton, S. R., II, J. L. Carter, S. A. Grotheer, T. F. Cuffney, and T. M. Short. 2000. Methods of analysis by the U.S. Geological Survey National Water-Quality Laboratory—processing, taxonomy, and quality control of benthic macroinvertebrate samples. U.S. Geological Survey Open-File Report 00–212, Denver.

Oemke, M. P., and T. M. Burton. 1986. Diatom colonization dynamics in a lotic system. Hydrobiologia 139:153–166.

Omernik, J. M. 1987. Ecoregions of the conterminous United State. Annals of the Association of American Geographers 77:118–125.

Ourso, R. T. 2001. Effects of urbanization on benthic macroinvertebrate communities in streams, Anchorage, Alaska. U.S. Geological Survey Water-Resources Investigation Report 01–4278, Anchorage, Alaska.

Paul, M. J., and J. L. Meyer. 2001. Streams in the urban landscape. Annual Review of Ecology and Systematics 32:333–365.

Santa Ana Watershed Project Authority. 2003. About the watershed; population. Available: http://www.sawpa.org/about/watershed.htm#Population. (June 2003)

Shelton, L.R. 1994. Field guide for collecting and processing stream-water samples for the National Water-Quality Assessment Program. U.S. Geological Survey Open-File Report 94–455, Sacramento, California.

Southern California Association of Governments. 1997. Draft 98 regional transportation plan. Southern California Association of Governments, Los Angeles.

Tate, C. M., T. F. Cuffney, G. McMahon, E. M. P. Giddings, J. F. Coles, and H. Zappia. 2005. Use of an urban intensity index to assess urban effects on streams in three contrasting environmental settings. Pages 291–315 in L. R. Brown, R. H. Gray, R. M. Hughes, and M. R. Meador, editors. Effects of urbanization on stream ecosystems. American Fisheries Society, Symposium 47, Bethesda, Maryland.

U.S. Army Corps of Engineers. 1994. Water control manual, Prado Dam and Reservoir, Santa Ana River, California. U.S. Army Corps of Engineers, Los Angeles.

U.S. Geological Survey. 1999. The quality of our nation's waters—nutrients and pesticides. U.S. Geological Survey Circular 1225, Reston, Virginia.

Van Dam, H., A. Mertens, and J. Sinkeldam. 1994. A coded checklist and ecological indicator values of freshwater diatoms from the Netherlands. Netherlands Journal of Aquatic Ecology 28:117–133.

Winter, J. G., and H. C. Duthie. 1998. Effects of urbanization on water quality, periphyton and invertebrate communities in a southern Ontario stream. Canadian Water Resources Journal 23:245–257.

Winter, J. G., and H. C. Duthie. 2000. Export coefficient modeling to assess phosphorus loading in an urban watershed. Journal of American Water Resources 36:1053–1061.

American Fisheries Society Symposium 47:263–287, 2005

Aquatic Assemblages of the Highly Urbanized Santa Ana River Basin, California

Larry R. Brown *

U.S. Geological Survey, Placer Hall, 6000 J Street, Sacramento, California 95819-6129, USA

Carmen A. Burton and Kenneth Belitz

U.S. Geological Survey, 5735 Kearny Villa Road, Suite O, San Diego, California 92123, USA

Abstract.—We assessed the structure of periphyton, benthic macroinvertebrate, and fish assemblages and their associations with environmental variables at 17 sites on streams of the highly urbanized Santa Ana River basin in Southern California. All assemblages exhibited strong differences between highly urbanized sites in the valley and the least-impacted sites at the transition between the valley and undeveloped mountains. Results within the urbanized area differed among taxa. Periphyton assemblages were dominated by diatoms (>75% of total taxa). Periphyton assemblages within the urbanized area were not associated with any of the measured environmental variables, suggesting that structure of urban periphyton assemblages might be highly dependent on colonization dynamics. The number of Ephemeroptera, Trichoptera, and Plecoptera (EPT) taxa included in macroinvertebrate assemblages ranged from 0 to 6 at urbanized sites. Benthic macroinvertebrate assemblages had significant correlations with several environmental variables within the urban area, suggesting that stream size and permanence were important determinants of distribution among the species able to survive conditions in urban streams. Only 4 of 16 fish species collected were native to the drainage. Fish assemblages of urbanized sites included two native species, arroyo chub *Gila orcuttii* and Santa Ana sucker *Catostomus santaanae,* at sites that were intermediate in coefficient of variation of bank-full width, depth, bed substrate, and water temperature. Alien species dominated urbanized sites with lesser or greater values for these variables. These results suggest that urban streams can be structured to enhance populations of native fishes. Continued study of urban streams in the Santa Ana River basin and elsewhere will contribute to the basic understanding of ecological principles and help preserve the maximum ecological value of streams in highly urbanized areas.

Introduction

As human population growth continues, urbanization and its effects on water quality and water quantity will increase in importance to biota, including humans, dependent on water resources (Naiman et al. 1995; Baer and Pringle 2000). Effects of urbanization on water quality and ecological conditions within watersheds are and will likely remain important scientific and policy issues in the foreseeable future (Grimm et al. 2000).

Urbanization can have a wide range of chemical and physical effects on stream systems (Klein 1979; Heany and Huber 1984). Increased storm water runoff due to large areas of impermeable surface can in-

crease the frequency and magnitude of storm flows (Arnold et al. 1982; Booth and Jackson 1997; Trimble 1997). Base flows can decline because of groundwater pumping and reduced recharge (Klein 1979; Finkenbine et al. 2000). Sediment regime, streambed composition, and stream channel morphology may change in response to altered hydrology and flood management practices (Arnold et al. 1982; Booth 1990, 1991; Booth and Jackson 1997; Finkenbine et al. 2000). Loss of riparian vegetation can lead to higher water temperatures through loss of shading (Booth 1991; Belt and O'Laughlin 1994; LeBlanc et al. 1996), loss of habitat for fish (Martin et al. 1986; Finkenbine et al. 2000), and changes in trophic processes (Kellar and Swanson 1979; Vannote et al. 1980). Urban runoff and treated wastewater may contain

* Corresponding author: lrbrown@usgs.gov

elevated levels of nutrients, pesticides, organic chemicals, and heavy metals (Klein 1979; Heany and Huber 1984; Field and Pitt 1990; Ahel et al. 2000; Lieb and Carline 2000; Shinya et al. 2000) that may affect aquatic biota.

Habitat and water quality alterations associated with urbanization have been linked to changes in aquatic biota. Early studies focused on effects of discharges from wastewater treatment plants on aquatic biota, but more recent studies have focused on other effects of urbanization. Urban stormwater runoff has been recognized as an important factor affecting biota (Heany and Huber 1984), as have hydrologic and land use changes associated with urbanization (Weaver and Garman 1994; Wichert 1994, 1995; Wang et al. 2000; Finkenbine et al. 2000; Sonneman et al. 2001; Walsh et al. 2001).

A common objective of many urbanization studies is to identify the level of urban land use in relatively natural watersheds that results in detectable degradation of aquatic communities. Such effects often occur at relatively low levels of urbanization (e.g., 10% of impervious surface, Limburg and Schmidt 1990; Booth and Jackson 1997; Wang et al. 2000; Wang and Lyons 2003). Although such information is important for understanding urban streams in the early stages of degradation, the information may not be useful in already developed, highly urbanized areas (Booth et al. 2002), especially in arid climates. For example, in the arid southwestern United States, many urban streams are channelized to transport large flows during low frequency, but large floods or natural surface flows are partially or completely replaced by discharges of treated wastewater or urban runoff. Managing such highly urbanized streams for maximum ecological integrity requires an understanding of ecological processes affecting them. The objective of this paper is to characterize the periphyton, benthic macroinvertebrate, and fish assemblages of selected streams in the highly urbanized Santa Ana River basin of Southern California and examine their relations with environmental variables. This general ecological approach is complementary to the metric-based assessment of the specific effects of stream channelization and water source on periphyton and benthic macroinvertebrates by Burton et al. (2005, this volume).

Study Area

The Santa Ana River basin (Figure 1) is the largest stream system in Southern California, with an area of about 6,900 km². The basin presently has a popula-

tion of more than 4.5 million people, and the population is expected to increase to almost 7 million people by 2025 (Santa Ana Project Watershed Authority 2003). The basin is divided between two ecoregions, the Southern California Coastal Plains and Hills and the Southern California Coastal Mountains. Most urban and agricultural land uses occur in the valleys and coastal plains of the Southern California Coastal Plains and Hills ecoregion. This area is more than 70% urban, and population density is about 1,160 people/km². Mountains of the Southern California Coastal Mountains ecoregion are generally too steep and unstable for development and remain open space (primarily forest and other natural vegetation), largely in national forests. Overall, land use in the basin is about 35% urban, 10% agricultural, and 55% open space. The basin has a Mediterranean climate, characterized by hot, dry summers and cool, wet winters. Average annual precipitation ranges from 25 to 60 cm in the coastal plains and inland valleys, and from 60 to 122 cm in the San Gabriel and San Bernardino mountains (U.S. Army Corps of Engineers 1994).

The hydrologic system of the basin has been highly altered, especially in the lowlands. In the mountains, the streams are relatively unaltered except for intense recreational use, including roads and housing, and some diversions for hydropower on the Santa Ana River. At the transition from mountains to valley, most streams are diverted directly to public drinking water supplies or are diverted to groundwater-recharge facilities (Figure 1). Groundwater is subsequently withdrawn for various urban uses. As a result of these alterations to the system and the natural Mediterranean climate, streams generally do not flow onto the valley floor, except during large floods that exceed the capacity of diversions.

Flow is reestablished in many low-elevation valley streams by various combinations of urban runoff, discharges from wastewater treatment plants (Figure 1), or groundwater forced upward by faulting or bedrock outcrops. Urban runoff includes water from rainfall runoff, landscape irrigation, and other residential and commercial activities. Water imported from outside the basin is occasionally discharged to a stream and further downstream is diverted for groundwater recharge. In some cases, urban runoff and treated wastewater have established perennial flows in stream channels that were historically intermittent or ephemeral. In addition to these changes in water source, many streams have been channelized and some concrete-lined for flood control.

Alterations in land use, hydrology, and stream

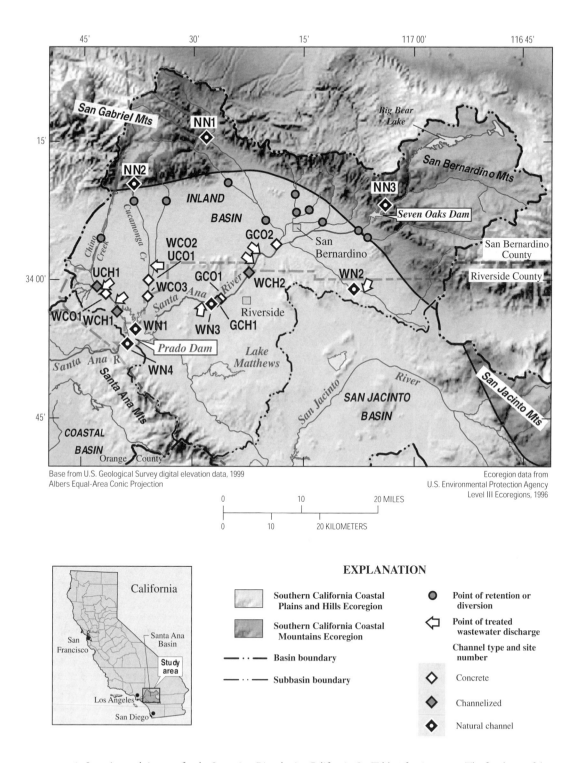

FIGURE 1. Location and site map for the Santa Ana River basin, California. See Table 1 for site names. The first letter of the site code denotes water source (N, natural; G, urban impacted groundwater; U, urban runoff; W, treated wastewater). The remaining letters denote channel type (N, natural; CH, channelized but unlined; CO, concrete-lined).

morphology have had significant impacts on ecological conditions. Terrestrial habitat has been converted to urban land uses. Riparian vegetation has
been removed or extensively altered. The natural seasonal and annual variations in streamflow have been
disrupted. Deliberately and accidentally introduced
alien species have invaded the disturbed terrestrial
and aquatic habitats. Toxic substances, such as pesticides, are now commonly found in both surface- and
groundwater. These changes have led to declines in
populations of various biota, including aquatic species. In aquatic systems, the most information exists
for fishes. Populations of anadromous Pacific lamprey *Lampetra tridentata* and steelhead rainbow trout
Oncorhynchus mykiss have been extirpated from most
southern California streams (Swift et al. 1993). Native freshwater resident species have also declined
(Swift et al. 1993), including Pacific brook lamprey
Lampetra pacifica (likely extirpated), prickly sculpin
Cottus asper, threespine stickleback *Gasterosteus
aculeatus*, arroyo chub *Gila orcuttii*, speckled dace
Rhinichthys osculus, and Santa Ana sucker *Catostomus
santaanae*. Santa Ana sucker and several populations
of threespine stickleback have been listed as threatened or endangered under federal or state endangered species legislation.

Methods

Study Design

Seventeen sites were selected to represent the available
combinations of water source (natural, urban runoff,
human impacted groundwater, and treated wastewater) and channel type (natural, channelized with natural bottom, and concrete-lined) available in the lower
urbanized part of the basin (Table 1). There were no
sites with little urban land use in the lowlands; therefore, three sites (sites NN1, NN2, and NN3) were
located near the interface with the uplands to represent least-impacted conditions (Table 1; Figure 1).
These three sites were located on streams with natural
channels and water sources.

Measurements of Environmental Variables

Because of the complex hydrology, basin area and
percent urban land use were calculated using two
methods. First, they were calculated based on the
natural, topographical drainage basin. Second, they
were calculated based on the actual contributing area
as defined by the existing urbanized hydrology. For

the three least-impacted sites, these areas are the same.
When a stream receives 100% treated wastewater, the
contributing basin area has no meaning because
water emerges from a pipe and urban land use is
necessarily 100% because all of the water is from
urban uses. Basin area and urban land use were determined using geographic information system databases.

Water samples for analysis of dissolved concentrations of major ions, nutrients, silica, and pesticides
were collected once, when algae samples were collected
(see below), using standard U.S. Geological Survey
(USGS) protocols (Shelton 1994). Field measurements
of specific conductance, pH, water temperature, dissolved oxygen, and discharge were made at each site
visit. Analyses of dissolved concentrations of major
ions, nutrients, and pesticides were conducted at the
USGS, National Water Quality Laboratory (NWQL),
Denver, Colorado.

Habitat variables (Table 2) were measured at
each of 11 transects within each sampling reach
(Fitzpatrick et al. 1998). Reaches ranged from 150
m for small streams and concrete-lined channels to
900 m for larger streams. Habitat variables were measured at the end of the study, after the benthic
macroinvertebrate artificial substrates had been collected (see below).

Collections of Biota

Periphyton and benthic macroinvertebrate samples
were collected between July and September 2000.
Artificial substrates were used to decrease the effect of
different substrate types among sites (cobbles, sand,
concrete) and facilitate comparisons between sites (Aloi
1990; Lowe and Pan 1996). Unglazed clay tiles (approximately 7.5 × 7.5 cm) attached to concrete paving blocks were used to collect periphyton. Four
paving blocks with two tiles each were placed at each
site. Water depth and mean water column velocity
were measured at each paving block when substrates
were deployed and when they were collected. After a
2-week colonization period, the clay tiles were removed
from the paving blocks. Periphyton was collected and
processed using the top-rock scrape method (Moulton
et al. 2002). Samples were preserved in 4% formalin.
Periphyton taxa were identified and enumerated at
the Philadelphia National Academy of Science according to Charles et al. (2002). Periphyton taxa were
identified to species in most cases.

Artificial substrates for benthic macroinvertebrates
consisted of a section of bristled plastic doormat (ap-

TABLE 1. Site name, site code, drainage area, urban land use, major water source, channel type and population density for sites sampled in the Santa Ana River basin, summer 2000. Drainage area and urban land use are reported for both the topographical and contributing basin. Population density is presented for the contributing basin only.

Station name	Site code[a]	Topographical basin		Contributing basin				
		Drainage area (km²)	Urban land use (%)	Major water source[b]	Channel type[c]	Drainage area (km²)	Urban land use (%)	Population density (people/km²)
Cajon Creek below Lone Pine	NN1	145	4	N	N	145	4	8
Cucamonga Creek near Upland	NN2	26	0	N	N	26	0	2.5
Santa Ana River at upper powerhouse	NN3	398	5	N	N	398	5	18
Sunnyslope Creek in regional park	GCH1	19	53	G	CH	19	53	872
Sunnyslope Creek near Rubidoux Nature Center	GCO1	19	52	G	CO	19	52	869
Warm Creek near San Bernardino	GCO2	32	94	G	CO	32	94	1,888
Little Chino Creek above pipeline	UCH1	16	46	U	CH	16	46	555
Cucamonga Creek at Chino Avenue, main channel	UCO1	180	58	U	CO	132	80	1,459
Mill Creek near Splatter S duck ponds	WN1	234	52	W	N	186	63	1,117
San Timoteo Creek near Eastside Ranch	WN2	141	20	W	N	NA[d]	100[e]	NA[d]
Santa Ana River at MWD crossing	WN3	2,136	25	W	N	960	49	727
Santa Ana River below Prado Dam	WN4	3,726	32	W	N	2,394	45	689
Chino Creek below Pine Road	WCH1	259	51	W	CH	191	69	1,515
Santa Ana River above Riverside Road	WCH2	1,918	21	W	CH	743	46	686
Chino Creek above Central Avenue	WCO1	234	55	W	CO	155	78	1,684
Cucamonga Creek at Chino Avenue, wastewater channel	WCO2	180	65	W	CO	NA[d]	100[e]	NA[d]
Cucamonga Creek near Mira Loma	WCO3	208	56	W	CO	160	72	1,277

[a] The site code is composed of the one letter water source code, followed by the channel type code and a numerical identifier.

[b] N, natural; G, urban impacted ground water; U, urban runoff; W, treated wastewater

[c] N, natural; CH, channelized but unlined; CO, concrete-lined

[d] Contributing area is not applicable because all flow in the channel comes from a wastewater treatment plant.

[e] Urban land use is 100% because all flow in the channel comes from wastewater treatment plant.

TABLE 2. The 14 environmental variables measured in the Santa Ana River basin, summer 2000, including the method used to measure the variable and the reason the variable was considered important.

Variable	Method	Reason for measurement
Discharge (m³/s)	Gaging station or instantaneous measurement	Stream size
Gradient (m/km)	Vertical drop along stream reach	General conditions
Channel width (m)	Mean wetted channel width at 11 equidistant cross-channel transects	Stream size
Coefficient of variation of bank-full width (%)	Coefficient of variation of bank-full width measured at 11 transects	Variability in stream width (channelization)
Open canopy (degrees)	Mean degrees of arc of sky (180 maximum) unobstructed by objects measured at 11 transects	Shading
Depth (m)	Mean of depths measured at three points along each of the 11 transects	General conditions
Coefficient of variation of depth (%)	Coefficient of variation of depths measured at three points along each of the 11 transects	Variability in depth (channelization)
Bed substrate	Mean dominant substrate type[a] measured at three points along each of the 11 transects	General conditions and channelization
Specific conductance (μS/cm)	Electronic meter	General water quality
Water temperature (°C)	Electronic meter	General conditions
Pesticides (number detected)	Analysis of water samples	Urbanization
Nitrite + Nitrate (mg/L as N)	Analysis of water samples	Urbanization and conditions for periphyton growth
ortho-Phosphate (mg/L as P)	Analysis of water samples	Urbanization and conditions for periphyton growth
Silica (mg/L)	Analysis of water samples	Conditions for diatom growth

[a] The dominant substrate was characterized as: 1, concrete; 2, silt, mud, or detritus; 3, sand (>0.063—2 mm); 4, fine/medium gravel (>2—16 mm); 5, coarse gravel (>16—32 mm); 6, very coarse gravel (>32—64 mm); 7, small cobble (>64—128 mm); 8, large cobble (>128—256 mm); 9, small boulder (>256—512 mm); 10, large boulder (>512 mm), irregular bedrock, irregular hardpan, or irregular artificial surface (Fitzpatrick et al. 1998).

proximately 15 × 15 cm) and an 18 cm length of 3.2-cm diameter polyvinyl chloride (PVC) pipe wrapped three times with plastic fencing (1.9-cm mesh) attached to a concrete paving block (see Figure 2 in Burton et al. 2005). This combination of materials provided a wide variety of habitats for colonization. Four substrates were placed at each site. Water depth and mean water column velocity were measured at each paving block when the substrates were deployed and when they were collected. Up to three substrates were removed after a 6-week colonization period. A 500-μm-mesh net was placed downstream of the substrate to collect any invertebrates dislodged in the removal process. The doormat and PVC pipe were removed from the paving block, and placed in a bucket. The doormat, PVC pipe, and fencing were scrubbed and inspected to remove invertebrates. Any material collected in the net was added to the sample. The sample was rinsed in a 500-μm sieve and preserved in 10% formalin (Moulton et al. 2002). Invertebrates were identified and enumerated at the NWQL following protocols for a 100-organism fixed count (Moulton et al. 2000). A 100-organism fixed count was used based on assessment of results from test substrates deployed the previous year and other sampling at the sites (Carmen Burton, unpublished data). Benthic macroinvertebrates were generally identified to genus. Some taxa, particularly noninsects, were identified at higher levels of taxonomy.

Fishes were primarily collected using single-pass electrofishing, which is generally adequate to document species richness in structurally simple channels (Meador et al. 2003). Small dip nets were used to collect fish in some very shallow concrete channels.

Seines (6-mm mesh) were used at one site (WN4) to supplement electrofishing. Fish were identified to species, counted, and released.

Data Analysis

More than 30 physical variables and more than 80 chemical variables, including concentrations of dissolved nutrients, major ions, and pesticides, were measured at the sites; however, many were redundant. Principle components analysis (PCA) and correlation analysis were used to identify a reduced set of 14 variables (Table 2) that captured the variability in physical habitat and water chemistry among the 17 sites. These variables were used in all subsequent statistical analyses. All variables were examined for normality, using normal probability plots. Discharge, channel width, dissolved concentration of nitrite + nitrate, and dissolved concentration of ortho-phosphate were log transformed to improve normality. A PCA was conducted on the 14 environmental variables to assess general environmental gradients among the sites. Only PCA axes with eigenvalues greater than one were retained for interpretation. Site scores on the first two PCA axes were plotted.

Periphyton and benthic macroinvertebrate assemblages were characterized using correspondence analysis (CA) or detrended correspondence analysis (DCA). Periphyton analyses were conducted on density (cells/cm^2), biovolume (cell volume/cm^2), and percent density and biovolume. Results were similar and only those for density are discussed. Benthic macroinvertebrate analyses used density data (organisms/m^2). Analyses were conducted using $\log_{10}(X + 1)$ transformed data. Only species found at two or more sites were included in analyses. This was a compromise between the value of rare species in separating sites (Cao et al. 2001) and the level of confidence that a species is collected if present. Complete species lists are available from the authors.

Relationships of benthic macroinvertabrate and periphyton assemblages with environmental variables were evaluated using indirect gradient analysis. Site scores on the first two ordination axes (CA or DCA) were correlated (Pearson's) with the 14 selected environmental variables. We also correlated site scores on the first two ordination axes with several metrics of the periphyton and macroinvertebrate assemblages. These metrics were calculated based on all species collected, varied with water source and channel type, and correlated with environmental variables in an independent analysis of these data (Burton et al.

2005). The periphyton metrics were number of taxa, number of diatom taxa, total density, diatom density, biovolume of blue-green algae, biovolume of green algae, percentage of nitrogen heterotrophic diatoms, percentage of eutrophic diatoms, and percentage of pollution intolerant diatoms. The macroinvertebrate metrics were number of taxa, number of Ephemeroptera, Trichoptera, and Plecoptera (EPT) taxa, number of trichoptera taxa, number of nonchironomid dipteran taxa, total density, trichoptera density, oligochaete density, density of orthoclad chironomids, noninsect density, shredder density, filterer density, and mean Environmental Protection Agency (EPA) species tolerance (Barbour et al. 1999) at the site. All variables were examined for normality, using normal probability plots. When needed, data were $\log_{10}(X + 1)$ to improve normality.

Fish presence/absence data were analyzed by group average cluster analysis of Jaccard similarities. This analysis is conservative and was chosen to avoid problems associated with inaccurate assessments of relative abundance that might occur with single-pass electrofishing. Differences in environmental variables among fish site groups were determined with analysis of variance (ANOVA). Subsequent pair-wise tests (Tukey Method) were performed for variables with significant ANOVA results.

Results

Environmental Variables

The sites varied widely for the 14 environmental variables (Table 3). A PCA of the 14 environmental variables resulted in four axes with eigenvalues greater than 1 (Table 4). These PCA axes accounted for 81% of the variance in the data. The first 2 PCA axes accounted for most of the variance (57%). Least-impacted and urban sites were clearly separated along PCA axis 1 (Figure 2). Least-impacted sites had higher channel gradients, more complex channels, larger bed substrate, lower water temperatures, less open canopy, fewer pesticides, and lower concentrations of nitrite + nitrate than urban sites. The second PCA axis separated urban sites based on discharge, depth, and orthophosphate concentrations (Figure 2). Sites with wastewater and a natural or channelized channel had high scores on PC axis 2 (>0). Sites with low scores (<0) had concrete channels with a mixture of water types. The third PCA axis indicated that sites with wider channels had lower specific conductance and silica concentrations (Table 4). The fourth PCA axis

TABLE 3. Values of 14 environmental variables for study sites in the Santa Ana River basin, summer 2000.

Station name	Site code	Discharge (m³/s)	Reach gradient (m/km)	Channel width (m)	CVᵃ of bank-full width (%)	Open canopy (degrees)	Depth (m)	CVᵃ of depth (%)	Bed Substrateᵇ	Number of pesticides	Specific conductance (µS/cm)	Water temperature (°C)	Nitrate + nitrate (as N, mg/L)	Ortho-phosphate (as P, mg/L)	Silica (mg/L)
Cajon Creek below Lone Pine	NN1	2.8	0.009	3.8	38	79	0.10	65	4.9	2	804	22.5	1.02	<0.01	20.84
Cucamonga Creek near Upland	NN2	1.0	0.036	3.7	33	10	0.10	56	7.0	0	343	19.0	0.19	<0.01	24.12
Santa Ana River at upper power-house	NN3	1.1	0.039	7.5	32	88	0.19	61	8.3	0	286	20.0	<0.05	<0.01	20.55
Sunnyslope Creek in regional park	GCH1	2.5	0.006	1.8	23	21	0.26	53	3.0	5	984	26.0	10.41	<0.01	31.79
Sunnyslope Creek near Rubidoux Nature Center	GCO1	2.3	0.001	5.3	5	150	0.14	17	1.7	5	943	30.0	10.50	<0.01	33.43
Warm Creek near San Bernardino	GCO2	0.8	0.002	3.8	0	109	0.05	39	1.0	3	993	29.5	0.25	<0.01	21.64
Little Chino Creek above pipeline	UCH1	2.0	0.004	5.1	27	157	0.20	45	4.1	6	1,250	24.5	1.12	0.09	28.33
Cucamonga Creek at Chino Avenue, main channel	UCO1	2.4	0.013	6.2	0	155	0.04	54	1.0	6	544	30.5	0.62	0.14	21.66
Mill Creek near Splatter S duck ponds	WN1	25.2	0.001	10.9	14	60	0.33	48	3.1	2	810	23.5	6.16	2.07	21.77

TABLE 3. Continued.

Station name	Site code	Discharge (m³/s)	Reach gradient (m/km)	Channel width (m)	CVª of bank-full width (%)	Open canopy (degrees)	Depth (m)	CVª of depth (%)	Bed Substrateᵇ	Number of pesticides	Specific conductance (µS/cm)	Water temperature (°C)	Nitrate + nitrate (as N, mg/L)	Ortho-phosphate (as P, mg/L)	Silica (mg/L)
San Timoteo Creek near Eastside Ranch	WN2	4.8	0.013	2.0	15	44	0.20	27	4.1	4	872	28.0	22.78	3.9	26.56
Santa Ana River at MWD crossing	WN3	67.0	0.003	42.4	24	142	0.12	36	3.0	5	927	31.5	5.71	0.91	24.28
Santa Ana River below Prado Dam	WN4	190.0	0.013	17.0	21	61	0.64	39	5.9	7	965	23.5	5.65	0.964	21.53
Chino Creek below Pine Road	WCH1	24.1	0.003	7.6	21	127	0.43	53	4.4	10	841	24.0	3.92	1.57	21.31
Santa Ana River above Riverside Road	WCH2	56.9	0.003	14.1	9	117	0.21	29	4.4	3	807	28.0	3.43	1.63	25.20
Chino Creek above Central Avenue	WCO1	13.2	0.004	24.4	6	161	0.05	27	1.0	5	670	31.0	3.14	1.00	21.60
Cucamonga Creek at Chino Avenue, wastewater channel	WCO2	36.2	0.011	7.6	0	123	0.15	56	1.1	4	709	29.0	6.85	0.79	23.64
Cucamonga Creek near Mira Loma	WCO3	31.0	0.009	20.0	0	156	0.10	30	1.0	5	730	27.0	7.82	1.05	23.15

ª CV, coefficient of variation.

ᵇ The dominant substrate was characterized as: 1, concrete; 2, silt, mud, or detritus; 3, sand (>0.063—2 mm); 4, fine/medium gravel (>2—16 mm); 5, coarse gravel (>16—32 mm); 6, very coarse gravel (>32—64 mm); 7, small cobble (>64—128 mm); 8, large cobble (>128—256 mm); 9, small boulder (>256—512 mm); 10, large boulder (>512 mm), irregular bedrock, irregular hardpan, or irregular artificial surface (Fitzpatrick et al. 1998).

TABLE 4. Loadings of original variables on principal component analysis (PCA) axes derived from PCA of the 14 environmental variables for sites in the Santa Ana River basin, summer 2000. Loadings greater than 0.5 are bolded.

Variable	PCA axis 1	PCA axis 2	PCA axis 3	PCA axis 4
Discharge (m³/s)[a]	**0.51**	**0.70**	−0.39	−0.02
Gradient (m/km)	**−0.84**	<0.01	−0.22	−0.27
Channel width (m)[a]	0.43	0.28	**−0.71**	0.07
Coefficient of variation of bank-full width (%)	**−0.71**	0.37	0.23	0.25
Open canopy (degrees)	**0.60**	−0.38	−0.42	0.38
Depth (m)	0.02	**0.89**	0.17	0.22
Coefficient of variation of depth	**−0.73**	0.04	−0.09	0.36
Bed substrate[b]	**−0.78**	**0.50**	0.06	0.01
Specific conductance (μS/cm)	**0.59**	0.15	**0.56**	0.40
Water temperature (°C)	**0.84**	−0.40	−0.09	−0.09
Pesticides (number detected)	**0.64**	0.27	0.11	**0.51**
Nitrite + Nitrate (mg/L as N)[a]	**0.64**	0.40	0.38	−0.42
ortho-Phosphate (mg/L as P)[a]	0.46	**0.60**	−0.16	−0.45
Silica (mg/L)	0.26	−0.19	**0.81**	−0.15
Percent variance explained by PC axis	38	19	15	9

[a] Variable log transformed for analysis.

[b] The dominant substrate was characterized as: 1, concrete; 2, silt, mud, or detritus; 3, sand (>0.063—2 mm); 4, fine/medium gravel (>2—16 mm); 5, coarse gravel (>16—32 mm); 6, very coarse gravel (>32—64 mm); 7, small cobble (>64—128 mm); 8, large cobble (>128—256 mm); 9, small boulder (>256—512 mm); 10, large boulder (>512 mm), irregular bedrock, irregular hardpan, or irregular artificial surface (Fitzpatrick et al. 1998).

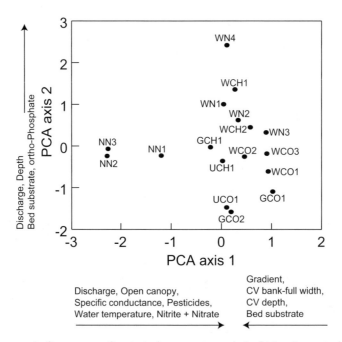

FIGURE 2. Site scores on the first two axes of a principal components analysis of 14 environmental variables measured at 17 sites in the Santa Ana River basin, summer 2000. See Table 1 for site codes. The first letter of the site code denotes water source (N, natural; G, urban impacted groundwater; U, urban runoff; W, treated wastewater). The remaining letters denote channel type (N, natural; CH, channelized but unlined; CO, concrete-lined).

summarized remaining variance in the number of pesticides detected (Table 4).

Periphyton

Artificial substrates collected a total of 62 algae taxa that were present at 2 or more sites (Table 5). Based on all taxa collected, 12–36 algae taxa were present from individual sites (Table 6). Diatoms were the dominant group contributing from 78% to 100% of the taxa found at each site. Both green algae and blue-green algae contributed from 0 to 3 taxa per site. Diatoms also tended to dominate percent density (27–100%) and biovolume (5–100%), with some exceptions. Percent density of blue-green algae was greater than diatoms at Mill Creek (42%), one site on

TABLE 5. Algae taxa (with species codes) collected from more than one site from artificial substrates in the Santa Ana River basin, summer 2000.

Species code	Taxon
	Chrysophyta (diatoms)
1	*Achnanthes exigua* Grunow
2	*Achnanthes exigua* var. *heterovalva* Krasske
3	*Achnanthes lanceolata* (Brébisson in Kützing) Grunow
4	*Achnanthes pusilla* (Grunow) DeToni
5	*Achnanthes lanceolata* subsp. *frequentissima* Lange-Bertalot
6	*Amphora veneta* Kützing
7	*Amphora inariensis* Krammer
8	*Caloneis bacillum* (Grunow) Cleve
9	*Cocconeis placentula* var. *lineata* (Ehrenberg) Van Heurck
10	*Cocconeis placentula* var. *euglypta* (Ehrenberg) Cleve
11	*Cocconeis pediculus* Ehrenberg
12	*Cyclotella meneghiniana* Kützing
13	*Cymbella affinis* Kütz.
14	*Cymbella* sp.1 JCK
15	*Fragilaria crotonensis* Kitton
16	*Gomphoneis olivaceum* (Lyngb.) P. Dawson ex Ross & Sims
17	*Gomphonema affine* Kütz.
18	*Gomphonema parvulum* (Kütz.) Kütz.
19	*Gomphonema minutum* (Ag.) Ag.
20	*Gomphonema kobayasii* Kociolek & Kingston
21	*Navicula atomus* (Kütz.) Grun.
22	*Navicula minima* Grun.
23	*Navicula seminulum* Grun.

TABLE 5. Continued.

Species code	Taxon
24	*Navicula tripunctata* (O. F. Müll.) Bory
25	*Navicula decussis* Østr.
26	*Navicula tenelloides* Hust.
27	*Navicula viridula* var. *rostellata* (Kütz.) Cl.
28	*Navicula veneta* Kütz.
29	*Navicula cryptotenella* L.B. in Kramm. & L.-B.
30	*Navicula subminuscula* Mang.
31	*Navicula erifuga* Lange-Bert.
32	*Navicula recens* Lange-Bert.
33	*Navicula* sp.1 ANS NAWQA DW
34	*Nitzschia amphibia* Grun.
35	*Nitzschia dissipata* (Kütz.) Grun.
36	*Nitzschia fonticola* Grun.
37	*Nitzschia frustulum* (Kütz.) Grun.
38	*Nitzschia palea* (Kütz.) W. Sm.
39	*Nitzschia umbonata* Lange-Bert.
40	*Nitzschia inconspicua* Grun.
41	*Nitzschia perminuta* (Grun.) Peragallo
42	*Nitzschia desertorum* Hust.
43	*Nitzschia archibaldii* Lange-Bertalot
44	*Reimeria sinuata* (Greg.) Kociolek & Stoermer
45	*Rhoicosphenia curvata* (Kütz.) Grun. ex Rabh.
46	*Synedra ulna* (Nitz.) Ehr.
47	*Thalassiosira weissflogii* (Grun.) Fryxell & Hasle
48	*Bacillaria paradoxa* Gmelin
49	*Encyonema reichardtii* (Kram.) Mann
50	*Luticola goeppertiana* Mann
51	*Pleurosira laevis* (Ehrenberg) Compere
52	*Sellaphora pupula* (Kütz.) Meresckowsky
53	*Staurosira construens* var. *venter* (Ehr.) Hamilton
54	*Diadesmis confervacea* Kütz.
55	*Encyonopsis microcephala* (Grun.) Kram.
	Chlorophyta (green algae)
56	*Cosmarium margaritatum* (Lund) Roy & Biss.
57	*Pediastrum biradiatum* Meyen
58	*Scenedesmus dimorphus* (Turp.) Kütz.
59	*Scenedesmus quadricauda* (Turp.) Bréb.
	Cyanophyta (blue-green algae)
60	*Chroococcus limneticus* Lemm.
61	*Lyngbya* sp. 1 ANS FWA
62	*Oscillatoria limnetica* Lemm.

TABLE 6. Values of macroinvertebrate metrics and periphyton metrics based on all taxa collected for study sites in the Santa Ana River basin, summer 2000.

Periphyton metrics

Station name	Site code	Total taxa	Diatom taxa[a]	Total algae density[a,b]	Diatom density[a]	Biovolume green algae[a,c]	Biovolume blue-green algae[a]	Nitrogen heterotrophic diatoms (%)	Eutrophic diatoms (%)	Motile diatoms (%)	Intolerant diatoms (%)
Cajon Creek below Lone Pine	NN1	33	32	4,137,834	3,304,886	0	0	11	67	37	46
Cucamonga Creek near Upland	NN2	20	20	464,862	464,862	0	0	41	57	27	8
Santa Ana River at upper powerhouse	NN3	17	14	24,557	17,372	0.012	0.001	0	13	33	80
Sunnyslope Creek in regional park	GCH1	23	21	182,898	163,879	0	0.003	29	56	37	7
Sunnyslope Creek near Rubidoux Nature Center	GCO1	23	18	1,156,759	661,704	38.844	0.005	37	41	49	3
Warm Creek near San Bernardino	GCO2	16	13	297,706	132,777	0.002	0.004	3	3	56	0
Cucamonga Creek at Chino Avenue, main channel	UCO1	18	16	365,037	99,372	1.542	0	66	87	81	3
Little Chino Creek above pipeline	UCH1	36	33	463,872	437,527	0	0.006	94	98	27	2
Mill Creek near Splatter S duck ponds	WN1	18	15	8,392,967	3,714,908	1.173	0.778	96	98	85	1
San Timoteo Creek near Eastside Ranch	WN2	13	12	187,230	160,341	0.028	0	84	94	72	0
Santa Ana River at MWD crossing	WN3	20	20	552,316	552,316	0	0.183	94	99	76	0
Santa Ana River below Prado Dam	WN4	32	30	982,102	944,568	0.003	0.012	65	89	84	1
Chino Creek below Pine Road	WCH1	27	23	1,694,796	1,327,293	0.167	0.044	62	66	55	<1
Santa Ana River above Riverside Road	WCH2	20	19	11,635	9,629	0	0.001	74	97	76	4
Chino Creek above Central Avenue	WCO1	23	20	9,575,518	5,764,422	2.691	0.096	96	97	68	<1
Cucamonga Creek at Chino Avenue, wastewater channel	WCO2	12	10	3,040,525	2,836,002	0.862	0.225	100	100	93	0
Cucamonga Creek near Mira Loma	WCO3	15	12	21,056,640	8,722,678	1.547	2.382	99	100	92	0

Macroinvertebrate metrics

Station name	Site code	Total taxa	EPT taxa	Trichoptera taxa	Non-chironomid diptera taxa	Total density[a,d]	Trichoptera density[a]	Oligochaete density[a]	Orthoclad density[a]	Non-insect density[a]	Shredder density[a]	Filterer density	Mean EPA tolerance
Cajon Creek below Lone Pine	NN1	15	6	4	3	22,866	14,375	0	0	2,112	22	10,905	4.8
Cucamonga Creek near Upland	NN2	24	9	4	1	10,500	531	219	0	3,115	1,802	1,742	4.9
Santa Ana River at upper powerhouse	NN3	19	6	4	2	49,147	14,231	0	705	719	353	11,382	5.1

TABLE 6. Continued.

Station name	Site code	Total taxa	EPT taxa	Trichoptera taxa	Non-chironomid diptera taxa	Total density[a,d]	Trichoptera density[a]	Oligochaete density[a]	Orthoclad density[a]	Non-insect density[a]	Shredder density[a]	Filterer density	Mean EPA tolerance
Sunnyslope Creek in regional park	GCH1	17	5	3	4	48,932	16,092	0	793	6,204	96	15,983	5.7
Sunnyslope Creek near Rubidoux Nature Center	GCO1	17	5	3	4	21,058	889	0	0	11,836	78	56	6.0
Warm Creek near San Bernardino	GCO2	–[c]	–	–	–	–	–	–	–	–	–	–	–
Cucamonga Creek at Chino Avenue, main channel	UCH1	14	1	1	0	31,215	597	16,840	2,743	19,458	2,771	0	7.1
Little Chino Creek above pipeline	UCO1	14	2	2	3	280,347	1,229	23,069	170,273	44,583	170,280	0	7.3
Mill Creek near Splatter S duck ponds	WN1	9	1	1	0	104,597	4,931	17,972	1,656	19,625	828	81,668	6.0
San Timoteo Creek near Eastside Ranch	WN2	11	1	1	2	69,396	728	37,413	11,087	37,938	11,087	1,981	7.3
Santa Ana River at MWD crossing	WN3	20	5	2	2	23,646	13,854	229	667	896	687	14,958	5.3
Santa Ana River below Prado Dam	WN4	8	2	1	0	39,187	31,306	507	5,375	965	2,405	32,583	5.5
Chino Creek below Pine Road	WCH1	5	2	1	0	49,021	40,833	0	2,042	0	2,042	41,243	4.8
Santa Ana River above Riverside Road	WCH2	14	5	2	0	21,925	18,163	199	271	268	320	18,302	5.5
Chino Creek above Central Avenue	WCO1	11	1	0	1	79,285	0	23,681	5,722	41,646	5,722	0	6.1
Cucamonga Creek at Chino Avenue, wastewater channel	WCO2	8	2	1	0	63,403	4,778	16,194	7,681	20,354	7,681	4,778	5.3
Cucamonga Creek near Mira Loma	WCO3	7	0	0	1	388,115	0	267,542	11,760	305,760	11,760	0	6.4

[a] Variable log transformed for statistical analyses.
[b] Periphyton densities are cells/cm².
[c] Periphyton biovolumes are μm³/cm².
[d] Macroinvertebrate densities are organisms/m².
[e] –, all macroinvertebrate substrates at this site were vandalized.

Cucamonga Creek (WCO3) (51%), and Warm Creek (55%), but they did not dominate biovolume because of small cell size. Green algae contributed most of the biovolume at two sites, GCO1 on Sunnyslope Creek (95%) and UCO1 on Cucamonga Creek (67%).

An initial CA analysis of periphyton density data exhibited a pronounced "arch effect," indicating that CA did not produce independent ordination axes. The data were reanalyzed with DCA, which corrected this problem. Detrended correspondence analysis resulted in four axes that explained a cumulative 36%

of the variance in the data (18%, 11%, 5%, and 2%, respectively). A plot of site scores on the first two DCA axes (Figure 3A) separated least-impacted sites from the other sites. There was no clear pattern related to water type or channel type among the urbanized sites. Most taxa scores were between 0 and 4 on DCA axis 1 and between –1 and 3 on DCA axis 2 (Figure 3B). Five diatom taxa had DCA axis 1 scores less than 0, including *Encyonopsis microcephala* (55), *Cymbella* sp.1 JCK (14), *Navicula cryptotenella* (29), *Encyonema reichardtii* (49), and *Gomphonema kobayasii* (20). Seven taxa had DCA axis 1 scores greater than 4, in-

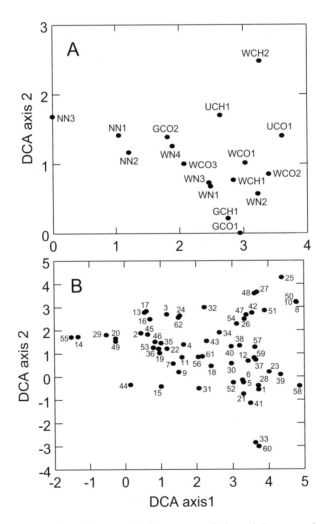

FIGURE 3. Site (A) and algae taxa (B) scores on the first two axes of a detrended correspondence analysis of log transformed periphyton densities from 17 sites in the Santa Ana River basin, summer 2000. See Table 1 for site codes and Table 5 for species codes. The first letter of the site code denotes water source (N, natural; G, urban impacted groundwater; U, urban runoff; W, treated wastewater). The remaining letters denote channel type (N, natural; CH, channelized but unlined; CO, concrete-lined).

cluding six diatoms—*Navicula seminulum* (23), *Nitzschia umbonata* (39), *Navicula decussis* (25), *Luticola goeppertiana* (50), *Caloneis bacillum* (8), *Cocconeis placentula* var. *euglypta* (10)—and one green alga, *Scenedesmus dimorphus* (58). Only three algae taxa had DCA axis 2 scores less than –1, including a blue-green alga, *Chroococcus limneticus* (60), and 2 diatoms *Navicula* sp.1 (33) and *Nitzschia perminuta* (41). Six diatom taxa had DCA axis 2 scores greater than 3, including *Caloneis bacillum* (8), *Cocconeis placentula* var. *euglypta* (10), *Luticola goeppertiana* (50), *Bacillaria paradoxa* (48), *Navicula viridula* var. *rostellata* (27), and *Navicula decussis* (25).

Periphyton DCA axis 1 scores were significantly correlated with 6 of the 14 environmental variables (Table 7) and three periphyton metrics. The significantly correlated metrics were percentage of nitrogen heterotrophic diatoms ($r = 0.69$, df = 15, $P < 0.05$), percent eutrophic diatoms ($r = 0.60$, df = 15, $P < 0.05$), and percent pollution intolerant diatoms ($r = -0.78$, df = 15, $P < 0.05$). All the significantly correlated environmental variables were associated with PCA axis 1 from the analysis of environmental variables (Table 4), suggesting that the correlations were prima-

rily a result of differences between the least-impacted and the urbanized sites. Similarly, significant periphyton metrics are associated with nitrite and nitrate, which was also associated with PCA axis 1 (Table 4). Examination of scatterplots for the univariate correlations (not shown) also suggested this. DCA axis 2 scores were not correlated with any environmental variables and only one periphyton metric, biovolume of green algae ($r = -0.49$, $P < 0.05$).

To evaluate the importance of the contrast between least-impacted and urbanized sites to the correlation results, we analyzed the data set with DCA after removing the three least-impacted sites. We then did the same set of correlations using only urbanized sites. None of the correlations were statistically significant.

Benthic Macroinvertebrates

Artificial substrates collected 43 taxa of benthic macroinvertebrates that were present at two or more sites (Table 8). Only data from 16 sites were available because all artificial substrates were vandalized at the Warm Creek site (GCO2). Based on all taxa collected,

TABLE 7. Correlations of algae DCA axis 1 scores and benthic macroinvertebrate CA axis 1 and 2 scores with environmental variables for sites in the Santa Ana River basin, summer 2000. Significant ($P < 0.05$) correlations are bolded.

Variable	Periphyton DCA axis 1	Benthic macro-invertebrate CA axis 1	Benthic macro-invertebrate CA axis 2
Discharge (m³/s)[a]	–0.31	0.27	**0.73**
Gradient (m/km)	**0.67**	–0.25	–0.32
Channel width (m)[a]	–0.08	0.23	0.36
Coefficient of variation of bank-full width (%)	**0.65**	**–0.65**	–0.13
Open canopy (degrees)	–0.36	0.43	–0.15
Depth (m)	0.01	–0.01	**0.73**
Coefficient of variation of depth	0.45	–0.23	–0.13
Bed substrate[b]	**0.69**	**–0.56**	0.06
Specific conductance (µS/cm)	–0.43	0.12	0.27
Water temperature (°C)	**–0.72**	0.33	<0.01
Pesticides (number detected)	**–0.59**	0.45	0.24
Nitrate + Nitrite (mg/L as N)[a]	**–0.56**	0.17	0.47
ortho-Phosphate (mg/L as P)[a]	–0.44	0.39	**0.68**
Silicate (mg/L)	0.37	–0.20	–0.20

[a] Variable log transformed for analysis.
[b] The dominant substrate was characterized as: 1, concrete; 2, silt, mud, or detritus; 3, sand (>0.063—2 mm); 4, fine/medium gravel (>2—16 mm); 5, coarse gravel (>16—32 mm); 6, very coarse gravel (>32—64 mm); 7, small cobble (>64—128 mm); 8, large cobble (>128—256 mm); 9, small boulder (>256—512 mm); 10, large boulder (>512 mm), irregular bedrock, irregular hardpan, or irregular artificial surface (Fitzpatrick et al. 1998).

TABLE 8. Benthic macroinvertebrate taxa (with taxon codes) collected from more than one site from artificial substrates in the Santa Ana River basin, summer 2000.

Taxon code	Taxon	Taxon code	Taxon
1	Turbellaria		Helicopsychidae
	Nemertea	21	*Helicopsyche* sp.
2	*Prostoma* sp.		Lepidoptera
3	Nematoda		Pyralidae
	Gastropda	22	*Petrophila* sp.
	Physidae		Coleoptera
4	*Physella* sp.		Dryopidae
	Oligochaeta	23	*Postelichus* sp.
5	Naididae		Elmidae
6	Tubificidae	24	*Optioservus* sp.
7	Arachnida		Diptera
	Amphipoda	25	Ceratopogonidae
	Talitridae		Chironomidae
8	*Hyalella* sp.		Chironominae
	Insecta	26	*Apedilum* sp.
	Ephemeroptera	27	*Chironomus* sp.
9	Leptophlebiidae	28	*Dicrotendipes* sp.
	Tricorythidae	29	*Polypedilum* sp.
10	*Tricorythodes* sp.	30	*Pseudochironomous* sp.
	Baetidae	31	*Rheotanytarsus* sp.
11	*Baetis* sp.	32	*Stempellinella* sp.
12	*Fallceon* sp.		Orthocladiinae
	Odanata	33	*Cricotopus* sp.
	Zygoptera	34	*Nanocladius* sp.
	Calopterygidae	35	*Rheocricotopus* sp.
13	*Hetaerina* sp.		Tanypodinae
14	Coenagrionidae	36	*Ablabesmyia* sp.
15	*Argia* sp.	37	*Pentaneura* sp.
	Anisoptera	38	Psychodidae
16	Libellulidae	39	Simuliidae
	Trichoptera		Empididae
	Hydroptilidae	40	*Hemerodromia* sp.
17	*Hydroptila* sp.		Stratiomyidae
18	*Oxyethira* sp.	41	*Caloparyphus* sp.
	Hydropsychidae	42	*Euparyphus* sp.
19	*Hydropsyche* sp.		Tabanidae
	Psychomyiidae	43	*Tabanus* sp.
20	*Tinodes* sp.		

the total number of taxa present at individual sites varied from 5 to 24 (Table 6). Values for other macroinvertebrate metrics varied widely (Table 6). The number of EPT taxa varied from 0 to 6 taxa. Insects contributed from 69% to 100% of the organisms collected from artificial substrates, except for site WCO3 on Cucamonga Creek (21%), site GCO1 on Sunnyslope Creek (45%), site UCH1 on Little Chino Creek (43%), and site WCO1 on Chino Creek (47%).

The CA analysis of macroinvertebrate density data resulted in four CA axes that explained 57% of the variance (22%, 14%, 11%, and 10%, respectively). The plot of site scores on CA axis 1 separated the sites into two major groups and CA axis 2 separated one of the major groups into two subgroups (Figure 4A). Sites with CA axis 1 scores less than 0 (hereinafter, less-impacted sites) include the least-impacted sites (NN1, NN2, and NN3), two urbanized

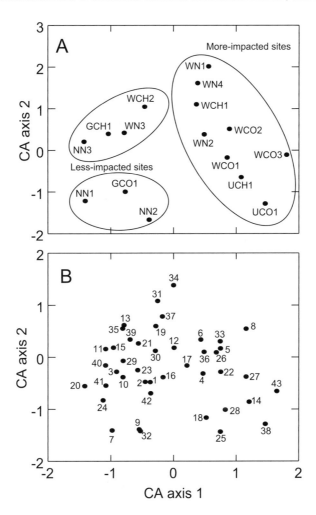

FIGURE 4. Site (A) and macroinvertebrate taxa (B) scores on the first two axes of a correspondence analysis of log transformed macroinvertebrate densities from 16 sites in the Santa Ana River basin, summer 2000. See Table 1 for site codes and Table 8 for species codes. The first letter of the site code denotes water source (N, natural; G, urban impacted groundwater; U, urban runoff; W, treated wastewater). The remaining letters denote channel type (N, natural; CH, channelized but unlined; CO, concrete-lined).

Santa Ana River sites (WCH2 and WN3), and both Sunnyslope Creek sites (GCH1 and GCO1). Sites with scores greater than 0 on CA axis 1 (hereinafter, more-impacted sites) include most sites receiving treated wastewater and all but one concrete-lined channel. Sites with CA axis 2 scores greater than 0 included all the Santa Ana River sites. Sites with CA axis 1 scores greater than 0 appeared to form a continuum along CA axis 2 with no clear breaks (Figure 4A).

Taxa scores on CA axis 1 exhibited a clear break at 0 (Figure 4B), similar to site scores. Taxa with scores greater than 0 were characteristic of the more-impacted sites and were dominated by noninsects and dipter-

ans, many of which are considered tolerant of environmental degradation (Barbour et al. 1999). These taxa included *Hyalella* sp. (8), *Chironomus* sp. (27), *Tabanus* sp. (43), and Psychodidae (38). Taxa having low scores on CA axis 1 were characteristic of the less-impacted sites and tended to be less tolerant of environmental degradation (Barbour et al. 1999). These taxa included *Optioservus* sp. (24), *Tinodes* sp. (20), *Caloparyphus* sp. (41), *Hemerodromia* sp., and *Baetis* sp. (11).

Taxa scores on CA axis 2 exhibited no clear groupings associated with the subgroups of less-impacted sites. The two taxa with high scores (>1) on CA axis 2 were both chironomids, *Nanocladius* sp. (34) and *Rheotanytarsus* sp. (31). Taxa with low scores (<–1) on CA axis 2 were a mixed group, including Arachnida (mites, 7), an ephemeropteran (Leptophlebiidae, 9), a chironomid (*Stempellinella* sp., 32), and two nonchironomid dipterans, Ceratopogonidae (25) and Psychodidae (38).

Benthic macroinvertebrate CA axis 1 scores were significantly negatively correlated with coefficient of variation of bank-full width and bed substrate (Table 7). Both variables were associated with PCA axis 1 from analysis of environmental variables (Table 4). The lack of significant correlations with water quality variables associated with PCA axis 1 suggests that benthic macroinvertebrates were mainly responding to habitat structures. The CA axis 1 scores were significantly correlated with nine macroinvertebrate metrics. These correlations (Table 9) indicated that the assemblages at the more-impacted sites had fewer total taxa, more tolerant taxa, fewer EPT taxa, fewer trichopteran taxa, higher total densities, lower trichopteran densities, higher densities of oligochaetes, and higher densities of orthoclad chironomids (Table 9).

Site scores on CA axis 2 were significantly positively correlated with discharge, depth, and ortho-phosphate concentration (Table 7). These environmental variables were associated with PCA axis 2 of the environmental analysis, which emphasized differ-

TABLE 9. Correlations of macroinvertebrate CA axis 1 and 2 site scores with 10 macroinvertebrate metrics for sites in the Santa Ana River basin, summer 2000. Significant ($P < 0.05$) correlations are bolded.

Metric	Macroinvertebrate CA axis 1	CA axis 2
Number of taxa	**–0.65**	**–0.57**
Number of EPT taxa	**–0.82**	–0.41
Number of trichoptera taxa	**–0.83**	–0.47
Number of nonchironomid dipteran taxa	–0.48	**–0.52**
Total density[a]	**0.71**	–0.15
Trichoptera density[a]	**–0.57**	0.35
Oligochaete density[a]	**0.85**	–0.08
Orthoclad chironomid density[a]	**0.71**	0.42
Noninsect density[a]	0.44	–0.33
Shredder density[a]	**0.86**	–0.03
Filterer density	–0.04	**0.75**
Mean EPA species tolerance	**0.63**	–0.15

[a] Variable log transformed for analysis.

ences among urban sites (Figure 2). The CA axis 2 scores were significantly correlated with 3 of the 10 macroinvertebrate metrics (Table 9). The metric correlations indicated that the larger streams had higher densities of filterers but fewer total taxa and fewer nonchironomid dipteran taxa (Table 9).

Similar to algae analyses, scatterplots (not shown) of CA axis 1 site scores with significantly correlated environmental variables suggested that correlations were strongly influenced by the least-impacted sites. The CA was recalculated without the least-impacted sites and the correlation analysis repeated. Positions of the urbanized sites in the site plot (not shown) and of the taxa in the taxa plot (not shown) were very similar to those in the plots using all the sites (Figure 4). There were no significant correlations of CA axis 1 site scores with environmental variables. The same three variables had significant correlations with CA axis 2 site scores (discharge, $r = 0.75$; depth, $r = 0.64$; and ortho-phosphate, $r = 0.66$, $n = 13$ and $P < 0.05$ for all). In addition, CA axis 2 was significantly negatively correlated with water temperature ($r = –0.57$; $n = 13$ and $P < 0.05$). The same metrics were correlated with CA axes 1 and 2, except Trichoptera density was no longer associated with CA axis 1 and mean EPA species tolerance was correlated with CA axis 2 rather than CA axis 1.

Fishes

Seventeen fish species were collected (Table 10). Only four species are native to the drainage. Fish were captured at 15 of the 17 sites sampled. No fish were collected at the Cucamonga Creek site just downstream of the wastewater discharge (WCO2) or at the San Timoteo Creek site (WN2), which was also just downstream of the wastewater discharge forming the stream. Of 2,242 fish collected, only 696 (31%) were native species. Alien fishes dominated (>66%) most sites.

The cluster analysis identified 5 clusters (Figure 5). The speckled dace cluster consisted of the Cajon Creek site (NN1), the only site where the species was captured. The trout cluster included the other two least-impacted sites. These sites were dominated by rainbow trout, with brown trout *Salmo trutta* also present at the Santa Ana River site (NN3). Urbanized sites formed three clusters with four sites each (Figure 5). The mosquitofish cluster included concrete-lined channels with only western mosquitofish *Gambusia affinis*. The alien species cluster included sites with natural or channelized streams and with three to nine species of alien fishes. The native species cluster in-

TABLE 10. Fishes collected in the Santa Ana River basin, summer 2000.

Scientific name	Common name	Native
Salmonidae		
Oncorhynchus mykiss	Rainbow trout	Yes[a]
Salmo trutta	Brown trout	No
Catostomidae		
Catostomus santaanae	Santa Ana sucker	Yes
Cyprinidae		
Carassius auratus	Goldfish	No
Cyprinus carpio	Common carp	No
Gila orcutti	Arroyo chub	Yes
Pimephales promelas	Fathead minnow	No
Rhinichthys osculus	Speckled dace	Yes
Ictaluridae		
Ameirus melas	Black bullhead	No
A. natalis	Yellow bullhead	No
Ictalurus punctatus	Channel catfish	No
Centrarchidae		
Lepomis cyanellus	Green sunfish	No
L. macrochirus	Bluegill	No
Micropterus salmoides	Largemouth bass	No
Poeciliidae		
Gambusia affinis	Western mosquitofish	No
Poecilia latipinna	Sailfin molly	No
Cichlidae		
Oreochromis mossambica	Mozambique tilapia	No

[a] Rainbow trout are native to the basin but hatchery strains have been widely introduced. The fish captured appeared to be wild, but their genetic heritage is unknown.

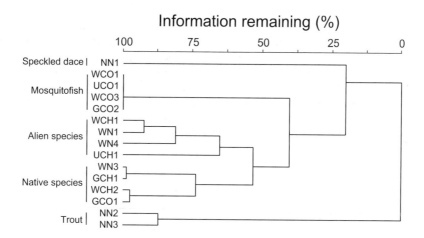

FIGURE 5. Results of a group average cluster analysis of Jaccard similarities for fishes captured at 15 sites in the Santa Ana River Basin, summer 2000. See Table 1 for site codes. The first letter of the site code denotes water source (N, natural; G, urban impacted groundwater; U, urban runoff; W, treated wastewater). The remaining letters denote channel type (N, natural; CH, channelized but unlined; CO, concrete-lined).

cluded sites with various channel and water types and with two to six species of alien fishes but also native arroyo chub. Three sites in the native species cluster also had native Santa Ana sucker (WN3, GCH1, and WCH2).

Analysis of variance was used to determine environmental differences between clusters. The two clusters including only least-impacted sites were omitted from analysis because they were clearly different from the other sites (Figure 2; Table 3). Significant differences were found for coefficient of variation of bank-full width, depth, bed substrate, and water temperature (Table 11). The mosquitofish cluster was clearly different from the others, reflecting that all the sites were in concrete-lined channels. These sites were uniform in shape and substrate and tended to be shallow and warm. The alien species cluster included the deepest most heterogeneous sites with the largest substrates and coolest temperatures. The native species cluster included sites with intermediate depth and bed substrate. Water temperatures were warm, similar to the mosquitofish cluster, but the coefficient of variation of bank-full width was similar to the alien species cluster because both site groups included primarily channelized or natural stream reaches.

Discussion

Biological assemblages of the highly urbanized streams of the Santa Ana basin responded to environmental gradients; however, different taxa showed different patterns. Periphyton primarily differed between least-impacted and urbanized sites. When the least-impacted sites were excluded from the analysis, no relationships were found between periphyton assemblages and environmental variables. Both benthic macroinvertebrate and fish assemblages exhibited associations with environmental variables even when the least-impacted sites were excluded from analysis. Different patterns between taxa are most likely related to different population dynamics.

Periphyton assemblages are well adapted to disturbance (Biggs 1996; Peterson 1996) and can rapidly disperse and recolonize disturbed habitats. Stevenson (1997) provided a theoretical framework for understanding how disturbance and other factors relate to heterogeneity often observed in periphyton assemblages. Dispersal ability is an important factor in this framework and is likely important in the Santa Ana River basin. Many algae species and other microorganisms, including small invertebrates, are widely distributed on large geographic scales because of wind dispersal of the organisms or specialized resting stages (Kristiansen 1996; Finlay 2002). Other likely dispersal mechanisms (Kristiansen 1996) within the Santa Ana River basin include downstream drift; intermittent connections with more permanent bodies of water such as detention, fishing, or water treatment ponds; and external and internal transport by wading birds, which are common even in concrete-lined channels. Although there is disagreement concerning the ubiquity of algae and other microorganisms at large geographic scales, such as continental and global distributions (Kociolek and Spaulding 2000; Hillebrand et al. 2001; Finlay 2002), it seems likely that all species have an equal probability of colonizing available habitat within the Santa Ana River basin.

Other studies have noted differences in the structure of periphyton assemblages between rural and urban land uses (Sonneman et al. 2001; Winter and Duthie 1998, 2000); however, similar to our study, Sonneman et al. (2001) did not find any strong patterns of periphyton assemblage composition when only urbanized sites were considered. In the Santa Ana River basin, when the least-impacted sites were excluded, nutrient concentrations did not appear limiting with detectable nitrite + nitrate available at every site and ortho-phosphate available at all but three sites (Table 3), presumably because of the dominance of treated wastewater. Similarly, most sites were quite open, so light was not a limiting factor. Thus, the particular taxa colonizing artificial substrates at a particular site

TABLE 11. Means (±SD) for variables with significant differences between fish site clusters for sites in the Santa Ana River basin, summer 2000. Different letters indicate groups significantly different in subsequent Tukey pairwise tests.

Variable	Fish site cluster		
	Mosquitofish	Native species	Alien species
Coefficient of variation of bank-full width (%)	1.5 ± 3.0 A	15.1 ± 10.0 B	20.7 ± 5.5 B
Depth (m)	0.06 ± 0.03 A	0.18 ± 0.06 A,B	0.40 ± 0.19 B
Bed substrate	1.0 ± 0.0 A	3.0 ± 1.1 A,B	4.4 ± 1.2 B
Water temperature (°C)	29.5 ± 1.8 A	28.9 ± 2.4 A	23.9 ± 0.5 B

were likely the result of random colonization and available taxa pool rather than a response to water or habitat quality. Interestingly, a metric approach to the data (Burton et al. 2005) suggested that the periphyton assemblage did respond to water source and channel type, within the urbanized subset of sites. This suggests that urbanization of stream environments creates conditions suitable for taxa with certain environmental optima but that the particular taxa having those characteristics at any particular site are determined by random colonization.

Macroinvertebrates appeared primarily responsive to habitat structure. Correlations of the primary gradient in assemblage structure (CA axis 1) with coefficient of variation of bank-full width and bed substrate (Table 7) suggest differences in macroinvertebrate assemblages related to stream channelization (low coefficient of variation of bank-full width) and concrete lining (low values for bed substrate). Correlations with the biological metrics suggest that the main difference in macroinvertebrate assemblages was a loss of EPT taxa, mainly trichopterans, at the more urbanized sites (more-impacted sites in Figure 4). The urbanized sites also tended to support more tolerant taxa. These metric results are consistent with other work documenting the effects of urbanization on stream macroinvertebrates (Walsh et al. 2001; Morley and Karr 2002; Wang and Lyons 2003). The grouping of several urbanized sites with the least-impacted sites (less-impacted sites in Figure 4) suggests that urbanized sites are capable of supporting relatively "natural" macroinvertebrate assemblages. Even the least-impacted sites can be quite stressful because of high water temperatures and low flows during the summer. Many native macroinvertebrates are likely tolerant of environmental stresses and could survive in urban streams if favorable habitats were available. In the analysis excluding least-impacted sites, the absence of correlations between CA axis 1 and the environmental variables makes it difficult to hypothesize about the specific conditions supporting more natural assemblages.

Correlations between the secondary gradient in macroinvertebrate assemblage structure (CA axis 2) and discharge, depth, ortho-phosphate, and water temperature, whether or not the least-impacted sites were included in the analysis, likely reflect a response to stream size. Discharge was greatest at sites supplied with treated wastewater and both depth and ortho-phosphate were correlated with discharge (Table 4). These results are similar to those of Burton et al. (2005). Although we did not measure variation in stream flow

directly, discharges of treated wastewater are one of the more consistent sources of water to these urban streams. Interactions between dispersal ability and permanence of flow may be important in the ecology of these streams. Dispersal ability can vary widely among aquatic macroinvertebrates, with important implications for population structure (Meyers et al. 2001; Miller et al. 2002; Rundle et al. 2002). Consistent wastewater flows may provide stable habitat for poor dispersers and a source of colonizers to more ephemeral habitats. Although this topic has not been addressed in urban streams, studies of aquatic macroinvertebrate dispersal between desert springs (Meyers et al. 2001; Miller et al. 2002) and dispersal of terrestrial macroinvertebrates between habitat patches in urban areas (Wood and Pullin 2002) provide useful models for pursuing such questions.

Exceptions to the general patterns of association between macroinvertebrate assemblages and environmental variables were largely due to site specific factors. The similarity of the Sunnyslope Creek site GCH1 to the least-impacted sites was not surprising because the channel and setting (a regional park) were fairly natural. The similarity of the upstream concrete-lined channel (GCO1) was more surprising but is understandable given the specific site conditions. The groundwater source at this site is apparently fairly constant and the lack of recent storm flows had resulted in accumulation of dense beds of filamentous algae and areas of fine substrate that had allowed emergent plants to grow within the concrete channel. The combination of complex habitat and a nearby, fairly natural source of colonists (GCH1) resulted in a macroinvertebrate assemblage similar to the least-impacted sites. The inclusion of the Santa Ana River above Riverside Road (WCH2) probably occurred for similar reasons. This site is located downstream of several wastewater treatment plants that supply a steady source of water and the channel, although very straight, had large amounts of gravel substrate in addition to sand. Thus, this site also represents a structurally complex, perennial habitat. The other Santa Ana River site (WN3) in this group is the most anomalous. The site is downstream from WCH2 so has similar hydrologic characteristics, but the channel is dominated by sand. There is some habitat complexity due to aquatic macrophytes and small amounts of gravel and woody debris. The main reason for the similarity between these two Santa Ana River sites may simply be downstream drift from one to the other.

Fish distribution in the basin exhibited several interesting features. Restriction of rainbow and brown trout to the least-impacted sites was expected. Water temperatures at urban sites were high enough to cause severe stress or even acute mortality of trout (Moyle 2002). The limited distribution of speckled dace was expected based on earlier descriptions of the distribution of this species in the region (Swift et al. 1993); however, the reasons for the limited distribution are unclear. Swift et al. (1993) suggested that appropriate habitat for this species has always been limited in Southern California.

Fish distribution among the urbanized sites was clearly associated with environmental conditions. Western mosquitofish was the only fish found in three of the four concrete-lined channels. This species is widely used for mosquito control and is actively planted by mosquito control agencies. The species is tolerant of high temperatures and low-dissolved oxygen (Moyle 2002). Its small size, omnivorous feeding habits, rapid generation time (3–4 generations per year), and the fact that it is a live-bearer make it the only species that can complete its life cycle in the shallow, homogeneous habitat of concrete-lined channels, which also lack appropriate spawning habitat for the other species (Moyle 2002). The only exception was the concrete channel on Sunnyslope Creek, which supported additional species but actually had fairly complex habitat as described above.

In the context of fish conservation, the ability of some highly urbanized streams to support native arroyo chub and Santa Ana sucker is important. Sites supporting these native species were similar to other sites in most characteristics; however, there were differences for coefficient of variation of bank-full width, depth, bed substrate, and water temperature. Rather than having the highest or lowest values for these variables, the sites with native fishes tended to be intermediate. Neither native species can complete its life cycle in concrete channels because appropriate spawning habitat is absent (Moyle 2002). The reasons for their absence from the other sites is unclear. The sites where the species were found included the Santa Ana River (WN3 and WCH2) and Sunnyslope Creek (GCH1 and GCO1). The occurrence of Santa Ana sucker may simply reflect that gravel in the area around WCH2 provides the best spawning habitat in the region (Moyle 2002) and that populations downstream in the Santa Ana River and nearby Sunnyslope Creek are dependent on this successful spawning for recruits. All four sites are within 10 km of each other and are hydrologically connected. This explanation does not hold for arroyo chub, which can also spawn over fine substrates or plants. Moyle

(2002) indicates that arroyo chub does not do well in the presence of alien species and similar observations have been made for Santa Ana sucker. Many of the alien species typically inhabit deeper, slower moving waters in their native habitats (Moyle 2002). The intermediate depths and perhaps other unmeasured characteristics of the sites with native species may favor native species over alien species. These results suggest that urban streams in the Santa Ana River basin can be configured to help in the conservation of native fishes.

Our study shows considerable variation in macroinvertebrate and fish assemblages of highly urbanized streams associated with variability in the environmental characteristics of those streams. Although not measured directly, the reliability and quantity of flow is likely an important environmental variable in this system. Of interest to managers is that treated wastewater, a reliable source of water in urban systems, appears to support valuable aquatic resources, including a threatened fish species. However, caution is warranted given concerns about the endocrine system disrupting effects of some chemicals often found in such waters. Any improvement in a specific habitat condition (e.g., water quality) for fish assemblages can be more than offset by habitat degradation caused by other human actions (Limburg and Schmidt 1990). For example, Trimble (1997) called for erosion control measures to protect property affected by increased rates of erosion due to urbanization. All too often, such measures have emphasized engineering solutions, such as channelization and concrete lining, which degrade the ecological and esthetic value of urban streams. Management should address all aspects of the environment simultaneously.

The study of urban systems provides ecologists the opportunity to observe the effects of intense rural-urban environmental gradients on ecological communities (McDonnell and Pickett 1990). Such studies provide opportunities to address basic ecological concepts such as disturbance, species invasions, and the effects of environmental stress. Similarly, Grimm et al. (2000) argue that ecological research in cities provides opportunities for advances in theoretical ecology and for the integration of ecological and social sciences. Continued study of urban streams in the Santa Ana River basin and elsewhere will help elucidate the fundamental principles of stream ecology and help develop the applied knowledge to conserve the ecological values of all streams as human populations continue to grow.

Acknowledgments

We thank Terry Maret, Ian Waite, Kurt Carpenter, and Bob Gray for reviews that significantly improved the quality of the paper. This work was funded by the National Water Quality Assessment Program of the U.S. Geological Survey.

References

Ahel, M., E. Molnar, S. Ibric, and W. Giger. 2000. Estrogenic metabolites of alkylphenol polyethoxylates in secondary sewage effluents and rivers. Water Science and Technology 42(7–8):15–22.

Aloi, J. E. 1990. A critical review of recent freshwater periphyton field methods. Canadian Journal of Fisheries and Aquatic Sciences 47:656–670.

Arnold, C. L., P. J. Boison, and P. C. Patton. 1982. Sawmill Brook: an example of rapid geomorphic change related to urbanization. Journal of Geology 90:155–160.

Baer, K. E., and C. M. Pringle. 2000. Special problems of urban river conservation: the encroaching megalopolis. Pages 385–402 in P. J. Boon, B. R. Davies, and G. E. Petts, editors. Global perspectives on river conservation: science policy, and practice. John Wiley, Chichester, New York.

Barbour, M. T., J. Gerritsen, B. D. Snyder, and J. B. Stribling. 1999. Rapid bioassessment protocols for use in streams and wadeable rivers: periphyton, benthic macroinvertebrates, and fish, 2nd edition. U.S. Environmental Protection Agency, Office of Water, EPA 841-B-99–002, Washington, D.C.

Belt, G. H., and J. O'Laughlin. 1994. Buffer strip design for protecting water quality and fish habitat. Western Journal of Applied Forestry 9:41–45.

Biggs, B. J. F. 1996. Patterns in benthic algae of streams. Pages 31–56 in R. J. Stevenson, M. L. Bothwell, and R. L. Lowe, editors. Algal ecology: freshwater benthic ecosystems. Academic Press, San Diego, California.

Booth, D. B. 1990. Stream-channel incision following drainage-basin urbanization. Water Resources Bulletin 26:407–417.

Booth, D. B. 1991. Urbanization and the natural drainage system—impacts, solutions, and prognoses. Northwest Environmental Journal 7:93–118.

Booth, D. B., and C. R. Jackson. 1997. Urbanization of aquatic systems–degradation thresholds, stormwater detention, and the limits of mitigation. Water Resources Bulletin 33:1077–1090.

Booth, D. B., D. Hartley, and C. R. Jackson. 2002. Forest cover, impervious-surface area, and the mitigation of stormwater impacts. Journal of the American Water Resources Association 38:835–845.

Burton, C., L. R. Brown, and K. Belitz. 2005. Assessing water source and channel type as factors affecting benthic macroinvertebrate and periphyton assemblages in the highly urbanized Santa Ana River basin, California. Pages 239–262 in L. R. Brown, R. Gray, R. M. Hughes, and M. R. Meador, editors. Effects of urbanization on stream ecosystems. American Fisheries Society, Symposium 47, Bethesda, Maryland.

Cao, Y., D. P. Larsen, and R. St.-J. Thorne. 2001. Rare species in multivariate analysis for bioassessment: some considerations. Journal of the North American Benthological Society 20:144–153.

Charles, D. F., C. Knowles, and R. S. Davis. 2002. Protocols for the analysis of algal samples collected as part of the U.S. Geological Survey National Water-Quality Assessment Program. Academy of Natural Sciences, Patrick Center for Environmental Research Report No. 02–06, Philadelphia.

Field, R., and R. E. Pitt. 1990. Urban storm-induced discharge impacts. Water Science Technology 22(3):1–7.

Finkenbine, J. K., J. W. Atwater, and D. S. Mavinic. 2000. Stream health after urbanization. Journal of the American Water Resources Association 36:1149–1160.

Finlay, B. J. 2002. Global disperal of free-living microbial eukaryote species. Science 5570:1061–1063.

Fitzpatrick, F. A., I. A. Waite, P. J. D'Arconte, M. R. Meador, M. A. Maupin, and M. E. Gurtz. 1998. Revised methods for characterizing stream habitat in the National Water-Quality Assessment Program. U.S. Geological Survey Water Resources Investigations Report 98–4052, Raleigh, North Carolina.

Grimm, N. B., J. M. Grove, and S. T. A. Pickett. 2000. Integrated approaches to long-term studies of urban ecological systems. BioScience 50:571–584.

Heany, J. P., and W. C. Huber. 1984. Nationwide assessment of urban runoff impact on receiving water quality. Water Resources Bulletin 20:35–42.

Hillebrand, H., F. Waterman, R. Karez, U.-G. Berninger. 2001. Differences in species richness patterns between unicellular and multicellular organisms. Oecologia 126:114–124.

Kellar, E. A., and F. J. Swanson. 1979. Effects of large organic material on channel form and alluvial process. Earth Surface Processes 4:361–380.

Klein, R. D. 1979. Urbanization and stream quality impairment. Water Resources Bulletin 15:948–963.

Kociolek, J. P., and S. A. Spaulding. 2000. Freshwater diatom biogeography. Nova Hedwigia 71:223–241.

Kristiansen, J. 1996. Dispersal of freshwater algae–a review. Pages 151–157 in J. Kristiansen, editor. Biogeography of freshwater algae. Kluwer Academic Publishers, Dordrecht, Belgium.

LeBlanc, R. T., R. D. Brown, and J. E. FitzGibbon. 1996. Modeling the effects of land use changes on the water temperature in unregulated urban streams. Journal of Environmental Management 49:445–469.

Lieb, D. A., and R. F. Carline. 2000. The effects of urban runoff from a detention pond on water quality, temperature, and caged *Gammurus minus* (Say) (Amphipoda) in a headwater stream. Hydrobiologia 441:107–116.

Limburg, K. E., and R. E. Schmidt. 1990. Patterns of spawning in Hudson River tributaries: response to an urban gradient? Ecology 71:1238–1245.

Lowe, R. L., and Y. Pan. 1996. Benthic algal communities as biological monitors. Pages 705–739 *in* R. J. Stevenson, M. L. Bothwell, and R. L. Lowe, editors. Algal ecology: freshwater benthic ecosystems. Academic Press, San Diego, California.

Martin, D. J., L. J. Wasserman, and V. H. Dale. 1986. Influence of riparian vegetation on posteruption survival of coho salmon fingerlings on the west-side streams of Mount St. Helens, Washington. North American Journal of Fisheries Management 6:1–8.

McDonnell, M. J., and S. T. A. Pickett. 1990. Ecosystem structure and function along urban-rural gradients: an unexploited opportunity for ecology. Ecology 71:1231–1237.

Meador, M. R., J. P. McIntyre, K. H. Pollock. 2003. Assessing the efficacy of single-pass backpack electrofishing to characterize fish community structure. Transactions of the American Fisheries Society 132:39–46.

Meyers, M. J., F. A. H. Sperling, and V. H. Resh. 2001. Dispersal of two species of Trichoptera from desert springs: conservation implications for isolated vs connected populations. Journal of Insect Conservation 5:207–215.

Miller, M. P., D. W. Blinn, and P. Keim. 2002. Correlations between observed dispersal capabilities and patterns of genetic differentiation in populations of four aquatic insect species from the Arizona White Mountains, U.S.A. Freshwater Biology 47:1660–1673.

Morley, S. A., and J. R. Karr. 2002. Assessing and restoring the health of urban streams in the Puget Sound basin. Conservation Biology 16(6):1–13.

Moulton, S. R. II, J. G. Kennen, R. M. Goldstein, and J. A. Hambrook. 2002. Revised protocols for sampling algal, invertebrate, and fish communities as part of the National Water-Quality Assessment Program. U.S. Geological Survey Open-File Report 02–150, Reston, Virginia.

Moulton, S. R., II, J. L. Carter, S. A. Grotheer, T. F. Cuffney, and T. M. Short. 2000. Methods of analysis by the U.S. Geological Survey National Water Quality Laboratory - processing, taxonomy, and quality control of benthic macroinvertebrate samples. U.S. Geological Survey Open-File Report 00–212, Denver.

Moyle, P. B. 2002. Inland fishes of California (2nd edition). University of California Press, Berkeley.

Naiman, R. J., J. J. Magnuson, D. M. McKnight, and J. A. Stanford. 1995. The freshwater imperative: a research agenda. Island Press, Washington, D.C.

Peterson, C. G. 1996. Response of benthic algal communities to natural physical disturbance. Pages 375–403 *in* R. J. Stevenson, M. L. Bothwell, and R. L. Lowe editors. Algal ecology: freshwater benthic ecosystems. Academic Press, San Diego, California.

Rundle, S. D., A. Foggo, V. Choiseul, and D. T. Bilton. 2002. Are distribution patterns linked to dispersal mechanism? An investigation using pond invertebrate assemblages. Freshwater Biology 47:1571–1581.

Santa Ana Watershed Project Authority. 2003. About the watershed: population. Available: http://www.sawpa.org/about/watershed.htm#population. (June 2003)

Shelton, L. R. 1994. Field guide for collecting and processing stream-water samples for the National Water-Quality Assessment Program. U.S. Geological Survey Open-File Report 94–455, Sacramento, California.

Shinya, M., T. Tsuchinaga, M. Kitano, Y. Yamada, and M. Ishikawa. 2000. Characterization of heavy metals and polycyclic aromatic hydrocarbons in urban highway runoff. Water Science and Technology 42(7–8):201–208.

Sonneman, J. A., C. J. Walsh, P. F. Breen, and A. K. Sharpe. 2001. Effects of urbanization on streams of the Melbourne region, Victoria, Australia. II. Benthic diatom communities Freshwater Biology 46:553–565.

Stevenson, R. J. 1997. Scale-dependent determinants and consequences of benthic algal heterogeneity. Journal of the North American Benthological Society 16:248–262.

Swift, C. C., T. R. Haglund, M. Ruiz, and R. N. Fisher. 1993. The status and distribution of the freshwater fishes of Southern California. Bulletin of the Southern California Academy of Sciences 92:101–172.

Trimble, S. W. 1997. Contribution of stream channel erosion to sediment yield from an urbanizing watershed. Science 278:1442–1444.

U.S. Army Corps of Engineers. 1994. Water control manual, Prado Dam and Reservoir, Santa Ana River, California. U.S. Army Corps of Engineers, Los Angeles.

Vannote, R. L., G. W. Minshall, K. W. Cummins, J. R. Sedell, and C. E. Cushing. 1980. The river continuum concept. Canadian Journal of Fisheries and Aquatic Sciences 37:130–137.

Walsh, C. J., A. K. Shape, P. F. Breen, and J. A. Sonneman. 2001. Effects of urbanization on streams of the Melbourne region, Victoria, Australia. I. Benthic macroinvertebrate communities. Freshwater Biology 46:535–551.

Wang, L., and J. Lyons. 2003. Fish and benthic macroinvertebrate assemblages as indicators of stream degradation in urbanizing watersheds. Pages 227–249 *in* T. P. Simon, editor. Biological response signatures: indicator patterns using aquatic communities. CRC Press, Boca Raton, Louisiana.

Wang, L., J. Lyons, P. Kanehl, R. Bannerman, and E. Emmons. 2000. Watershed urbanization and changes in fish communities in southeastern Wisconsin streams. Journal of the American Water Resources Association 36:1173–1189.

Weaver, L. A., and G. C. Garman. 1994. Urbanization of a watershed and historical changes in a stream fish assemblage. Transactions of the American Fisheries Society 123:162–172.

Wichert, G. A. 1994. Fish as indicators of ecological sustainability: historical sequences in Toronto area streams. Water Pollution Research Journal of Canada 29:599–617.

Wichert, G. A. 1995. Effects of improved sewage effluent management and urbanization on fish associations of Toronto streams. North American Journal of Fisheries Management 15:440–456.

Winter, J. G., and H. C. Duthie. 1998. Effects of urbanization on water quality, periphyton and invertebrate communities in a southern Ontario stream. Canadian Water Resources Journal 23:245–257.

Winter, J. G., and H. C. Duthie. 2000. Epilithic diatoms as indicators of stream total N and P concentration. Journal of the North American Benthological Society 19:32–49.

Wood, B. C., and A. S. Pullin. 2002. Persistence of species in a fragmented urban landscape: the importance of dispersal ability and habitat availability for grassland butterflies. Biodiversity and Conservation 11:1451–1468.

Regional Comparisons

American Fisheries Society Symposium 47:291–315, 2005
© 2005 by the American Fisheries Society

Use of an Urban Intensity Index to Assess Urban Effects on Streams in Three Contrasting Environmental Settings

Cathy M. Tate*

U.S. Geological Survey, Box 25046, Mail Stop 415, Denver, Colorado 80225, USA

Thomas F. Cuffney, Gerard McMahon, Elise M. P. Giddings

U.S. Geological Survey, 3916 Sunset Ridge Road, Raleigh, North Carolina 27607, USA

James F. Coles

U.S. Geological Survey, c/o USEPA New England, Suite 1100 (HBS)
1 Congress Street, Boston, Massachusetts 02114, USA

Humbert Zappia

1162 Rock Cliff Drive, Martinsburg, West Virginia 25401, USA

Abstract.—To assess the effects of urbanization on assemblages (fish, invertebrate, and algal), physical habitat, and water chemistry, we investigated the relations among varying intensities of basin urbanization and stream ecology in three metropolitan areas: the humid northeastern United States around Boston, Massachusetts; the humid southeastern United States around Birmingham, Alabama; and the semiarid western United States around Salt Lake City, Utah. A consistent process was used to develop a multimetric urban intensity index (UII) based on locally important variables (land-use/land-cover, infrastructure, and socioeconomic variables) in each study area and a common urban intensity index (CUII) based on a subset of five variables common to all study areas. The UII was used to characterize 30 basins along an urban gradient in each metropolitan area. Study basins were located within a single ecoregion in each of the metropolitan areas. The UII, ecoregions, and site characteristics provided a method for limiting the variability of natural landscape characteristics while assessing the magnitude of urban effects. Conditions in Salt Lake City (semiarid climate and water diversions) and Birmingham (topography) required nesting sites within the same basin. The UII and CUII facilitated comparisons of aquatic assemblages response to urbanization across different environmental settings.

Introduction

Urbanization represents a complex environmental gradient that provides a framework for assessing changes in the physical, chemical, and biological characteristics of ecosystems (McDonnell and Pickett 1990). Numerous studies have documented specific physical, chemical, or biological responses to urbanization within a stream or among streams within a region (e.g., Wang et al. 2000; Paul and Meyer 2001; Walsh et al. 2001; Center for Watershed Protection 2003). Few studies have examined the physical, chemical, and bio-

logical characteristics to urbanization in contrasting geographic areas (Paul and Meyer 2001). The nature and magnitude of urban effects on streams vary widely, depending on the geographic area studied and the initial ecosystem conditions represented within it. Understanding the differences and similarities of how urbanization affects physical, chemical, and biological characteristics of streams across the United States is important for managing aquatic resources.

A gradient approach has been used to assess the effects of urbanization on geomorphic conditions and aquatic assemblages (e.g., Booth and Jackson 1997; Wang et al. 2000; Walsh et al. 2001; Fitzpatrick et al. 2004; Taylor et al. 2004). Understanding and com-

* Corresponding author: cmtate@usgs.gov

paring urban effects on streams and associated aquatic assemblages can be complicated by how urban influences are quantified or defined (e.g., human population density, percent urban land, percent impervious area, etc.). In addition, the relations among population density, percent urban land, and percent impervious area in a basin may not be understood and depend on regional and historical differences in development of urban areas as well as natural factors such as climate, physiography, geological setting, vegetation types, and soils (Harding et al. 1998; Fitzpatrick et al. 2004). Thus, providing a comprehensive understanding of regional responses to urbanization that are comparable among different environmental settings requires multiple regional urban studies using a common design and sample collection techniques (Cuffney et al. 2005, this volume).

Most studies have used a single measure of urban intensity, such as population density, percent urban land, and percent imperviousness (Arnold and Gibbons 1996), to interpret responses to urbanization. Yoder and Rankin (1995), however, noted that interpretation of ecosystems effects could vary depending on which single measure was used to quantify urban effects. Although impervious area was commonly used to represent urban intensity (Arnold and Gibbons 1996), Karr and Chu (2000) suggested that impervious area alone does not account for all aspects of urbanization. Patterns of development within a metropolitan area are a function not only of the amount of developed land, but also of differences in infrastructure (e.g., roads, sewers, storm water drainage), human population, and socioeconomic (e.g., income, housing) characteristics (McMahon and Cuffney 2000). Multimetric indices have been used to describe the overall condition of complex systems (Karr 1981; Simon and Lyons 1994; Ward 1996; Karr and Chu 1999) and land-use intensities (Ometo et al. 2000; Morley and Karr 2002). A multimetric indicator of urban intensity combines individual condition measures that provide distinct information about the different dimensions of complex systems (McMahon and Cuffney 2000). This approach aids integration of multiple, commonly used sources of information about the urban landscapes, such as land-cover, infrastructure, population, and socioeconomic variables, into a single measure of urban intensity index (Cuffney et al. 2000; McMahon and Cuffney 2000).

In 2000, we initiated a series of studies that used a common design to examine the regional effects of urbanization on aquatic assemblages, physical habitat, and water chemistry in three metropolitan areas that represent contrasting environmental settings. These studies were conducted in the humid northeastern United States around Boston, Massachusetts; the humid southeastern United States around Birmingham, Alabama; and the semiarid western United States around Salt Lake City, Utah. This study was unique in its use of urban intensity indexes (UIIs) to select sites along urban gradients while minimizing differences in natural basin features and local disturbances within three markedly different climatic regions of the United States. The UII was intended to provide an a priori basis for ranking the relative intensity of urban development from low to high (McMahon and Cuffney 2000). A common urban intensity index (CUII) was also calculated using a subset of urban indicators common to all study areas to allow direct comparisons of urban intensities among regions. Once sites were selected, aquatic assemblages, physical habitat, and water chemistry were sampled using the same protocols so that these ecological responses to urbanization could be compared among study areas.

This paper describes the application of the urban intensity gradient design of McMahon and Cuffney (2000) across different environmental settings. The next four chapters (Short et al. 2005; Potapova et al. 2005; Cuffney et al. 2005; Meador et al. 2005; all this volume) compare ecological responses (habitat, algal, invertebrate, and fish) along the urban intensity gradients in three contrasting environmental settings.

Methods

Study Areas

Boston (BOS).—The BOS study area was in Massachusetts, New Hampshire, Maine, and Connecticut in the northeastern United States (Figure 1). The major metropolitan area is Boston, Massachusetts, with a 1992 population of 5.7 million (Flanagan et al. 1999). The study area is in the Northeastern Coastal Zone ecoregion (Omernik 1987), which is characterized by low hills, forests, cropland and pasture, and urban lands and inceptisol soils (Flanagan et al. 1999). Elevation ranges from about 6–61 m above sea level. The climate is cool and humid, with mean annual precipitation of 107 cm evenly distributed throughout the year. Highest flows in all rivers occur in April as a result of spring runoff and snowmelt, and lowest flows occur in July through September (Flanagan et al. 1999). More than 1,600 dams in the area regulate flows in mid-sized to large rivers (basin areas > 250 km², Flanagan et al. 1999). Streams

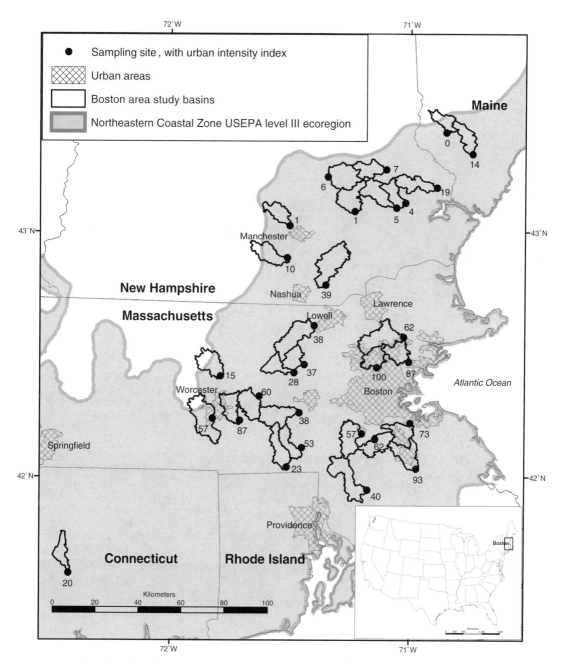

FIGURE 1. Location of study basins and sampling sites in relation to urban areas and U.S. Environmental Protection Agency (USEPA) level III ecoregions in the Boston, Massachusetts study area. Site numbers correspond to urban intensity index in Table 3.

in this region support warmwater fish assemblages (Flanagan et al. 1999).

Birmingham (BIR).—The BIR study area is in Georgia and Alabama in the southeastern United States (Figure 2). Major metropolitan areas include Birmingham, Anniston, and Gadsden, Alabama, with 1990

populations of 839,942, 116,032, and 99,840, respectively (Johnson et al. 2002). The study area is in the Ridge and Valley ecoregion (Omernik 1987), where mountain ridges are typically sandstone, valley floors are primarily limestone or shale, and elevation ranges from about 183 to 488 m above sea level

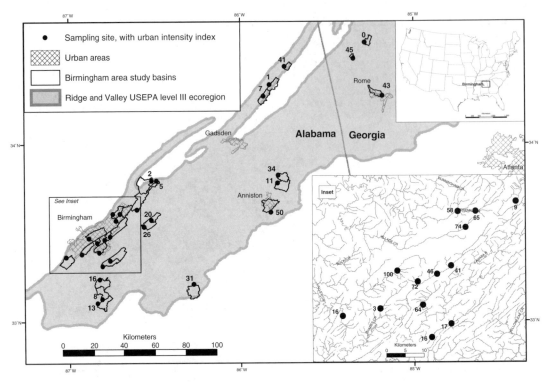

FIGURE 2. Location of study basins and sampling sites in relation to urban areas and U.S. Environmental Protection Agency (USEPA) level III ecoregions in the Birmingham, Alabama study area. Site numbers correspond to the urban intensity index in Table 3.

(Johnson et al. 2002). The dominant natural vegetative cover is Appalachian oak forest, and land use is predominantly cropland and pasture and urban lands (Johnson et al. 2002). The climate is warm and humid with mean annual rainfall of 139 cm, evenly distributed throughout the year, except for a dry period in August to October. Highest flows occur in February, and lowest flows occur in June to September (Johnson et al. 2002); however, flows during 1999–2001 were below the long-term (>50 years) average due to drought conditions in the region (Atkins et al. 2004). Streams in this region support warmwater fish assemblages.

Salt Lake City (SLC).—The SLC study area is located in north-central Utah in the western United States (Figure 3). The three largest cities in Utah, Salt Lake City, Provo, and Ogden, combined with their suburbs, have a total population of about 1.6 million people. These cities are along the western edge of the Wasatch Range, which rises from an elevation of about 1,280 m above sea level at the valley floor to more than 3,300 m (Baskin et al. 2002). The study area is in the Central Basin and Range ecoregion (Omernik 1994; Figure 3), which is characterized by xeric basins, scattered low and

high mountains, and salt flats. Natural vegetation consists of sagebrush, saltbrush, and greasewood on dry alkaline soils, although vegetation in the urban areas is highly altered. Land use in the ecoregion is primarily irrigated agriculture and urban (Baskin et al. 2002). The climate of the study area is semiarid, with precipitation ranging from 30 to 41 cm on the valley floor to greater than 150 cm in the mountains. Summer months are typically dry, with precipitation occurring as thunderstorms (Baskin et al. 2002). Highest flows occur in May and June from snowmelt, and lowest flow from October to March in the Wasatch Range (Baskin et al. 2002). Streams in the study area arise in the Wasatch Range and flow westerly through the urban areas, where they support cool- and coldwater fish assemblages. Typical of arid and semiarid urban areas in the western United States, an array of reservoirs, diversions, and canals, alters the hydrologic regime of most SLC streams (Baskin et al. 2002).

Site Selection

We selected study basins through an iterative process of identifying candidate study basins. We used avail-

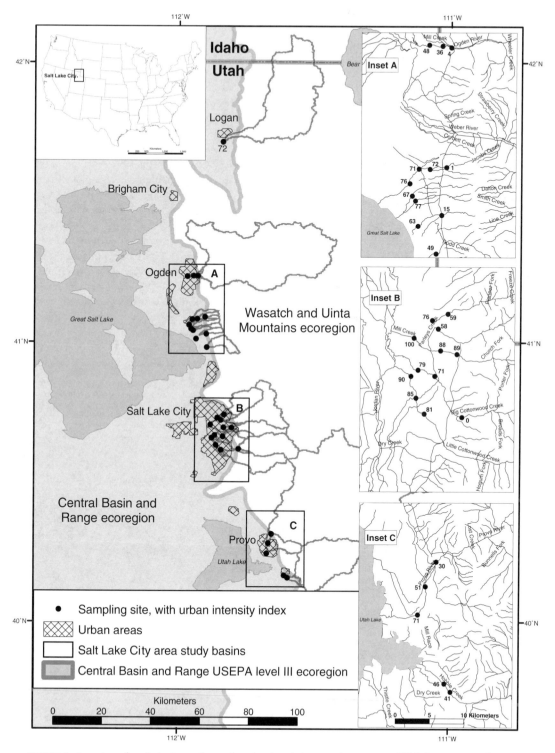

FIGURE 3. Location of study basins and sampling sites in relation to urban areas and U.S. Environmental Protection Agency (USEPA) level III ecoregions in the Salt Lake City, Utah study area. Site numbers correspond to the urban intensity index in Table 3.

able Geographic Information System (GIS) data to group basins with similar natural characteristics (environmental setting). We then used additional GIS data to rank candidate basins by the UII, examined environmental setting groups, and selected a subset of candidate basins with similar natural characteristics that covers the range of UII. We visited candidate sites to validate GIS data and assessed site characteristics and access. Finally, we shifted site locations if necessary, refined basin boundaries, and repeated GIS analyses and UII calculations for the final set of sites.

Basin delineation.—A population of candidate basins in the BOS and BIR were delineated using 30-m digital elevation models (DEMs, U.S. Geological Survey 2000) and GIS programs to approximate 2nd–5th-order basins. We selected 206 candidate basins (50–250 km² in area) in the BOS study area and 375 candidate basins (5–130 km² in area) in the BIR study area. The process for SLC was different because the semiarid conditions of the SLC severely limited the number of streams that were available for study. To develop a population of candidate basins in SLC, we visited every stream in the Central Basin and Range ecoregion between Provo and Logan, Utah and as-

sessed their suitability for inclusion in the urban gradient. To get the range of urban intensity values needed, we had to nest sites and use a larger range of basin sizes (4–1,764 km²) than recommended by the original design. Once sites were selected, basin boundaries were delineated using 30-m DEMs and GIS programs.

Reducing natural variability.—To reduce natural variability for each study area, we grouped candidate basins on the basis of soil drainage characteristics (U.S. Department of Agriculture 1994), bedrock geology (lithology, BOS: Robinson 1997; SLC: Johnson and Raines 1995), topography, and ecoregions (Omernik 1987; Keys et al. 1995) (Table 1) to produce relatively homogeneous groups based on natural features in each study area.

The resulting groups (environmental setting) were consistent with U.S. Environmental Protection Agency (USEPA) level III ecoregion (Omernik 1987) or U.S. Forest Service (USFS) ecological units (Keys et al. 1995). Ecoregions provide a coarse framework of relatively homogenous climate, elevation, soils, geology, and vegetation and have been used to investigate regional water quality patterns (Hughes et al. 1994).

In BOS, we first located candidate basins in the

TABLE 1. Sources of digital mapped information for calculating basin variables.

Basin characteristic	Maps	Scale	Reference
Watershed boundaries and topography	Developed from digital elevation models	100,000	U.S. Geological Survey 2000
Soils	U.S. Department of Agriculture State Soil Data Base (STATSGO)	250,000	U.S. Department of Agriculture 1994
Lithology	Bedrock lithology groups	~250,000	Johnson and Raines 1995; Robinson 1997
Ecological regions	U.S. Environmental Protection Agency (USEPA) level III ecoregions	7,000,000	Omernik 1987
	USEPA level IV ecoregions	1,700,000	Griffith et al. 2001
	U.S. Forest Service subsections (level IV)	3,500,000	Keys et al. 1995
Land-cover data	National land-cover data	100,000	Vogelman et al. 2001; U.S. Geological Survey 2002
Infrastructure	Roads (Census TIGER roads)	100,000	GeoLytics 1999
	Point source dischargers	Point	USEPA 1999
	USEPA Toxic Release Inventory	Point	USEPA 1997; Price and Clawges 1999
	Dams	Point	U.S. Army Corps of Engineers 1996
Census block group	Population, housing unit density, income, socio-economic indices	100,000	GeoLytics 1999

USEPA level III Northeastern Coastal Zone ecoregion (Omernik 1987) that corresponds to the USFS Southern New England Coastal Hills and Plains ecological unit (Keys et al. 1995). To ensure a further degree of homogeneity among natural features, candidate basins were categorized using the 12 USFS ecological subsections that are analogous to higher resolution USEPA level IV ecoregions. This second categorization step provided a mechanism to reduce candidate basins to a subset of basins having relatively little variability in their natural features. The Gulf of Maine Coastal Plain ecological subsection was selected as the primary area for the site network because it included basins that covered a range of urban intensity, including a significant portion of the urban, suburban, and rural areas in the BOS study area. Study basins were selected within 128 km of Boston. Low urban intensity basins are forested. One characteristic unique to BOS was the large number of small, historical millponds that substantially modify the natural hydrology. No streams were identified in central Boston either because they were not in the appropriate size range or were highly modified (e.g., concrete culvert).

In BIR, candidate basins were located in a geologically complex area of the southern Appalachians (USEPA level III Ridge and Valley ecoregion, Omernik 1987), where mountain ridges typically are composed of sandstone and the valley floors tend to be primarily limestone or shale. Candidate basins were then subdivided into relatively homogeneous groups based on four USEPA level IV subecoregions (Griffith et al. 2001) and through analysis of natural features data (e.g., geology, topography). The Southern Limestone/Dolomite Valleys and Low Rolling Hills subecoregion was selected as the primary area for the site network. We also restricted candidate basins to a single surficial geology type that included urban, suburban, and rural areas in the BIR study area. The Ridge and Valley topography lead to the sampling of multiple sites within the same basin. In this nested design, the downstream site integrated the inflows from many upstream tributaries. Sewer overflows and sedimentation from construction were two obvious local alterations in BIR; also, the 2000 sampling coincided with a severe drought that required dropping two sites that went dry during the study.

The SLC urban study focused on streams draining the western edge of the Wasatch Mountains (Figure 3). The mountainous terrain concentrates urban development at the lower end of the river basins in the USEPA level III Central Basin and Range ecoregion (Omernik 1994; Figure 3), but the upper portion of each basin and the source of most of the water are in the Wasatch and Uinta ecoregion. The ecoregion junction is an abrupt transition from an area with little or no urbanization to one with moderate to high urbanization. The SLC study area is heavily affected by water withdrawal, and some streams are piped beneath urban areas or confined by concrete channels. Large irrigation canals run along the edge of the Wasatch Mountains, and streams may receive irrigation overflows or return flows varying hourly and representing marked changes in water source, quantity, and quality. Because of the semiarid environment and numerous water diversions, only 13 perennial streams were suitable for study between Provo and Logan, Utah, requiring us to select one to three sites in each stream to meet the design goal of 30 sites covering the range of urban intensity. In addition, a much wider range in basin area (4–1764 km^2) was required, and one site lacked riffles. Sampling sites ranged in elevation from 1,250 m to 1,539 m because older and more intense urbanization was generally located near the valley floor and newer and less intense residential development was located closer to the mountains. In this nested design, downstream sites were used to represent increasing urban intensity even though they were not independent of conditions at upstream sites (Figure 3). Although we observed many low head dams and diversions, we located no quantification of their number or flows into or away from our study streams.

Urban intensity indices (UIIs).—Infrastructure, land-cover/land-use, and socioeconomic data were used as potential variables in our UIIs (Table 1). Infrastructure measures included road density, the number of point-source dischargers (USEPA 1999), the number of dams (U.S. Army Corp of Engineers 1996), and the number of Toxic Release Inventory sites (USEPA 1997; Price and Clawges 1999). Land-use/land-cover data came from National Land-Cover Data (NLCD; Vogelmann et al. 2001; U.S. Geological Survey 2002), which is based on Landsat Thematic Mapper satellite images from the early 1990s. Land use/land cover was characterized for the entire basin and for a 250-m buffer (125 m on either side of the stream channel) along all streams in the basin mapped at a 1:100,000 scale.

Census counts (1990) and estimates (1999) for population, labor, income, and housing variables, based on census block group areas, were used to characterize socioeconomic features of the urban landscape (GeoLytics 1999). Socioeconomic indices (SEI) were also derived for each basin using principal components analysis (PCA) of social, income, and housing variables (Anson 1991). Socioeconomic indices values were site scores along the PCA axes. Each axis represented a different combination of social, income, housing, and labor variables that characterize the major patterns of change across the urban gradient. We included these variables in the UII because socioeconomic conditions shape perceptions of degree (e.g., density) and character (e.g., affluence) of development within a drainage basin and may also affect factors that can influence water quality (Grove and Burch 1997; McMahon and Cuffney 2000). For example, population and housing density may provide a direct measure of development intensity that is likely correlated with impervious areas (Stankowski 1972). McMahon and Cuffney (2000) suggest that residential use of fertilizers and pesticides may vary according to the income levels of neighborhoods.

We developed separate UIIs for each study area in a consistent five-step process. First, all available GIS data for a study area that were associated with urbanization were normalized: areas into percent basin area, total counts to counts per 100 km², and socioeconomic index = SEI – minimum (SEI). Second, to focus on variables associated with population density (urban intensity), we only included variables that were at least moderately correlated ($|r| \geq 0.5$) with 1999 population density and not strongly correlated with basin area ($|r| < 0.5$). Third, we then range-standardized the remaining data so that values ranged from 0 to 100 (low to high): $Y = (X - X_{min}) \div (X_{max} - X_{min}) \times 100$, where X is the value of variable X for the site, Y is the transformed variable for the site, X_{min} is the minimum values of variable X over all sites, and X_{max} is the maximum values of X over all sites (McMahon and Cuffney 2000). Fourth, values for variables that were negatively correlated with population density were subtracted from 100 so all variables increased with increasing urban intensity. Fifth, we next averaged all of the range-standardized variables for each site and then range-standardized site values over all sites to produce a UII that ranged from 0 to 100 (McMahon and Cuffney 2000). This was the UII score for that site.

UII variables were selected on the basis of their correlation with population density because urbanization is characterized as the number of people using ecosystem resources and services in a defined space and time. We chose to use a multimetric UII and not population density as our sole indicator of urbanization for several reasons. Population density causes landscape changes that affect water quality, but it is not the direct cause of water quality degradation. Also, there are multiple causes of urban water quality degradation and we wanted to include multiple indicators to define urbanization. Variables that were highly correlated with each other were not omitted because by definition all variables included in the UII were correlated with changes in population density.

Reducing the number of sites.—We reduced the number of sites from 206 and 375 in BOS and BIR, respectively, to a more manageable number (<100) for site reconnaissance by examining sites within the different environmental setting groups in each study area. Environmental setting groups were based on sites with similar natural features (e.g., topography, geology, and soils) within an ecoregion. Sites in environmental setting groups were also examined to determine coverage along the urban gradient; that is, six sites distributed within five blocks along the length of gradient (i.e., 0–20, 20–40, 40–60, 60–80, 80–100) or as close an approximation as we could achieve. In this step, related environmental settings were combined to get the coverage of the urban gradient needed while maintaining as homogenous an environmental setting as possible. We then prioritized sites to include in the reconnaissance.

Reconnaissance.—Once the subset of candidate basins were identified, basins were visited to select 30 study sites in each study area, get site permissions, and assess physical access and local stream conditions such as land-use, point sources, riparian condition, and instream habitat characteristics. Criteria for selecting a sampling reach were that the stream reach was free-flowing for 150 m, had no signs of recent anthropogenic modification, had natural substrates, had riffle habitat, and had a well-defined bank with relatively complete (≥50%) vegetation cover. These criteria ensured that ecological differences within the sampling reach resulted from changes in the urban intensity in the basin rather than from differences within the reach (e.g., concrete lined channels).

Index recalculation and final site selection.—The reconnaissance visits caused shifts in the location of some sampling sites. This required redrawing basin boundaries and repeating the five-step process of scoring the UII for all 30 basins in a study area. The final sites represented the gradient in basin-scale urbanization with minimal differences in natural basin features (e.g., ecoregion, climate, topography, stream size) and local disturbances (e.g., major point sources, modifications to channels, bank, or bed).

Common urban intensity index (CUII) calculation.—Urban intensity indexes were developed individually for each study area to reflect the unique land-use, land-cover, infrastructure, population, and socioeconomic data available in each. These UIIs represent the range of urban intensity in each study area, but the variables comprising the index differed among study areas. Consequently, the level of urban intensity described by the UII may not be comparable among study areas. To address this issue, a CUII was also calculated based on a subset of five urban variables common to all three study areas: percentage of basin area in urban, percentage of basin area in forest + shrub land, percentage of stream network buffer in developed, percentage of stream network buffer in forest + shrub lands, and road density. The CUII provided a measure of urban intensity that was calculated in the same way as the UII, but was consistent among the study areas.

Data analyses.—Spearman rank correlations (*r*) were used to examine the strength of relations among population density or basin area and infrastructure, land-use, land-cover, socioeconomic, basin soil, and lithology variables. Spearman rank correlation was used to summarize the relations among variables because it was able to detect associations even when the underlying responses were not linear. Regression analysis (R^2) was used to examine population density as a predictor of UII, and UII as a predictor of land use, road density, and CUII. A significance level of 0.05 was used for regression analyses. Spearman rank correlations and

regression analyses were performed using SYSTAT 9 (SPSS 1999). Principal components analysis used to derive socioeconomic indices was performed using SAS (SAS Inc. 1990).

Results

Natural Variability within Study Areas

In BOS, most basins were in the Gulf of Maine Coastal Plain ecological subsection with the exceptions of two basins that were located in the Southeast New England Coastal Hills and Plains and Worcester-Monadock Plateau ecological subsections (Table 2). Basin area, elevation, and slope varied relatively little among basins (Table 2) and stream sizes ranged from 3rd to 5th order (Table 3). Soil drainage characteristics and lithology, however, varied among basins (Table 2).

In BIR, most basins were in the Southern Limestone/Dolomite Valleys and Hills subecoregion with the exception of two basins that were located in the Southern Shale Valleys and the Southern Sandstone Ridges subecoregions. Basin size, elevations, slopes and soils varied relatively little among basins (Table 2) and stream sizes were mostly 2nd and 3rd order (Table 3).

TABLE 2. Minimum (Min.), maximum (Max.), and median (Med.) of basin variables used to characterize the environmental setting and the urban intensity index for Boston (BOS), Birmingham (BIR), and Salt Lake City (SLC) studies. Variables for SLC are based on the Central Basin and Range ecoregion portion of the basin except for the range and mean elevation in the basin. See Table 1 for data sources.

Basin variables (units)	BOS			BIR			SLC		
	Min.	Max.	Med.	Min.	Max.	Med.	Min.	Max.	Med.
Environmental setting variables									
Basin area (km²)	45.8	124.7	73.0	4.7	66.1	33.5	0.3	29.0	4.5
Topography									
Elevation (m)									
Sampling site	6	144	53	136	254	192	1,250	1,539	1,345
Range in basin	76	485	156	85	428	205	33	1,351	222
Mean in basin	31	237	105	163	324	241	1,376	2,355	1,467
Basin slope (% of basin area)									
Slope < 1%	2	31	11	1	29	3	0	12	2
Slope < 1%, > midpoint elevation (uplands)	0	6	1	0	7	0	0	1	0
Slope < 1%, ≤ midpoint elevation in the basin (lowlands)	1	29	10	0	29	3	0	12	2
Soils									
Hydrologic soil groups (% of basin area)									
A, minimum infiltration rate									
8–12 mm/h	0	74	19	–	–	–	0	7	0

TABLE 2. Continued.

Basin variables (units)	BOS			BIR			SLC		
	Min.	Max.	Med.	Min.	Max.	Med.	Min.	Max.	Med.
B, minimum infiltration rate 4–8 mm/h	0	92	0	6	100	86	0	100	90
C, minimum infiltration rate 1–4 mm/h	0	88	0	0	94	0	0	100	0
D, minimum infiltration rate 0–1 mm/h	0	55	1	0	65	0	0	95	0
Soil drainage (% of basin area)									
Well-drained soils	5	98	45	6	100	86	0	100	90
Poorly drained soils	2	95	54	0	94	14	0	100	9
Average soil volume proportion of sand	19	45	34	4	18	14	7	38	25
Lithology (% of basin area)									
Quartzite	–	–	–	–	–	–	0	31	0
Alluvium	–	–	–	–	–	–	0	84	12
Lake sediment and playa	–	–	–	–	–	–	0	94	56
Granitic gneiss	–	–	–	–	–	–	0	100	0
Carbonate rich	0	90	0	–	–	–	–	–	–
Carbonate poor, clastic sedimentary, depositonal basins	0	74	0	–	–	–	–	–	–
Mafic igneous and metamorphic equivalents	0	64	3	–	–	–	–	–	–
Ultramafic	0	87	1	–	–	–	–	–	–
Metamorphosed clastic sedimentary	0	97	47	–	–	–	–	–	–
Felsic igneous and plutonic	0	94	0	–	–	–	–	–	–
Ecoregions (% of basin area)									
U.S. Forest Service ecological units									
Southern New England Coastal Hills and Plains									
Boston Basin	0	68	0	–	–	–	–	–	–
Narragansett/Bristol Lowlands	0	61	0	–	–	–	–	–	–
Southeast New England Coastal Hills and Plains	0	100	0	–	–	–	–	–	–
Worcester/Monadnock Plateau	0	100	0	–	–	–	–	–	–
Gulf of Maine Coastal Plain	0	100	99	–	–	–	–	–	–
U.S. Envrionmental Protection Agency ecoregions									
Ridge and Valley									
Southern Limestone/ Dolomite Valleys	–	–	–	0	100	72	–	–	–
Southern Shale Valleys	–	–	–	0	98	0	–	–	–
Southern Sandstone Ridges	–	–	–	0	100	0	–	–	–
Plateau Escarpment	–	–	–	0	35	0	–	–	–
Southern Table Plateaus	–	–	–	0	43	0	–	–	–
Central Basin and Range	–	–	–	–	–	–	100	100	100

TABLE 2. Continued.

Basin variables (units)	BOS			BIR			SLC		
	Min.	Max.	Med.	Min.	Max.	Med.	Min.	Max.	Med.
Urban intensity index variables									
Land use/land cover (National Land-Cover Data)									
Basin level (% of basin area)									
Developed	2	67	15	0	73	11	0	87	40
Low intensity residential	1	50	10	0	34	7	0	77	30
High intensity residential	0	4	0	0	17	1	0	0	0
Commercial/industrial/									
transportation	0	14	3	0	23	3	0	19	4
Forest	23	86	65	18	93	64	2	47	11
Deciduous	14	60	28	9	55	27	0	16	5
Evergreen	1	32	5	1	26	12	1	31	3
Mixed	7	42	18	6	33	24	0	12	1
Shrubland	0	0	0	–	–	–	1	68	12
Deciduous	–	–	–	–	–	–	0	67	8
Herbaceous planted/cultivated									
Pasture/hay	0	6	1	0	26	7	0	38	6
Row crops	0	9	4	0	8	3	0	0	0
Urban/recreational grasses	0	10	2	0	11	3	0	25	8
Stream buffers (250 m, % of buffer area)									
Developed	2	60	12	0	68	16	0	78	32
Forest	25	82	60	22	89	62	4	57	14
Shrubs	–	–	–	–	–	–	3	58	14
Infrastructure									
Road density in basin (km/km²)	1	9	3	5	50	15	0	45	20
Point source discharger density									
(number/100 km²)	0	15	0	–	–	–	–	–	–
USEPA Toxic Release Inventory									
density (number/100 km²)	0	40	3	–	–	–	–	–	–
Dam density (number/100 km²)	0	18	6	–	–	–	–	–	–
Socioeconomic indices (SEI) variables									
SEI2	–3.6	1.5	–0.6	–3.7	3.7	–0.9	–4.4	3.3	0.4
SEI3	–1.3	2.8	1.2	–	–	–	–	–	–
SEI5	–0.7	1.8	1.0	–	–	–	–	–	–
Population and housing variables									
1999 population density									
(people/km²)	25	1,261	205	10	1,543	214	13	2,251	813
Change in population density 1990									
to 1999 (people/km²)	–2	82	12	–47	129	6	1	278	166
Percent of families with female head									
of household	5	19	8	–	–	–	–	–	–
Percent of minorities in 1999	0	10	2	–	–	–	–	–	–
Percent occupied housing units that									
are renter occupied, 1990	5	28	16	–	–	–	–	–	–
Percent of 1990 housing units built									
before 1980	58	88	71	–	–	–	–	–	–
Percent of housing units on public									
sewers, 1990	–	–	–	3	97	42	1	100	94

TABLE 3. Urban intensity index (UII), common urban intensity index (CUII), and selected characteristics for study basins. UII values correspond to sampling site locations in each basin in Figures 1, 2, and 3.

Site name	Urban intensity index (UII)	Common urban intensity index (CUII)	1999 population density (number/ km²)	Total basin area (km²)	Basin area in Central Basin and Range eco-region (km²)	Stream order
Boston, Massachusetts						
Little River near Lebanon, ME	0	1	41	45.8	–	4
Black Brook Dunbarton Road near Manchester, NH	1	5	55	53.7	–	4
Lamprey River Cotton Road near Deerfield, NH	1	4	27	83.1	–	4
Little River at Cartland Road at Lee, NH	4	7	39	52.2	–	3
North River at Route 152 near Nottingham, NH	5	6	31	74.9	–	5
Little Suncook River Blackhall Road at Epsom, NH	6	11	34	101.4	–	4
Isinglass River Batchelder Road near center Strafford, NH	7	8	25	59.4	–	3
Baboosic River Bedford Road near Merrimack, NH	10	11	123	73.0	–	4
Greatworks River near North Berwick, ME	14	11	95	60.2	–	4
Stillwater River near Sterling, MA	15	9	60	78.7	–	3
Bellamy River at Bellamy Road near Dover, NH	19	14	87	68.5	–	4
Blackledge River above Lyman Brook near North Westchester, CT	20	12	94	49.2	–	3
Mill River at Summer Street near Blackstone, MA	23	15	204	73.7	–	5
Elizabeth Brook off White Pond Road near Stow, MA	28	14	91	48.5	–	4
Fort Pond Brook at River Road near South Acton, MA	37	19	228	53.7	–	4
Stony Brook at North Pelham, NH	38	27	193	107.7	–	4
Sudbury River at Concord Street at Ashland, MA	38	22	212	89.6	–	5
Beaver Brook at North Pelham, NH	39	38	349	121.7	–	4
Wading River (head of Threemile River) near Norton, MA	40	23	208	113.4	–	4
Charles River at Maple Street at North Bellingham, MA	53	32	529	54.2	–	4
Middle River off Sutton Lane at Worcester, MA	57	34	499	124.7	–	5

TABLE 3. Continued.

Site name	Urban intensity index (UII)	Common urban intensity index (CUII)	1999 population density (number/ km²)	Total basin area (km²)	Basin area in Central Basin and Range eco- region (km²)	Stream order
Neponset River at Norwood, MA	57	36	477	84.9	–	5
Assabet River at Allen Street at Northborough, MA	60	34	295	76.4	–	5
East Branch Neponset River at Canton, MA	62	43	605	72.9	–	5
Ipswich River at South Middleton, MA	63	47	445	115.3	–	4
Monatiquot River at River Street at Braintree, MA	73	50	808	71.2	–	4
Quinsigamond River at North Grafton, MA	87	52	781	66.2	–	4
Saugus River at Saugus Ironworks at Saugus, MA	87	63	1,015	60.4	–	4
Matfield River at North Central Street at East Bridgewater, MA	93	56	1,261	79.8	–	4
Aberjona River (head of Mystic River) at Winchester, MA	100	75	1,204	58.2	–	5
Birmingham, Alabama						
Chappel Creek at Long Branch Road near Trion, GA	0	6	35	14.3	–	2
Mush Creek near Portersville, AL	1	5	10	24.5	–	3
Big Canoe Creek at Canoe Creek Road near Springville, AL	2	2	55	54.3	–	4
Little Shades Creek at State Highway 150 near Bessemer, AL	3	0	46	21.7	–	2
Unnamed Tributary to Big Canoe Creek near Springville, AL	5	8	45	10.5	–	2
Little Wills Creek at Collins Chapel Road at Collinsville, AL	7	10	14	27.9	–	3
Spring Creek at County Road 16 near Moores Crossroads, AL	8	16	102	33.1	–	3
Cahaba River above Trussville, AL	9	–	94	50.1	–	–
Little Tallaseehatchee Creek near Weaver, AL	11	5	66	38.1	–	3
Dry Creek at Spring Creek Road near Montevallo, AL	13	15	74	34.7	–	2

TABLE 3. Continued.

Site name	Urban intensity index (UII)	Common urban intensity index (CUII)	1999 population density (number/ km²)	Total basin area (km²)	Basin area in Central Basin and Range eco- region (km²)	Stream order
Five Mile Creek at Nevel Road near McCalla, AL	16	22	96	33.9	–	2
Cahaba Valley Creek at Cross Creek Road at Pelham, AL	16	15	50	66.0	–	3
Buck Creek at Buck Creek Road at Alabaster, AL	16	16	224	38.7	–	3
Cahaba Valley Creek at Indian Trail Road near Indian Springs, AL	17	15	40	36.9	–	3
Little Cahaba River near Braggsville, AL	20	32	420	15.7	–	2
Little Cahaba River below Leeds, AL	26	31	205	43.9	–	2
Shirtee Creek near Odena, AL	31	32	189	43.3	–	3
Williams Branch near Jacksonville, AL	34	29	303	23.9	–	2
Unnamed Tributary to Big Wills Creek at State Route 35 near Fort Payne, AL	41	44	358	12.1	–	2
Shades Creek at Lakeshore Drive near Mountain Brook, AL	41	36	498	42.1	–	2
Little Dry Creek at US 27 at Rome, GA	43	–	295	20.0	–	–
Town Branch near Summerville, GA	45	44	351	4.7	–	2
Shades Creek at Samford University at Homewood, AL	46	40	536	56.3	–	3
Snow Creek below Anniston, AL	50	51	426	44.7	–	2
Fivemile Creek at Lawson Road near Tarrant City, AL	58	52	768	48.6	–	3
Patton Creek near Bluff Park below Patton Chapel, AL	64	61	824	28.8	–	2
Fivemile Creek at Fivemile Road near Huffman, AL	65	58	857	25.0	–	3
Unnamed Tributary to Shades Creek near Oxmoor, AL	72	68	560	6.0	–	2
Village Creek at East Lake in Birmingham, AL	74	72	826	14.2	–	2
Valley Creek at Cleburn Avenue at Powderly, AL	100	100	1,543	52.1	–	3

Salt Lake City, Utah
  Big Cottonwood Creek above

TABLE 3. Continued.

Site name	Urban intensity index (UII)	Common urban intensity index (CUII)	1999 population density (number/ km²)	Total basin area (km²)	Basin area in Central Basin and Range eco- region (km²)	Stream order
Water Treatment Plant at Salt Lake City, UT	0	15	13	128.7	0.3	3
South Fork Kays Creek at Fernwood Picnic Area at Layton, UT	1	10	53	3.9	3.9	2
Ogden River at Valley Drive Ogden, UT	4	29	23	855.2	0.8	6
Baer Creek at 1800 East at Fruit Heights, UT	15	21	45	9.3	0.3	2
Provo River at Highway 189 at Provo, UT	31	29	212	1,709.9	3.6	5
Ogden River at Harrison Avenue at Ogden, UT	36	43	635	857.5	3.1	6
Hobble Creek at 800 East at Springville, UT	41	37	270	319.1	9.6	5
Hobble Creek at Center Street at Springville, UT	46	42	389	320.1	10.6	5
Ogden River at Washington Avenue at Ogden, UT	48	52	862	858.8	4.4	6
Farmington Creek at Frontage Road at Farmington, UT	49	42	443	32.6	3.1	3
Provo River at 3700 North at Provo River, UT	51	42	765	1,714.1	7.8	5
Parleys Creek at Sugarhouse Park at Salt Lake City, UT	58	55	839	139.9	4.7	4
Emigration Creek at 1300 South at Salt Lake City, UT	59	60	635	72.5	3.1	3
Baer Creek at Frontage Road at Kaysville, UT	63	54	748	12.7	3.6	2
North Fork of Holmes Creek at Main Street at Layton, UT	67	53	611	14.2	7.0	2
Kays Creek at 1000 East at Layton, UT	71	55	786	23.8	10.1	3
Provo River at 800 North at Salt Lake City, UT	71	37	1,515	1,764.0	24.1	5
Big Cottonwood Creek at Cottonwood Mall at Salt Lake City, UT	71	65	1,178	160.3	14.5	3
Logan River at Golf Course Road at Salt Lake City, UT	72	77	993	562.3	4.7	5
South Fork of Kays Creek at Layton, UT	72	61	596	12.9	3.1	3
Kays Creek at Layton, UT	76	59	1,033	28.0	3.1	3
Emigration Creek at 1200 East at Salt Lake City, UT	76	75	1,334	73.6	4.1	3

TABLE 3. Continued.

Site name	Urban intensity index (UII)	Common urban intensity index (CUII)	1999 population density (number/km²)	Total basin area (km²)	Basin area in Central Basin and Range eco-region (km²)	Stream order
Holmes Creek at Main Street at Layton, UT	77	64	1,165	8.8	2.3	3
Big Cottonwood Creek at 900 East at Salt Lake City, UT	79	63	1,436	184.1	26.7	3
Little Cottonwood Creek at Crestwood Park at Salt Lake City, UT	81	75	1,553	93.8	9.8	3
Little Cottonwood Creek at Wheeler Farm at Salt Lake City, UT	85	76	1,724	97.6	13.7	3
Mill Creek at 2000 East at Salt Lake City, UT	88	79	1,749	60.1	2.1	4
Mill Creek at 3060 East at Salt Lake City, UT	89	80	1,700	59.6	1.6	4
Little Cottonwood Creek at Murray Park at Salt Lake City, UT	90	83	1,906	112.9	29.0	3
Mill Creek at 300 East at Salt Lake City, UT	100	96	2,251	84.7	25.1	4

In contrast to BOR and BIR, total basin area and elevation (Table 2), and stream sizes (2nd–6th order; Table 3) in SLC varied widely among basins. Basin area in the Central Basin and Range ecoregion portion of the SLC basin also varied (0.3–29 km²; Table 2). In the SLC, only data from the portions of the basins in the Central Basin and Range ecoregion (Tables 2 and 3) were used to calculate scores for the UII and CUII. This was done because the upper extent of urbanization approximates the junction between the Wasatch and Uinta Mountain ecoregion and the Central Basin and Range ecoregion, leading to an abrupt transition from an area with little or no urbanization to one with moderate to high levels of urbanization (Figure 3). The Wasatch and Uinta Mountain ecoregion was such a large proportion of total basin area that it diluted the measures of urban intensity. In addition, Wasatch and Uinta Mountain waters were variably diverted among basins, confounding their contributions to downstream sampling sites. The site visits and recalculations of basin characteristics for the Central Basin and Range ecoregion also aided in narrowing the natural variability among sites.

Comparison of Components of UIIs among Study Areas

The UII component variables were selected on the basis of correlation with population density (Table 4). Variables included in the final UII varied (23 for BOS, 15 for BIR, 13 for SLC), but each study area included land-use/land-cover, infrastructure, and socioeconomic variables. In all study areas, the amount of developed land (basin level or stream buffer), road density, and SEI2 increased whereas the amount of natural land cover (forest or shrubs) in the basin or stream buffers decreased with increasing population density (Table 4). Differences in variables included in the UII were related to local data availability and natural differences among study areas. In contrast to BOS and BIR, the limited number of streams, nested design, and water management features in SLC made reducing the number of sites on the basis of using the homogeneous environmental setting impractical, and therefore basin soils and lithology variables were included in the calculation of the UII. Water diversions and dams were common in SLC; however, the information needed to quantify these water management features were not

TABLE 4. Spearman rank correlation coefficients for variables correlated with 1999 population density for the Boston (BOS), Birmingham (BIR), and Salt Lake City (SLC) study areas. Variables with correlation coefficients in bold were included in the urban intensity index. *, variable was included in common urban intensity index; –, variable not used.

Variables	Correlation coefficients		
	BOS	BIR	SLC
Land-use/land-cover variables			
Basin level (% of basin area)			
*Developed	**0.965**	**0.891**	**0.960**
Low intensity residential	**0.963**	**0.845**	–
High intensity residential	**0.888**	**0.852**	–
Commercial/industrial/transportation	**0.872**	**0.789**	–
*Forest	**–0.939**	**–0.868**	**–0.577**
Deciduous forest	–0.229	**–0.678**	–
Evergreen forest	**–0.717**	–0.451	–
Mixed forest	**–0.767**	**–0.574**	–
*Shrub	0.247	–	**–0.693**
Deciduous shrubland	0.247	**–0.685**	–
Herbaceous planted/cultivated			
Pasture/hay	–0.411	**–0.685**	–
Row crops	**–0.680**	–0.346	–
Urban/recreational grasses	**0.695**	**0.796**	–
Stream buffers (% of buffer area)			
*Developed	**0.942**	**0.877**	**0.957**
*Forest	**–0.865**	**–0.788**	**–0.595**
*Shrub	–	–	**–0.816**
Infrastructure variables			
*Road density in basin (km/km^2)	**0.964**	**0.908**	**0.759**
Toxic release inventory site density (number/100 km^2)	**0.858**	–	–
Point source discharger density (number/100 km^2)	**0.613**	–	–
Dam density (number/100 km^2)	**0.621**	–	–
Socioeconomic variables			
Socioeconomic index 2	**0.707**	**0.789**	**0.848**
Socioeconomic index 3	**–0.878**	–0.121	0.168
Socioeconomic index 5	**–0.712**	–0.482	0.264
Population and housing variables			
Change in population density from 1990 to 1999	**0.927**	–0.179	**0.893**
Percent of families with female head of household	**0.772**	–	–
Percent of 1999 population of minorities	**0.811**	–	–
Percent occupied housing units that are renter occupied, 1990	**0.690**	–	–
Percent of 1990 housing units built before 1980	**0.751**	–	–
Percent of housing units on public sewer, 1990	–	**0.763**	**0.626**
Basin soil and lithology variables (% of basin area)			
Soil group B, minimum infiltration rate 8–12 mm/h	–	–	**0.559**
Well-drained soils	–	–	**0.630**
Lake sediment and playa	–	–	**0.606**

available so they were not included in the UII. The BOS included dam density in the UII because it is an important landscape feature as urban intensity increased within the area. In contrast, no measure of dams or other water management features were included in the UII for BIR.

Each study area had at least one socioeconomic index included in the UII, and BOS had three (Tables 4 and 5). Eigenvalues for the PCA axes ranged from 2.63 to 10.42 (Table 5), and the percent of variance explained among block groups ranged from 4.8 to 18.9. In all study areas, the SEI2 had high loadings

TABLE 5. Variables included in the socioeconomic indices (SEIs) for the Boston (BOS), Birmingham (BIR), and Salt Lake City (SLC) study areas. The SEIs were derived from principal component analyses (PCA) of Census block group variables for each drainage basin. Variables with relatively high (≥0.2) or low (≤–0.2) loadings on each axis are in bold.

| Variable | BOS | | | BIR | SLC |
	SEI2	SEI3	SEI5	SEI2	SEI2
PCA	axis 2	axis 3	axis 5	axis 2	axis 2
Eigenvalue	8.54	5.24	2.63	9.64	10.42
Percent variance explained by PCA axis (%)	15.4	9.5	4.8	17.6	18.9
Socioeconomic variables					
1990 population density (people/km^2)	**0.323**	–0.138	0.020	**0.248**	**0.264**
1999 population density (people/km^2)	**0.315**	–0.155	0.000	**0.252**	**0.257**
Percent of population 65 or older, 1990	–0.003	0.039	**0.387**	–0.004	0.087
Number of families/km^2, 1990	**0.319**	–0.153	0.020	**0.253**	**0.269**
Percent of total population with rural residence, 1990	–0.164	**–0.323**	0.112	**–0.249**	**–0.244**
Percent of total population with urban residence, 1990	0.164	**0.323**	–0.112	**0.249**	**0.224**
Households/km^2, 1990	**0.316**	–0.162	0.028	**0.252**	**0.262**
Households/km^2, 1999	**0.311**	–0.177	0.014	**0.255**	**0.263**
Number of housing units/km^2, 1990	**0.315**	–0.163	0.027	**0.245**	**0.255**
Percent occupied housing units that are renter occupied, 1990	0.130	**0.221**	–0.056	0.133	0.107
Percent of housing units on public sewers, 1990	0.169	**0.333**	0.088	**0.238**	**0.208**
Percent of housing units using septic systems, 1990	–0.168	**–0.332**	0.085	**–0.233**	**–0.203**
No vehicles available to household, 1990	0.082	0.142	**0.284**	0.055	0.101
One vehicle available to household, 1990	0.068	0.111	**0.261**	0.077	0.159
Two vehicles available to household, 1990	0.003	0.023	**0.310**	0.036	0.110
Three vehicles available to household, 1990	–0.051	–0.066	**0.320**	–0.019	0.034
Per capita income/km^2, 1999	**0.279**	**–0.202**	–0.002	0.151	**0.220**
Drug expenditures per household, 1999	–0.014	–0.060	**–0.200**	–0.032	0.002
Proportional change in per capita income between 1990 and 1999	0.006	0.046	**0.270**	0.051	0.087

for variables that represented increasing population and housing density.

Comparison of UIIs with Population Density and Other Variables

The UII was related to 1999 population density for each study area (BOS: $Y = 0.080X + 11.1$, $R^2 = 0.88$; BIR: $Y = 0.069X + 7.8$, $R^2 = 0.88$; SLC: $Y = 0.040X + 22.6$, $R^2 = 0.80$; Y = UII, X = 1999 population density). This was expected because component variables were selected based on correlation with population density. There was not, however, a 1:1 relation (slope ≠ 1) between UII and 1999 population density (Figure 4). The rate of change in urban intensity as measured by the UII was greater at low (<500 people/km^2) compared to high (>500 people/km^2) 1999 population densities for all study areas (Figure 4). The 1999 population density ranged from 10 to 102 people/km^2 at low urban intensities (UIIs < 10) and was similar for all study areas (Table 3). In con-

trast, SLC had the highest population density at a UII of 100 compared to BOS and BIR (Table 3; Figure 4).

Infrastructure and socioeconomic (SEI2, population, and housing) variables increased with increasing UII (Table 4). Developed land (BOS: $Y = 0.60X – 2.41$, $R^2 = 0.92$; BIR: $Y = 0.70X – 3.52$, $R^2 = 0.98$; SLC: $Y = 0.84X – 9.59$, $R^2 = 0.83$; Y = developed land, X = UII) and road density ($Y = 0.07 + 0.96$, $R^2 = 0.94$; BIR: $Y = 0.41X + 5.11$, $R^2 = 0.93$; $Y = 0.26X + 4.78$, $R^2 = 0.41$; Y = road density, X = UII) increased whereas natural vegetation (forest in BOS: $Y = 0.56X + 82.2$, $R^2 = 0.95$; forest in BIR: $Y = 0.57X + 82.7$, $R^2 = 0.83$; forest + shrub in SLC: $Y = 0.62X + 63.4$, $R^2 = 0.60$; Y = forest + shrub, X = UII) decreased as UII increased in all study areas (Figure 5). The rate of change for some variables in relation to the UII, however, differed among study areas and demonstrated differences in patterns of urbanization among study areas. For example, the range in road density in BOS (1–9 km/km^2) was much narrower compared to BIR (5–50 km/km^2) and SLC (0–

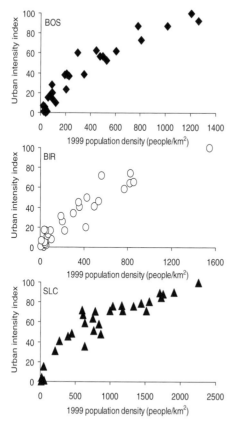

FIGURE 4. Relation of urban intensity index to 1999 population density for the Boston (BOS), Birmingham (BIR), and Salt Lake City (SLC) study areas.

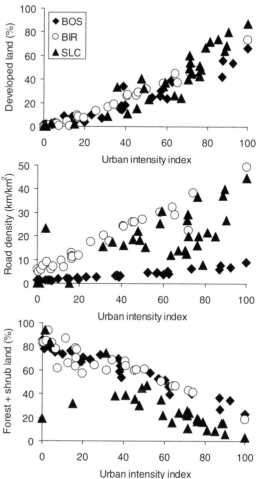

FIGURE 5. Relations of developed land use, road density, and forest + shrub land use with the urban intensity index for the Boston (BOS), Birmingham (BIR), and Salt Lake City (SLC) study.

45 km/km²; Table 2; Figure 5). Further, the strength of the relation (R^2) of developed land, road density, and forest + shrub versus the UII was less for SLC than BOS and BIR (Figure 5).

Comparing UII to CUII among Urban Areas

The CUII was strongly related to the UII for each study area (BOS: $Y = 1.52X - 1.90$, $R^2 = 0.98$; BIR: $Y = 1.06X - 1.93$, $R^2 = 0.97$; SLC: $Y = 1.19X - 5.69$, $R^2 = 0.86$; $Y =$ UII, $X =$ CUII; Figure 6). Intercepts were all relatively close to zero indicating correspondence at low levels of urban intensity. There was almost a 1:1 relation between CUII and UII in BIR and SLC, but not in BOS where a unit of CUII corresponds to 1.52 units of UII. Consequently, the rate of change in urban intensity in BOS is higher when expressed as CUII than as UII. In addition, maximum levels of urban intensity (Table 3), as measured by CUII and UII, were different in BOS (CUII = 75; UII = 100) but

not in BIR (CUII = 100, UII = 100) or SLC (CUII = 96, UII = 100). This is important when comparing the rate of response of aquatic assemblage, water chemistry, or physical habitat to urban intensity among study areas. Response rates that are similar for all study areas based on the UII will be greater in BOS compared to BIR or SLC when using the CUII.

The cumulative distribution of sites across the urban gradients expressed either as UII (Figure 7) or CUII (Figure 7) showed that BOS and BIR were similar, but SLC was different. The SLC had a higher proportion of sites (57% for UII, 43% for CUII) located at the high end (UII or CUII > 60 units) and a lower proportion (20% for UII and CUII) at the low end (UII or CUII < 40 units) of the urban gradient.

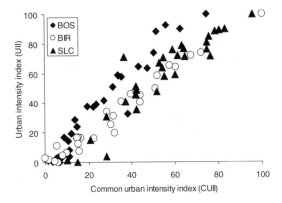

FIGURE 6. Relation of the common urban intensity index (CUII) derived from land use and infrastructure variables common to all three urban studies to the urban intensity index (UII) derived from study-specific land use, infrastructure, and socioeconomic variables for the Boston (BOS), Birmingham (BIR), and Salt Lake City (SLC) study areas.

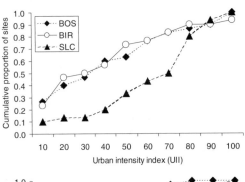

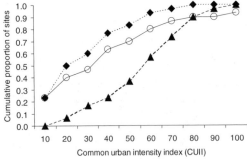

FIGURE 7. Cumulative distribution of sampling sites across the study-specific urban intensity index (UII) and the common urban intensity index (CUII) for the Boston (BOS), Birmingham (BIR), and Salt Lake City (SLC) study areas.

In contrast, BOS and BIR had 60% of sites for UII and 76% (BOS) and 64% (BIR) of sites for CUII at the low end (UII or CUII < 40) and few sites (4 and 1 sites using UII; 0 and 1 site using CUII, for BOS and BIR, respectively) at the high end (UII or CUII > 80 units) of the gradient. Thus, we did not find sites that were evenly distributed along an urban intensity gradient within each study area despite our efforts.

Discussion

For several reasons, we used a multimetric UII that was based on basin variables that correlated with population density rather than rely solely on population density as our indicator of urbanization. Population density causes landscape changes that affect water quality (aquatic assemblages, physical habitat, water chemistry), but it is not the direct cause of stream-quality degradation. We also wanted to provide managers with insight into what variables associated with urbanization were most strongly associated with water quality changes and could be manipulated to improve water quality. Finally, there are multiple causes of urban water quality degradation, and we wanted to include multiple indicators to define urbanization. The UII provides a mechanism of summarizing a variety of variables that are associated with changes in population density that is similar to deriving an index of biotic integrity (IBI) to describe biological conditions, where limited redundancy is acceptable.

Variables included in UII were correlated with population density, however, the UII did not show a 1:1 association with population density (Figure 4). In all study areas, the UII was a more sensitive indicator of urban intensity than population density at low levels of urbanization (Figure 4), where changes in water quality due to urbanization have been reported to occur (e.g., Paul and Meyer 2001 and reference within).

Comparison of variables included in the UII demonstrated similarities and differences in patterns of urbanization among the study areas (Tables 2 and 4; Figures 4 and 5). For example, the pattern of increased developed land and decreased natural vegetation with increasing UII was relatively similar among study areas (Figure 5). The range and rate of increase in road density with increasing UII, however, varied greatly among study areas with BIR > SLC > BOS (Table 2; Figure 5). Population density was greater at the high end of the UII in SLC compared to BOS and BIR (Figure 4). In addition, the BOS UII included point source discharger density, dam density, and more socioeconomic variables than BIR and SLC UIIs whereas the SLC

UII included soil and lithology variables not included in BOS and BIR UIIs (Tables 2 and 4).

The UII provides a measure of urban intensity that maximizes use of locally available information, but is not directly comparable among study areas. The CUII provides a measure of urban intensity that is directly comparable among study areas. The UII and CUII were strongly related to one another because the CUII was based on a subset of the UII variables (Figure 6). The strong relation between the CUII and UII within each study basin dictates that correlations between response variables (e.g., aquatic assemblages, physical habitat, water chemistry) will be similar whether urban intensity is characterized by the CUII or UII. The rate of response between these water quality variables and increasing urban intensity, however, would be greater in BOS compared to BIR or SLC, when using the CUII, because the response would occur over a smaller range of urban intensity (Figure 6).

The application of the urban land-use gradient design of McMahon and Cuffney (2000) differed among the three study areas because of regional differences in the environmental setting and patterns of urbanization. The use of the UII to define an urban intensity gradient within a homogenous environmental setting within a study area worked relatively well in the humid eastern part of the United States (BOS and BIR), although BIR had some nested basins due to topography and both had a limited number of sites at the high end of the urban scale (Figure 7). In contrast, the semiarid climate of the Central Basin and Range ecoregion and the abrupt transition with the Wasatch-Uintah ecoregion limited the number of SLC basins from which to choose. Fewer basins contributed to a number of study design differences, including nested sites, greater variability in basin size, the inability to use homogeneous environmental settings, and the lack of sites on the low end of the urban scale. In all studies, however, the UII and CUII were calculated using the same procedure, sites were distributed across a range of urban intensity, and differences in local site characteristics (e.g., instream habitat and anthropogenic alterations) were minimized so that aquatic assemblage responses to increasing urban intensity could be compared among studies.

Our study design differed from other studies of aquatic assemblages in urban streams in the use of a UII to define a gradient of urban intensity while limiting the variability of natural factors among selected basins within a region. The UII captures many of the complex stressors associated with urbanization that were unique to a study area and could have cumulative effects on aquatic assemblages. The design allows comparison of patterns of responses of aquatic assemblages to urban intensity among different geographic regions even when specific variables included in the UII differed. Other studies have used single measures of urban intensity to assess the effects of urbanization on aquatic assemblages. Degradation of aquatic assemblages was related to percent urban land (e.g., Kennen 1999; Diamond et al. 2002; Morley and Karr 2002; Roy et al. 2003; Snyder et al. 2003; Fitzpatrick et al. 2004), population density (e.g., Fitzpatrick et al. 2004), and impervious area (e.g., Booth and Jackson 1997; Wang et al. 2000, 2001; Sonneman et al. 2001; Morse et al. 2003; Ourso and Frenzel 2003; Taylor et al. 2004).

Impervious area (effective and total) has emerged as a key indicator of urbanization (Arnold and Gibbons 1996) that has been widely used to associate urbanization with changes in aquatic assemblages (Klein 1979; Pratt et al. 1981; Duda et al. 1982; Whiting and Clifford 1983; Garie and McIntosh 1986; Pedersen and Perkins 1986; Jones and Clark 1987; Maxted and Shaver 1997; May et al. 1997; Wang et al. 2000; Paul and Meyer 2001; Walsh et al. 2001; Center for Watershed Protection 2003; Morse et al. 2003; Ourso and Frenzel 2003; Taylor et al. 2004). It is an ecologically appealing indicator of urbanization because it bears a direct relation to runoff and its effects on transport to the stream (e.g., litter, sediments, microbes, nutrients, organic matter, surfactants, heavy metals, pesticides, hydrocarbons), transport within the stream (e.g., rates of downstream transport and exchanges with floodplains and riparian areas), and hydrology and instream habitat (e.g., changes in frequency and severity of extreme flows, changes in sediment transport, changes in channel geomorphology). Unfortunately, the measurement of impervious surface is not a trivial task, particularly over large areas, and most estimates are totally or partially dependent upon applying conversion factors to land-use or land-cover data. The national land-cover data (U.S. Geological Survey 2002) that were available for our urban studies did not include estimates of impervious surface area. We estimated impervious surface area by applying conversion factors to land-cover data (McMahon and Cuffney 2000). However, when we examined the relations between these estimates of impervious surface and UII, we found very strong correspondence (BOS: $Y = 0.445X + 0.4143$, $R^2 = 0.96$; BIR: $Y = 0.5406X + 0.9799$, $R^2 = 0.98$; SLC: $Y = 0.4267X + 2.9513$, $R^2 = 0.95$; where X = UII, Y = % impervious surface) due to the underlying mathematical relations with land cover. Consequently, estimated impervious surface area did not provide any additional explanatory power beyond that of the UII and was dropped from subsequent analyses in favor of variables that were directly measured from census data and remote-sensing images.

Many studies have demonstrated an adverse effect on aquatic assemblages when impervious area in a basin area reaches anywhere from 5% to18% (Klein 1979; Pratt et al. 1981; Duda et al. 1982; Whiting and Clifford 1983; Garie and McIntosh 1986; Pedersen and Perkins 1986; Jones and Clark 1987; Maxted and Shaver 1997; May et al. 1997; Wang et al. 2000; Paul and Meyer 2001; Walsh et al. 2001; Morse et al. 2003; Ourso and Frenzel 2003; Taylor et al. 2004). Using the equations (UII versus % impervious surface) described above for each study area, adverse effects on aquatic assemblages would be expect to occur between UIIs of 10–40 in BOS, 7–35 in BIR, and 5–35 in SLC.

The scale at which urbanization affects aquatic assemblages can vary depending on the geographic setting, the scale at which urbanization is most intense, and the range of that intensity. Our design was set up to minimize the local-scale effects (e.g., habitat) and maximize the detection of basin-scale effects of urbanization. In the Puget Sound basin (Washington, USA), macroinvertebrate assemblages as measured by a benthic IBI responded to changes in land cover at the basin and local scales (Morley and Karr 2002). Similarly, Roy et al. (2003) found strong negative relations between basin landcover and stream macroinvertebrate indices in Georgia streams (USA); however, biotic indices were better predicted by reach scale variables than single, basin-scale land cover. In contrast, diatoms were better indicators of nutrient enrichment, whereas macroinvertebrates were better indicators of basin-scale urban disturbances in Melbourne, Australia streams (Sonneman et al. 2001; Walsh et al. 2001). Fish assemblages in Opequon Creek watershed, West Virginia, USA were strongly associated with the extent of urban land use in the basin; however, urban land use was more disruptive to fish assemblages in basins with steeper channel slopes (Synder et al. 2003).

Many factors can be associated with urban disturbances, which makes it difficult to predict how ecological components will respond to specific aspects of urbanization, particularly in different geographic locations across the United States. The value of the UII versus other urban disturbance measures (e.g., single variables used in the index, impervious area, population density) that affect aquatic assemblages, physical habitat, and water chemistry re-sponses awaits further evaluation. The UII might be used instead of single or multiple measures of urban disturbance, once associations between the index, individual stressors, and aquatic assemblages are established.

Acknowledgments

The authors gratefully acknowledge the assistance provided by the many colleagues participating in the urban gradient studies. We also thank Robert Hughes, Anne Brasher, Larry Brown, and two anonymous reviewers for providing suggestions and criticism to earlier drafts of the manuscript and James Falcone for preparation of the figures. Funding was provided by the U.S. Geological Survey's National Water-Quality Assessment (NAWQA) Program. The use of firm, trade, or brand names in this article is for identification purposes only and does not constitute endorsement by the U.S. Geological Survey.

References

Anson, J. 1991. Demographic indices as social indicators. Environment and Planning A 23:433–446.

Arnold, C. L., and C. J. Gibbons. 1996. Impervious surface coverage: the emergence of a key environmental indicator. American Planners Association Journal 62:243–258.

Atkins, J. B., H. Zappia, J. L. Robinson, A. K. McPherson, R. S. Moreland, D. A. Harned, B. F. Johnston, and J. S. Harvill. 2004. Water quality in the Mobile River basin, Alabama, Georgia, Mississippi, and Tennessee, 1999–2001. U.S. Geological Survey, Circular 1231, Montgomery, Alabama.

Baskin, R. L., K. M. Waddell, S. A. Thiros, E. M. Giddings, H. K. Hadley, D. W. Stephens, and S. J. Gerner. 2002. Water-quality assessment of the Great Salt Lake basins, Utah, Idaho, and Wyoming – environmental setting and study design. U.S. Geological Survey, Water-Resources Investigations Report 02–4115, West Valley City, Utah.

Booth, D. B., and C. R. Jackson. 1997. Urbanization of aquatic systems: degradation thresholds, stormwater detection, and the limit of mitigation. Journal of the American Water Resources Association 33:1077–1090.

Center for Watershed Protection. 2003. Impacts of impervious cover on aquatic ecosystems. Watershed Protection Research Monograph No. 1, Center for Watershed Protection, Ellicott City, Maryland.

Cuffney, T. F., M. R. Meador, S. D. Porter, and M. E. Gurtz. 2000. Responses of physical, chemical, and biological indicators of water quality to a gradient of agricultural land use in the Yakima River basin, Washington. Environmental Monitoring and Assessment 64:259–270.

Cuffney, T. F., H. Zappia, E. M. P. Giddings, and J. F. Coles. 2005. Effects of urbanization on benthic macroinvertebrate assemblages in contrasting environmental settings: Boston, Massachusetts; Birmingham, Alabama; and Salt Lake City, Utah. Pages 361–407 in L. R. Brown, R. H. Gray, R. M. Hughes, and M. R. Meador, editors. Effects of urbanization on stream ecosystems. American Fisheries Society, Symposium 47, Bethesda, Maryland.

Diamond, J. M., D. W. Bressler, and V. B. Serveiss. 2002. Assessing relationships between human land uses and the decline of native mussels, fish, and macroinvertbrates in the Clinch and Powell River watershed, USA. Environmental Toxicology and Chemistry 21:1147–1155.

Duda, A. M., D. R. Lenat, and D. L. Penrose. 1982. Water quality in urban streams – what can we expect? Journal of the Water Pollution Federation 54:1139–1147.

Flanagan, S. M., M. G. Nielsen, K.W. Robinson, and J. F. Cole. 1999. Water-quality assessment of the New England coastal basins in Maine, Massachusetts, New Hampshire, and Rhode Island: environmental settings and implications for water quality and aquatic biota. U.S. Geological Survey, Water-Resources Investigations Report 98–4249, Pembroke, New Hampshire.

Fitzpatrick, F. A., M. A. Harris, T. L. Arnold, and K. D., Richards. 2004. Urbanization influences on aquatic communities in northeastern Illinois streams. Journal of the American Water Resources Association 40:461–475.

Garie, H. L., and A. McIntosh. 1986. Distribution of benthic macroinvertebrates in a stream exposed to urban runoff. Water Resources Bulletin 22:447–455.

GeoLytics. 1999. Census CD + Maps, Release 3.0 [CDROM]. Geolytics, Inc., East Brunswick, New Jersey.

Griffith, G. E., J. M. Omernik, J. A. Comstock, S. Lawrence, G. Martin, A. Goddard, V. J. Hulcher, and T. Foster. 2001. Ecoregions of Alabama and Georgia (poster). U.S. Geological Survey, Reston, Virginia [map scale 1:1,700,000].

Grove, J. M., and W. R. Burch, Jr. 1997. A social ecology approach and application of urban ecosystem and landscape analyses: a case study of Baltimore, Maryland. Urban Ecosystems 1:259–275.

Harding, J. S., E. F. Benfield, P.V. Bolstad, G. S. Helfman, and E. B. D. Jones. 1998. Stream biodiversity: the ghost of land use past. Proceedings of the National Academy of Sciences 95:14843–14847.

Hughes, R. M., S. A. Heiskary, W. J. Matthews, and C. O. Yoder. 1994. Use of ecoregions in biological monitoring. Pages 125–151 in S. L. Loeb and A. Spacie, editors. Biological monitoring of aquatic systems. Lewis Publishers, Boca Raton, Florida.

Johnson, G. C., R. E. Kidd, C. A. Journey, H. Zappia, and J. B. Atkins. 2002. Environmental setting and water-quality issues of the Mobile River basin, Alabama, Georgia, Mississippi, and Tennessee. U.S. Geological Survey, Water-Resources Investigations Report 02–4162, Montgomery, Alabama.

Johnson, B. R., and G. L. Raines. 1995. Digital map of major bedrock lithologic units for the Pacific Northwest: a contribution to the Interior Columbia River Basin Ecosystem Management Project. U.S. Geological Survey, Open-File Report 95–680, digital map, West Valley City, Utah.

Jones, R. C., and C. C. Clark. 1987. Impact of watershed urbanization on stream insect communities. Water Resources Bulletin 23:1047–1055.

Karr, J. R. 1981. Assessment of biotic integrity using fish communities. Fisheries 6:21–27.

Karr, J. R., and E. W. Chu. 1999. Restoring life in running waters: better biological monitoring. Island Press, Covelo, California.

Karr, J. R., and E. W. Chu. 2000. Sustaining living rivers. Hydrobiologia 422:1–14.

Kennen, J. G. 1999. Relation of macroinvertebrate community impairment to catchment characteristics in New Jersey streams. Journal of the American Water Resources Association 35:939–955.

Keys, J. E., Jr., C. A. Carpenter, S. L. Hooks, F. G. Koenig, W. H. McNab, W. E. Russell, and M. L. Smith. 1995. Ecological units of the eastern United States–first approximation. U.S. Department of Agriculture, Forest Service, Technical Publication R8-TP 21, [Map Scale 1:3,500,000], Atlanta.

Klein, R. D. 1979. Urbanization and stream quality impairment. Water Resources Bulletin 15:948–963.

Maxted, J., and E. Shaver. 1997. The use of retention basins to mitigate stormwater impacts on aquatic life. Pages 494–512 in L. A. Roesner, editor. Effects of watershed development and management on aquatic ecosystems. American Society of Civil Engineers, New York.

May, C. W., R. Horner, J. R. Karr, B. Mar, and W. Welch. 1997. Effects of urbanization on small streams in the Puget Sound Lowland ecoregion. Watershed Protection Techniques 2:483–494.

McDonnell, M. J., and S. T. A. Pickett. 1990. Ecosystem structure and function along urban-rural gradients: an unexploited opportunity for ecology. Ecology 71:1232–1237.

McMahon, G., and T. F. Cuffney. 2000. Quantifying urban intensity in drainage basins for assessing stream ecological conditions. Journal of the American Water Resources Association 36:1247–1261.

Meador, M. R., J. F. Coles, and H. Zappia. 2005. Fish assemblage responses to urban intensity gradients in contrasting metropolitan areas: Birmingham, Alabama and Boston, Massachusetts. Pages 409–423 *in* L. R. Brown, R. H. Gray, R. M. Hughes, and M. R. Meador, editors. Effects of urbanization on stream ecosystems. American Fisheries Society, Symposium 47, Bethesda, Maryland.

Morley, S. A., and J. R. Karr. 2002. Assessing and restoring the health of urban streams in the Puget Sound basin. Conservation Biology 16:1498–1509.

Morse, C. C., A. D. Huryn, and C. Cronan. 2003. Impervious surface area as a predictor of the effects of urbanization on stream insect communities in Maine, U.S.A. Environmental Monitoring and Assessment 89:95–127.

Omernik, J. M. 1987. Ecoregions of the conterminous United States. Annals of the Association of American Geographers 77:118–125.

Omernik, J. M. 1994. Ecoregions: a spatial framework for environmental management. Pages 49–62 *in* W. S. Davis and T. P. Simon, editors. Biological assessment and criteria: tools for water resource planning and decision making. Lewis Publishers, Boca Raton, Florida.

Ometo, J. P. H. B., L. A. Martinelli, M. V. Ballester, A. Gessner, A. V. Krusche, R. L. Victoria, and M. Williams. 2000. Effects of land use on water chemistry and macroinvertebrates in two streams of the Piracicaba River basin, south-east Brazil. Freshwater Biology 44:327–337.

Ourso, R. T., and S. A. Frenzel. 2003. Identification of linear and threshold responses in streams along a gradient of urbanization in Anchorage, Alaska. Hydrobiologia 501:117–131.

Paul, M. J., and J. L. Meyer. 2001. Streams in the urban landscape. Annual Review of Ecology and Systematics 32:333–365.

Pedersen, E. R., and M. A. Perkins. 1986. The use of benthic macroinvertebrate data for evaluating impacts of urban runoff. Hydrobiologia 139:13–22.

Potapova, M., J. F. Coles, E. M. P. Giddings, and H. Zappia. 2005. A comparison of the influences of urbanization in contrasting environmental settings on stream benthic algal assemblages. Pages 333–359 *in* L. R. Brown, R. H. Gray, R. M. Hughes, and M. R. Meador, editors. Effects of urbanization on stream ecosystems. American Fisheries Society, Symposium 47, Bethesda, Maryland.

Pratt, J. M., R. A. Coler, and P. J. Godfrey. 1981. Ecological effects of urban stormwater runoff on benthic

macroinvertebrates inhabiting the Green River, Massachusetts. Hydrobiologia 83:29–42.

Price, C. V., and R. M. Clawges. 1999. Digital data sets describing water use, toxic chemical releases, metropolitan areas, and population density of the conterminous United States. U.S. Geological Survey, Open-File Report 99–78, Rapid City, South Dakota.

Robinson, G. R., Jr. 1997. Portraying chemical properties of bedrock for water-quality and ecosystem analysis: an approach for the New England region. U.S. Geological Survey, Open-File Report 97–154, Pembroke, New Hampshire.

Roy, A. H., A. D. Rosemond, M. J. Paul, D. S. Leigh, and J. B. Wallace. 2003. Stream macroinvertebrate response to catchment urbanization (Georgia, U.S.A.). Freshwater Biology 48:329–346.

SAS Inc. 1990. SAS Language Reference, Version 6. SAS Institute Inc., Cary, North Carolina.

Short, T. M., E. M. P. Giddings, H. Zappia, and J. F. Coles. 2005. Urbanization effects on stream habitat characteristics in Boston, Massachusetts; Birmingham, Alabama; and Salt Lake City, Utah. Pages 317–332 *in* L. R. Brown, R. H. Gray, R. M. Hughes, and M. R. Meador, editors. Effects of urbanization on stream ecosystems. American Fisheries Society, Symposium 47, Bethesda, Maryland.

Simon, T. P., and J. Lyons. 1994. Application of the index of biotic integrity to evaluate water resource integrity in freshwater ecosystems. Pages 245–262 *in* W.S. Davis and T. P. Simon, editors. Biological assessment and criteria: tools for water resource planning and decision making. Lewis Publishers, Boca Raton, Florida.

Snyder, C. D., J. A. Young, R. Villella, and D. P. Lemarie. 2003. Influences of upland and riparian land use patterns on stream biotic integrity. Landscape Ecology 18:647–664.

Sonneman, J. A., C. J. Walsh, P. F. Breen, and A. K. Sharpe. 2001. Effects of urbanization on streams of the Melbourne region, Victoria, Australia. II. Benthic diatom communities Freshwater Biology 46:553–565.

SPSS. 1999. SYSTAT 9 Statistics I & II. SPSS Inc., Chicago.

Stankowski, S. J. 1972. Population density as an indirect indicator of urban and suburban land-surface modification. U.S. Geological Survey, Professional Paper 800-C:B219–B224, Washington, D.C.

Taylor, S. L., S. C. Roberts, C. J. Walsh, and B. E. Hatt. 2004. Catchment urbanisation and increased benthic algal biomass in streams: linking mechanisms to management. Freshwater Biology 49:835–851.

U.S. Army Corps of Engineers. 1996. Water Control

Infrastructure, National Inventory of Dams, 1995–96. U.S. Federal Emergency Management Agency, [CDROM], Arlington, Virginia.

U.S. Department of Agriculture. 1994. State Soil Geographic (STATSGO) Data Base data use information. U.S. Department of Agriculture-Natural Resources Conservation Service Miscellaneous Publications 1492, Fort Worth, Texas.

USEPA (U.S. Environmental Protection Agency). 1997. 1987–1995 Toxics Release Inventory. EPA 749-C-97–003, Washington, D.C., [CDROM].

USEPA (U.S. Environmental Protection Agency). 1999. Permit Compliance System Homepage. U.S. Environmental Protection Agency. Available: http://www.epa.gov/envirofw/html/water.html (November 1999).

U.S. Geological Survey. 2000. National elevation dataset. U.S. Geological Survey, Available: http://gisdata.usgs.gov/ned/ (March 2000).

U.S. Geological Survey. 2002. National Land Cover Characterization Project. U.S. Geological Survey. Available: http://landcover.usgs.gov/nationallandcover.html (December 2002).

Vogelmann, J. E., S. M. Howard, L. Yang, C. R. Larson, B. K. Wylie, and N. Van Driel. 2001. Completion of the 1990s National Land Cover Data set for the conterminous United States from Landsat Thematic Mapper data and ancillary data sources. Photogrammetric Engineering and Remote Sensing 67:650–652.

Walsh, C. J., A. K. Sharpe, P. F. Breen, and J. A. Sonneman. 2001. Effects of urbanization on streams of the Melbourne region, Victoria, Australia. I. Benthic macroinvertebrate communities. Freshwater Biology 46:535–551.

Wang, L., J. Lyons, P. Kanehl, R. Bannerman, and E. Emmons. 2000. Watershed urbanization and changes in fish communities in southeastern Wisconsin streams. Journal of the American Water Resources Association 35:1173–1189.

Wang, L., J. Lyons, P. Kanehl, and R. Bannerman. 2001. Impacts of urbanization on stream habitat and fish across multiple spatial scales. Environmental Management 28:255–266.

Ward, R. C. 1996. Water quality monitoring: where's the beef? Water Resources Bulletin 32:673–680.

Whiting, E. R., and H. J. Clifford. 1983. Invertebrates and urban runoff in a small northern stream, Edmonton, Alberta, Canada. Hydrobiologia 102:73–80.

Yoder, C. O., and E. T. Rankin. 1995. Biological response signatures and the area of degradation value: new tools for interpreting multimetric data. Pages 263–286 in W. S. Davis and T. P. Simon, editors. Biological assessment and criteria: tools for water resource planning and decision making. Lewis Publishers, Boca Raton, Florida.

American Fisheries Society Symposium 47:317–332, 2005

Urbanization Effects on Stream Habitat Characteristics in Boston, Massachusetts; Birmingham, Alabama; and Salt Lake City, Utah

TERRY M. SHORT*

U.S. Geological Survey, 345 Middlefield Road, Menlo Park, California 94025, USA

ELISE M. P. GIDDINGS

U.S. Geological Survey, 3916 Sunset Ridge Road, Raleigh, North Carolina 27607, USA

HUMBERT ZAPPIA

1162 Rock Cliff Drive, Martinsburg, West Virginia 25401, USA

JAMES F. COLES

U.S. Geological Survey, c/o USEPA New England, Suite 1100 (HBS)
1 Congress Street, Boston, Massachusetts 02114, USA

Abstract.—Relations between stream habitat and urban land-use intensity were examined in 90 stream reaches located in or near the metropolitan areas of Salt Lake City, Utah (SLC); Birmingham, Alabama (BIR); and Boston, Massachusetts (BOS). Urban intensity was based on a multi-metric index (urban intensity index or UII) that included measures of land cover, socioeconomic organization, and urban infrastructure. Twenty-eight physical variables describing channel morphology, hydraulic properties, and streambed conditions were examined. None of the habitat variables was significantly correlated with urbanization intensity in all three study areas. Urbanization effects on stream habitat were less apparent for streams in SLC and BIR, owing to the strong influence of basin slope (SLC) and drought conditions (BIR) on local flow regimes. Streamflow in the BOS study area was not unduly influenced by similar conditions of climate and physiography, and habitat conditions in these streams were more responsive to urbanization. Urbanization in BOS contributed to higher discharge, channel deepening, and increased loading of fine-grained particles to stream channels. The modifying influence of basin slope and climate on hydrology of streams in SLC and BIR limited our ability to effectively compare habitat responses among different urban settings and identify common responses that might be of interest to restoration or water management programs. Successful application of land-use models such as the UII to compare urbanization effects on stream habitat in different environmental settings must account for inherent differences in natural and anthropogenic factors affecting stream hydrology and geomorphology. The challenge to future management of urban development is to further quantify these differences by building upon existing models, and ultimately develop a broader understanding of urbanization effects on aquatic ecosystems.

Introduction

Despite the fact that urbanization represents a relatively small component of human-caused landscape change (U.S. Environmental Protection Agency 2000),

urban development has a profoundly degrading influence on stream ecosystems (Grimm et al. 2000; Paul and Meyer 2001). The disproportionately large influence of urbanization on surface water systems can be attributed to dramatic changes in land surface characteristics, such as soil properties, vegetative cover, and runoff potential as impervious surface area increases,

---

* Corresponding author: tmshort@usgs.gov

and to changes in water management practices implemented to offset adverse effects of population growth on domestic water resources (McDonnell et al. 1997; Grimm et al. 2000). Physical properties of streams are particularly vulnerable to landscape disturbance caused by urbanization, and the detrimental effects of urban development on stream hydrology and geomorphology have been documented in numerous studies (Hammer 1972; Klein 1979; Gregory et al. 1992; Booth and Jackson 1997; Finkenbine et al. 2000). However, relatively few studies have examined differences in the effects of urbanization on stream habitat in widely contrasting land-use settings, where differences in climate, physiography, and geology could modify how hydrologic and geomorphic conditions are changing in response to urban development (Paul and Meyer 2001). Landscape disturbances in these complex and heterogeneous environments are highly variable (McDonnell and Pickett 1990; Zipperer et al. 2000), and it is unclear whether urbanization affects stream habitat similarly in different environmental settings.

To characterize the effects of urbanization on stream ecology in contrasting environmental settings, the National Water-Quality Assessment (NAWQA) Program of the U.S. Geological Survey investigated the relations between urbanization and the physical, chemical, and biological conditions of streams in the metropolitan areas of Boston, Massachusetts; Birmingham, Alabama; and Salt Lake City, Utah. These urban areas provided contrasting conditions of climate, physiography, geological setting, vegetation types, and soils (Tate et al. 2005, this volume). This study presents results of the effects of urbanization on stream physical habitat. The objectives were to (1) characterize and compare habitat conditions in urban streams in different urban areas, (2) examine relationships between stream habitat and urbanization using a multi-metric index of urban intensity, and (3) compare physical responses to urbanization in contrasting environmental settings to identify common indicators of urbanization effects on stream habitat.

Study Areas

Study sites consisted of stream reaches located in the metropolitan and surrounding areas of Boston (BOS), Birmingham (BIR), and Salt Lake City (SLC). Sites in each urban area were selected from a pool of candidate watersheds representing a gradient of urbanization defined by an urban intensity index (UII) described in McMahon and Cuffney (2000). The UII is a multi-metric index that combines measures of watershed

land use, infrastructure (e.g., numbers of sewers, roads, and stormwater drains), population and socioeconomic condition (e.g., income levels and home ownership) into a single measure of urban intensity. Values for each measure are standardized and scaled to a numerical range of urban intensity from 0 (low intensity) to 100 (high intensity). Additional details describing the calculation of the urban intensity index for each of the three urban areas, and maps of the study sites and basin boundaries, are provided in Tate et al. (2005).

Sites were located primarily on 3rd- to 5th-order streams (Strahler 1957), although a few 2nd- and 6th-order streams were included. Boundaries for each candidate watershed were delineated using 30-m digital elevation model (DEM) data in conjunction with geographic information system (GIS) programs (U.S. Geological Survey 2000). It was possible in the BOS study area to locate sites in each of 30 different drainage basins. Severe drought conditions occurred in the southeast during the summer of 2000, and as a result, 2 of the 30 candidate sites in BIR went dry and were excluded from the study. Owing to the relative paucity of perennial flowing streams in the SLC study area, it was necessary to locate more than one site within some drainage basins. This resulted in 30 sites being located in 17 different drainages. Streams in the SLC area have their headwaters in the Wasatch and Uinta Mountains and flow westerly to their eventual terminus in Great Salt Lake (Tate et al. 2005). The mountainous terrain adjacent to the Salt Lake City metropolitan area resulted in study sites having a relatively wide range of water-surface gradients (0.4% to 16.6%) compared to streams in BOS and BIR where basin slopes were generally lower and considerably less variable (Table 1).

Median reach lengths were similar among study areas and ranged from 150 to 163 m. While it was possible to establish reaches of 150 m for all sites in BOS, reach lengths varied for BIR (140–300 m) and SLC (81–295 m). Median basin areas for SLC streams were small (4.5 km^2) compared to streams in BOS (72.0 km^2) and BIR (33.5 km^2). Much of the water contributing to streamflows in SLC was diverted prior to entering the study area. The relatively small basin sizes for streams in SLC (Table 1) resulted from the use of modified basin boundaries that more accurately reflected catchment contributions to streamflow in the urban area (see Tate et al. 2005 for details). In spite of the fact that drainage basin areas were generally larger in BIR than SLC, drought conditions in BIR resulted in relatively low median flows (0.086 m^3/s). Median discharge for BOS streams (0.680 m^3/s) was the highest of the three study areas.

TABLE 1. Characteristics of study sites in the Boston (BOS), Birmingham (BIR), and Salt Lake City (SLC) areas. Median values with ranges given in parentheses.

Study area	Sites	Basin area (km²)	Basin elevation range (m)	Segment length (m)	Reach length (m)	Reach gradient (%)	Discharge (m³/s)
BOS	30	73.0	156	1,203	150[a]	0.54	0.680
		(45.8–124.7)	(76–485)	(200–5,871)		(0.12–1.62)	(0.018-2.847)
BIR	28	33.5	205	1,567	160	0.36	0.086
		(4.7–66.1)	(85–428)	(260–5,320)	(140–300)	(0.03–0.67)	(0.001–1.723)
SLC	30	4.5[b]	222	1,352	163	1.01	0.242
		(0.3–29.0)	(33–1,351)	(131–3,507)	(81–295)	(0.40–16.6)	(0.002–3.874)

[a] All reach lengths were 150 m.
[b] Basin areas based on modified boundary delineations (see Tate et al. 2005).

In order to minimize local-scale differences in physical properties that might confound interpretation of broader-scale urbanization effects, sampling locations were limited to reaches that were free-flowing for at least 150 m, showed no evidence of recent anthropogenic modification, and had relatively well-defined banks with at least 50% mature vegetation cover. In addition, biological sampling was facilitated by selecting reaches with natural substrates and riffle habitats. The presence of riffles for biological sampling was necessary to reduce among-site variability in substrate size and composition of benthic habitats, thereby minimizing substrate-dependent effects on invertebrate and algae community richness (Ward 1992; Burkholder 1996; Cuffney et al. 2005; Potapova et al. 2005; both this volume).

Methods

Habitat Parameters

Habitat assessments were conducted in the three study areas during June to August 2000. Base flow conditions were predominant for most streams during this period. Lowest flows typically occur in the BOS area in July through September (Flanagan et al. 1999), and in June through September in BIR (Johnson et al. 2002). Flow regimes for streams in BIR were altered by drought conditions resulting in flows below the long-term (>50 year) average (Atkins et al. 2004). Streams in the SLC area generally experience lowest flows during October to March (Baskin et al. 2002); however, many of the smaller streams become intermittent during this period, and sampling during June to August ensured that flows would be sufficient for completing habitat and biological assessments. Sampling during base flow conditions was desirable because it represented a period of relative hydrologic

stability that allowed for greater consistency in application of habitat and biological survey methods.

Determinations of hydraulic parameters, channel morphology, bank characteristics, substrate particle size, and instream cover were based on methods described in Fitzpatrick et al. (1998). Eleven equidistant transects perpendicular to the direction of flow were established within the longitudinal boundaries of each reach. Bank-full width, bank-full depth, and wetted channel width were measured at each transect location. In addition, wetted depth and flow velocity were recorded at three locations along each transect. Aspect of stream flow (compass heading in degrees) was determined at mid-channel between adjacent transects. Standard deviation of average stream aspect was used as a relative measure of reach sinuosity, with higher values representing greater sinuosity. At each transect, the presence of a habitat cover type (overhanging vegetation, undercut banks, woody debris, boulders, macrophytes, artificial structures) that could provide refuge for fish or other organisms was recorded at channel margins near the edge of water and at three other locations in the main channel (limited to woody debris, boulders, macrophytes, and artificial structures). Twenty-four types of habitat cover were possible at each transect location. The proportion of cover types occurring within a stream reach was calculated as percent cover.

Visual estimates of dominant substrate particle size, percent siltation, and percent embeddedness were conducted at three locations along each transect. Particle size was based on a categorical scale of 1–10, with 1 representing the smallest particles (silt/clay) and 10 representing the largest (large boulder). Percent composition of the substrate consisting of sand and smaller-sized particles was used as an estimate of percent fines. Percent composition of sand and smaller-sized particles were summed as percent fines. The presence or absence of predominantly silt- and clay-sized particles (<1 mm) on bottom surfaces was recorded at each location, averaged for all locations in the reach, and reported as percent siltation. Embeddedness (nearest 10%) was determined for gravel and larger-sized particles, and averaged for each reach. The ratio of dominant particle size to wetted depth was used as an estimate of streambed roughness, with higher values indicating greater hydraulic roughness (Leopold et al. 1992).

Riparian vegetation density (percent) was measured near stream channel margins at each transect location using a hemispherical densiometer (Platts et al. 1987). Bank characteristics were determined at each transect, and consisted of bank angle, bank height, dominant substrate size (as described for bed substrate), and percent vegetative cover. These variables were used to calculate a multimetric index of bank stability (Fitzpatrick et al. 1998). Index values ranged from 4 to 22, with higher values representing greater bank instability.

Change in water surface elevation between reach boundaries was determined by surveying and used to calculate reach gradient. Lengths of major fluvial geomorphic features (riffles, runs, pools) were measured and used to determine the proportion of these features in each reach. Occurrences of riffles and runs are not reported in this study. Average reach discharge was calculated based on measurements of wetted cross-sectional area and flow velocities taken at each transect (Gordon et al. 1993). Additional calculated variables were wetted volume, flow stability, and stream power. Wetted volume represents a gross measure of total hydrologic habitat available in each of the study reaches (Church 1995) and was calculated as the product of the mean wetted-channel width, mean depth of water, and reach length. The ratio of maximum wetted depth to bank-full depth was used as an estimate of relative flow stability. As the ratio becomes larger, stability increases, and presumably the stream channel is less subject to hydrologic disturbance that might arise from storm runoff or other related events (Leopold et al. 1992). Stream power was calculated for each reach as an indication of general channel stability (Gordon et al. 1993), where higher values indicate increased potential for channel scouring.

Data Analysis

Habitat conditions were described based on a total of 28 measured and derived physical variables. Variables were selected to represent conditions of physical habitat relating to channel properties (15), hydraulic properties (5), and streambed properties (6). Additional variables were percent cover and percent pool habitat. A description of these variables is provided in Appendix 1.

Discriminant function analysis (DA) was conducted to identify physical variables most responsible for discriminating site conditions among urban areas. Discriminant analysis can be useful for classifying observations into one of several groups (e.g., urban areas) according to which group they most closely resemble with respect to a set of measurements, such as those related to physical habitat variables (ter Braak 1995). Stepwise forward-selection discriminant analysis was used to select the best subset of predictive variables. All variables were standardized prior to analysis by transforming site measurements into z-scores (mean = 0, SD = 1). Separation of groups was evaluated based on Wilk's lambda (l), which ranges from zero (perfect separation of groups) to one (no separation of groups). Significance of group separations was tested with a chi-square approximation (Manley 1986). Correct classification of canonical variable scores was evaluated using a jackknifed classification data matrix. Calculations were performed using SYSTAT 9 (SPSS 1999).

Relations between physical variables and the urban intensity index were examined using Spearman's rank correlation analysis (r_s). Principal components analysis (PCA; ter Braak 1995) was used to identify gradients of physical habitat characteristics within urban areas. Habitat variables that were highly correlated (Spearman's Rho greater than |0.4|) were reduced in number to a single variable that we felt best characterized conditions for a given physical property (e.g., channel morphology, hydraulics, streambed condition). This resulted in a total of 19 variables used for PCA (see Table 4). Results are based on standardized data (correlation matrix) and reported for axes having eigenvalues greater than one (Legendre and Legendre 1983). Habitat variables accounting for the greatest variance for each axis were identified as those having absolute loading scores greater than 0.3. Relations between PCA axes scores and the UII were examined using Spearman's rank correlation analysis.

Results

Habitat Conditions in Study Areas

Discriminant analysis identified three site clusters that corresponded to differences in habitat conditions in BOS, BIR, and SLC (Figure 1). Urban areas differed

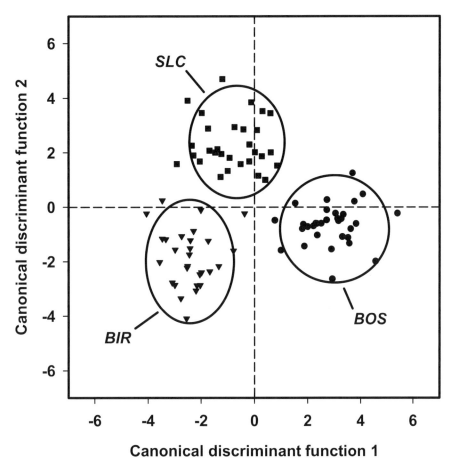

FIGURE 1. Canonical discriminant function biplot based on stepwise forward-selection analysis of physical characteristics of sites in the Boston (BOS), Birmingham (BIR), and Salt Lake City (SLC) areas. Site groups are enclosed within 90% confidence ellipses. Description of variables accounting for site-group separations is provided in Table 2.

primarily in channel size (based on bank-full cross-sectional area) and shape (based on bank-full width to depth ratio), discharge, stream power, flow stability, percent siltation, heterogeneity of substrate particle size (based on coefficient of variation of particle size), percent embeddedness, and riparian vegetation density (Table 2). The first and second canonical functions accounted for 62% and 38%, respectively, of the total variance associated with site group dispersion. A low Wilk's Lambda (0.038) indicated that these habitat variables were highly effective in discriminating among study areas. Classification analysis of jackknifed site-variable scores indicated that 97% of BOS sites, 93% of BIR sites, and 97% of SLC sites were classified correctly.

Average bank-full cross-sectional area of BIR streams was approximately twice that of streams in BOS and SLC (Table 3). Bank-full area was not re-

lated to discharge at the time of sampling for streams in BIR ($r_s = 0.198$; $P = 0.115$), but discharge was significantly correlated with bank-full area for streams in BOS ($r_s = 0.496$; $P = 0.015$) and SLC ($r_s = 0.704$; $P < 0.001$). Average stream power was relatively low in all urban areas (2.53–7.63 W/m) and probably reflected low-flow conditions prevalent during summer sampling. Flow stability was lowest for streams in BIR, suggesting that streams in this urban area were the least hydrologically stable, although drought conditions likely contributed to low stability values. Siltation was low in BOS (22.4%), intermediate in SLC (53.1%), and high in BIR (86.3%). Substrates in BOS streams consisted primarily of small cobble-sized particles (mean size = 7.2, where category 7 = small cobble; Fitzpatrick et al. 1998) with relatively homogeneous distributions (CVSUB = 17.9%). Gravel-sized particles were prevalent in BIR and SLC streams (mean

TABLE 2. Standardized discriminant function coefficients for habitat variables accounting for site separations among urban study areas shown in Figure 1. Results based on stepwise forward-selection analysis. Evaluation of group separation was based on Wilk's lambda[a] and tested for significance using a chi-square approximation[b].

Variable[c]	Discriminant function 1	Discriminant function 2
BFWD	0.657	0.427
BFAREA	–0.244	–0.766
DSCHR	0.341	0.721
POWER	–0.741	0.000
FLOSTAB	0.291	–0.394
SILT	–0.456	–0.063
CVSUB	–0.408	0.250
EMBED	–0.100	0.382
VEG	0.330	–0.779
Eigenvalues	5.236	3.257
Variance explained (%)	61.7	38.3

[a] Wilk's lambda = 0.038.
[b] $F_{18,158}$ = 36.448; $P < 0.001$.
[c] Variables described in Appendix 1.

size = 5.4 and 4.3, respectively, where categories 4–5 = medium to coarse gravel). However, heterogeneity of particle size was relatively high for sites in BIR (CVSUB = 45.6%) and SLC (CVSUB = 57.4%). Substrates were less embedded in BOS streams (35.7%) than in BIR (62.2%) and SLC (62.0%). Streambanks in BOS and BIR were relatively well vegetated (VEG = 91.1% and 87.9%, respectively) compared to SLC (VEG = 62.9%).

Habitat Variables and UII

Numbers and types of habitat variables that significantly correlated with the UII varied among urban areas. None of the variables was significantly correlated with the UII in all three study areas (Table 4). Moreover, the number of significant correlations between habitat variables and the UII was markedly greater for the BOS study (46%) compared to BIR (7%) and SLC (11%). Effects of drought conditions on instream flows in BIR, and the necessity of nesting some site locations within the same drainages in SLC, may have weakened correlations between the UII and variables characterizing channel and hydraulic properties for these areas.

Channel properties.—Several channel variables were significantly correlated with the UII in the BOS study area (Table 4). Segment sinuosity and bank-full width to depth ratios decreased with increasing urbanization. Significant correlations between the UII and bank-full depth, wetted depth, and maximum wetted depth indicated that stream channels were deepening with increasing urbanization in the BOS area. In contrast, changes in channel size did not appear to be a significant effect of urbanization in BIR or SLC. Reach sinuosity decreased in BIR streams with increasing urban intensity; however, correlations between variability in bank-full cross-sectional area (CVBFAREA) and the UII for all study areas were not significant suggesting that urbanization effects on stream channelization were not pronounced. The lack of significant correlations in all three study areas between riparian vegetation density and the UII was not unexpected given that sites were chosen on the basis of having relatively well-established riparian vegetation. Ability to identify urbanization effects on riparian vegetation was limited because vegetation density was high (>60%) in all urban areas, and the range of vegetation density among sites was relatively narrow (Table 3).

Hydraulic properties.—Responses of stream hydraulic properties to urbanization were evident only in BOS streams (Table 4). Wetted volume and discharge increased with increasing urban intensity, consistent with concomitant changes in channel deepening. Wetted volume and discharge were not significantly correlated to basin area ($r_s = 0.326$, $P = 0.081$; $r_s = 0.287$, $P = 0.110$, respectively), suggesting that flow regimes in the BOS area may be under the influence of more local controls, such as inputs from wastewater treatment facilities or interbasin transfers (see Tate et al. 2005). Even though bank-full depth increased significantly with urbanization in BOS streams, accompanying higher discharge and flow volume resulted in lower wetted depth to bank-full depth ratios, suggesting that flow stability also increased.

In contrast, flow stability for streams in BIR was negatively correlated ($r_s = -0.344$, $P = 0.085$) with the UII, although atypically low flow conditions during sampling may have accentuated differences between base flow and bank-full discharge. Hydraulic properties of streams in BIR were poorly correlated with the UII (Table 4). Wetted volume was highly correlated to basin area ($r_s = 0.621$, $P < 0.001$), although discharge was not ($r_s = 0.210$, $P = 0.107$). Discharge at 50% of the sites in the BIR area was less than 0.09 m³/s (Table 1), and differences in discharge among sites may not have been sufficient to support a

TABLE 3. Means of habitat variables (ranges in parenthesis) for study sites in the Boston (BOS), Birmingham (BIR), and Salt Lake City (SLC) areas.

Variables[a]	BOS (N = 30)	BIR (N = 28)	SLC (N = 30)
Channel properties			
SEGSINU	1.14 (1.01–1.54)	1.23 (1.00–1.57)	1.18 (1.00–1.36)
RCHSINU	23.7 (8.8–57.8)	15.8 (0–54.4)	21.2 (7.6–59.3)
GRAD (%)	0.62 (0.12–1.62)	0.38 (0.03–0.67)	2.25 (0.40–16.6)
BFD (m)	0.96 (0.64–1.52)	1.67 (0.84–2.81)	1.04 (0.36–1.83)
CVBFD (%)	16.5 (6.9–35.5)	20.5 (7.8–36.0)	18.6 (4.2–42.9)
BFW (m)	12.55 (8.13–16.39)	13.76 (5.86–26.59)	9.42 (2.81–21.76)
BFWD	13.9 (7.0–21.7)	3.7 (1.4–9.1)	9.2 (3.5–16.9)
BFAREA (m^2)	9.05 (6.17–17.02)	18.39 (5.29–47.19)	7.98 (0.71–25.83)
CVBFAREA (%)	22.5 (12.8–62.7)	29.1 (13.9–89.3)	28.2 (9.6–68.6)
WETD (m)	0.30 (0.11–0.62)	0.25 (0.05–0.44)	0.25 (0.06–0.56)
MAXWETD (m)	0.38 (0.15–0.77)	0.34 (0.12–0.56)	0.34 (0.08–0.75)
WETW (m)	9.24 (4.75–12.53)	8.29 (3.92–15.11)	5.78 (1.22–13.49)
VOL (m^3)	425 (80–1,127)	395 (94–991)	390 (6–1,581)
BANK	11.6 (8.5–14.8)	16.5 (14.4–18.6)	12.3 (9.2–14.8)
VEG (%)	91.1 (77.8–99.7)	87.9 (50.6–100)	62.9 (40.1–80.1)
Hydraulic properties			
DSCHR (m^3/s)	0.720 (0.018–2.847)	0.229 (0.001–1.723)	0.714 (0.002–3.874)
VEL (m/s)	0.294 (0.050–0.496)	0.127 (0.002–0.557)	0.299 (0.026–0.671)
CVVEL (%)	71.3 (31.8–127.3)	136.7 (0–387.9)	86.2 (38.9–228.5)
FLOSTAB	0.37 (0.16–0.51)	0.22 (0.10–0.47)	0.34 (0.10–0.78)
POWER (W/m)	4.45 (0.07–12.89)	2.53 (0.01–20.65)	7.63 (0.16–53.91)
Streambed properties			
FINE (%)	5.3 (0–45.5)	23.0 (0–79.3)	20.8 (0–100)
EMBED (%)	35.7 (15.8–86.4)	62.2 (8.8–100)	62.0 (26.1–100)
SILT (%)	22.4 (0–84.8)	86.3 (30.3–100)	53.1 (0–100)
SUB	7.2 (5.1–8.6)	5.4 (2.3–8.8)	4.3 (0.5–8.0)
CVSUB (%)	17.9 (4.8–49.1)	45.6 (15.0–123.4)	57.4 (17.2–148.1)
ROUGH	35.2 (11.5–71.5)	45.6 (18.0–140.8)	53.3 (6.7–204.2)
Cover and pools			
COVER (%)	11.3 (2.9–23.8)	7.4 (0–21.7)	12.2 (2.1–20.8)
POOL (%)	11.1 (0–36.4)	19.3 (0–73.5)	14.1 (0–45.5)

[a] Definitions provided in Appendix 1.

stronger correlation. None of the hydraulic properties of streams in SLC was significantly correlated with the UII. Stream discharge and wetted volume were strongly related to basin area (r_s = 0.698, $P < 0.001$; r_s = 0.808, $P < 0.001$, respectively).

Streambed properties.—Variables related to streambed condition were among the most responsive to urbanization, and significant relationships with the UII were found for streams in all study areas (Table 4). Average substrate particle size decreased with increasing urbanization for sites in SLC, but particle size was not highly correlated with the UII for sites in BOS and BIR. In spite of relatively low variability of substrate particle sizes in BOS streams (CVSUB = 17.9%), particle size variability significantly increased with increasing urbanization. Particle size variability was not significantly correlated with the UII for streams in BIR and SLC. Percent fines significantly increased with increasing urbanization for sites in BOS and SLC. The increase in percent fines was due primarily to increases in the relative abundance of sand-size particles. Sand comprised 91% of fine-grained substrates in BOS and 78% in SLC; however, fines comprised a greater percentage of the overall substrate composition in SLC streams (20.8% compared to 5.3% in BOS). Although the relative abundance of fines increased with urban-

TABLE 4. Correlations (Spearman's Rho) between urbanization intensity index values (UII) and selected physical habitat variables for the Boston (BOS), Birmingham (BIR), and Salt Lake City (SLC) areas. Asterisks indicate significance of correlation analysis (*, $P < 0.05$; **, $P < 0.01$; ***, $P < 0.001$). Bolded variables were used in principal components analysis.

Variables[a]	BOS ($N = 30$)	BIR ($N = 28$)	SLC ($N = 30$)
Channel properties			
SEGSINU	−0.421*	−0.362	0.098
RCHSINU	−0.236	−0.456*	0.178
GRAD	−0.199	0.067	−0.187
BFD	0.581***	0.245	−0.127
CVBFD	0.347	−0.039	0.309
BFW	−0.231	0.282	−0.147
BFWD	−0.504**	−0.050	−0.067
BFAREA	0.147	0.293	−0.114
CVBFAREA	0.055	−0.093	0.234
WETD	0.626***	−0.214	0.022
MAXWETD	0.553**	−0.235	0.002
WETW	−0.159	0.101	−0.053
VOL	0.419*	−0.043	−0.003
BANK	−0.030	−0.128	0.036
VEG	0.023	−0.134	−0.122
Hydraulic properties			
DSCHR	0.481**	0.025	−0.141
VEL	0.433*	0.027	−0.299
CVVEL	−0.210	−0.187	0.106
FLOSTAB	0.415*	−0.344	0.060
POWER	0.221	0.027	−0.291
Streambed properties			
FINE	0.542**	−0.174	0.433*
EMBED	0.292	0.410*	−0.017
SILT	−0.111	0.099	0.475**
SUB	−0.196	0.134	−0.437*
CVSUB	0.450**	0.118	0.352
ROUGH	−0.703***	0.160	−0.137
Cover and pools			
COVER	0.451**	0.029	0.089
POOL	0.034	−0.206	0.129

[a] Definitions provided in Appendix 1.

ization at sites in BOS and SLC, significant increases in substrate embeddedness were observed only for streams in the BIR area. With increasing urban development increases in runoff potential can result in greater channel erosion and sedimentation (Booth and Jackson 1997; Trimble 1997). It was expected that increases in streambed siltation would be a common response to urbanization; however, a significant increase in siltation was observed only for sites in SLC. A decline in relative roughness was highly correlated with increasing urban intensity at sites in BOS (Table 4), but was not significantly related to urbanization in BIR and SLC. Streambed roughness increases with increasing substrate particle size and decreasing depth of water. Since average substrate particle size for streams in BOS did not increase with urbanization intensity, the decline in roughness in this study area is likely due to the significant increase in wetted depth.

Instream cover and pools.—Abundance of habitat cover types was poorly correlated with the UII for streams in BIR and SLC (Table 4). However, habitat cover significantly increased in BOS streams with increasing urbanization. Most of this increase was due to greater numbers of boulder-size rocks in the stream channel (boulders comprised 54% of all habitat cover types). Percent of pool habitats was not significantly correlated with the UII for streams in any of the study areas.

Multivariate Gradients and UII

For BOS and BIR, the primary PCA axis site scores were strongly correlated with the UII (Table 5), suggesting that urban intensity was likely a factor affecting the variance in these data. Urbanization effects were most apparent for BOS where the gradient described by the habitat data was relatively strong (eigenvalue = 6.630). The greatest proportion of the variance described by axis 1 (34.9%) was accounted for by trends in maximum wetted depth, discharge, percent fines, and relative roughness. Each of these variables was significantly correlated with the UII (Table 4), which in part accounts for the strong relationship between the UII and the gradient defined by the primary axis of the habitat ordination. Secondary axes scores were poorly correlated with the UII, suggesting that these habitat gradients were not strongly influenced by urbanization. The physical gradient defined by axis 1 for BIR was somewhat weaker (eigenvalue = 3.787). Trends in bank-full width, bank-full cross-

sectional area, substrate particle size, embeddedness, and relative roughness accounted for most of the variance (21.0%). Although PCA axis 1 scores for sites in BIR significantly correlated with the UII, the strength of the association appears to be driven largely by the significant relationship between the UII and embeddedness (Table 4). Moreover, strengths of the habitat-site gradients defined by secondary axes were similar to that of the primary axis (secondary axes eigenvalues ranged from 2.206 to 3.600), suggesting that habitat gradients for BIR were not strongly influenced by urbanization.

The gradients defined by the primary and secondary axes for the site-habitat ordinations for SLC were relatively strong (eigenvalues = 7.209 and 5.053), and together account for 61.3% of the total variance. Channel properties (bank-full width, bank-full depth, and bank-full cross-sectional area) and discharge were the primary physical variables defining the habitat gradient for axis 1, whereas streambed properties (substrate particle size, percent fines, embeddedness, relative roughness) and bank stability accounted for most of the variance defining the axis 2 gradient. Component scores from either axis were not significantly related to the UII. Urbanization intensity was significantly

TABLE 5. Spearman rank correlations between PCA axes scores for site-habitat[a] ordinations and the urban intensity index (UII). Asterisks indicate significance of correlation analysis (*, $P < 0.05$; **, $P < 0.01$; ns, $P > 0.1$).

Study area	Parameters	Axis 1	Axis 2	Axis 3	Axis 4
BOS	Eigenvalues	6.630	4.218	1.779	1.413
	Variance explained (%)	34.9	22.2	9.4	7.4
	Variables with component loadings > |0.3|	MAXWETD, DSCHR, FINE, ROUGH	POOL, VEL, CVVEL, SILT	GRAD, SUB, RCHSINU, POOL, CVBFD	RCHSINU, BFW, BFAREA, SILT
	Correlation with UII	−0.63**	−0.19 ns	0.01 ns	0.08 ns
BIR	Eigenvalues	3.787	3.600	2.574	2.206
	Variance explained (%)	21.0	19.9	14.3	12.3
	Variables with component loadings > |0.3|	BFW, BFAREA, SUB, EMBED, ROUGH	DSCHR, VEL, FLOSTAB, SILT, COVER	MAXWETD, BFD, CVVEL, CVSUB	GRAD, VEL, CVVEL, BANK, COVER
	Correlation with UII	−0.47*	0.03 ns	−0.13 ns	0.03 ns
SLC	Eigenvalues	7.209	5.053	2.289	1.173
	Variance explained (%)	36.0	25.3	11.5	5.9
	Variables with component loadings > |0.3|	BFW, BFD, BFAREA, DSCHR	SUB, FINE, EMBED, ROUGH, BANK	CVBFD, VEL, FLOSTAB, SILT	GRAD, SILT, RCHSINU, CVSUB, EMBED, BANK
	Correlation with UII	−0.12 ns	0.29 ns	0.12 ns	−0.44*

[a] Definitions provided in Appendix 1.

correlated with component scores for axis 4 (Table 5); however, the strength of the gradient was relatively weak (eigenvalue = 1.173), and the primary physical variables defining the gradient (reach gradient, percent siltation, reach sinuosity, variation in substrate particle size, embeddedness, and bank stability) accounted for only 5.9% of the total variance. Based on these results, it appeared that urbanization was not having a significant effect on stream habitat in the SLC study area.

Discussion

Urbanization Effects on Channel Properties

Increase in impervious area and surface runoff can result in more frequently occurring extreme flow events (Hammer 1972; Arnold and Gibbons 1996) and contribute to channel enlargement. There was no strong evidence that channel enlargement was occurring in response to urbanization in any of the three study areas. Structural reinforcement of streambanks using riprap or wire netting was not extensive but may have confined lateral expansion of stream channels in some areas. Bank stability was not significantly correlated with the UII, and it appeared that urbanization effects on bank erosion and channel widening were minimal at most. Changes in channel morphology in response to urbanization were most apparent for streams in the BOS area. Although bank-full area for these streams did not significantly increase, channels tended to become more incised (narrower and deeper) with increasing urbanization, which is consistent with urbanization effects reported for other areas (Hammer 1972; Arnold et al. 1982; Booth 1990).

Channelization is a common practice in urban areas to reduce flooding and facilitate transport of water and sediments (Paul and Meyer 2001). If channel straightening was occurring, there would be corresponding increase in reach gradient and flow velocity (Pizzuto et al. 2000). Based on measurements of reach sinuosity, water-surface gradient, and flow velocity, it did not appear that urbanization was contributing to marked increases in channelization in BOS and SLC. The best evidence of urbanization effects on channel straightening was for streams in BIR where reach sinuosity significantly declined with increasing urbanization intensity. Reach gradient and flow velocity did not increase with decreasing sinuosity, but extremely low flows at the time of sampling may have masked these effects.

Although it has been argued that the majority of disturbances to streams in urban environments may be more local in scale (Kemp and Spotila 1997; Wang et al. 2001; Townsend et al. 2003), in BOS we found that segment-level sinuosity was more highly correlated to urbanization (i.e., significant decline) than reach-level sinuosity. Despite the fact that segment and reach sinuosity were not markedly different among study areas (Table 3), reach sinuosity was more highly correlated to urbanization for streams in BIR. These differences between reach- and segment-level responses to urbanization may be indicative of differences among urban areas in water-management infrastructures, specifically controls on water movement and storage that may alter connectivity of stream networks and contribute to increase variability in segment length and relative linear shape of stream channels (Hirsch et al. 1990; Paul and Meyer 2001).

Urbanization Effects on Hydraulic Properties

Flow regimes can be dramatically altered in urbanized watersheds due to increases in runoff potential as land surfaces become increasingly impervious (Seaburn 1969; Booth and Jackson 1997; Moscrip and Montgomery 1997). Groundwater recharge can decrease with increasing impervious surface area resulting in a reduction of base flow discharge (Barringer et al. 1994). A decline in base flow discharge with increasing urbanization was evident only for streams in SLC, but the relationship was weak ($r_s = -0.141$). Flow modifications from diversions, impoundments, and groundwater abstraction were pervasive in the SLC study area (see Tate et al. 2005) and likely contributed to the high variability in average discharge among sites (CV = 154%) and to the corresponding weak relations between urbanization intensity and stream hydraulic properties. Although effects of these modifications on flow characteristics were difficult to quantify, it was expected that severe alterations of flow patterns would result in poor correlation between drainage basin size and discharge (Petts and Bravard 1996). Discharge was highly correlated with basin area ($r_s = 0.698$) for streams in SLC, suggesting that flow modification effects were probably local in scope (reach level) and of low to moderate intensity. Elevation changes among SLC streams corresponded to changes in land use along a gradient of urban intensity with lower intensity urbanization occurring in the higher elevation foothills and higher urbanization in the lower elevation valley floor. Consequently, it was difficult to separate the effects of elevation change on hydraulic properties of discharge and velocity from urbanization effects. Similar results were observed for BIR streams where none of the hydraulic variables was significantly correlated with the UII; however, unseasonably low flows in this study area limited the range of flow conditions with which to test relationships with the UII.

Urbanization appeared to be more closely linked to flow regimes for streams in the BOS area. In this urban setting, discharge increased significantly with urbanization intensity and varied in magnitude independent of basin area. These findings suggest that urbanization in BOS was affecting flow conditions, perhaps by increasing surface runoff from rainfall and irrigation, increasing input volume from wastewater treatment facilities, or augmenting flows by interbasin transfers (Hirsch et al. 1990; Dennehy et al. 1998). The increase in base flow discharge with urbanization intensity resulted in a significant increase in flow stability; however, flow regimes can be highly unpredictable over short time scales (Leopold et al. 1992), and inferences about long-term flow conditions based on short-term estimates of flow stability are speculative at best.

Urbanization Effects on Streambed Properties

Effects of urbanization on stream habitat were most evident in responses of the streambed substrate, particularly substrate size, embeddedness, and siltation; however, responses were not consistent among urban areas. Although the site selection process favored reaches with riffles and coarser-grained substrates, we felt that variability in substrate size among sites was sufficient to determine if urbanization was affecting substrate composition (see Table 3). An increase in percent fines significantly correlated with increasing urbanization intensity for streams in BOS and SLC, and similar results have been reported for other urban studies (Finkenbine et al. 2000; Pizzuto et al. 2000). Although results were similar for streams in BOS and SLC, it is likely that the factors responsible for the increase in percent fines were different between the two urban areas. For example, urban development in SLC proceeds along an increasing elevation gradient from the valley floor to the foothills. Accordingly, surface water gradients and flow velocities tend to decrease with decreasing elevation, resulting in a natural sorting of particles with finer-grained particles being deposited in the more downstream reaches (Leopold et al. 1992). In contrast,

elevation differences among sites for BOS streams were not great and would not account for site differences in sediment composition. Sand comprised a relatively large proportion (median = 34%) of the soil volume for drainages in BOS (see Tate et al. 2005), and increases in sand-based fines in more urbanized areas could reflect local differences in sediment sources to stream channels. Differences in substrate properties may also be indicative of differences in the age of urban development. Introduction of fine sediments to stream channels can result from construction activities in the watershed during early stages of urban development (Wolman and Schick 1967; Waters 1995), whereas in older urban areas (corresponding to higher UII), increases in surface runoff and peak flows as a result of more impervious surfaces could increase inputs of coarser-grained sediments (Klein 1979; Arnold and Gibbons 1996). Percent siltation did not increase with urbanization intensity in BOS streams, which is consistent with results expected for older urban areas. The propensity of streambed materials to be mobilized and displaced by elevated flow velocities decreases as substrate particle size becomes smaller or larger than sand-size materials (Leopold et al. 1992); accordingly, streambed stability may also have declined with urbanization in the BOS area, owing to the introduction of predominantly sand-size particles to the stream channel.

Substrate embeddedness has been reported to increase in urban areas as a result of increased sediment loading to stream channels (Wolman and Schick 1967; Klein 1979). Significant increases in embeddedness were found only for streams in the BIR area. Low correlation ($r_s = 0.181$) between percent fines and embeddedness suggested that sediment loading was not a primary factor responsible for increased embeddedness. Instead, greater embeddedness in more urbanized areas may reflect remnant conditions of bed armoring and channel incision caused by high discharge flows during nondrought conditions (Montgomery and Buffington 2001).

Urbanization Effects on Instream Cover and Pools

The complexity and stability of the biotic environment are in large part a function of the numbers and types of habitat structures occurring within the stream channel (Cummins 1979; Maddock 1999; Rosenfeld 2003). A decline in the richness of habitat structures in urban and urbanizing landscapes could significantly alter the structure of stream biotic assemblages. Previous studies have shown that the types and availability of habitat structures and channel features that can act as cover for aquatic biota may diminish in some urban settings as channel complexity is reduced through modifications to facilitate water transfer and mitigate local flooding (Booth and Jackson 1997; Wang et al. 1997; Finkenbine et al. 2000; Pizzuto et al. 2000). We found no evidence that urbanization significantly reduced percent cover in any of the study areas. To the contrary, percent cover increased with urbanization in BOS streams, owing primarily to greater numbers of boulder-size rocks and concrete pieces in the more highly urbanized areas. Abundance of cover in study reaches was low (average = 7% to 12%), and the relative paucity of these features likely contributed to poor correlations with the UII.

Channel enlargement through widening or deepening of the stream channel can alter the relative abundance and distribution of fluvial habitat features such as riffles and pools (Gregory et al. 1994). There were no significant effects of urbanization on the occurrence of pool habitats, even for streams in the BOS area where channel deepening occurred. Urbanization effects may have been less pronounced because of the low number of sites with pools (72% of all sites) and the relatively low number of pools at each site (median ≤ 2 for all sites).

Habitat Properties as Indicators of Urbanization Effects

These results illustrate the physical complexities of urban streams and the difficulties in comparing urbanization effects on stream habitat in contrasting urban environments. The magnitude and type of hydrologic and geomorphic responses vary within a stream network according to differences in age of development, drainage basin slope, surficial geology, sediment characteristics, type of urbanization, and land use history (Gregory et al. 1992). The model of urban intensity described by McMahon and Cuffney (2000) and discussed in Tate et al. (2005) incorporates elements of these landscape features into a common index that accounts for these differences by providing a scale of landscape intensity that can be used as a comprehensive measure of urbanization effects. Despite the fact that study site locations were based on a common model of land-use intensity that constrained natural variability in hydrologic and geomorphic conditions, streams in the three urban study areas differed in channel shape and size, discharge, and substrate type and composition. For streams in SLC and BIR,

these differences are less indicative of urbanization effects and probably reflect the overwhelming influences of basin slope (SLC) and prolonged drought (BIR) on flow regimes. The influence of these natural factors on modifying the hydrology of streams in SLC and BIR limited our ability to effectively compare habitat responses among different urban settings and identify common responses as targets for restoration or water management programs.

Flow regimes in the BOS study area were not unduly influenced by climate and physiography, and habitat conditions in these streams were more responsive to urbanization. Strong relations between urbanization and stream habitat were evident from correlations between PCA axes scores and the UII. Urbanization in the BOS area contributed to higher baseflows, channel deepening, and increased loading of fine-grained particles.

Despite some successes in applying the urban intensity model to identify habitat responses to urbanization, our study would have benefited from a better understanding of factors affecting hydrologic connectivity of streams in the study areas. Human modification to flow regime, resulting from dams, diversions, and surface- and groundwater abstractions are commonplace in urban settings and can fragment stream networks by disrupting linkages between streams, tributaries, and drainage basins. Although it is recognized that alteration of flow regimes is a fundamental outcome of landscape change, there is a general lack of a more predictive understanding of the ecological implications of hydrologic connectivity in urban systems (Pringle 2003). Difficulties in characterizing urbanization effects on habitat for the BIR and SLC studies underscore the need to supplement this understanding. While the urban intensity model developed by McMahon and Cuffney (2000) provides a relatively comprehensive means with which to characterize urban land use, identification of habitat responses to urbanization across multiple landscapes and scales must account for inherent differences in natural and anthropogenic factors affecting stream hydrology and geomorphology at basin and site scales. The challenge to future management of urban development is to further quantify these differences by building upon existing models and ultimately develop a broader understanding of urbanization effects on aquatic ecosystems.

Acknowledgments

The authors gratefully acknowledge the numerous colleagues who provided assistance in all aspects of this and associated urban studies. This study was conducted as part of a broader-scale ecological investigation of urban environments by the National Water-Quality Assessment Program of the U.S. Geological Survey.

References

Arnold, C. L., P. J. Boison, and P. C. Patton. 1982. Sawmill Brook: an example of rapid geomorphic change related to urbanization. Journal of Geology 90:155–166.

Arnold, C. L., and C. J. Gibbons. 1996. Impervious surface coverage: the emergence of a key environmental indicator. Journal of the American Planning Association 62:243–258.

Atkins, J. B., H. Zappia, J. L. Robinson, A. K. McPherson, R. S. Moreland, D. A. Harned, B. F. Johnston, and J. S. Harvill. 2004. Water quality in the Mobile River basin, Alabama, Georgia, Mississippi, and Tennessee, 1999–2001. U. S. Geological Survey, Circular 1231, Montgomery, Alabama.

Barringer, T. H., R. G. Reiser, and C. V. Price. 1994. Potential effects of development on flow characteristics of two New Jersey streams. Water Resources Bulletin 30:283–295.

Baskin, R. L., K. M. Waddell, S. A. Thiros, E. M. Giddings, H. K. Hadley, D. W. Stephens, and S. J. Gerner. 2002. Water-quality assessment of the Great Salt Lake basins, Utah, Idaho, and Wyoming — environmental setting and study design. U.S. Geological Survey, Water-Resources Investigations Report 02–4115, Salt Lake City, Utah.

Booth, D. B. 1990. Stream channel incision following drainage-basin urbanization. Water Resources Bulletin 26:407–417.

Booth, D. B., and C. R. Jackson. 1997. Urbanization of aquatic systems: degradation thresholds, stormwater detection, and the limits of mitigation. Journal of the American Water Resources Association 33:1077–1090.

Burkholder, J. M. 1996. Interactions of benthic algae with their substrata. Pages 253–297 in R. J. Stevenson, M. L Bothwell, and R. L. Lowe, editors. Algal ecology: freshwater benthic ecosystems. Academic Press, San Diego, California.

Church, M. 1995. Channel morphology and typology. Pages 126–143 in P. Calow, and G. E. Petts, editors. The rivers handbook: hydrological and ecological principles. Blackwell Scientific Publications, Ltd., London.

Cuffney, T. F., H. Zappia, E. M. P. Giddings, and J. F. Coles. 2005. Effects of urbanization on benthic macroinvertebrate assemblages in contrasting environmental settings: Boston, Massachusetts; Birmingham, Alabama; and Salt Lake City, Nevada. Pages 361–407 in L. R. Brown, R. H. Gray, R. M. Hughes, and M. R. Meador, editors. Effects of urbanization on stream ecosystems. American Fisheries Society, Symposium 47, Bethesda, Maryland.

Cummins, K. W. 1979. The natural stream ecosystem. Pages 7–24 in J. V. Ward, and J. A. Stanford, editors. The ecology of regulated streams. Plenum, New York.

Dennehy, K. F., D. W. Litke, C. M. Tate, S. L. Qi, P. B. McMahon, B. W. Bruce, R. A. Kimbrough, and J. S. Heiny. 1998. Water quality in the South Platte River basin, Colorado, Nebraska, and Wyoming, 1992–95. U.S. Geological Survey Circular 1167, Washington, D.C.

Finkenbine, J. K., J. W. Atwater, and D. S. Mavinic. 2000. Stream health after urbanization. Journal of the American Water Resources Association 36:1149–1160.

Fitzpatrick, F. A., I. R. Waite, P. J. D'Arconte, M. R. Meador, M. A. Maupin, and M. E. Gurtz. 1998. Revised methods for characterizing stream habitat in the National Water-Quality Assessment Program. U.S. Geological Survey, Water-Resources Investigations Report 98–4052, Raleigh, North Carolina.

Flanagan, S. M., M. G. Nielsen, K. W. Robinson, and J. F. Cole. 1999. Water-quality assessment of the New England Coastal Basins in Maine, Massachusetts, New Hampshire, and Rhode Island: environmental settings and implications for water quality and aquatic biota. U.S. Geological Survey, Water-Resources Investigations Report 98–4249, Northborough, Massachusetts.

Gordon, N. D., T. A. McMahon, and B. L. Finlayson. 1993. Stream hydrology: an introduction for ecologists. Wiley, New York.

Gregory, K. J., R. J. Davis, and P. W. Downs. 1992. Identification of river channel change due to urbanization. Applied Geography 12:299–318.

Gregory, K. J., A. M. Gurnell, C. T. Hill, and S. Tooth. 1994. Stability of the pool-riffle sequence in changing river channels. Regulated Rivers Research and Management 9:35–43.

Grimm, N. B., J. M. Grove, S. T. A. Pickett, and C. L. Redman. 2000. Integrated approaches to long term studies of urban ecological systems. BioScience 50:571–584.

Hammer, T. R. 1972. Stream channel enlargement due to urbanization. Water Resources Research 8:1530–1540.

Hirsch, R. M., J. F. Walker, J. C. Day, and R. Kallio. 1990. The influence of man on hydrologic systems. Pages 329–359 in M. G. Wolman and H. C. Riggs, editors. Surface water hydrology (The geology of America), volume 0–1. Geological Society of America, Boulder, Colorado.

Johnson, G. C., R. E. Kidd, C. A. Journey, H. Zappia, and J. B. Atkins. 2002. Environmental setting and water-quality issues of the Mobile River basin, Alabama, Georgia, Mississippi, and Tennessee. U.S. Geological Survey, Water-Resources Investigations Report 02–4162, Washington, D.C.

Kemp, S. J., and J. R. Spotila. 1997. Effects of urbanization on brown trout *Salmo trutta*, other fishes and macroinvertebrates in Valley Creek, Valley Forge, Pennsylvania. American Midland Naturalist 138:55–68.

Klein, R. D. 1979. Urbanization and stream quality impairment. Water Resources Bulletin 15:948–963.

Legendre, P., and L. Legendre. 1983. Numerical ecology. Elsevier, Amsterdam.

Leopold, L. B., M. G. Wolman, and J. P. Miller. 1992. Fluvial processes in geomorphology. Dover Publications, New York.

Maddock, I. 1999. The importance of physical habitat assessment for evaluating river health. Freshwater Biology 41:373–391.

Manley, B. F. J. 1986. Multivariate statistical methods. Chapman and Hall, New York.

McDonnell, M. J., and S. T. A. Pickett. 1990. Ecosystem structure and function along urban-rural gradients: an unexploited opportunity for ecology. Ecology 71:1232–1237.

McDonnell, M. J., S. T. A. Pickett, R. V. Pouyat, W. C. Zipperer, R. W. Parmelee, M. M. Carreiro, and K. Medley. 1997. Ecosystem processes along an urban-to-rural gradient. Urban Ecosystems 1:21–36.

McMahon, G., and T. F. Cuffney. 2000. Quantifying urban intensity in drainage basins for assessing stream ecological conditions. Journal of the American Water Resources Association 36:1247–1261.

Montgomery, D. R., and J. M. Buffington. 2001. Channel processes, classification, and response. Pages 13–42 *in* R. J. Naiman and R. E. Bilby, editors. River ecology and management: lessons from the Pacific coastal ecoregion. Springer-Verlag, New York.

Moscrip, A. L., and D. R. Montgomery. 1997. Urbanization, flood frequency, and salmon abundance in Puget lowland streams. Journal of the American Water Resources Association 33:1289–1297.

Paul, M. J., and J. L. Meyer. 2001. Streams in the urban landscape. Annual Review of Ecology and Systematics 32:333–364.

Petts, G. E., and J. P. Bravard. 1996. A drainage basin perspective. Pages 13–36 *in* G. E. Petts and C. Amaros, editors. Fluvial hydrosystems. Chapman and Hall, London.

Pizzuto, J. E., W. C. Hession, and M. McBride. 2000. Comparing gravel-bed rivers in paired urban and rural catchments of southeastern Pennsylvania. Geology 28:79–82.

Platts, W. S., C. Amour, G. D. Booth, M, Bryant, J. L. Buford, P. Cuplin, S. Jensen, G. W. Lienkaemper, W. G. Minshall, S. B. Monsen, R. L. Nelson, J. R. Sedell, and J. S. Tuhy. 1987. Methods for evaluating riparian habitats with applications to management. U.S. Forest Service General Technical Report INT-138, Ogden, Utah

Potapova, M., J. F. Coles, E. M. P. Giddings, and H. Zappia. 2005. A comparison of the influences of urbanization in contrasting environmental settings on stream benthic algal assemblages. Pages 333–359 *in* L .R. Brown, R. H. Gray, R. M. Hughes, and M. R. Meador, editors. Effects of urbanization on stream ecosystems. American Fisheries Society, Symposium 47, Bethesda, Maryland.

Pringle, C. 2003. The need for a more predictive understanding of hydrologic connectivity. Aquatic Conservation: Marine and Freshwater Ecosystems 13:467–471.

Rosenfeld, J. 2003. Assessing the habitat requirements of stream fishes: an overview and evaluation of different approaches. Transactions of the American Fisheries Society 132:953–968.

Seaburn, G. E. 1969. Effects of urban development on direct runoff to East Meadow Brook, Nassau County, New York. U.S. Geological Survey Professional Paper 627-B, Washington, D.C.

SPSS. 1999. SYSTAT 9 Statistics I. SPSS Inc., Chicago.

Strahler, A. N. 1957. Quantitative analysis of watershed geomorphology. Transactions of the American Geophysical Union 38:913–920.

Tate, C. M., T. F. Cuffney, G. McMahon, E. M. P. Giddings, J. F. Coles, and H. Zappia. 2005. Use of an urban intensity index to assess urban effects on streams in three contrasting environmental settings. Pages 291–315 *in* L. R. Brown, R. H. Gray, R. M. Hughes, and M. R. Meador, editors. Effects of urbanization on stream ecosystems. American Fisheries Society, Symposium 47, Bethesda, Maryland.

ter Braak, C. J. F. 1995. Ordination. Pages 91–173 *in* R. H. G. Jongman, C. J. F. ter Braak, and O. F. R. van Tongeren, editors. Data analysis in community and landscape ecology. Cambridge University Press, Cambridge, UK.

Townsend, C. R., S. Doledec, R. Norris, K. Peacock, and C. Arbuckle. 2003. The influence of scale and geography on relationships between stream community composition and landscape variables: description and prediction. Freshwater Biology 48:768–785.

Trimble, S. W. 1997. Contribution of stream channel erosion to sediment yield from an urbanizing watershed. Science 278:1442–1444.

U.S. Environmental Protection Agency. 2000. The quality of our nation's waters. EPA 841-S-00–001, Washington, D.C.

U.S. Geological Survey. 2000. National elevation dataset. U.S. Geological Survey. Available: http://gisdata.usgs.gov/ned/ (March 2000).

Wang, L., J. Lyons, P. Kanehl, and R. Gatti. 1997. Influences of watershed land use on habitat quality and biotic integrity in Wisconsin streams. Fisheries 22(6):6–12.

Wang, L., J. Lyons, P. Kanehl, and R. Bannerman. 2001. Impacts of urbanization on stream habitat and fish across multiple spatial scales. Environmental Management 28:255–266.

Ward, J. V. 1992. Aquatic insect ecology, volume 1. Biology and habitat. Wiley, New York.

Waters, T. F. 1995. Sediment in streams: source, biological effects, and control. American Fisheries Society, Monograph 7, Bethesda, Maryland.

Wolman, M. G., and A. P. Schick. 1967. Effects of construction on fluvial sediment, urban and suburban areas of Maryland. Water Resources Research 3:451–464.

Zipperer, W. C., J. Wu, R. V. Pouyat, and S. T. A. Pickett. 2000. The application of ecological principles to urban and urbanizing landscapes. Ecological Applications 10:685–688.

APPENDIX 1. Selected habitat variables measured at or calculated for each study reach.

Variables	Description
Channel properties	
Segment sinuosity (SEGSINU)	Ratio of curvilinear channel length to valley centerline length (Platts et al. 1983).
Reach sinuosity (RCHSINU)	Standard deviation of mean difference in streamflow direction (degrees) measured at mid-channel between reach transects; increasing values represent increasing sinuosity.
Reach gradient (GRAD)	Percent change in elevation (m) between lower and upper reach boundaries.
Bank-full depth (BFD)	Average depth (m) at deepest part of stream channel to top of bank at bank-full stage; calculated from 11 transects.
Coefficient of variation in bank-full depth (CVBFD)	Percent variation of reach-averaged bank-full depth.
Bank-full width (BFW)	Average width (m) of stream channel at bank-full stage from top edge of left bank to top edge of right bank; calculated from 11 transects.
Bank-full width to depth ratio (BFWD)	Average bank-full width to depth ratio; calculated from 11 transects.
Bank-full cross-sectional area (BFAREA)	Average area (m^2) based on product of bank-full depth and bank-full width; calculated from 11 transects.
Coefficient of variation in bank-full cross-sectional area (CVBFAREA)	Percent variation of reach-averaged bankfull cross-sectional area.
Wetted depth (WETD)	Average depth (m) of wetted channel; measured at three locations at each of 11 transects.
Maximum wetted depth (MAXWETD)	Average depth (m) at deepest part of wetted channel; calculated from 11 transects.
Wetted width (WETW)	Average width (m) of wetted channel; calculated from 11 transects.
Wetted volume (VOL)	Stream volume (m^3) based on product of reach length, average wetted width, and average wetted depth.
Bank stability (BANK)	Multimetric index representing average bank stability; based on combination of characteristics consisting of bank angle, bank height, dominant substrate (ordinal), and percent vegetative cover (Fitzpatrick et al. 1998); index values range from 4 to

APPENDIX 1. Continued.

Variables	Description
	22, with scores 4–7 = stable, 8–10 = at risk, 11–15 = unstable, 16–22 = highly unstable; calculated from 11 transects.
Percent vegetation density (VEG)	Percent riparian vegetation density near wetted channel margins (see Methods); measured at two locations at each of 11 transects.
Hydraulic properties	
Discharge (DSCHR)	Average discharge (m^3/s) based on product of wetted cross-sectional area and mean velocity (Gordon et al. 1993); calculated from 11 transects.
Velocity (VEL)	Average velocity (m/s) measured at six-tenths depth at three locations at each of 11 transects.
Coefficient of variation in velocity (CVVEL)	Percent variation of reach-averaged velocity.
Flow stability (FLOSTAB)	Average ratio of maximum wetted depth to bank-full depth; values range from 0 to 1, with increasing values representing more hydrologically stable conditions; calculated from 11 transects.
Stream power (POWER)	Power per unit of stream length (W/m) (Gordon et al. 1993).
Streambed properties	
Percent fines (FINE)	Average percent of total substrate composition (categorical) consisting of sand and smaller-sized particles; calculations based on visual determinations at three locations at each of 11 transects.
Percent embeddedness (EMBED)	Average percentage (nearest 10%) to which larger substrate particles ($\geq$ coarse gravel) are surrounded or covered by fine sediment (< 2 mm); calculations based on visual determinations at three locations at each of 11 transects.
Percent siltation (SILT)	Proportion (presence or absence) of fine sediment (<1 mm) on bottom surfaces; calculations based on visual determinations at three locations at each of 11 transects.
Substrate size (SUB)	Average substrate particle size (ordinal) with size categories ranging from 1 to 10, where 1 = smooth bedrock and 10 = large boulder (Fitzpatrick et al. 1998); calculations based on visual determinations at three locations at each of 11 transects.
Coefficient of variation in substrate size (CVSUB)	Percent variation in reach-averaged substrate size.
Relative roughness (ROUGH)	Average ratio of dominant particle size (categorical) to wetted depth; higher values represent increasing hydraulic roughness of streambed; calculations based on measurements at three locations at each of 11 transects.
Cover and pools	
Percent cover (COVER)	Percent occurrence (based on total number of observations) of habitat cover (overhanging vegetation, undercut banks, woody debris, boulders, macrophytes, artificial structures) at five locations (two for undercut banks and overhanging vegetation) at each of 11 transects; a maximum of 24 cover types was possible at each transect.
Percent pool (POOL)	Proportion of total pool length to reach length, for pools comprising $\geq$ 50% of wetted channel width.

American Fisheries Society Symposium 41:333–359, 2005

A Comparison of the Influences of Urbanization in Contrasting Environmental Settings on Stream Benthic Algal Assemblages

MARINA POTAPOVA

Patrick Center for Environmental Research, the Academy of Natural Sciences
1900 Benjamin Franklin Parkway, Philadelphia, Pennsylvania 19103, USA

JAMES F. COLES

U.S. Geological Survey, c/o USEPA New England, Suite 1100 (HBS)
1 Congress Street, Boston, Massachusetts 02114, USA

ELISE M. P. GIDDINGS

U.S. Geological Survey, 3916 Sunset Ridge Road, Raleigh, North Carolina 27607, USA

HUMBERT ZAPPIA

1162 Rock Cliff Drive, Martinsburg, West Virginia 25401, USA

Abstract.—Patterns of stream benthic algal assemblages along urbanization gradients were investigated in three metropolitan areas—Boston (BOS), Massachusetts; Birmingham (BIR), Alabama; and Salt Lake City (SLC), Utah. An index of urban intensity derived from socioeconomic, infrastructure, and land-use characteristics was used as a measure of urbanization. Of the various attributes of the algal assemblages, species composition changed along gradients of urban intensity in a more consistent manner than biomass or diversity. In urban streams, the relative abundance of pollution-tolerant species was often higher than in less affected streams. Shifts in assemblage composition were associated primarily with increased levels of conductivity, nutrients, and alterations in physical habitat. Water mineralization and nutrients were the most important determinants of assemblage composition in the BOS and SLC study areas; flow regime and grazers were key factors in the BIR study area. Species composition of algal assemblages differed significantly among geographic regions, and no particular algal taxa were found to be universal indicators of urbanization. Patterns in algal biomass and diversity along urban gradients varied among study areas, depending on local environmental conditions and habitat alteration. Biomass and diversity increased with urbanization in the BOS area, apparently because of increased nutrients, light, and flow stability in urban streams, which often are regulated by dams. Biomass and diversity decreased with urbanization in the BIR study area because of intensive fish grazing and less stable flow regime. In the SLC study area, correlations between algal biomass, diversity, and urban intensity were positive but weak. Thus, algal responses to urbanization differed considerably among the three study areas. We concluded that the wide range of responses of benthic algae to urbanization implied that tools for stream bioassessment must be region specific.

Introduction

Streams go through hydrological and water quality changes as they become part of the urban landscape (Paul and Meyer 2001). Alterations of stream habitat inevitably lead to transformations in stream biota, including algal assemblages. Although the presence of harmful chemicals in streams or the disappearance of important fish species attracts attention, changes in algal assemblages usually do not cause public concern

* Corresponding author: potapova@acnatsci.org

unless excessive amounts of algae diminish the esthetic value of streams, clog water supplies, or cause secondary water pollution. Algae are sensitive, however, to water chemistry and habitat disturbance and, thus, have a long history of being used in water quality monitoring (Lowe and Pan 1996). Algae also play an important role in the function of stream ecosystems. Algae are a source of organic matter and provide habitat for other organisms, such as nonphotosynthetic bacteria, protists, invertebrates, and fish. The crucial role in stream ecosystems and excellent indicator properties of algae make them an important component of environmental studies to assess the effects of human activities on stream health.

Relations among lotic benthic algal assemblages and various environmental factors associated with water pollution and landscape alteration have been studied intensively (Stevenson et al. 1996), but only a few studies have focused specifically on the effects of urbanization. Algal vegetation in running waters has been studied in many urban areas, including temperate zones (e.g., Whitton 1984; Sabater et al. 1987; Lobo et al. 1995; Vis et al. 1998; Winter and Duthie 1998; Fukushima 1999; Siva et al. 2001; Sonneman et al. 2001) and tropics (Nather Khan 1991; Wu 1999). Studies in individual urban streams or individual metropolitan areas generally have been carried out to determine which attributes of algal assemblages are indicative of human influences for use in future monitoring programs. Many of these described changes in taxonomic composition of assemblages in flowing waters influenced by municipal or industrial wastes when compared to less affected sites. Some also reported declining diversity of algae in severely polluted urban rivers (Whitton 1984; Nather Khan 1991) and increased algal biomass (Taylor et al. 2004). It is not clear, however, whether stream algal assemblages are affected by urbanization in a similar way in different geographic areas. If they are, then it should be possible to identify the attributes of assemblages that can be used as universal indicators of the effects of urbanization. Urban areas differ, however, in their environmental settings and history of development. Climate, geology, and human influences are considered to be ultimate environmental factors that determine biomass and composition of algal assemblages in streams (Biggs 1990; Stevenson 1997). These factors may modify the patterns of algal assemblage variations along urbanization gradients. To understand to what degree the responses of stream algal assemblages to urbanization vary geographically, it is necessary to conduct studies based on a common approach and methodology in various urban areas.

We studied stream algal assemblages in three metropolitan areas of contrasting climate and geography. This investigation was part of the Urban Land Use Gradient (ULUG) study conducted in 2000 as part of the U.S. Geological Survey's (USGS) National Water-Quality Assessment (NAWQA) Program (Tate et al. 2005; this volume). Our goals were to (1) describe relations between urbanization and attributes of stream algal assemblages, such as biomass, diversity, and species composition; and (2) determine whether patterns of algal assemblages along urbanization gradients were different in three metropolitan areas. Uniform responses of particular attributes of algal assemblages to urbanization indicate the possibility of using these attributes as universal bioassessment tools in urban streams. Conversely, large differences among patterns of algal assemblages in three metropolitan areas indicate the overriding influence of local environmental and historical conditions and the need to develop region-specific bioassessment tools.

Methods

Site Selection

The study was conducted in three diverse metropolitan areas in terms of climate and geography—Boston (BOS), Massachusetts, representing the cool and humid Northeast; Birmingham (BIR), Alabama, representing the warm and humid Southeast; and Salt Lake City (SLC), Utah, representing the arid West. In each area, 30 stream sites were selected along gradients of urban intensity quantified by using the multimetric urban intensity index (UII). The UII combined several land-cover, population, socioeconomic, and infrastructure variables (McMahon and Cuffney 2000). In each study area, a group of candidate basins was established to represent a gradient from low (background) to high urban intensity within a relatively homogeneous environmental setting, and several variables characterizing human influences and natural variability were calculated for these basins by using geographic information system (GIS) programs. Variables selected to derive the UII were different among the three study areas; in each case, however, they correlated with population density and did not correlate with basin area. The variables were combined to calculate UII values using formulas from McMahon and Cuffney (2000). The calculated values then were adjusted to range from 0 to 100. The final set of 30 sites was selected in each study area with the goal of minimizing variability in soils, geology, ecoregion, physiographic province, climate, drainage area, and topography, which influence the physical, chemical, and biological characteristics of streams. Finally, the UII was recalculated so the values ranged from 0 to 100 in each set of 30 sites. Greater details of the process of index development, site selection, and lists of variables used to derive the UII in each study area are provided in Tate et al. (2005).

All 30 sites in the BOS study are within or adjacent to ecological subsection 221Ai, Gulf of Maine Coastal Plain, of the U.S. Forest Service ecological unit 221A, Southern New England Coastal Hills and Plain (Keys et al. 1995), which corresponds to the U.S. Environmental Protection Agency (USEPA) level III ecoregion, Northeastern Coastal Zone (Omernik 1995). The BIR study sites are within the USEPA level IV ecoregion, Southern Limestone/Dolomite Valleys and Low Rolling Hills. The final number of sampling sites in BIR area was 27 because of logistical problems. Streams sampled in the SLC originate in the Wasatch Mountain range in the USEPA level III ecoregion, Wasatch and Uinta Mountains, but the urban areas mostly are in lower parts of stream drainage basins in the Central Basin and Range ecoregion. Only 13 perennial streams were available for study in this area because of the dry climate and numerous water diversions. One to three sites were selected in each of the stream basins in the SLC study area for a total number of 30 sites.

Sample Collection and Laboratory Analyses

Benthic algae were sampled as described by Porter et al. (1993). At each site, two quantitative samples were collected—one from hard substrates, mostly rocks located in a riffle or run (richest-targeted habitat or RTH sample), and the other from soft sediment in a depositional area (depositional-targeted habitat or DTH sample). Richest-targeted habitat samples were collected by scraping algae from cobble-size stones selected from five riffle areas of the sampling reach. The scraped area was determined by the foil-template method. Depositional-targeted habitat samples were collected from five depositional areas in the same sampling reach by pressing an inverted petri dish into the sediment and sliding a spatula under the petri dish to isolate the upper layer of sediment. Additionally, a multihabitat qualitative sample (QMH) was collected

from various substrates in the sampling reach. Subsamples of RTH samples were taken for determinations of chlorophyll a. The other samples and remaining portion of RTH samples were preserved with a 5% solution of formalin for identification and enumeration of algae. Algal samples were collected in low-flow conditions from August 1 to September 1, 2000, in the BOS study area; from June 6 to June 12, 2000, in the BIR study area, and from July 17 to August 9, 2000, in the SLC study area.

Algae were identified and enumerated following protocols in Charles et al. (2002) by taxonomic specialists in the Phycology Section of the Patrick Center for Environmental Research, Academy of Natural Sciences, Philadelphia, and in the Department of Zoology at Michigan State University. Algae were identified and enumerated using the Palmer-Maloney counting cell. Diatoms were identified from permanent slides; only the total number of live and dead diatoms was recorded using the Palmer-Maloney counting cell. Cell density was expressed as number of cells/cm^2 and cell biovolume as mm^3/cm^2. Chlorophyll a (mg/m^2) was measured at the USGS Water Quality Laboratory in Lakewood, Colorado, using standard methods (Arar and Collins 1997).

Invertebrates and fish were sampled concurrently with algae. The data used in this study include absolute abundance of invertebrate scrapers in all three study areas and abundance of herbivorous fish in the BIR study area. Herbivorous fish were absent in the BOS and SLC study areas.

Water quality samples were collected in August 2000 in the BOS area, in May 2000 in the BIR area, and in July 2000 in the SLC area. Dissolved oxygen, alkalinity, pH, and conductivity were measured in the field according to Shelton (1994). Nutrient concentrations, major ions, and pesticides were analyzed at the USGS Water Quality Laboratory in Lakewood, Colorado, following methods described in Fishman (1993). Water quality characteristics that were used as explanatory environmental variables for this investigation are listed in Table 1.

Physical habitat characteristics were measured according to Fitzpatrick et al. (1998) close to the time of algal sampling. Physical habitat characteristics were measured at 11 equally spaced transects along the sampling reaches and consisted of measurements of current velocity, discharge, channel morphology, bed substrate, and canopy cover. Means and coefficients of variation (CV) were calculated from these data to characterize general habitat conditions of the reaches. Channel shape index was calculated as W/D $^{D/Dmax}$,

TABLE 1. Environmental characteristics used as explanatory variables in the analyses of algal data. Physical habitat variables were derived from measurements made at 11 transects at each sampling site. Abbreviations are given for some variables shown in tables and graphs.

Variable group and description	Abbreviation
Basin-scale characteristics	
Urban intensity index	UII
Basin area (km²)	
1999 population density (people/km²)	Population
Road density (km/km²)	
Number of dams (number/100km²)	
Land use/land cover (% of basin area)	
Water and wetlands	
Urban	
Barren	
Forest	
Shrub land	
Herbaceous upland/grassland	Grassland
Herbaceous planted/cultivated	Cultivated
Wetlands	
Elevation (m)	
Sampling site	
Mean in basin	
Range in basin	Relief
Percentage of the basin area with slope less than 1%	
Percentage of the basin area with slope less than 1% at elevations above average	Uplands
Percentage of the basin area with slope less than 1% at elevations below average	
Stream order	
Physical habitat characteristics	
Segment sinuosity	
Reach sinuosity	
Surface-water gradient (m/km)	Gradient
Percentage of reach area as pools	
Percentage of reach area as riffles	
Percentage of reach area as runs	
Wetted width (m)	
Coefficient of variation of wetted width	
Maximum wetted width (m)	
Bank-full width (m)	
Coefficient of variation of bank-full width	
Maximum bank-full width (m)	
Wetted depth (m)	
Coefficient of variation of wetted depth	
Maximum wetted depth (m)	
Bank-full depth (m)	
Coefficient of variation of bank-full depth	
Maximum bank-full depth (m)	
Depth at the sampling location (m)	
Wetted width–depth ratio	
Coefficient of variation of wetted width–depth ratio	
Bank-full width–depth ratio	
Coefficient of variation of bank-full width–depth ratio	
Channel shape index	
Coefficient of variation of channel shape index	

TABLE 1. Continued.

Variable group and description	Abbreviation
Discharge (m³/s)	
Coefficient of variation of discharge	
Mean flow velocity (m/s)	
Coefficient of variation of flow velocity	
Maximum flow velocity (m/s)	
Flow velocity at the sampling location (m/s)	
Shear stress	
Froude number	
Stream power (W/m)	
Flow-stability index	
Mean dominant substrate size	
Coefficient of variation of dominant substrate size	
Silt occurrence	
Percentage of nonporous substrate	
Percentage of fine sediments	% fine
Percentage of silt-clay size particles	% silt + clay
Percentage of sand size particles	% sand
Percentage of gravel size particles	% gravel
Percentage of cobble size particles	% gravel
Percentage of boulder size particles	
Percentage of silt-gravel size particles	% silt + gravel
Percentage of gravel-cobble size particles	
Percentage of cobble-boulder size particles	
Embeddedness (%)	
Manning's channel roughness	
Channel relative roughness	
Hydrological channel radius	
Canopy closure (%)	
Coefficient of variation of canopy closure	
Light intensity (photosynthetically active radiation, mmol s⁻¹ m⁻²)	Light

$$\text{Light intensity (photosynthetically active radiation, mmol s}^{-1}\text{ m}^{-2}\text{)}$$

Hydrological (stage-related) characteristics

Variation of stage values	
Skew of stage values	
Number of time periods when stage rises by at least 0.03 m/h	periodr1
Number of time periods when stage rises by at least 0.09 m/h	periodr3
Number of time periods when stage rises by at least 0.15 m/h	periodr5
Number of time periods when stage rises by at least 0.21 m/h	periodr7
Number of time periods when stage rises by at least 0.27 m/h	periodr9
Number of time periods when stage falls by at least 0.03 m/h	periodf1
Number of time periods when stage falls by at least 0.09 m/h	periodf3
Number of time periods when stage falls by at least 0.15 m/h	periodf5
Number of time periods when stage falls by at least 0.21 m/h	periodf7
Number of time periods when stage falls by at least 0.27 m/h	periodf9
Maximum duration of low stage pulses with discharge < 5th percentile as low flow (h)	Mxl5
Maximum duration of low stage pulses with discharge < 10th percentile as low flow (h)	Mxl10
Maximum duration of low stage pulses with discharge < 25th percentile as low flow (h)	Mxl25
Median duration of low stage pulses with discharge < 5th percentile as low flow (h)	Mdl5
Median duration of low stage pulses with discharge < 10th percentile as low flow (h)	Mdl10
Median duration of low stage pulses with discharge < 25th percentile as low flow (h)	Mdl25

TABLE 1. Continued.

Variable group and description	Abbreviation
Maximum duration of high stage pulses with discharge > 75th percentile as high flow (h)	Mxh75
Maximum duration of high stage pulses with discharge > 90th percentile as high flow (h)	Mxh90
Maximum duration of high stage pulses with discharge > 95th percentile as high flow (h)	Mxh95
Median duration of high stage pulses with discharge > 75th percentile as high flow (h)	Mdh75
Median duration of high stage pulses with discharge > 90th percentile as high flow (h)	Mdh90
Median duration of high stage pulses with discharge > 95th percentile as high flow (h)	Mdh95
Water chemical and physical characteristics	
Phosphorus as total phosphorus (mg/L as P)	TP
Phosphorus as orthophosphate, dissolved (mg/L as P)	PO_4
Nitrogen as total nitrogen (mg/L as N)	TN
Nitrogen as total organic nitrogen + dissolved ammonia (mg/L as N)	TKN
Nitrogen as nitrite + nitrate nitrogen, dissolved (mg/L as N)	$NO_2 + NO_3$
Nitrogen as ammonia, dissolved (mg/L as N)	NH_4
Conductivity (mS/cm)	Cond
Alkalinity (mg/L as $CaCO_3$)	
pH (standard units)	
Sulfate, dissolved (mg/L)	SO_4
Chloride, dissolved (mg/L)	Cl
Calcium, dissolved (mg/L)	Ca
Magnesium, dissolved (mg/L)	Mg
Sodium, dissolved (mg/L)	Na
Potassium, dissolved (mg/L)	K
Fluoride, dissolved (mg/L)	F
Iron, dissolved (mg/L)	Fe
Silica as silica dioxide, dissolved (mg/L)	SiO_2
Residue on evaporation at 180°C (mg/L)	
Total herbicide concentration (mg/L)	HerbConc
Number of herbicide detections per sample	HerbHits
Total pesticide concentration (mg/L)	
Number of pesticide detections	
Oxygen, dissolved (mg/L)	O_2
Water temperature (°C)	
Turbidity (NTU)	
Grazers	
Abundance of invertebrate scrapers (number/m²)	Scrapers
Abundance of herbivorous fish largescale stoneroller (in BIR, number/reach)	Stoneroller

where W is wetted channel width, D is mean water depth, and Dmax is maximum water depth. Smaller values of the shape index generally indicate more pool-like conditions, whereas larger values indicate more riffle-like conditions. The flow-stability index characterized high-flow events and was calculated as D_{lf}/D_{bf}, where D_{lf} is depth of water at low flow, and D_{bf} is bank-full depth. Current velocity, water depth, and light intensity also were measured at the sampling location (except light intensity in the BIR study area).

Mean light intensity (photosynthetically active radiation, PAR) measured near the stream bottom with light meters was used in the analyses. More detailed information on the physical habitat characterization can be found in Short et al. (2005, this volume) and in Fitzpatrick et al. (1998).

Stream stage (water level) was recorded at 15-min intervals at each site using USGS gauges or stage transducers (McMahon et al. 2003). Summary hydrological variables were calculated from the recorded stage data and used in our analyses as measures of flow stability. Watershed-scale land-use, population, infrastructure, and socioeconomic variables in each watershed were derived from GIS data. All environmental variables used in this study are listed in Table 1.

Data Analysis

Algal biomass was characterized by the amount of chlorophyll *a* in RTH samples and the total algal biovolume in RTH and DTH samples. Relations between algal biomass and environmental variables were evaluated by using correlation analysis (Pearson's *r*). The number of environmental variables in our data set was higher (>100) than the number of observations in each of the regional data sets (27–30). Thus, some correlations may be spurious, caused by chance alone. To avoid overinterpretation, we sought combinations of a few variables that could explain biomass variability. This was accomplished by stepwise forward selection of variables in multivariate regression analysis. Initially, we selected 10–12 variables representing different classes, such as nutrients (TP and TN), major ion chemistry (conductivity and alkalinity), pH, light, sediment size, channel morphology, flow variability, and abundance of grazers. These variables were chosen so that they were not highly intercorrelated with each other but had significant correlation with algal biomass. The criteria for variable inclusion in the model was $F > 0.05$, and for exclusion, $F < 0.1$. Resulting models had one to three variables that explained observed biomass variability in the most parsimonious way. The low number of variables is reasonable for small data sets such as ours. Total algal biovolume and concentration of nutrients, ions, alkalinity, and conductivity were log-transformed prior to analyses. Correlation and multiple regression procedures were conducted using SPSS for Windows, version 11.0.

Algal diversity was estimated by species richness, which is the total number of species in a sample, and Shannon-Wiener diversity index, which is a function of both species richness and evenness of species distribution. Both metrics are commonly used in water quality bioassessment (Stevenson and Bahls 1999). We also calculated relative abundance of algal taxa that are currently considered as possibly endemic. Trends in algal diversity along urban gradient were evaluated by calculating Kendall's correlations between these diversity measures and UII.

To evaluate patterns in taxonomic composition of algal assemblages and their relations with stream environment, we used nonmetric multidimensional scaling (NMS, Kruskal 1964; Mather 1976). Nonmetric multidimensional scaling is a nonparametric iterative technique using ranked distances, and this technique is used increasingly in ecological studies (McCune and Mefford 1999). Nonmetric multidimensional scaling solution is based on minimizing stress, which is a measure of poorness of fit between the ordination matrix and original data matrix. To run NMS, we used the "slow-and-thorough" autopilot mode available in PC-ORD 4.0 (McCune and Mefford 1999) and the quantitative Sørensen (Bray-Curtis) distance measure. Three-dimensional solutions were optimal in all NMS runs. Four algal data sets from each study area were used, representing samples from two habitats (RTH and DTH) and including either diatom proportions or all algal taxa proportions. Species relative abundance was square root transformed. We rotated ordinations to load the variable UII on a single (horizontal) axis and illustrated relations between algal assemblages and environment with the joint plots. These plots showed the positions of taxa and selected environmental variables most strongly correlated with ordination axes and related to different aspects of stream environment (e.g., hydrology, substrate composition, light regime, ionic composition, nutrients). Variance explained by ordination was expressed by the coefficient of determination (r^2) between Euclidean distances in the ordination space and Sørensen distances in the original species spaces. Algal taxa shown in the ordination plots are those that had the highest correlations with ordination axes and were found in at least three samples in each data set. The relative importance of environmental variables in explaining assemblage composition patterns was estimated by the sum of squared correlations between a variable and all ordination axes (Σr^2).

Kendall's correlations between relative abundance of most abundant (reaching 15% or 20%) algal taxa and UII were calculated to identify which taxa were associated with urban gradient in each study area. Autecological characteristics of algal taxa, such as trophic categories, relations to water mineral content and pollution tolerance, were obtained from the works of Sládecek (1973), Lange-Bertalot (1979), and van Dam et al. (1994). These sources are useful for characterizing the autecology of cosmopolitan taxa; however, metrics calculated from these characteristics, such as percentage of pollution-sensitive, pollution-tolerant, oligo- and polysaprobic (tolerance to organic pollution), and oligo- and eutraphentic (tolerance to nutrient enrichment) taxa, must be considered with caution. These sources provide no autecological information for many algal taxa found in American streams.

Results

Habitat Characteristics

The three study areas differed in climate, topography, and geology, and therefore, in water chemistry and flow regime (Table 2). Water-mineral content, as measured by conductivity, was generally higher in the SLC area than in the other two study areas because of the arid climate. In the BIR area, conductivity and pH were relatively high because of the prevalence of carbonate bedrock. In the BOS area, conductivity and pH were lowest among three areas because of the prevalence of noncarbonate bedrock and the cool, humid climate. Conductivity was significantly positively correlated with the UII in all three study areas (Table 2). Water pH tended to be higher in urbanized streams in all three study areas, but we found no significant correlation between pH and the UII (Table 2).

Streams in the SLC area had the steepest channels, whereas streams in the BIR area had the lowest gradients and flow velocities. Flow stability, as quantified by the flow-stability index derived from channel morphology, increased with urbanization in the BOS study area, and showed no pattern in the BIR and SLC areas (Table 2).

Streams in the BIR area had, in general, a higher proportion of sand in the bed sediment than streams in the BOS and SLC areas (Table 2). In BOS and SLC, proportions of sand were low in the nonurban streams but increased along gradients of urbanization. Some of the high-gradient nonurban stream sites in the SLC area had very rough channels with numerous boulders.

The dominant natural land-cover type in the two eastern study areas was forest; in the SLC study area, the dominant natural land-cover type was shrub land (Table 2). Cultivated land cover was present in all three study areas, but it was significantly negatively correlated with the UII only in the BIR area. In correspondence with this pattern, nutrient concentrations increased with urbanization in the BOS and SLC areas, but not in the BIR area. Median nutrient concentrations were comparable in all study areas. One site with exceptionally high phosphorus and ionic (NaCl) content was in the BIR area. Concentrations of herbicides were higher in urbanized streams than in less urbanized streams, but significant positive correlations

between herbicide concentrations and UII were found only in the BIR and SLC areas.

Biomass of Benthic Algae in Streams

Regional differences.—Median algal biovolume was highest in the BIR study area and lowest in the BOS study area (Figure 1A). Total algal biovolume was consistently higher in DTH samples than in RTH samples in all three areas, although the difference in biovolume between DTH and RTH samples was not large in the SLC area. In the BOS and BIR study areas, algal biovolume was approximately one order of magnitude higher in DTH samples than in RTH samples. Median chlorophyll *a* was lowest in the BOS area and highest in the SLC area (Figure 1B). A chlorophyll-*a* concentration of 200 mg/m^2, commonly considered a nuisance level (Biggs 1996; Dodds et al. 1998), occurred in only two BIR streams of relatively low urban intensity (UII = 16.5–16.8) and in five SLC streams of moderate to high urban intensity (UII = 45.5–71.3). Values between 50 and 200 mg/m^2, which also can be regarded as a nuisance level (Biggs 1996), were observed at nine sites of varying degrees of urbanization in the SLC area, at seven sites in the BIR area, and at three sites of rather high urban intensity (UII = 62.7–92.6) in the BOS area.

Boston study area.—In the BOS area, algal biomass increased along the urban intensity gradient. Positive correlation between the UII and total algal biovolume was significant for RTH samples ($r = 0.53$, $P < 0.01$) but not significant for DTH samples ($r = 0.12$). Chlorophyll *a* concentration in RTH samples also was significantly positively correlated with the UII ($r = 0.48$, $P < 0.01$). Diatoms were the most abundant algae in DTH samples and the second most abundant algae in RTH samples (Figure 2A, B). Red algae constituted most of the algal biomass in RTH samples (Figure 2A).

In the BOS study area, total algal biovolume in RTH samples was significantly positively correlated with nutrients (all measured forms of phosphorus and nitrogen, $r = 0.36$–0.50, $P < 0.05$), alkalinity ($r = 0.45$, $P < 0.05$), conductivity ($r = 0.52$, $P < 0.01$), water depth ($r = 0.47$, $P < 0.05$), flow-stability index ($r = 0.57$, $P < 0.01$), proportion of fine sediments ($r = 0.53$, $P < 0.01$), number of dams ($r = 0.44$, $P < 0.05$), and light intensity ($r = 0.44$, $P < 0.05$). Total algal biovolume was significantly negatively correlated with channel width ($r = -0.36$, $P < 0.05$). The significance of these correlations, however, must be regarded with caution. The high number of tested variables increased the possibility of a spurious correlation.

TABLE 2. Selected characteristics of streams in three study areas and correlations of these characteristics (Kendall's correlation coefficient, tau) with the urban intensity index. Abbreviations for variables are in Table 1. Median values are in bold. **, $P < 0.01$; *, $P < 0.05$.

Characteristics	Boston				Birmingham				Salt Lake City			
	Min	Median	Max	Tau	Min	Median	Max	Tau	Min	Median	Max	Tau
Urban (%)	1	**15**	67	0.87**	0	**13**	73	0.93**	0	**40**	87	0.81**
Forest (%)	23	**65**	86	-0.89**	18	**64**	93	-0.74**	2	**11**	47	-0.49**
Shrub land (%)	0	**0**	0		0	**0**	0		1	**12**	68	-0.68**
Grassland (%)	2	**7**	17	-0.28*	0	**0**	0		0	**4**	26	-0.52**
Cultivated (%)	3	**8**	16	0.01	3	**13**	34	-0.31*	0	**16**	53	0.09
Number of dams	0	**5**	17	0.45**								
Surface-water gradient (m/km)	1.2	**5.8**	16.2	-0.16	0.3	**3.9**	6.7	0.03	4.0	**10.1**	166.1	-0.12
Wetted width (m)	5.0	**9.3**	12.5	-0.13	3.9	**5.6**	15.1	0.08	1.2	**4.4**	13.5	-0.05
Wetted depth (m)	0.16	**0.30**	0.62	0.57**	0.05	**0.25**	0.44	-0.14	0.05	**0.21**	0.56	-0.02
Discharge (m³/s)	0.18	**0.68**	2.85	0.32*	0.001	**0.27**	4.19	0.04	0.001	**0.24**	3.87	-0.10
Mean flow velocity (m/s)	0.12	**0.31**	0.50	0.33*	0.001	**0.07**	0.56	0.01	0.03	**0.29**	0.67	-0.20
Flow-stability index	0.24	**0.37**	0.51	0.32*	0.10	**0.19**	0.47	-0.23	0.10	**0.32**	0.78	-0.01
% silt + clay	0	**0**	15	0.19	0	**0**	27	-0.27	0	**0**	21	0.25
% sand	0	**2**	45	0.42**	0	**13**	79	-0.03	0	**3**	88	0.31*
% cobbles	18	**67**	100	-0.28	0	**19**	70	-0.17	0	**38**	91	-0.01
% boulders	0	**12**	52	0.09	0	**9**	64	0.26	0	**17**	76	-0.21
Embeddedness (%)	16	**34**	86	0.30*	9	**66**	100	0.31*	26	**61**	100	0.02
Channel relative roughness	11	**33**	68	-0.53**	18	**35**	141	0.07	7	**37**	204	-0.07
Conductivity (mS/cm)	47	**224**	643	0.69**	168	**314**	1,710	0.42**	89	**540**	1,110	0.37**
pH	6.4	**6.9**	7.6	0.26	7.5	**8.0**	8.3	0.14	7.3	**8.1**	8.6	0.13
TP (mg/L as P)	0.01	**0.03**	0.25	0.34*	0.01	**0.02**	8.93	0.08	0.01	**0.04**	0.13	0.35**
TN (mg/L as N)	0.32	**0.60**	5.40	0.45**	0.22	**0.78**	3.54	0.21	0.17	**0.75**	3.51	0.15
Total herbicide concentration (mg/L)	0.000	**0.003**	0.324	0.27	0.022	**0.030**	0.060	0.44**	0.001	**0.027**	1.372	0.49**
Number of herbicide detections	0	**1**	4	0.20	0	**3**	7	0.53**	1	**3**	7	0.42**
Light (mmol s⁻¹ m⁻²)	0.4	**7.5**	101	0.15	2	**73**	706	0.61**	2.1	**23.2**	670.4	-0.26
Number of herbivorous fish												

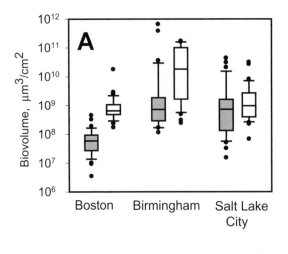

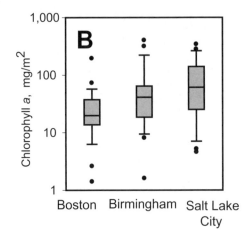

EXPLANATION

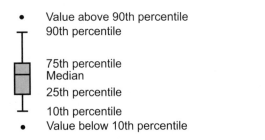

- • Value above 90th percentile
- — 90th percentile
- 75th percentile
- Median
- 25th percentile
- 10th percentile
- • Value below 10th percentile

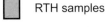

■ RTH samples

□ DTH samples

FIGURE 1. Box plots of the (A) total algal biovolume and (B) chlorophyll *a* in streams in three study areas—Boston *n* = 30; Birmingham *n* = 27; and Salt Lake City *n* = 30 for RTH samples, *n* = 28 for DTH samples.

For the stepwise multiple regression analysis, the following variables were selected initially as possible independent variables: TP, TN, alkalinity, wetted channel width, flow-stability index, percentage of fine sediments, current velocity and depth at the sampling location, light, and abundance of invertebrate scrapers. Variables finally chosen by the stepwise forward-selection procedure as those best predicting total algal biovolume on rocks were flow stability and TN (Table 3). Final variables in the chlorophyll-*a* model were light and TP (Table 3). Total algal biovolume in DTH samples could not be predicted from measured environmental factors. Although the relatively low number of observations in our data sets did not allow us to create highly predictive models, results of the selection of variables indicated that the main factors associated with increased algal biomass on rocks in urban streams of the BOS area were nutrients, light, and flow stability.

Birmingham study area.—In the BIR study area, algal biovolume was lower in streams at the high end of

the urban gradient (Figure 2C, D). Negative correlation between the UII and total algal biovolume was significant for DTH samples (*r* = –0.53, *P* < 0.01) but not significant for RTH samples (*r* = –0.33). No trend was detected in chlorophyll *a* along the urban gradient. Correlation analysis showed that algal biovolume was positively correlated (*P* < 0.05) with a number of variables that had decreasing values along the urban gradient, including segment sinuosity (*r* = 0.43, *P* < 0.05 in RTH samples and *r* = 0.44, *P* < 0.05 in DTH samples), turbidity (*r* = 0.42, *P* < 0.05 in RTH samples and *r* = 0.39, *P* < 0.05 in DTH samples), concentration of suspended solids (*r* = 0.42, *P* < 0.05 in both RTH and DTH samples), percentage of gravel in the sediment (*r* = 0.40, *P* < 0.05 in RTH samples), and variation in discharge (*r* = 0.46, *P* < 0.05 in RTH samples), and was negatively correlated with variables that had increasing values along the urban gradient, such as surface water gradient (*r* = –0.41, *P* < 0.05 in DTH samples) and channel width (*r* = –0.42, *P* < 0.05 in RTH samples

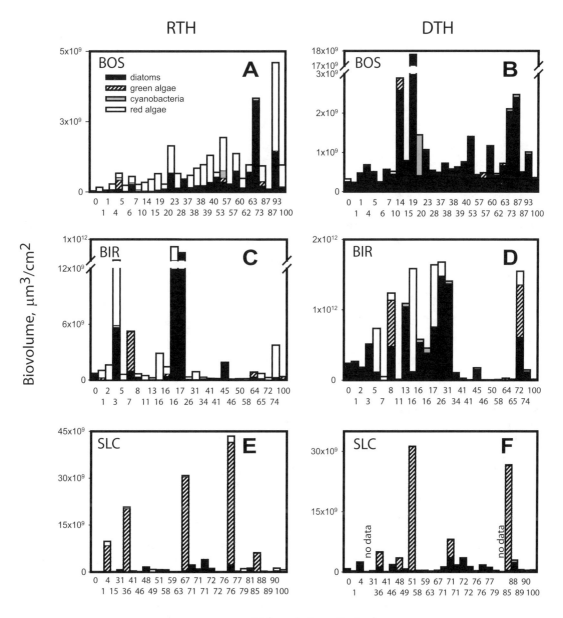

FIGURE 2. Algal biovolume in streams in (A, B) Boston (BOS); (C, D) Birmingham (BIR); and (E, F) Salt Lake City (SLC); A, C, E—hard substrata (RTH samples); B, D, F—soft sediments (DTH samples). The order of the sampling sites is by increasing UII.

and $r = -0.51$, $P < 0.01$ in DTH samples). The strongest correlations occurred between algal biovolume and abundance of the herbivorous fish, the largescale stoneroller *Campostoma oligolepis* ($r = -0.50$, $P < 0.01$ in RTH samples and $r = -0.77$, $P < 0.01$ in DTH samples). Stepwise forward selection of variables in

multiple regression analysis confirmed that abundance of largescale stoneroller most likely explained the decrease in algal biovolume in the BIR streams (Table 3). Potential explanatory variables tested in the multiple regression model were TP, TN, alkalinity, channel width, flow stability, canopy closure, turbidity, percentage of

TABLE 3. Results of the stepwise multiple regression analysis with three algal biomass characteristics (biovolume of algae in RTH and DTH samples, and chlorophyll *a*) as dependent variables. Explanatory variables were selected by the stepwise forward procedure as best predictors of algal biomass. No environmental variables were selected as predictors in two data sets—algal biovolume of DTH samples in the BOS study area and chlorophyll *a* in the BIR study area.

Dependent variable	Model r^2	Adjusted model r^2	Explanatory variables	Beta	r^2
		Boston			
Total algal biovolume, RTH	0.44	0.40	Flow-stability index	0.47	0.33
			Log TN	0.35	0.11
Chlorophyll *a*	0.72	0.70	Light	0.69	0.62
			Log TP	0.33	0.10
		Birmingham			
Total algal biovolume, RTH	0.25	0.22	Stoneroller abundance	−0.51	0.25
Total algal biovolume, DTH	0.67	0.56	Stoneroller abundance	−0.77	0.58
			Alkalinity	0.31	0.09
		Salt Lake City			
Total algal biovolume, RTH	0.16	0.13	Stream width		0.16
Total algal biovolume, DTH	0.42	0.37	Stream width	1.12	0.29
			Stream depth	−0.68	0.13
Chlorophyll *a*	0.19	0.16	Basin area with slope < 1%	0.43	0.19

fine-grained sediments, abundance of largescale stoneroller, stream depth, and current velocity at the sampling site. The final model for algal biovolume in RTH samples included only largescale stoneroller abundance as an explanatory variable, and the model for DTH samples includes abundance of largescale stoneroller and alkalinity. Diatoms and red algae most often dominated algal assemblages in this area, showing no particular pattern of relative abundance along the urban gradient (Figure 2C, D).

Salt Lake City study area.—No pattern was observed in algal biomass along the urban gradient in streams of the SLC study area. The filamentous green alga *Cladophora glomerata* occasionally proliferated in streams with various degrees of urban intensity (Figure 2E, F). Weak positive correlations ($r = 0.37$–0.53, $P < 0.05$) were identified between algal biomass variables (total algal biovolume and chlorophyll *a*) and several variables representing stream width and flatness of the watershed estimated as percentage of watershed area with slopes less than 1%. Biovolume in RTH samples was negatively associated with hydrologic variables related to flow stability, but the number of sites with hydrologic data were too low to ascertain the significance of these correlations. Stepwise multiple regression analysis did not reveal any relations between algal biomass and environmental factors except for a tendency toward higher biomass in wider streams and streams with flatter watersheds (Table 3). Variables initially con-

sidered for inclusion in the models were TP, TN, alkalinity, light, percentage of fine-grained sediment, stream width, stream depth, and current velocity at the sampling site, flow-stability index, percentage of the watershed with slope less than 1%, and abundance of invertebrate scrapers. Only stream depth, width, and percentage of the watershed with slope less than 1% were selected by the stepwise procedure for the final equations (Table 3).

Algal Diversity

The diversity of stream algal assemblages differed among the three study areas (Figure 3). The total number of species in a sample (species richness) was higher in the BIR study area compared with the other two areas (Figure 3A). Total number of algal species (gamma diversity) reported for the BIR data set also was higher (358 taxa) than for the BOS (278 taxa) and SLC (291 taxa) data sets. The Shannon-Wiener diversity index, however, was similar in all study areas. This index was somewhat higher in soft-sediment samples in the BOS area (Figure 3B), which can be explained by the absence of filamentous green algae. Evenness usually is low when there is an abundant growth of filamentous algae and high when filamentous algae are absent.

The strongest positive correlation between diversity of algal assemblages and urban gradient occurred in streams of the BOS study area (Tables 4, 5). In the SLC area, algal assemblages in DTH and QMH

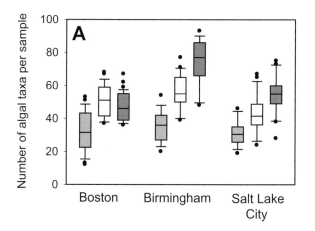

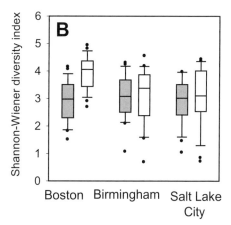

EXPLANATION

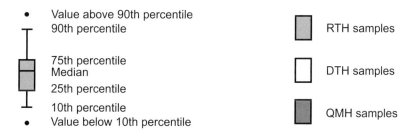

FIGURE 3. Median values and ranges of (A) total species richness and (B) Shannon-Wiener diversity index in streams of three study areas: Boston $n = 30$; Birmingham $n = 27$ for RTH and DTH samples and $n = 17$ for QMH samples; and Salt Lake City $n = 30$ for RTH samples, $n = 28$ for DTH samples, and $n = 27$ for QMH samples.

samples also had higher diversity in urban rivers. In the BIR area, only species richness in DTH samples was lower in urban streams than in nonurban streams.

Taxa with the highest number of occurrences in all study areas generally were cosmopolitan diatoms, such as *Achnanthidium minutissimum, Cocconeis placentula* var. *lineata, Navicula cryptotenella,* and *Gomphonema parvulum,* which are common in temperate rivers. There were, however, obvious regional differences in the taxonomic composition of algal as-

semblages. In the BOS study area, the list of taxa with the highest occurrences included a number of oligohalobous (salt intolerant) taxa, such as *Tabellaria flocculosa, Achnanthidium rivulare,* and *Eunotia incisa.* Conversely, in the BIR and SLC study areas, diatoms known to prefer high water-mineral content were common, including *Rhoicosphenia abbreviata, Achnanthidium deflexum, Nitzschia paleacea,* and *N. dissipata.* Besides these widely distributed taxa, some species with limited geographic distribution were found. The

TABLE 4. Kendall rank correlation between the Shannon-Wiener diversity index of algal assemblages and the urban intensity index in the three study areas. **, $P < 0.01$, *, $P < 0.05$.

	All algal taxa		Diatoms only	
Study area	RTH	DTH	RTH	DTH
Boston ($n = 30$)	0.59**	0.26*	0.63**	0.30*
Birmingham ($n = 27$)	−0.05	−0.09	0.03	−0.24
Salt Lake City ($n = 30$ for RTH; $n = 28$ for DTH)	0.24	0.05	0.24	0.42**

TABLE 5. Kendall rank correlation coefficients between species richness of algal assemblages and the urban intensity index in the three study areas. **, $P < 0.01$, *, $P < 0.05$.

Study area	All algal taxa			Diatoms only		
	RTH	DTH	QMH	RTH	DTH	QMH
Boston (n = 30)	0.66**	0.27*	0.30*	0.67**	0.28*	0.30*
Birmingham (n = 27 for RTH and DTH; n = 17 for QMH)	−0.02	−0.29*	−0.31	−0.04	−0.32*	−0.33
Salt Lake City (n = 30 for RTH; n = 28 for DTH; n = 27 for QMH)	0.21	0.47**	0.35*	0.22	0.44**	0.39*

highest number of rare and yet undescribed taxa was found in the BIR area. At least six diatom species, one green alga, and one chrysophyte were undescribed species, currently found only in the southeastern United States. Correlations (Kendall's tau), however, between the UII and relative abundance (RTH and DTH samples) and occurrence (RTH, DTH, and QMH samples) of these possibly endemic taxa in the BIR data set were not significant.

In the SLC study area, one diatom species (*Navicula* sp.) was found that is new to science and possibly endemic in the western United States. Its occurrence and abundance did not correlate with UII. No species of limited distribution were found in the BOS area.

Trends in Taxonomic Composition

Boston study area.—Algal taxa reaching the highest (20% in at least one sample) relative abundance of cells in the RTH samples collected in streams of the BOS study area were the diatoms *Achnanthidium minutissimum, A. rivulare, Cocconeis placentula* var. *lineata, Gomphonema parvulum;* filamentous cyanobacteria *Homoeothrix simplex, Calothrix fusca, Phormidium formosum, P. aeruginosum, Lyngbya hieronymusii, Lyngbya* sp.; and some red algae not identifiable because of the absence of reproductive structures in the summer. Among these taxa, only relative abundances of *Achnanthidium minutissimum* and *Calothrix fusca* were negatively correlated with UII (Kendall's tau, $P < 0.05$); eutraphentic *Gomphonema parvulum* was positively correlated with UII. In the DTH samples, the most abundant species (a relative abundance of 15% at least once) were the diatoms *Achnanthidium minutissimum, A. rivulare, Cocconeis placentula* var. *lineata, Fragilaria capucina* var. *rumpens, Tabellaria flocculosa, Staurosira construens* var. *venter, Psammothidium subatomoides, Sellaphora seminulum, Brachysira microcephala,* and *Melosira varians.* Among these, only *Achnanthidium minutissimum* and oligotraphentic *Psammothidium subatomoides* were

negatively correlated (Kendall's tau, $P < 0.05$) with the UII, and no taxa showed significant positive correlations with the UII.

In the BOS study area, NMS ordinations of both data sets (diatoms and all algal taxa) from the RTH samples produced similar results (Table 6). Variance in species data explained by all-taxa ordination was 87%, and variance explained by diatom ordination was 91%. Both ordinations had strong correlations with the UII. The axis aligned with the UII explained 52% of the variation in the all-taxa and 57% in the diatom data set. Variables strongly correlated with the UII-aligned ordination axis included alkalinity, conductivity, road density, TN, wetted channel width-to-depth ratio, shape index, and channel relative roughness (Table 6). Variables that showed strong association with algal assemblage composition in the BOS study area, but not strongly correlated with the UII, were TP, number of herbicide detections, and some variables characterizing flow regime (Table 6; Figure 4A). Eutraphentic and pollution-tolerant diatoms (*Navicula minima, N. gregaria, Sellaphora seminulum*) were positioned at the high end of the urban gradient. Some species in the left side of the ordination diagram, corresponding to the low end of the urban gradient, were oligotraphentic taxa (*Brachysira microcephala* and *B. serians*). Abundance of filamentous cyanobacteria, such as *Lyngbya bergei* and *Calothrix fusca*, was lower in urban streams.

Ordination of DTH samples indicated similar environmental gradients explaining variation in algal assemblages as ordination of RTH samples, although taxa that had the highest ordination scores were different between the two ordinations (compare Figure 4A, B). Diatoms positioned at the high end of the urban gradient were mostly eutraphentic, pollution-tolerant, and halophilic species (*Navicula lanceolata, Rhoicosphenia abbreviata, Nitzschia bremensis*). The all-taxa and diatom ordinations extracted 85% and 91% variability in species data, respectively. After rotation, the first axis aligned with UII extracted 28% and 33% of the varia-

TABLE 6. Correlations of environmental variables and NMS ordination axes for the RTH 30-sample data set for the Boston study area. Ordinations were rotated to maximize loadings of the first axis on the urban intensity index. Only environmental variables with highest multiple r^2 (Σr^2) are shown. Significant correlations ($P < 0.05$) are in bold. Abbreviations for variables and variable units are in Table 1.

Environmental variable	All taxa				Diatoms only			
	axis 1	axis 2	axis 3	Σr^2	axis 1	axis 2	axis 3	Σr^2
Alkalinity	**0.72**	−0.20	0.18	0.59	**0.81**	0.02	**0.38**	0.79
Wetted width–depth ratio	**−0.66**	0.08	−0.27	0.52	**−0.72**	0.02	−0.22	0.57
Channel shape index	**−0.62**	0.09	−0.29	0.48	**−0.66**	0.09	−0.23	0.49
Urban intensity index	**0.67**	0.00	0.07	0.45	**0.83**	−0.03	0.17	0.71
Conductivity	**0.63**	−0.13	0.18	0.44	**0.83**	−0.02	**0.42**	0.87
Road density	**0.64**	0.02	0.10	0.42	**0.74**	−0.11	0.11	0.56
Coefficient of variation of bank-full width–depth	**0.49**	−0.33	0.23	0.40	**0.53**	−0.05	0.34	0.40
TN	**0.50**	−0.33	0.18	0.39	**0.74**	−0.06	**0.49**	0.79
Dissolved oxygen	**−0.51**	0.28	−0.20	0.38	**−0.54**	0.11	−0.10	0.31
Channel relative roughness	**−0.58**	0.12	−0.15	0.37	**−0.70**	−0.08	−0.18	0.54
NO_2+NO_3	**0.49**	−0.32	0.15	0.36	**0.71**	0.01	**0.49**	0.74
TKN	**0.50**	−0.25	0.23	0.36	**0.64**	−0.11	0.30	0.51
SO_4	**0.55**	−0.09	−0.23	0.36	**0.62**	**0.44**	0.11	0.59
Mean flow velocity	**0.50**	−0.28	−0.15	0.35	**0.50**	**0.43**	0.29	0.52
Maximum flow velocity	**0.47**	−0.27	−0.21	0.34	**0.51**	**0.41**	0.31	0.52
Mxh90	0.29	0.18	**0.47**	0.34	0.28	−0.18	0.25	0.17
TP	**0.39**	**−0.38**	0.18	0.33	**0.67**	0.00	**0.51**	0.71
Number of herbicide detections	**0.36**	**−0.41**	0.19	0.33	−0.17	−0.03	−0.15	0.05
Population	**0.56**	0.04	0.04	0.32	**0.71**	−0.10	0.03	0.51
Forest	**−0.52**	−0.21	0.01	0.31	**−0.44**	0.08	0.11	0.21
Segment sinuosity	**−0.52**	0.18	−0.02	0.31	**−0.51**	−0.03	−0.15	0.29
Coefficient of variation of bank-full width	**0.40**	−0.21	0.31	0.31	0.19	−0.20	0.22	0.12
Bank-full width–depth ratio	**−0.51**	0.05	−0.19	0.30	**−0.60**	0.07	−0.16	0.39
Mxl5	−0.33	**0.42**	−0.10	0.29	**−0.44**	0.02	**−0.36**	0.32
Water temperature	**0.42**	−0.26	0.20	0.28	**0.47**	0.20	0.18	0.29
Wetted depth	**0.51**	−0.06	0.14	0.28	**0.66**	−0.17	0.01	0.46
Discharge	**0.36**	−0.34	−0.17	0.27	**0.50**	0.16	0.09	0.28
% silt+gravel	**0.47**	−0.07	0.21	0.26	**0.45**	−0.27	−0.13	0.29
Wetted width	**−0.41**	−0.05	−0.29	0.25	−0.29	0.00	−0.25	0.14
% sand	**0.41**	−0.24	0.11	0.24	**0.45**	−0.18	−0.11	0.25
Maximum wetted depth	**0.46**	−0.05	0.10	0.23	**0.63**	−0.18	−0.01	0.42

tion in all-taxa and diatom data sets, respectively. Similar to the RTH ordination, the variation of algal assemblage along urban gradient was mostly associated with water-mineral content, nitrogen content, and channel morphology (Table 7). Variation in assemblages not directly related to urban intensity gradient was mostly associated with several characteristics of flow regime in both diatom and all-taxa ordinations, with silt occurrence in the all-taxa ordination, and with percentage of riffles in the diatom ordination.

Birmingham study area.—In the BIR study area, the most abundant taxa in both RTH and DTH

samples were diatoms *Achnanthidium minutissimum* and *A. deflexum*; filamentous cyanobacteria *Homoeothrix simplex, Phormidium autumnale,* and unidentified *Leptolyngbia*; green alga *Scenedesmus acutus*; and the chantransia stage of red algae. Among these, only relative abundance of *Scenedesmus acutus* increased significantly with urbanization.

Ordinations of RTH samples in the all-taxa and diatom data sets showed that algal assemblages were more related to physical habitat characteristics and the presence of grazers than to the urban gradient (Table 8). The all-taxa ordination extracted more variability

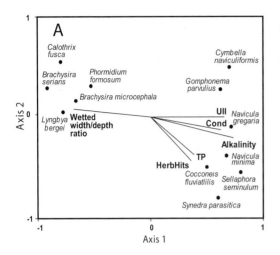

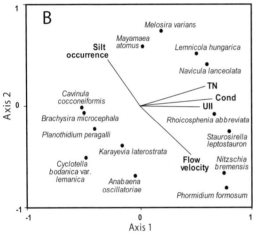

FIGURE 4. Results of nonmetric multidimensional scaling ordinations for (A) RTH and (B) DTH samples from 30 streams in the Boston study area. Joint plots of species and environmental variables were obtained by rotating ordinations to align the UII variable with the first ordination axis. Abbreviations for variables are listed in Table 1.

of species data (86%) than the diatom ordination (77%). The ordination axis aligned with the UII extracted only a low amount of variation of species data— 21% in the all-taxa data set and 19% in the diatom data set. The relatively short line for the UII (Figure 5A), corresponding to its low correlation with ordination (Table 8), indicated that this variable was not associated with considerable variation in the assemblage composition. Variation of algal assemblages along the gradient of urban intensity was associated mostly with hydrological variables, such as frequency of stream level (stage) above or below particular values (Table 8). Positive correlation between stage-related charac-

teristics and the UII-aligned axis indicated that streams were more flashy in urban settings than in nonurban settings and that this factor could cause shifts in the composition of algal assemblages along the urban gradient. Abundance of invertebrate scrapers and herbivorous fish were important factors in ordination of the all-taxa data set but not in the diatom data set (Table 8), indicating that grazers may exert a selective pressure on particular nondiatom taxa, most probably macroscopic algae. Abundance of the largescale stoneroller was positively correlated and abundance of invertebrate scrapers was negatively correlated with the UII-aligned axis; therefore, these variables could be associated with algal assemblage composition along the urban gradient. Other variables that had strong correlations with ordination but were not associated with urbanization gradient were several characteristics of channel morphology and canopy closure.

Ordination of DTH samples indicated that assemblages in soft sediments were more strongly related to the urban intensity gradient than assemblages on rocks (Table 9). Ordinations of the all-taxa and diatom data sets accounted for 83% and 75% of variability in species data, respectively. The axis aligned with the UII extracted 36% and 39% of the variation of the all-taxa and diatom ordinations, respectively. The UII variable in both ordinations was associated with the highest amount of variability in the species data compared to all other measured variables (Table 9). Other variables that had highest correlations with ordination but were not strongly aligned with the UII-aligned axis were characteristics of flow regime, channel morphology and sediment composition, concentration and number of herbicide detections, water-mineral content, and nitrogen content (Table 9; Figure 5B). Algal taxa at the high end of the urban gradient were common pollution-tolerant species, such as *Navicula veneta* and *Scenedesmus acutus*, whereas some of those at the low end were taxa of limited geographic distribution (*Surirella stalagma*, *N. repentina*) that could be indicators of natural conditions in the BIR study area.

Salt Lake City study area.—The taxa with the highest relative abundances in streams of the SLC study area were the diatoms *Achnanthidium minutissimum*, *Amphora pediculus*, *Rhoicosphenia abbreviata*, and *Nitzschia inconspicua*; filamentous cyanobacteria *Homoeothrix janthina*, *Phormidium autumnale*, and *Calothrix parietina*; an unidentified coccoid cyanobacterium; and the chantransia stage of red algae. *Phormidium autumnale* had a significant negative correlation (Kendall's tau, $P <$ 0.05) with the UII in the RTH sample data set. Two

TABLE 7. Correlations of environmental variables and NMS ordination axes for the DTH 30-sample data set for the Boston study area. Ordinations were rotated to maximize loadings of the first axis on the urban intensity index. Only environmental variables with highest multiple r^2 (Σr^2) are shown. Significant correlations ($P < 0.05$) are in bold. Abbreviations for variables and variable units are in Table 1.

Environmental variable	All taxa				Diatoms only			
	axis 1	axis 2	axis 3	Σr^2	axis 1	axis 2	axis 3	Σr^2
$NO_2 + NO_3$	**0.60**	0.28	0.30	0.53	**0.55**	0.12	−0.16	0.34
Conductivity	**0.66**	0.07	0.30	0.52	**0.64**	0.06	−0.15	0.43
SO_4	**0.66**	−0.22	−0.13	0.49	**0.51**	0.20	**0.37**	0.43
TN	**0.59**	0.19	0.31	0.48	**0.61**	0.11	−0.22	0.43
Mean flow velocity	**0.46**	**−0.48**	0.03	0.45	**0.52**	**0.46**	0.29	0.57
Maximum flow velocity	**0.49**	**−0.45**	0.05	0.45	**0.50**	**0.41**	0.33	0.52
Alkalinity	**0.62**	0.15	0.15	0.43	**0.71**	0.25	−0.15	0.59
Mxh95	−0.33	0.15	0.53	0.41	−0.09	−0.14	**−0.48**	0.26
Dissolved oxygen	**−0.58**	0.14	0.05	0.37	**−0.54**	−0.04	0.12	0.31
Coefficient of variation of discharge	**−0.47**	0.35	0.02	0.35	−0.23	−0.18	0.00	0.09
Channel relative roughness	**−0.50**	0.28	−0.10	0.33	**−0.62**	0.01	0.09	0.39
Coefficient of variation of flow velocity	−0.34	**0.46**	−0.06	0.33	−0.26	**−0.46**	−0.22	0.33
TP	**0.48**	0.17	0.25	0.32	**0.51**	0.11	−0.13	0.29
Discharge	**0.41**	**−0.37**	−0.06	0.31	**0.47**	0.09	0.18	0.26
Wetted width–depth ratio	**−0.52**	0.15	−0.13	0.31	**−0.68**	−0.03	0.11	0.48
Urban intensity index	**0.55**	−0.02	0.00	0.30	**0.67**	−0.02	0.00	0.45
Silt occurrence	−0.27	**0.44**	−0.15	0.29	−0.34	−0.24	−0.07	0.02
Bank-full width–depth ratio	**−0.50**	0.15	−0.10	0.28	**−0.54**	0.03	0.17	0.32
Channel shape index	**−0.49**	0.09	−0.14	0.27	**−0.64**	−0.03	0.13	0.43
Forest	**−0.50**	−0.04	0.05	0.25	**−0.58**	0.09	−0.01	0.34
Road density	**0.46**	0.06	0.02	0.22	**0.64**	−0.04	−0.05	0.41
TKN	**0.43**	0.10	0.13	0.21	**0.61**	0.10	−0.28	0.46
Population density	**0.45**	−0.04	−0.05	0.20	**0.59**	−0.12	−0.01	0.37
Wetted depth	**0.42**	−0.11	−0.01	0.19	**0.57**	−0.21	−0.11	0.39
Maximum wetted depth	**0.39**	−0.10	0.01	0.16	**0.54**	−0.25	−0.08	0.36
Coefficient of variation of bank-full width–depth	0.20	−0.02	0.32	0.14	**0.54**	0.27	−0.15	0.38
% silt + gravel	0.31	−0.04	−0.05	0.10	**0.53**	−0.19	−0.24	0.37
% sand	0.28	−0.10	−0.05	0.09	**0.53**	−0.11	−0.14	0.31
% gravel + boulder	−0.29	0.06	0.04	0.09	**−0.51**	0.19	0.23	0.35
Percentage of reach area as riffles	0.09	−0.11	−0.26	0.09	0.21	**0.50**	**0.40**	0.45
% fine	0.27	−0.05	−0.08	0.08	**0.53**	−0.19	−0.18	0.35
Number of herbicide detections	0.24	−0.01	0.12	0.07	0.40	**0.41**	−0.18	0.36

diatoms commonly associated with sandy sediments, *Amphora pediculus* and *Nitzschia inconspicua,* correlated positively with the UII.

Algal assemblages on hard substrates in urban streams of the SLC area were apparently influenced by the increased concentrations of ions and nutrients (Table 10). Both NMS ordinations of the all-taxa and diatom data sets extracted a high percentage of variability—87% and 84%, respectively. The ordination axis aligned with the UII extracted 43% of the vari-

ability in the all-taxa data set and 41% in the diatom data set. Several variables related to water-mineral content, TP, and the percentage of fine-grained sediments were positively correlated with the UII-aligned axis (Table 10). Water-mineral content could be considered the most probable cause of the shift in the algal assemblage composition along the urban gradient in the SLC. Algal taxa at the high end of the urban gradient were diatoms commonly found in waters of high ionic strength, such as *Diatoma moniliformis* and

TABLE 8. Correlations of environmental variables and NMS ordination axes for the RTH 27-sample data set from the Birmingham study area. Ordinations were rotated to maximize loadings of the first axis on the urban intensity index. Only environmental variables with highest multiple r^2 (Σr^2) are shown. Significant correlations ($P < 0.05$) are in bold. Abbreviations for variables and variable units are in Table 1.

Environmental variable	All taxa				Diatoms only			
	axis 1	axis 2	axis 3	Σr^2	axis 1	axis 2	axis 3	Σr^2
Coefficient of variation of canopy closure	0.20	0.04	**−0.64**	0.45	0.09	0.04	0.02	0.01
Canopy closure	−0.10	−0.05	**0.65**	0.44	−0.07	0.06	0.02	0.01
Dissolved oxygen	−0.07	**−0.56**	−0.28	0.39	−0.32	0.08	0.30	0.20
% silt + clay	**−0.51**	0.02	−0.34	0.38	−0.20	−0.29	0.10	0.13
Scrapers	**−0.41**	**0.40**	−0.24	0.38	−0.09	−0.35	−0.36	0.26
Mxl5	**0.61**	0.04	−0.08	0.37	0.37	**0.44**	0.07	0.33
Wetted depth	**−0.48**	0.32	−0.13	0.35	−0.03	−0.27	−0.17	0.10
Stoneroller	**0.44**	−0.37	−0.10	0.34	0.33	0.25	0.14	0.19
Channel relative roughness	**0.39**	−0.36	0.13	0.30	0.25	0.06	0.28	0.14
Flow-stability index	−0.32	0.25	−0.33	0.28	−0.27	−0.32	0.08	0.18
Maximum wetted depth	**−0.46**	0.20	−0.11	0.27	−0.13	−0.26	−0.08	0.09
Periodr7	**0.50**	0.07	0.09	0.27	**0.53**	**0.38**	−0.05	0.43
Periodr9	**0.49**	0.06	0.10	0.26	**0.50**	0.37	−0.04	0.38
Periodr5	**0.48**	0.09	0.08	0.25	**0.56**	0.36	−0.05	0.45
Segment sinuosity	−0.23	**0.43**	−0.05	0.24	−0.10	−0.36	−0.06	0.14
Periodf9	**0.45**	0.03	0.09	0.21	**0.46**	0.37	−0.04	0.35
Periodr3	**0.43**	0.01	0.15	0.21	**0.59**	0.36	−0.09	0.48
Mean basin elevation	0.29	−0.35	0.05	0.21	**−0.40**	0.30	0.02	0.25
Periodf7	**0.43**	0.01	0.09	0.19	**0.46**	0.34	−0.05	0.33
Periodf3	**0.42**	0.01	0.11	0.19	**0.52**	0.31	−0.06	0.37
Silt occurrence	0.15	0.36	0.20	0.19	0.17	−0.10	**−0.49**	0.28
Periodf1	0.10	0.31	0.18	0.14	**0.49**	0.16	**−0.47**	0.48
Coefficient of variation of bank-full width–depth ratio	0.20	−0.01	0.32	0.14	−0.16	0.13	**0.66**	0.47
Periodr1	0.04	0.32	0.16	0.13	**0.41**	0.11	−0.45	0.38
Percentage of reach area as riffles	−0.01	−0.33	0.00	0.11	−0.02	0.34	**0.51**	0.38
Urban intensity index	0.29	−0.01	−0.05	0.09	**0.52**	0.01	0.00	0.27
Basin area	0.07	0.24	0.18	0.09	**0.47**	−0.02	−0.42	0.39
Periodf5	−0.13	−0.03	−0.26	0.08	**0.49**	0.33	−0.06	0.35
Coefficient of variation of channel shape index	0.17	−0.19	0.09	0.08	0.03	0.12	**0.54**	0.30
Uplands	−0.25	−0.12	−0.08	0.08	−0.04	−0.16	**0.51**	0.28
Road density	0.22	−0.03	−0.15	0.07	**0.54**	−0.03	−0.03	0.29
Variation in wetted width	0.22	−0.10	−0.01	0.06	−0.15	0.07	**0.62**	0.42
Bank-full width	0.19	−0.13	0.00	0.05	**0.56**	−0.03	0.06	0.32
Total herbicide concentration	0.21	−0.07	0.03	0.05	**0.55**	0.06	0.01	0.30
Coefficient of variation of bank-full width	0.03	−0.14	−0.07	0.02	−0.14	−0.02	**0.60**	0.38

Encyonema auerswaldii (Figure 6A). Taxa at the low end of the urban gradient, such as *Diatoma mesodon* and *Homoeothrix janthina,* were typical inhabitants of cold, oligotrophic, and fast-flowing streams.

Ordination of DTH samples showed weaker relations of algal assemblages to the urban gradient in the SLC area (Table 11). The all-taxa and diatom ordinations extracted 84% and 85% of variance, respectively. After rotation, the first ordination axis aligned with the UII extracted 22% and 31% of variance, respectively. The all-taxa ordination was related mostly to light conditions, canopy closure, stream size

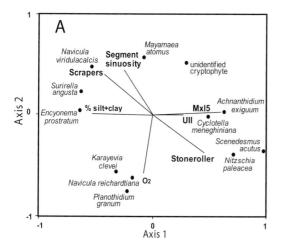

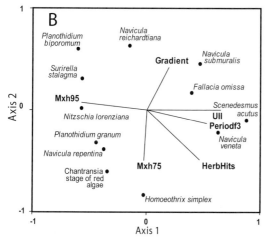

FIGURE 5. Results of nonmetric multidimensional scaling ordinations for (A) RTH and (B) DTH samples from 27 streams in the Birmingham study area. Joint plots of species and environmental variables were obtained by rotating ordinations to align the UII variable with the first ordination axis. Abbreviations for variables are listed in Table 1.

(as stream order, basin area and discharge, stream depth and width), and some chemical characteristics, such as F, pH, and NH_4. The variables most closely aligned with the UII-axis were those related to stream size and canopy closure (negative correlation) and residue on evaporation (positive correlation). Light reaching the stream bottom had a strong relation to algal assemblage structure. Light conditions generally were worse in the urban streams, despite less canopy closure, because of increased suspended sediments. Some cyanobacteria (*Calothrix parietina, Homoeothrix janthina*) and the diatom *Cocconeis neodiminuta*, which often is associated with sandy sediments, were positioned at the high

end of the urban gradient (Figure 6B). Although this analysis did not indicate very strong relations between algal assemblages and stream environment, the higher concentration of dissolved solids (measured as residue on evaporation and concentrations of Na, K, Cl, SO_4, and SiO_2) was a likely factor related to the assemblage patterns revealed by this ordination. In the diatom ordination, variables related to stream size and residue on evaporation were the most important factors, but concentration of nutrients (TKN, TP, SiO_2) and some ions (Na, K, Cl, SO_4) and sediment size also had high correlations with ordination axes.

Percentages of pollution-sensitive, oligosaprobous, and oligotraphentic diatoms mostly decreased, while percentages of pollution-tolerant, α-mesosparobous + polysaprobous, and eutraphentic diatoms increased with urbanization (Table 12). This pattern was most pronounced in the BOS study area, less obvious in the SLC area, and weakest in the BIR area. Percentages of pollution-tolerant and saprophilous taxa were always higher in urban streams, although other metrics showed less consistency.

Discussion

The results of this study indicate that patterns in algal assemblages along urban intensity gradients vary regionally. Of the various attributes of algal assemblages tested, only proportions of taxa tolerant to general and organic pollution consistently tended to be higher in urban streams than in nonurban streams, although correlations of these attributes with UII were not always statistically significant. Algal biomass and diversity increased or decreased along the urban gradient depending on natural factors and human influences.

Our work demonstrates that climate and geology imposed ultimate constraints on the structure of algal assemblages in streams as predicted by the conceptual models of Biggs (1990) and Stevenson (1997). Lower algal biomass in the BOS study area in comparison to algal biomass in the SLC and BIR areas was in agreement with a generally observed pattern of lower biomass levels in streams of higher latitudes where climate is harsher and nutrients are lower compared to streams of lower latitudes (Dodds et al. 1998). Higher species diversity in the BIR area in comparison to diversity in the BOS and SLC areas confirmed previous observations that highest diversity of stream algae in the United States occurs in the warm, humid Southeast (Potapova and Charles 2004). The higher proportion of oligohalobous algal taxa in the BOS area compared to

TABLE 9. Correlations of environmental variables and NMS ordination axes for the DTH 27-sample data set from the Birmingham study area. Ordinations were rotated to maximize loadings of the first axis on the urban intensity index. Only environmental variables with highest multiple r^2 (Σr^2) are shown. Significant correlations ($P < 0.05$) are in bold. Abbreviations for variables and variable units are in Table 1.

Environmental variable	All taxa				Diatoms only			
	axis 1	axis 2	axis 3	Σr^2	axis 1	axis 2	axis 3	Σr^2
Urban intensity index	**0.65**	−0.02	−0.37	0.55	**0.71**	−0.03	0.00	0.51
Forest	**−0.62**	0.11	**0.38**	0.53	**−0.63**	0.15	0.10	0.43
Periodf3	**0.51**	−0.13	**−0.42**	0.45	**0.66**	0.04	−0.07	0.44
Periodf5	**0.50**	−0.14	**−0.42**	0.44	**0.65**	0.08	−0.05	0.43
Number of herbicide detections	**0.46**	**−0.47**	0.00	0.44	0.28	**−0.46**	−0.22	0.34
Periodr5	**0.52**	−0.12	**−0.38**	0.43	**0.65**	0.11	−0.13	0.45
Periodr3	**0.50**	−0.18	−0.37	0.42	**0.64**	0.02	−0.16	0.44
Periodf9	**0.46**	−0.15	**−0.40**	0.40	**0.62**	0.12	−0.07	0.40
Periodf7	**0.47**	−0.14	**−0.40**	0.40	**0.63**	0.11	−0.04	0.40
Periodr9	**0.47**	−0.15	**−0.38**	0.40	**0.62**	0.12	−0.09	0.40
Periodr7	**0.48**	−0.12	**−0.39**	0.39	**0.63**	0.12	−0.11	0.42
Mean basin elevation	−0.29	0.33	**−0.42**	0.36	0.13	**−0.52**	**0.54**	0.58
Mxh95	**−0.56**	0.07	0.19	0.35	**−0.53**	0.09	0.15	0.31
% cobbles	−0.34	−0.17	**−0.41**	0.32	0.13	−0.13	0.02	0.04
Stoneroller	0.22	0.18	**−0.48**	0.31	**0.63**	0.23	0.27	0.52
Mg	**0.51**	−0.17	−0.04	0.29	0.36	−0.08	−0.08	0.14
Relief	−0.26	0.36	−0.30	0.28	0.08	**0.45**	0.24	0.26
Cultivated	**−0.31**	−0.33	0.27	0.28	**−0.46**	−0.23	−0.12	0.27
Mxl5	0.12	0.07	**−0.50**	0.26	**0.46**	0.15	−0.07	0.24
Segment sinuosity	−0.05	0.07	**0.51**	0.26	−0.35	−0.26	−0.26	0.26
Mxh75	−0.02	**−0.50**	−0.05	0.25	−0.07	−0.08	−0.04	0.01
% gravel	0.13	0.22	**0.43**	0.25	**−0.41**	−0.01	−0.04	0.17
Bank-full depth	−0.03	0.07	**−0.48**	0.24	**0.53**	−0.02	−0.09	0.28
Surface-water gradient	0.21	**0.41**	−0.09	0.22	0.21	0.22	**0.41**	0.26
% silt + gravel	−0.16	0.02	0.44	0.22	**−0.58**	0.21	−0.34	0.49
Total herbicide concentration	0.27	−0.17	−0.34	0.21	**0.48**	−0.30	−0.18	0.36
Flow-stability index	0.01	0.15	**0.43**	0.21	**−0.43**	−0.24	0.00	0.24
Bank-full width	0.27	−0.05	−0.35	0.20	**0.60**	−0.18	−0.13	0.41
Wetted width	0.31	−0.08	−0.31	0.20	**0.49**	−0.29	−0.24	0.38
$NO_3 + NO_2$	0.04	−0.12	**0.43**	0.20	−0.24	**−0.41**	−0.12	0.24
Scrapers	−0.32	0.06	0.28	0.18	**−0.46**	0.01	−0.34	0.32
Discharge	0.16	0.08	0.36	0.16	−0.04	**−0.52**	−0.02	0.27
Wetted width–depth ratio	0.29	−0.03	−0.22	0.13	**0.43**	−0.14	0.21	0.24
TN	0.10	−0.08	0.31	0.12	−0.05	**−0.50**	−0.19	0.28
Basin area	0.09	−0.20	−0.23	0.10	0.25	−0.06	**−0.52**	0.33
Residue on evaporation	0.26	−0.10	0.13	0.09	0.24	**−0.44**	**−0.39**	0.40
Uplands	0.03	0.07	0.30	0.09	−0.02	**−0.48**	0.05	0.23
Conductivity	0.21	−0.06	0.08	0.05	0.23	**−0.41**	−0.37	0.35
Periodf1	0.17	−0.03	−0.04	0.03	0.19	−0.10	**−0.50**	0.30
Ca	0.10	−0.10	0.11	0.03	0.05	**−0.44**	−0.20	0.23
Dissolved oxygen	0.03	0.02	0.13	0.02	0.02	−0.06	**0.48**	0.23

the dominance of halophilic species in the two other study areas reflected differences in the bedrock composition and, therefore, in water mineralization among the study areas. Biotic interactions, such as the presence of grazers, also influenced algal assemblages. In the BIR study area, the herbivorous largescale stoneroller was able to tolerate urban-related habitat disturbance (Meador et al. 2005, this volume). The

TABLE 10. Correlations of environmental variables and NMS ordination axes for the RTH 30-sample data set from the Salt Lake City study area. Ordinations were rotated to maximize loadings of the first axis on the urban intensity index. Only environmental variables with highest multiple r^2 (Σr^2) are shown. Significant correlations ($P < 0.05$) are in bold. Abbreviations for variables and variable units are in Table 1.

Environmental variable	All taxa				Diatoms only			
	axis 1	axis 2	axis 3	Σr^2	axis 1	axis 2	axis 3	Σr^2
Na	**0.63**	0.05	0.22	0.44	**0.48**	−0.02	0.15	0.26
Cl	**0.64**	0.20	0.06	0.44	**0.51**	0.04	0.11	0.27
SiO$_2$	**0.59**	0.21	0.13	0.40	0.30	−0.06	−0.07	0.10
Residue on evaporation	**0.58**	0.24	−0.01	0.39	**0.55**	0.15	−0.13	0.34
Conductivity	**0.58**	0.20	−0.02	0.37	**0.58**	0.22	−0.07	0.39
K	**0.52**	−0.06	0.28	0.36	**0.40**	−0.02	0.37	0.30
% gravel + boulders	**−0.55**	−0.18	−0.05	0.34	**−0.57**	−0.10	0.19	0.37
% silt + gravel	**0.55**	0.18	0.05	0.34	**0.57**	0.10	−0.19	0.37
Mg	**0.51**	0.24	−0.13	0.34	**0.57**	0.31	−0.17	0.45
F	**0.47**	−0.21	0.25	0.32	0.21	−0.28	**0.49**	0.36
% sand	**0.55**	0.15	−0.05	0.32	0.49	−0.02	−0.12	0.25
Mean dominant substrate size	**−0.54**	−0.17	0.02	0.32	**−0.63**	−0.05	0.21	0.44
Alkalinity	**0.38**	0.34	−0.25	0.32	**0.54**	**0.44**	−0.33	0.60
% fine	**0.54**	0.17	−0.01	0.32	**0.49**	0.11	−0.15	0.27
Coefficient of variation of flow velocity	−0.28	**−0.48**	−0.10	0.32	−0.28	**−0.53**	**0.37**	0.49
Grassland	−0.45	0.27	−0.16	0.30	0.03	**0.49**	−0.03	0.24
Coefficient of variation of bank-full width	**0.39**	0.37	0.01	0.29	**−0.61**	−0.24	0.30	0.52
Ca	0.33	0.33	−0.26	0.28	**0.51**	**0.40**	−0.42	0.60
Bank-full width–depth ratio	−0.26	**−0.42**	−0.19	0.28	−0.39	0.21	0.17	0.23
TP	**0.49**	0.00	0.17	0.27	**0.53**	0.00	0.14	0.31
Fe	−0.16	**−0.37**	0.34	0.27	0.26	−0.27	0.03	0.14
Channel shape index	−0.34	−0.36	−0.16	0.27	**−0.48**	−0.35	**0.48**	0.59
Wetted width–depth ratio	−0.30	**−0.40**	−0.11	0.26	**−0.41**	**−0.51**	**0.56**	0.74
Segment sinuosity	0.28	0.28	0.33	0.26	**0.54**	0.28	−0.12	0.39
Urban intensity index	**0.50**	0.06	−0.07	0.26	**0.54**	0.00	0.00	0.29
Embeddedness	0.26	**0.43**	0.00	0.25	**0.61**	**0.50**	−0.33	0.73
Coefficient of variation of discharge	−0.24	**−0.43**	−0.08	0.25	−0.31	**−0.65**	**0.47**	0.73
Depth at sampling location	0.16	**0.46**	−0.22	0.25	0.09	**0.34**	−0.13	0.14
Channel relative roughness	**−0.37**	−0.33	0.08	0.25	−0.36	**−0.55**	0.32	0.53
TKN	0.25	−0.18	0.21	0.14	**0.38**	−0.15	**0.38**	0.31
Manning's channel roughness	−0.15	−0.34	−0.04	0.14	−0.37	−0.27	0.25	0.27
Maximum wetted depth	0.08	0.35	0.00	0.13	−0.08	**0.50**	−0.24	0.32
Wetted depth	0.08	0.36	0.00	0.13	−0.06	**0.50**	−0.24	0.32
% silt + clay	0.32	0.05	−0.10	0.12	**0.44**	0.03	−0.35	0.32
Number of herbicide detections	0.16	−0.24	0.14	0.10	**0.38**	−0.13	0.42	0.33
Velocity at sampling location	0.10	0.29	0.06	0.10	−0.04	**0.39**	−0.38	0.30
Flow velocity	−0.04	0.25	0.18	0.09	−0.27	0.33	−0.34	0.30
Maximum flow velocity	−0.09	0.22	0.15	0.08	−0.30	0.28	−0.34	0.29
Silt occurrence	0.20	0.09	−0.07	0.05	**0.53**	0.09	0.32	0.39

presence of this grazer was not only associated with reduced algal biomass, but also with shifts in taxonomic composition and diversity of algae.

Nonuniform responses of stream algal assemblages to urbanization reflected the regional differences in human influences. The gradient of urban intensity in

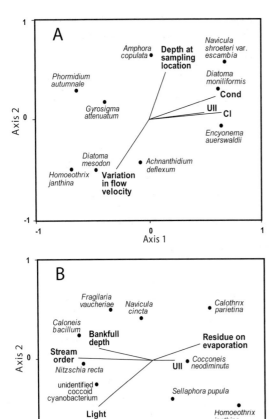

FIGURE 6. Results of nonmetric multidimensional scaling ordinations for (A) 30 RTH and (B) 28 DTH samples from streams in the Salt Lake City study area. Joint plots of species and environmental variables were obtained by rotating ordinations to align the UII variable with the first ordination axis. Abbreviations for variables are listed in Table 1.

related to urban intensity. In the BIR area, patterns of algal composition along the urban gradient were related more to physical habitat characteristics and the presence of grazers. Taxonomic composition of algal assemblages in the BOS study area showed a clear pattern along the conductivity gradient, which was collinear with the gradient of urban intensity. The process of site selection for the BOS area ensured homogeneity of natural conditions of the data set, meaning that increased conductivity at the urban sites was caused primarily by human influence. Thus, the ability of algae to indicate water-mineral content may be exploited successfully to monitor water mineralization in affected streams of the BOS area. The composition of algal assemblages also was related to water-mineral content in the SLC study area. However, urban development was concentrated in lower elevations, while nonurban sampling was conducted in higher elevations. Water-mineral content naturally increases downstream; therefore, we could not be sure that an increase in water-mineral content at the urban sites was a result of human influence alone. Abundance of halophilic diatoms on hard substrates of SLC urban streams can be considered a sign of human influences with caution only.

We found that while algal assemblages in the BOS and SLC study areas had higher biomass and diversity in urban streams than in less affected streams, assemblages in the BIR streams exhibited opposite patterns. Evidently, algae in the nonurban BOS and SLC streams were nutrient-limited, and increases in nutrient concentrations in urban streams were at least partly associated with higher algal abundance and diversity. Patterns in species composition of algal assemblages also were closely associated with nutrients. The strongest correlations occurred in the BOS area where nutrient concentrations increased significantly with urbanization. In the SLC and BIR study areas, even in the absence of strong correlations between nutrient concentrations and urban intensity, most algal taxa occurring at the upper end of the urban gradient were eutraphentic diatoms. The composition of benthic algae has potential as an indicator of nutrient concentrations in running waters (Kelly and Whitton 1995; Pan et al. 1996; Winter and Duthie 2000; Soininen and Niemelä 2002), but detailed, regional-scale studies are needed to create reliable algae-based monitoring tools. In particular, many species typical of nutrient-rich waters are broadly distributed and well known, whereas oligotraphentic species often are characteristic of more limited geographic areas and are not sufficiently studied (Potapova and Charles 2004). This may explain why, in this study, we sometimes did not observe decreases in relative abundance of

the BOS and SLC study areas was associated mostly with the transition from natural landscapes (forest and shrub land) to urban areas. In the BIR area, not only natural landscapes, but also percentages of agricultural land decreased along an urban gradient. In agreement with this pattern, concentrations of nutrients and major ions significantly increased along gradients of urban intensity in the BOS and SLC study areas, but not in the BIR area. Presumably, agricultural inputs were replaced by urban inputs in BIR. Taxonomic composition of the stream algal assemblages changed especially along the urban gradient in the BOS and SLC study areas where water chemistry was

TABLE 11. Correlations of environmental variables and NMS ordination axes for the DTH 28-sample data set from the Salt Lake City study area. Ordinations were rotated to maximize loadings of the first axis on the urban intensity index. Only environmental variables with highest multiple r^2 (Σr^2) are shown. Significant correlations ($P < 0.05$) are in bold. Abbreviations for variables are in Table 1.

Environmental variable	All taxa				Diatoms only			
	axis 1	axis 2	axis 3	Σr^2	axis 1	axis 2	axis 3	Σr^2
Light	**−0.48**	**−0.48**	0.34	0.57	**−0.41**	**0.39**	0.05	0.32
Stream order	**−0.66**	0.03	−0.16	0.47	**−0.72**	−0.28	**0.53**	0.87
Grassland	**−0.65**	0.11	0.16	0.46	**−0.56**	0.00	0.37	0.44
F	**0.43**	−0.05	**−0.42**	0.36	**0.45**	0.36	−0.32	0.43
Basin area	**−0.56**	−0.03	−0.18	0.35	**−0.60**	−0.15	**0.44**	0.57
pH	−0.22	0.06	**−0.53**	0.33	−0.29	−0.11	0.29	0.18
Canopy closure	**−0.51**	−0.18	0.12	0.30	−0.19	−0.10	**0.52**	0.31
Discharge	**−0.45**	−0.04	−0.29	0.29	**−0.56**	−0.11	**0.45**	0.53
NH_4	−0.09	−0.30	**0.43**	0.28	0.14	0.28	−0.07	0.10
Uplands	−0.12	**0.45**	−0.24	0.27	0.10	0.13	0.20	0.07
Bank-full width	**−0.44**	0.06	−0.25	0.25	**−0.59**	0.01	0.25	0.41
Wetted width	**−0.42**	0.01	−0.27	0.25	**−0.59**	−0.02	0.27	0.43
Bank-full depth	**−0.45**	0.12	−0.01	0.22	−0.11	**0.39**	0.07	0.16
TKN	−0.03	−0.20	−0.37	0.18	0.16	**0.74**	0.01	0.57
Na	0.37	0.08	−0.32	0.25	**0.65**	0.30	−0.08	0.52
K	0.16	−0.12	**−0.39**	0.19	0.39	**0.58**	−0.04	0.49
Cl	0.30	0.10	−0.32	0.20	**0.62**	0.31	0.01	0.48
Residue on evaporation	**0.43**	0.15	−0.10	0.22	**0.67**	−0.09	−0.16	0.48
Velocity at sampling location	−0.30	0.19	−0.26	0.19	−0.30	−0.20	**0.50**	0.38
SiO_2	**0.42**	−0.05	−0.02	0.17	**0.62**	0.02	−0.21	0.43
Relative channel roughness	0.37	0.05	0.16	0.17	0.13	−0.01	**−0.54**	0.31
Coefficieint of variation of flow velocity	0.23	0.06	0.32	0.16	0.26	0.16	**−0.47**	0.31
SO_4	**0.38**	0.08	−0.05	0.15	**0.51**	−0.24	−0.20	0.36
Embeddedness	−0.36	−0.09	0.12	0.15	0.14	0.14	**0.53**	0.32
Wetted depth	−0.37	−0.09	0.02	0.15	**−0.39**	−0.11	0.36	0.29
Coefficient of variation of discharge	0.25	0.14	0.23	0.14	0.32	0.25	**−0.41**	0.33
Conductivity	0.26	0.20	−0.19	0.14	**0.56**	0.07	0.01	0.32
TP	0.06	−0.23	−0.28	0.13	0.34	**0.57**	0.05	0.45
Maximum wetted depth	−0.36	−0.06	0.01	0.13	**−0.40**	−0.13	0.35	0.30
Flow velocity	−0.20	−0.14	−0.23	0.11	**−0.44**	−0.27	0.27	0.34
Water temperature	0.01	−0.17	−0.21	0.07	0.19	**0.58**	0.16	0.40
Number of herbicide detections	0.22	0.04	−0.14	0.07	0.35	**0.40**	−0.30	0.37
Maximum flow velocity	−0.11	−0.13	−0.19	0.06	**−0.43**	−0.32	0.13	0.30
% silt + gravel	0.19	−0.09	0.08	0.05	**0.50**	0.21	0.10	0.31
% gravel + boulder	−0.18	0.09	−0.08	0.05	**−0.50**	−0.21	−0.11	0.31
Mean dominant substrate size	−0.11	0.01	−0.18	0.04	**0.52**	−0.20	−0.13	0.32
Urban intensity index	0.18	0.00	−0.01	0.03	**0.54**	0.00	0.00	0.29

pollution-sensitive, oligosaprobic, and oligotraphentic species along urban gradients when using metrics based on European studies.

The three study areas in this investigation also differed in the hydrological modifications to urban streams that affect patterns of flow regime along urban gradi-

ents. Dams in the watersheds of urban streams in the BOS study area stabilized discharges. Stable flow commonly promotes accumulation of algal biomass in streams (Biggs 1996), a pattern that we observed in the urban streams of the BOS study area. In contrast, urban streams in the BIR study area had more variable flow patterns.

TABLE 12. Kendall rank correlation coefficients between selected autecological diatom metrics and the urban intensity index in the three study areas. **, $P < 0.01$;*, $P < 0.05$.

Metrics	Boston		Birmingham		Salt Lake City	
	RTH $n = 30$	DTH $n = 30$	RTH $n = 27$	DTH $n = 27$	RTH $n = 30$	DTH $n = 28$
Pollution-sensitive[a]	−0.50**	−0.35**	0.08	−0.08	−0.17	−0.25
Pollution-tolerant[a]	0.55**	0.27*	0.18	0.12	0.11	0.14
Oligosaprobous[b]	0.38**	−0.15	−0.17	−0.17	−0.30*	0.01
α-meso + polysaprobous[b]	0.66**	0.33**	0.18	0.11	0.44**	0.41**
Oligotraphentic[b]	0.12	−0.18	−0.15	−0.32*	−0.39**	−0.16
Eutraphentic[b]	0.42**	0.35**	0.13	−0.01	0.21	−0.06

[a] From Lange-Bertalot (1979)
[b] From van Dam et al. (1994)

Higher disturbance levels associated with stream flashiness may lower algal biomass and diversity and affect species membership (Biggs et al. 1998), as was observed in the BIR urban streams. Flow variability, measured as discharge or stage variability, may affect algal assemblages at different temporal scales (Clausen and Biggs 1997; Matthaei et al. 2003). Flow variability in the days or weeks preceding algal sampling often determines at which successional stage the algal assemblages will be found and which life forms will dominate. Long-term flow variability, measured over seasons and years, and current velocity may control the local species pool, favoring species best adapted for a particular hydrological stream type. In our study, streams were sampled within relatively short time periods in each study area and during periods of stable flow; thus, short-term flow conditions were not considered as explanatory variables in our analyses. Flow regime was quantified by using long-term stage observations and channel morphology. Stage-related variables, such as the number of periods when stage rose above or fell below specific levels, characterized urban streams in the BIR area as having a less stable flow regime than the background streams. This flow variability apparently was reflected in the composition of algal assemblages. The correlative nature of this study, however, only allows us to hypothesize about the causal relations between long-term flow regime and the composition of algal assemblages.

Our study differed fundamentally from other studies of algal assemblages in urban streams in that we used the multimetric index of urban intensity based on several infrastructure, socioeconomic, and land-use characteristics. Studying relations between biological assemblages and a general measure of human influences could be enlightening for several reasons. Various stressors associated with human influence may have a cumulative effect on biota. A single disturbance-quantifying index, such as the UII, may be used instead of the multiple characteristics of impairment once strong relations have been established among such an index, individual stressors, and biological assemblages. Our analyses demonstrated, however, that individual environmental factors associated with urbanization more often than the UII showed strong relations to algal assemblage composition, biomass, and diversity. In almost all data sets in this study, a number of proximate environmental factors had higher correlations with the NMS ordination axes than with the UII. Similarly, Sonneman et al. (2001) found that diatom communities in Australian urban streams were more strongly related to water chemistry than to a gradient of urban intensity, quantified as the proportion of impervious surface in the watershed.

Results of this study imply that no universal algae-based indicators can be used successfully in bioassessment across different geographic zones and environmental settings. The relative abundance of some taxa, recognized worldwide as reliable indicators of nutrient-rich and generally polluted or unpolluted waters, was the single attribute of algal assemblages showing the most consistent response to urbanization in this study. Our gradient analyses demonstrated, however, that a large amount of additional information on the relations between various habitat variables and algal assemblages in each area could be explored and then used in bioassessment. For instance, algal assemblages in our study showed distinct responses to many physical habitat characteristics. Further observational and experimental studies may clarify the significance of these responses and their usefulness for stream monitoring.

The design of this pilot study allowed us to compare patterns of biota along urban gradients in different environmental settings, but not to develop metrics for immediate use in bioassessment. Such work requires not only exploratory, but also confirmatory analyses and larger data sets specifically collected to investigate the effects of particular stressors on stream algal assemblages. Our work illustrated, however, the importance of developing regional-scale methods of bioassessment that are based on the detailed investigations of biological community responses to specific stresses associated with human influences.

Acknowledgments

Frank Acker, Kalina Manoylov, Eduardo Morales, Lont Marr, Jackie White-Reimer, and Diane Winter identified and enumerated algae. Cathy Tate, David Mueller, David Litke, Gerard McMahon, Tom Cuffney, Michael Meador, Peter Ruhl, Stephen Moulton, and Terry Short provided environmental information. Robert Gray, Julie Hambrook Berkman, Donald Charles, Karin Ponader, and an anonymous reviewer provided helpful comments on earlier drafts of the manuscript. The use of firm, trade, or brand names in this article is for identification purposes only and does not constitute endorsement by the U.S. Geological Survey.

References

Arar, E. J., and G. B. Collins. 1997. U.S. Environmental Protection Agency method 445.0, in vitro determination of chlorophyll *a* and pheophytin *a* in marine and freshwater algae by fluorescence, rev. 2.2. U.S. Environmental Protection Agency, National Exposure Research Laboratory, Office of Research and Development, Cincinnati, Ohio.

Biggs, B. 1990. Periphyton communities and their environments in New Zealand rivers. New Zealand Journal of Marine and Freshwater Research 24:367–386.

Biggs, B. 1996. Patterns of benthic algae in streams. Pages 31–56 *in* R. J. Stevenson, M. L. Bothwell, and R. L. Lowe, editors. Algal ecology: freshwater benthic ecosystems. Academic Press, San Diego, California.

Biggs, B., R. J. Stevenson, and R. L. Lowe. 1998. A habitat matrix conceptual model for stream periphyton. Archiv für Hydrobiologie 143:1–56.

Charles, D. F., C. Knowles, and R. Davis. 2002. Protocols for the analysis of algal samples collected as part of the U.S. Geological Survey National Water-Quality Assessment Program. The Academy of Natural Sciences, Patrick Center for Environmental Research Report No. 02–06, Philadelphia, Pennsylvania. Available: http://diatom.acnatsci.org/nawqa/. (January 2004).

Clausen, B., and B. Biggs. 1997. Relationships between benthic biota and hydrological indices in New Zealand streams. Freshwater Biology 38:327–342.

Dodds, W. K., J. R. Jones, and E. B. Welsh. 1998. Suggested classification of stream trophic status: distributions of temperate stream types by chlorophyll, total nitrogen, and phosphorus. Water Research 32:1455–1462.

Fishman, M. J., editor. 1993. Methods of analysis by the U.S. Geological Survey National Water Quality Laboratory–determination of inorganic and organic constituents in water and fluvial sediments. U.S. Geological Survey, Open-File Report 93–125, Denver, Colorado.

Fitzpatrick, F. A., I. R. Waite, P. J. D'Arconte, M. R. Meador, M. A. Maupin, and M. E. Gurtz. 1998. Revised methods for characterizing stream habitat in the National Water-Quality Assessment Program. U.S. Geological Survey, Water-Resources Investigations Report 98–4052, Raleigh, North Carolina. Available: http://water.usgs.gov/nawqa/protocols/WRI98–4052. (January 2004).

Fukushima, S. 1999. Change in the diatom assemblage of an urban river with utilization of treated sewage as maintenance water. Pages 277–289 *in* S. Mayama, M. Idei, and I. Koizumi, editors. Proceedings of the 14th International Diatom Symposium. Koeltz Scientific Books, Koenigstein, Germany.

Kelly, M. G., and B. A. Whitton. 1995. The Trophic Diatom Index: a new index for monitoring eutrophication in rivers. Journal of Applied Phycology 7:433–444.

Keys, J. E., Jr., C. A. Carpenter, S. L. Hooks, F. G. Koenig, W. H. McNab, W. E. Russell, and M. L. Smith. 1995. Ecological units of the eastern United States—first approximation. U.S. Department of Agriculture, Forest Service, Map (scale 1:3,500,000) and booklet of tables, Atlanta.

Kruskal, J. B. 1964. Nonmetric multidimensional scaling: a numerical method. Psychometrika 29:115–129.

Lange-Bertalot, H. 1979. Pollution tolerance of diatoms as a criterion for water quality estimation. Nova Hedwigia Beiheft 64:285–304.

Lobo, E. A., K. Katoh, and Y. Aruga. 1995. Response of epilithic diatom assemblages to water pollution in rivers in the Tokyo metropolitan area, Japan. Freshwater Biology 34:191–204.

Lowe, R. L., and Y. Pan. 1996. Benthic algal communities as biological monitors. Pages 705–739 *in* R. J. Stevenson, M. L. Bothwell, and R. L. Lowe, editors. Algal ecology: freshwater benthic ecosystems. Academic Press, San Diego, California.

Mather, P. M. 1976. Computational methods of multivariate analysis in physical geography. J. Wiley & Sons, London.

Matthaei, C. D., C. Guggelberger, and H. Huber. 2003. Local disturbance history affects patchiness of benthic river algae. Freshwater Biology 48:1514–1526.

McCune, B., and M. J. Mefford. 1999. Multivariate analysis of ecological data, Version 4. MjM Software, Gleneden Beach, Oregon.

McMahon, G., and T. F. Cuffney. 2000. Quantifying urban intensity in drainage basins for assessing stream ecological conditions. Journal of the American Water Resources Association 36:1247–1261.

McMahon, G., J. D. Bales, J. F. Coles, E. M. P. Giddings, and H. Zappia. 2003. Use of stage data to characterize hydrologic conditions in an urbanizing environment. Journal of the American Water Resources Association 39:1529–1546.

Meador, M. R., J. F. Coles, and H. Zappia. 2005. Fish assemblage responses to urban intensity gradients in contrasting metropolitan areas: Birmingham, Alabama and Boston, Massachusetts. Pages 409–423 in L. R. Brown, R. H. Gray, R. M. Hughes, and M. R. Meador, editors. Effects of urbanization on stream ecosystems. American Fisheries Society, Symposium 47, Bethesda, Maryland.

Nather Khan, I. S. A. 1991. Effect of urban and industrial wastes on species diversity of the diatom community in a tropical river, Malaysia. Hydrobiologia 224(3):175–184.

Omernik, J. M. 1995. Ecoregions: a spatial framework for environmental management. Pages 49–62 in W. S. Davis and T. P. Simon, editors. Biological assessment and criteria: tools for water resource planning and decision making. Lewis Publishers, Inc., Boca Raton, Florida.

Pan, Y., R. J. Stevenson, B. H. Hill, A. T. Herlihy, and G. B. Collins. 1996. Using diatoms as indicators of ecological conditions in lotic systems: a regional assessment. Journal of the North American Benthological Society 15:481–495.

Paul, M. J., and J. L. Meyer. 2001. Streams in the urban landscape. Annual Review of Ecology and Systematics 32:333–365.

Porter S. D., T. F. Cuffney, M. E. Gurtz, and M. R. Meador. 1993. Methods for collecting algal samples as part of the National Water-Quality Assessment Program. U.S. Geological Survey, Open-File Report 93–409, Raleigh, North Carolina. Available: http://water.usgs.gov/nawqa/protocols/bioprotocols.html (January 2004).

Potapova, M. G., and D. F. Charles. 2004. Potential use of rare diatoms as environmental indicators in U.S.A. rivers. Pages 281–295 in M. Poulin, editor. Proceedings of the 17th International Diatom Symposium. Biopress, Bristol, UK.

Sabater, S., F. Sabater, and X. Tomas. 1987. Water qual-

ity and diatom communities in two Catalan rivers (N.E. Spain). Water Research 21:901–911.

Shelton, L. R. 1994. Field guide for collecting and processing stream-water samples for the National Water-Quality Assessment Program. U.S. Geological Survey, Open-File Report 94–455, Sacramento, California. Available: http://ca.water.usgs.gov/pnsp/pest.rep/sw-t.html. (January 2004).

Short, T. M., E. M. P. Giddings, H. Zappia, and J. F. Coles. 2005. Urbanization effects on stream habitat characteristics in Boston, Massachusetts; Birmingham, Alabama; and Salt Lake City, Utah. Pages 317–332 in L. R. Brown, R. H. Gray, R. M. Hughes, and M. R. Meador, editors. Effects of urbanization on stream ecosystems. American Fisheries Society, Symposium 47, Bethesda, Maryland.

Siva, C. J., V. Mylvaganam, and J. John. 2001. Urban land use and periphytic diatom communities: a comparative study of three metropolitan streams in Perth, Western Australia. Pages 125–134 in J. John, editor. Proceedings of the 15th International Diatom Symposium. Koeltz Scientific Books, Koenigstein, Germany.

Sládecek, V. 1973. System of water quality from the biological point of view. Archiv für Hydrobiologie 7:1–218.

Soininen, J., and P. Niemelä. 2002. Inferring the phosphorus levels of rivers from benthic diatoms using weighted averaging. Archiv für Hydrobiologie 154(1):1–18.

Sonneman, J. A., C. J. Walsh, P. F. Breen, and A. K. Sharpe. 2001. Effect of urbanization on streams of the Melbourne region, Victoria, Australia. II. Benthic diatom communities Freshwater Biology 46:553–565.

Stevenson, R. J. 1997. Scale-dependent causal frameworks and the consequences of benthic algal heterogeneity. Journal of the North American Benthological Society 16:248–262.

Stevenson, R. J., and L. L. Bahls. 1999. Periphyton protocols. Pages 6/1–6/22 in M. T. Barbour, J. Gerritsen, B. D. Snyder, and J. B. Stribling, editors. Rapid bioassessment protocols for use in wadeable streams and rivers: periphyton, benthic macroinvertebrates, and fish. 2nd edition. U.S. Environmental Protection Agency, Office of Water, EPA 841-B-99–002, Washington, D.C.

Stevenson, R. J., M. L. Bothwell, and R. L. Lowe, editors. 1996. Algal ecology: freshwater benthic ecosystems. Academic Press, San Diego, California.

Tate, C. M., T. F. Cuffney, G. McMahon, E. M. P. Giddings, J. F. Coles, and H. Zappia. 2005. Use of an urban intensity index to assess urban effects on streams in three contrasting environmental settings.

Pages 291–316 *in* L. R. Brown, R. H. Gray, R. M. Hughes, and M. R. Meador, editors. Effects of urbanization on stream ecosystems. American Fisheries Society, Symposium 47, Bethesda, Maryland.

Taylor, S. L., S. C. Roberts, C. J. Walsh, and B. E. Hatt. 2004. Catchment urbanization and increased benthic algal biomass in streams: linking mechanisms to management. Freshwater Biology 49:835–851.

van Dam, H., A. Mertens, and J. Sinkeldam. 1994. A coded checklist and ecological indicator values of freshwater diatoms from the Netherlands. Netherlands Journal of Aquatic Ecology 28(1):117–133.

Vis, C., C. Hudon, A. Cattaneo, and B. Pinel-Alloul. 1998. Periphyton as an indicator of water quality in the St. Lawrence River (Quebec, Canada). Environmental Pollution 101:13–24.

Whitton, B. A., editor. 1984. Ecology of European rivers. Blackwell Scientific Publications, Oxford, UK.

Winter, J. G., and H. C. Duthie. 1998. Effects of urbanization on water quality, periphyton and invertebrate communities in a southern Ontario stream. Canadian Water Resources Journal 23:245–257.

Winter, J. G., and H. C. Duthie. 2000. Epilithic diatoms as indicators of stream total N and total P concentration. Journal of the North American Benthological Society 19:32–49.

Wu, J. T. 1999. A generic index of diatom assemblages as bioindicator of pollution in the Keelung River of Taiwan. Hydrobiologia 397:79–97.

American Fisheries Society Symposium 47:361–407, 2005

Effects of Urbanization on Benthic Macroinvertebrate Assemblages in Contrasting Environmental Settings: Boston, Massachusetts; Birmingham, Alabama; and Salt Lake City, Utah

THOMAS F. CUFFNEY*

U.S. Geological Survey, Water Resources Discipline
3916 Sunset Ridge Road, Raleigh, North Carolina 27607, USA

HUMBERT ZAPPIA

1162 Rock Cliff Drive, Martinsburg, West Virginia 25401, USA

ELISE M. P. GIDDINGS

U.S. Geological Survey, Water Resources Discipline
3916 Sunset Ridge Road, Raleigh, North Carolina 27607, USA

JAMES F. COLES

U.S. Geological Survey, c/o USEPA New England, Suite 1100 (HBS)
1 Congress Street, Boston, Massachusetts 02114, USA

Abstract.—Responses of invertebrate assemblages along gradients of urban intensity were examined in three metropolitan areas with contrasting climates and topography (Boston, Massachusetts; Birmingham, Alabama; Salt Lake City, Utah). Urban gradients were defined using an urban intensity index (UII) derived from basin-scale population, infrastructure, land-use, land-cover, and socioeconomic characteristics. Responses based on assemblage metrics, indices of biotic integrity (B-IBI), and ordinations were readily detected in all three urban areas and many responses could be accurately predicted simply using regional UIIs. Responses to UII were linear and did not indicate any initial resistance to urbanization. Richness metrics were better indicators of urbanization than were density metrics. Metrics that were good indicators were specific to each study except for a richness-based tolerance metric (TOLr) and one B-IBI. Tolerances to urbanization were derived for 205 taxa. These tolerances differed among studies and with published tolerance values, but provided similar characterizations of site conditions. Basin-scale land-use changes were the most important variables for explaining invertebrate responses to urbanization. Some chemical and instream physical habitat variables were important in individual studies, but not among studies. Optimizing the study design to detect basin-scale effects may have reduced the ability to detect local-scale effects.

Introduction

Urban lands represent only a small component of human engendered landscape alteration in the United States (U.S. Environmental Protection Agency 2000), but these lands have a disproportionate effect on stream condition. It is estimated that 1 km² of urbanized basin

impairs three times (0.15 km) the length of stream that would be impaired by a similar amount of agricultural land (National Resources Conservation Service 2000; U.S. Environmental Protection Agency 2000). The extent of urbanized land is also increasing rapidly (about 101,000 km² between 1987 and 1997). Consequently, urbanization is a significant source of stream impairment in the United States that will be steadily increasing for the foreseeable future. Understanding how

* Corresponding author: tcuffney@usgs.gov

urbanization affects physical, chemical, and biological characteristics of streams and the similarities and differences in these effects throughout the United States is important for managing aquatic resources.

The number of urban stream studies has increased substantially in recent years and the effects of urbanization are well documented for selected urban areas (Paul and Meyer 2001) and for invertebrate assemblages (Klein 1979; Jones and Clark 1987; Schueler and Galli 1992; Lenat and Crawford 1994; Yoder and Rankin 1996; Horner et al. 1997; Kemp and Spotila 1997; Kennen 1999; Yoder et al. 1999; Beasley and Kneale 2002; Huryn et al. 2002; Kennen and Ayers 2002; Morley and Karr 2002; Morse et al. 2003; Ourso and Frenzel 2003; Roy et al. 2003; Vølstad et al. 2003). While the effects of urbanization have been well established, the intensity of development that brings about ecological changes, the rate and form of these changes, and regional differences in responses are less clearly understood (Karr and Chu 1999, 2000). Single variable surrogates for urban intensity, such as population density or measures of impervious surface (Arnold and Gibbons 1996), are often used to represent urban intensity and interpret responses to urbanization. However, a comprehensive understanding of the ecological effects of urbanization (i.e., rates and forms of responses) requires an understanding of the interactions of a large variety of physical, chemical, and biological factors that change along gradients of urbanization and that vary locally and regionally. These, along with differences in study design and sampling methods, hinder extrapolating study results from one region of the country to another. Multiple regional urban studies using a common design and sample collection techniques are needed to provide a comprehensive understanding of regional responses to urbanization that are comparable among different environmental settings.

In 1999, the U.S. Geological Survey's (USGS) National Water-Quality Assessment (NAWQA) Program initiated a series of studies that used a common design to examine the regional effects of urbanization on aquatic biota (fish, invertebrates, and algae) and chemical and physical habitat in three metropolitan areas in different environmental settings. These urban gradient studies were conducted in the Boston, Massachusetts (BOS), Birmingham, Alabama (BIR), and Salt Lake City, Utah (SLC) metropolitan areas. A multimetric urban intensity index (UII) was used to identify representative gradients of urbanization within relatively homogeneous environmental settings (McMahon and Cuffney 2000; Tate et al. 2005, this volume) associated with each urban

area. The objectives of these studies were to (1) determine if physical, chemical, and biological characteristics of streams responded to urban intensity as defined by the UII; (2) describe the form and rate of these responses; (3) determine which characteristics are useful indicators of urbanization; (4) identify characteristics of urbanization that are most strongly associated with biological responses; and (5) compare responses among urban areas.

This paper describes the responses of invertebrate assemblages. Responses of algae, fish, and physical habitat structure are described in Potapova et al. (2005, this volume), Meador et al. (2005, this volume), and Short et al. (2005, this volume). Tate et al. (2005) describe the design of these urban land-use gradient studies.

Methods

Site Selection

Sampling sites were chosen from populations of candidate basins (2nd–5th order) defined using 30-m digital elevation models (U.S. Geological Survey 2003). Natural and anthropogenic basin characteristics were derived from publicly available information sources. A UII was used to select 30 study basins that represented a gradient of urban intensity from low (0) to high (100). The UII was derived from a combination of land use, infrastructure, population, and socioeconomic variables (McMahon and Cuffney 2000; Tate et al. 2005) that were associated with changes in population density. Study sites were chosen to minimize differences in natural basin features (e.g., ecoregion, climate, topography, stream size) and local disturbances (e.g., major point sources or modifications to riparian vegetation, channels, banks, or beds) as a means of maximizing the ability to detect basinwide urban effects as opposed to local-scale effects (Morley and Karr 2002). The different urban intensities represented by the spatially distributed sampling network are intended to represent changes in urbanization through time (i.e., substitute space for time).

Urban intensity indexes were developed individually for each study area to take full advantage of the unique land-use, land-cover, infrastructure, population, and socioeconomic data available in each. These UIIs represent the range of urban intensity in each study area, but the variables comprising the index differed among study areas. A common urban intensity index (CUII) was also calculated based on a set of five urban indicator variables that were common to all three study areas (Tate et al. 2005). The CUII provides a measure of urban intensity that is consistent among the study areas, whereas the UII provides a measure of urban intensity that makes maximum use of local indicators of urbanization.

Water Samples

Water column chemistry data (i.e., nitrogen species, phosphorus species, major ions, and pesticides) were collected during summer low flows (BOS August, BIR May, SLC July) in 2000. Additional samples were collected in BOS (April 2000) and BIR (May 2001). These samples were collected from equal-width increments across the stream channel, composited, and processed on site in accordance with standard NAWQA Program protocols (Shelton 1994). Water samples were sent to the USGS National Water Quality Laboratory in Denver, Colorado, for analysis. Dissolved oxygen, pH, specific conductance, and alkalinity were measured during each site visit (every 2–4 weeks). Water temperature was measured continuously every 15 min at each site using temperature probes and data recorders. Stream-stage measurements were recorded at 15-min intervals at each site using either existing USGS streamgages or a stage transducer. Temperature and stage recorders were removed from SLC during winter. Water chemistry, temperature, and stage measurements were collected for approximately 1 year prior to collecting biological samples. Because of equipment malfunctions, the temperature data collection in BOS was extended through 2001 to characterize the annual thermal cycle. Chemical characteristics were summarized as the mean of all values collected during the study.

Stream Physical Habitat Characterization

Stream physical habitat characteristics were quantified during summer low flows using standard NAWQA Program protocols (Fitzpatrick et al. 1998). Data were collected from 11 transects at each site, and 65 habitat metrics were calculated from these data. Details on habitat sampling and the derivation of habitat metrics are given in Short et al. (2005).

Invertebrate Samples

Standard NAWQA Program sampling protocols were used to collect benthic macroinvertebrates (Cuffney et al. 1993) during summer low flows in 2000: BOS August, BIR June, and SLC July. Two types of macroinvertebrate samples were collected—a quantitative sample collected from multiple representatives

of the stream habitat that contained the richest assemblage of invertebrates (richest targeted habitat, RTH) and a qualitative multihabitat (QMH) sample that collected invertebrates from as many habitats in the stream reach as were accessible. The RTH sample consisted of Slack (Cuffney et al. 1993) samples (0.25 m^2, 425-μm-mesh net) collected from five separate riffle areas in the sampling reach and combined to form a single composite sample of 1.25 m^2. One SLC site (Kays Creek at Layton; Tate et al. 2005) did not have enough riffle habitat, so the RTH sample was collected from at least two woody snags at each of five locations along the stream reach. The QMH sample collected invertebrates using a 212-μm-mesh dip net supplemented with hand-picking of substrates. Sampling effort (time) was apportioned as equally as possible among accessible habitats in the sampling reach. Data from the QMH and RTH samples were combined to form a qualitative composite sample (QRC) that provided a comprehensive list of invertebrates in each sampling reach. Samples were preserved in 10% buffered formalin and sent to the USGS National Water Quality Laboratory in Denver, Colorado for taxa identification and enumeration. Invertebrate samples were processed using standard NAWQA Program protocols (Moulton et al. 2000) for RTH (randomized 300-organism count) and QMH (fixed processing time designed to maximize the number of taxa enumerated) samples.

Resolving Taxonomic Ambiguities

Taxonomic ambiguities arise when results (abundance or presence) are reported at multiple taxonomic levels. For example, an ambiguity would exist in a sample when data are reported for the species *Hydropsyche sparna* and *H. betteni*, the genus *Hydropsyche*, and the family Hydropsychidae. In this example, *Hydropsyche* and Hydropsychidae are ambiguous parent taxa because they may belong to either *betteni*, *sparna*, or to another unidentified child species or genus in the case of Hydropschidae. Taxa richness in this sample could range from 1 (Hydropsichidae) to 4 depending on how the analyst decides to resolve ambiguities. The method used to resolve ambiguous taxa can strongly influence the analysis and interpretation of assemblage data.

Taxonomic ambiguities were resolved using the Invertebrate Data Analysis System software (IDAS; Cuffney 2003). Ambiguities in RTH samples were resolved separately for each study area using option RC3. This option combines RTH samples from a study area, identifies ambiguities in the combined data, and determines whether to delete or combine ambiguous taxa depending on their abundances. If the combined abundance of the children is greater than the abundance of the parent, the parent is deleted and the children are retained. If the abundance of the parent is greater than the combined abundance of the children, the abundances of the children are added to the parent and the children are dropped. The decision of which taxa to keep, combine, or delete are then applied to each of the samples individually.

Ambiguities in qualitative samples (QMH or QRC) were resolved separately for each study area using method RC1. This method combines samples from a study area, identifies ambiguous parents in the combined data, and tags them for deletion. Decisions on which taxa to delete are then applied to each sample individually. If a sample contains an ambiguous parent but no associated children, the most commonly occurring child is substituted for the ambiguous parent. This method is appropriate for qualitative samples because the presence of children implies the existence of parents and there is no quantitative information to lose.

Data Analysis

Invertebrate responses were analyzed using a combination of multivariate (ordination) and multimetric analyses that reduced assemblage data into a series of simple response variables. The correspondence between response variables and the UII was examined to determine if assemblages were responding to urbanization and, if so, the form and rate of the response. Invertebrate responses were then compared to land-use, land-cover, topographic, lithologic, soils, population, socioeconomic, habitat, and chemical variables to ascertain which variables were important in explaining responses and how responses and explanatory variables compared among studies. Quantitative data were converted to densities (number/m^2) and taxonomic ambiguities were resolved prior to calculating metrics or conducting ordinations.

Multivariate analysis.—Indirect gradient analysis (ter Braak 1995) was used to investigate the relations between invertebrate responses and explanatory variables separately for each urban study area. This is a two-part procedure that uses ordination to derive response gradients (latent environmental variables) that summarize the assemblages and then relates these gradients to explanatory variables using correlation and/or regression analysis. The response gradients derived from ordination are the site scores whose position along the axis is determined by dissimilarity among assemblages at each site. That is, sites with similar assemblages are located close together on an ordination axis and sites with dissimilar assemblages are located far apart.

Ordinations were conducted for both qualitative (QRC) and quantitative (RTH) data using correspondence analysis (CA) and detrended correspondence analysis (DCA; CANOCO v. 4.0, ter Braak and Šmilauer 1998). Rare taxa were downweighted in all ordinations using the methods of ter Braak and Šmilauer (1998). Ordination of the BOS and BIR RTH samples required transformation of the data (log x + 1) and detrending (DCA). RTH data from SLC were square-root transformed but did not require detrending. Data from QRC samples did not require transformation or detrending. Scaling was focused on intersample distances and detrending was by segments.

The ordination site scores (derived response gradients) for ordination axes 1–4 were correlated (Spearman rank correlation, ρ) with the UII to determine which axis was most strongly associated with urban intensity, the strength of the association, and the sign of the association. If the association was positive, the site scores were transformed (i.e., individual site scores were subtracted from the maximum site score for each study area) to produce responses that were similar and consistent with the response of the EPTr metric (i.e., decrease in value as urbanization increases, Paul and Meyer 2001; Morse et al. 2003). If the ordination contained negative values for site scores, they were adjusted to positive values by subtracting the minimum site score from all site scores. These transformations do not alter the relation (ecological distances) among sites, but are required to produce consistent and comparable responses among ordinations derived using different procedures (i.e., DCA, CA) and data transformations. If an axis was at least moderately associated with UII ($|\rho| \geq 0.5$), regression analysis was used to determine if there was a statistically significant response (slope, $b \neq 0$, $P \leq 0.05$)). Analysis of covariance (ANCOVA) and Newman-Keuls multiple range test (Zar 1974) were used to determine if there were significant differences in responses (slopes) among urban areas.

Associations between invertebrate responses and explanatory variables (e.g., land-use, land-cover, topography, elevation, chemistry, soils, and habitat variables) were identified based on Spearman rank correlations (ρ). These correlations provided an effective means of summarizing relations between variables even when the underlying responses were not linear or contained outliers. Spearman rank correlations and regression analyses were calculated using SYSTAT 9 (SPSS 1999). Spearman correlations were considered to be strong when $|\rho| \geq 0.7$ and moderate when $0.7 > |\rho| \geq 0.5$, after rounding correlations to the nearest tenth. These criteria provided an effective and efficient mechanism for selecting a subset of variables that merited more intensive investigation as potential explanatory variables.

Assemblage metrics.—The IDAS program was used to calculate 137 invertebrate metrics (Table 1) that are commonly used in bioassessment (Rosenberg and Resh 1993; Davis and Simon 1995; Barbour et al. 1999). Tolerance and functional group metrics were calculated using data from Barbour et al. (1999), supplemented with tolerance data from the North Carolina Department of Environment and Natural Resources (NCDENR 2003). The tolerance metrics reported herein were based on averages of regional values reported in Barbour et al. (1999). Tolerances were calculated on the basis of richness (average of tolerance values assigned to each taxon) and density (density-weighted tolerances; Cuffney 2003).

Associations between metrics and explanatory variables were investigated using correlation and regression analysis. Spearman rank correlations were used to reduce the large number of comparisons to a manageable number that could be investigated using regression analysis. The significance and strength of responses were determined in the same manner as for ordinations.

Multimetric analysis.—Invertebrate responses were evaluated using a multimetric response index (B-IBI) that combined all metrics (excluding tolerance-based metrics and diversity measures) that were at least moderately correlated ($|\rho| \geq 0.5$) with urban intensity. The response of each metric was adjusted so that the value of all metrics decreased as urban intensity increased (i.e., $M_{adj-i} = M_{max} - M_i$ when $\rho > 0$). The component metrics were range standardized ($[M_i - M_{min}]/[M_{max} - M_{min}] \times 100$) over all sites so that all metrics were equally weighted. The standardized metrics were averaged over all sites, and the resulting values were again range standardized to produce a B-IBI that varied from 100 (minimum urban) to 0 (maximum urban). This is the same procedure that was

TABLE 1. Abbreviations used to identify invertebrate assemblage metrics based on density. Abbreviations for taxonomy-based and functional-group metrics that are based on other units of measurement are designated by appending lowercase letters to these abbreviations: *r*, richness; rp, % richness; *p*, % density. For example, EPT density, % density, richness, and % richness are abbreviated as EPT, EPTp, EPTr, and EPTrp, respectively.

Metric	Abbreviation	Metric	Abbreviation
Taxonomy-based metrics		Taxonomy-based metrics	
Total	RICH	Amphipoda	AMPHI
Ephemeroptera, Plecoptera, Trichoptera	EPT	Isopoda	ISOPOD
Ratio of EPT to Chironomidae	EPT_CH	Oligochaeta	OLIGO
Ephemeroptera	EPEM	Functional-group metrics	
Plecoptera	PLECO	Parasites	PA
Pteronarcidae	PTERY	Predators	PR
Trichoptera	TRICH	Omnivores	OM
Odonata	ODONO	Collector-gatherers	CG
Coleoptera	COLEOP	Filtering-collectors	FC
Diptera	DIP	Scrapers	SC
Chironomidae	CH	Shredders	SH
Orthocladiinae	ORTHO	Piercers	PI
Orthocladiinae/Chironomidae	ORTHO_CH	Dominance metrics	
Tanytarsanii	TANY	Most abundant taxa	DOM1
Tanytarsanii/Chironomidae	TANY_CH	Two most abundant taxa	DOM2
Nonchironomid Diptera	NCHDIP	Three most abundant taxa	DOM3
Noninsects	NONINS	Four most abundant taxa	DOM4
Nonchironomid Diptera and noninsects	ODIPNI	Five most abundant taxa	DOM5
Mollusca and Crustacea	MOLCRU	Tolerance metrics	
Gastropoda	GASTRO	Average tolerance of taxa	TOLr
Bivalvia	BIVALV	Density-weighted tolerance	TOL
Corbicula	CORBIC	Shannon diversity	SHANND

used to calculate the UII (McMahon and Cuffney 2000; Tate et al. 2005). This B-IBI is analogous to other multimetric indices (e.g., IBI, B-IBI, and ICI) that have proven to be valuable tools for assessing biological responses to changes in water quality (Karr 1981; Kerans and Karr 1994; Fore et al. 1996; Barbour et al. 1999; Morley and Karr 2002).

Three versions of the B-IBI were calculated. The "full" B-IBI (B-IBI-f) used all metrics that were at least moderately correlated with UII in a study area. The "common" B-IBI (B-IBI-c) used only those metrics that at least moderately correlated with UII in all three study areas. The "reduced" B-IBI (B-IBI-r) used the "common" model metrics but eliminated metrics that differ only in units of measurement: richness, percent richness, density, or percent density. The common and reduced IBIs were constructed to investigate the possibility of establishing a nationally consistent B-IBI.

Response thresholds.—Locally weighted least squares smoothing (LOWESS) was used to identify possible thresholds (i.e., points of abrupt change) in the invertebrate responses and to identify the approximate UII value that corresponded to the threshold (Coles et al. 2004). Once a potential threshold was identified, a two-slope linear regression analysis was used to determine if the threshold corresponded to a statistically significant ($P \leq 0.05$) change in the rate of response. This involved dividing the data into two subsets associated with the different sides of the threshold. A linear regression then was calculated for each subset of data and the slopes were compared using ANCOVA. LOWESS and regression analyses were done with SYSTAT 9.0 (SPSS 1999).

Urban tolerance values for invertebrates.—Tolerance values specific to urbanization were derived using weighted-averaging (WA) calibration (Juggins 2003) to estimate the optimum urban intensity (CUII or UII) for the occurrence of each taxon. Optima were derived separately for each sample type (QRC, QMH, and RTH) within a study area for taxa that occurred at five or more sites. Tolerance values were calculated by range standardizing the optima (CUII or UII) and multiplying by 10 to produce a tolerance index with a range that matched tolerance values reported in Barbour et al. (1999): 0 (very intolerant) to 10 (very tolerant of urbanization). Tolerance values derived from UII were range standardized separately for each study area. Tolerances based on CUII were range standardized using the range of optima encompassed by the three study areas combined.

Results

Taxonomic Richness and Composition

A total of 423 invertebrate taxa were collected from the three urban study areas (Table 2; Appendix 1). BOS had the most taxa (240) of which 85% were insects, BIR had 208 taxa (86% insects), and SLC had 185 taxa (88% insects). Very few taxa were common to all three study areas (50 of 423), and most taxa (263 of 423) were found in only one of the three study areas. The greatest commonality in taxonomic composition among study areas was in the Chironomidae, where 54% of the taxa were common to all study areas.

Richness metrics at background sites (UII ≤ 10) were substantially higher for BOS than for BIR and SLC, though percent richness metrics were comparable among study areas (Figure 1). Density and percent density metrics were highly variable, particularly in SLC, and did not show consistent differences among study areas (Figure 1; Appendix 2).

Invertebrate Responses Based on Ordination

Most variation in invertebrate assemblages was accounted for in the first two ordination axes (Table 3) for all sample types and study areas. Analyses of the RTH and QRC data gave similar results in terms of the strength of the ordination axes (eigenvalues), amount of assemblage variation explained (13–17%), and correlation with UII. The UII was strongly correlated with the first ordination axis derived from QRC data for each study area and with RTH data from BOS and BIR. In contrast, the second ordination axis derived from SLC RTH data were most strongly correlated with UII and the first axis with elevation ($r = 0.77$).

The best-fit relation between ordination site scores and UII was linear for both the RTH and QRC data (Figure 2). The UII accounted for a very high proportion of the variability in ordination site scores for BOS (86–87%) and BIR (74–80%) and a modest amount for SLC (45–51%). In all cases the slopes were statistically significant ($P \leq 0.05$, analysis of variance (ANOVA), Zar 1974). The response rates (slopes) were not statistically different among the study areas (ANCOVA, $P > 0.05$) for either RTH or QRC data. Despite large regional differences in environmental conditions and in the composition of the invertebrate assemblages, the rate of change associated with increasing urbanization was the same for all three study areas (common slope = –0.019 for RTH samples and –0.015 for QRC samples).

TABLE 2. Assemblage richness characteristics (number of taxa in QRC samples) summarized by major taxonomic groupings for the Boston (BOS), Birmingham (BIR), and Salt Lake City (SLC) urban study areas.

Taxon	Taxa richness				Taxa unique to a study area				Taxa common to all study areas
	BOS	BIR	SLC	Total	BOS	BIR	SLC	Total	
Cnidaria	1	0	1	1	0	0	0	0	0
Platyhelminthes	1	1	1	1	0	0	0	0	1
Nemertea	1	0	1	1	0	0	0	0	0
Nematoda	1	1	1	1	0	0	0	0	1
Gastropoda	10	9	5	17	5	4	2	11	1
Bivalvia	3	3	1	5	2	2	0	4	1
Annelida	10	7	7	12	3	1	0	4	4
Arachnida	1	1	1	1	0	0	0	0	1
Decapoda	2	2	1	5	2	2	1	5	0
Isopoda	1	2	1	2	0	1	0	1	1
Amphipoda	4	3	3	5	1	1	0	2	2
Collembola	1	1	1	1	0	0	0	0	1
Ephemeroptera	21	28	17	51	9	17	12	38	2
Odonata	18	17	4	30	9	9	3	21	0
Plecoptera	10	4	12	23	7	2	11	20	0
Hemiptera	12	10	6	22	7	5	4	16	0
Megaloptera	4	4	0	5	1	1	0	2	0
Trichoptera	39	25	30	73	22	9	23	54	2
Lepidoptera	1	1	0	2	1	1	0	2	0
Coleoptera	28	25	21	54	11	5	18	34	0
Non-midge Diptera	13	15	24	36	2	7	16	25	5
Chironomidae	58	49	47	75	9	5	10	24	28
Total insects	205	179	162	372	78	61	97	236	38
Total invertebrates	240	208	185	423	91	72	100	263	50

Ordination analysis indicated that invertebrate responses to urbanization can be predicted using UII and that a comprehensive qualitative depiction of the assemblages (QRC) provided a representation of response that was at least as good as an intensive single-habitat quantitative sample (RTH).

Invertebrate Responses Based on Assemblage Metrics

A variety of invertebrate assemblage metrics were strongly ($|\rho| \geq 0.7$) associated with UII for both RTH and QRC data (Appendices 3 and 4). More metrics were strongly correlated with urban intensity in BOS (34 richness, 16 density) than in BIR (15 richness, 2 density) or SLC (3 richness, 1 density). Richness metrics were, in all cases, much more frequently correlated with UII than were metrics based on density. There was little correspondence among the three study areas in terms of the assemblage metrics that were correlated with the UII either when considering all metrics with

$|\rho| \geq 0.7$ or the 12 metrics most strongly correlated with urban intensity in each study area (Appendices 3 and 4). Only one metric (richness-based tolerance, TOLr) appeared in the top 12 metrics for each urban study area. This metric was strongly related to the UII in the BOS urban study, but less strongly related in BIR and SLC (Figure 3). There was little correspondence between metrics that were strongly correlated with UII based on RTH and QRC data (i.e., less than half of the 12 metrics most strongly correlated with UII were similar for RTH and QRC data). Generally speaking, metrics based on EPT and its components, Coleoptera, noninsects, oligochaetes, mollusks plus crustaceans, and tolerances were the best indicators of changes in urban intensity.

Effects of urbanization were qualitatively similar when differences between mean values of assemblage metrics from background (UII $\leq$ 10) and and highly urbanized (UII $\geq$ 70) sites were compared (Table 4). Total, EPT, Ephemeroptera, Plecoptera, Trichoptera, and Diptera taxa richness decreased in all three urban

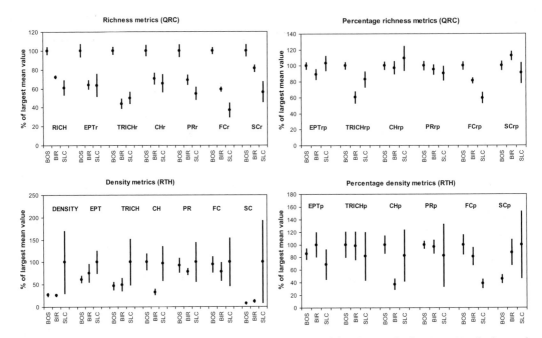

FIGURE 1. Mean values with standard errors for selected metrics at sites with low (UII ≤ 10) urban intensities (background sites) for the Boston (BOS), Birmingham (BIR), and Salt Lake City (SLC) urban study areas. Values are expressed as a percentage of the largest mean associated with the three study areas for each metric. Metric abbreviations are explained in Table 1.

TABLE 3. Correspondence analysis results for invertebrate assemblages and Spearman rank correlations between site scores and the urban intensity index (UII) for the Boston (BOS), Birmingham (BIR), and Salt Lake City (SLC) urban study areas.

Study	Parameter	Axis 1	Axis 2	Axis 3	Axis 4
Quantitative (RTH) samples					
BOS	Eigenvalues	0.272	0.079	0.056	0.037
	Variance explained (%)	17.4	5.0	3.6	2.4
	Correlation with UII	−0.91	−0.29	0.08	−0.04
BIR	Eigenvalues	0.262	0.171	0.085	0.059
	Variance explained (%)	15.5	10.1	5.0	3.5
	Correlation with UII	−0.78	0.01	−0.03	−0.02
SLC	Eigenvalues	0.322	0.307	0.231	0.161
	Variance explained (%)	13.7	13.0	9.8	6.9
	Correlation with UII	−0.12	−0.73	−0.07	−0.05
Qualitative (QRC) samples					
BOS	Eigenvalues	0.242	0.124	0.084	0.080
	Variance explained (%)	14.8	7.6	5.2	4.9
	Correlation with UII	−0.92	−0.11	−0.02	−0.16
BIR	Eigenvalues	0.236	0.164	0.116	0.111
	Variance explained (%)	13.0	9.0	6.3	6.1
	Correlation with UII	−0.84	−0.01	−0.02	0.17
SLC	Eigenvalues	0.259	0.179	0.127	0.112
	Variance explained (%)	13.7	9.4	6.7	5.9
	Correlation with UII	−0.54	−0.29	−0.32	0.12

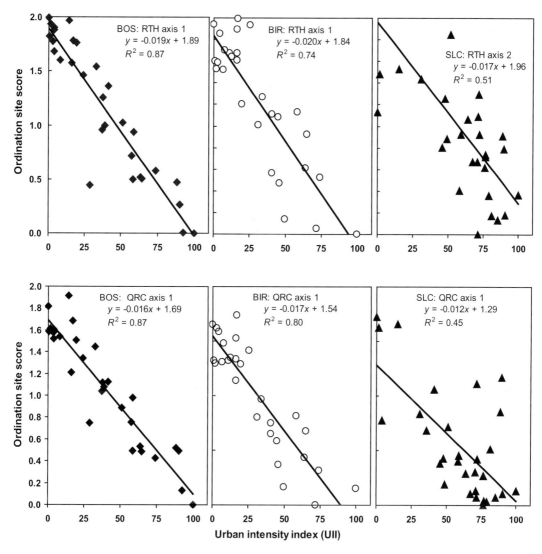

FIGURE 2. Relations between ordination (CA) axis site scores and urban intensity (UII) for assemblages based on RTH and QRC data for the Boston (BOS), Birmingham (BIR), and Salt Lake City (SLC) urban study areas. All slopes are statistically significant ($b \neq 0$, $P < 0.05$).

study areas regardless of whether richness was characterized by QRC or RTH data. Noninsect taxa richness increased with UII in all studies areas. Generally, BOS lost the most taxa over the urban gradient and SLC lost the least. Differences expressed as density were not consistent across the three study areas. Total density at high-intensity urban sites increased in BOS, primarily because of increases in densities of Trichoptera (hydropsychids) and noninsects. Total density decreased in BIR and SLC with SLC exhibiting very large decreases in the density of noninsects, primarily the gastropod family Hydrobiidae.

The B-IBI-f exhibited a very strong response to urban intensity for all study areas and for both RTH and QRC data (Figure 4), and in most cases, the correspondence (R^2) between UII and B-IBI-f was equal to or greater than the maximum observed for any of the component metrics (Figure 5). The advantages attributed to multimetric indices are clearly evident in the B-IBI-f results. The "common" and "reduced" versions of the B-IBI included far fewer metrics (3 quantitative, 14 qualitative, Table 5) than the "full" model (23–68 metrics, Figure 5; Appendices 3 and 4). However, the correlations between the B-IBI and urban

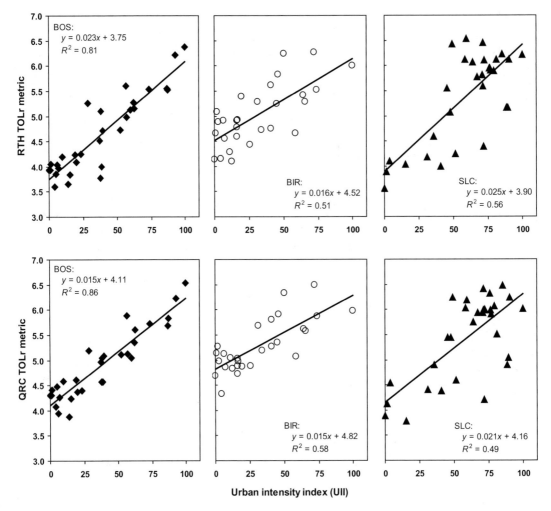

FIGURE 3. Relations between the richness-based tolerance metric (TOLr) and urban intensity (UII) for assemblages based on RTH and QRC samples for the Boston (BOS), Birmingham (BIR), and Salt Lake City (SLC) urban study areas. All slopes are statistically significant ($b \neq 0$, $P < 0.05$).

intensity for the "common" and "reduced" models were, generally, only slightly less than that of the "full" model (Table 6) and were nearly as strong, if not stronger, than the component metric with the best linear fit to urban intensity (Figure 6).

As with ordinations, invertebrate assemblage metrics and B-IBI indices could be predicted using UII. However, the individual metrics that were the best indicators of urbanization varied among study areas. Measures of taxa richness, whether from QRC or RTH data, provided the best indications of response. Quantitative metrics were highly variable and did not give results that were as comparable across study areas.

Response Thresholds

Response thresholds were only observed in the BOS urban study area and only for a few invertebrate metrics (CGr RTH, CGrp RTH, DOM5 RTH) that exhibited exhaustion thresholds at UII levels of about 35–40 (e.g., Figure 7). No assemblage metrics, B-IBIs, or ordinations displayed any initial resistance to urbanization (i.e., no threshold at the low end of the urban gradient) in any of the urban study areas. There was no level of urbanization that did not adversely affect the invertebrate assemblage in any of the three study areas. Invertebrate assemblages began to degrade as soon as the native vegetation, typically forest (BOS, BIR) or shrub land (SLC), began to be replaced with

TABLE 4. Average number of taxa or density lost (negative) or gained (positive values) between background (UII ≤ 10: BOS *n* = 8, BIR *n* = 7, SLC *n* = 3) and high intensity urban (UII ≥ 70: BOS *n* = 5, BIR *n* = 3, SLC *n* = 11) sites for selected taxonomic groups in the Boston (BOS), Birmingham (BIR), and Salt Lake City (SLC) urban study areas. Values in parentheses are percentages of the background values lost (negative) or gained (positive). No odonates were found at SLC background sites, so the percentage departure from background conditions could not be calculated (NA).

Metric	BOS		BIR		SLC	
Richness: Qualitative (QRC) samples						
Total	−34	(−41)	−25	(−42)	−10	(−21)
EPT	−20	(−75)	−14	(−81)	−11	(−66)
Ephemeroptera	−8	(−86)	−9	(−93)	−4	(−62)
Plecoptera	−2	(−63)	−1	(−100)	−3	(−87)
Trichoptera	−10	(−70)	−4	(−59)	−4	(−57)
Odonata	−5	(−79)	−2	(−48)	1	(NA)
Diptera	−12	(−45)	−5	(−24)	−2	(−10)
Chironomidae	−10	(−45)	−2	(−15)	1	(4)
Noninsects	9	(100)	3	(45)	4	(54)
Richness: Quantitative (RTH) samples						
Total	−25	(−52)	−7	(−34)	−8	(−24)
EPT	−13	(−78)	−6	(−67)	−9	(−69)
Ephemeroptera	−4	(−92)	−4	(−100)	−3	(−69)
Plecoptera	−2	(−100)	−1	(−100)	−3	(−90)
Trichoptera	−6	(−66)	−2	(−44)	−3	(−54)
Odonata	−1	(−80)	−1	(−7)	1	(NA)
Diptera	−11	(−58)	−1	(−18)	−1	(−5)
Chironomidae	−9	(−62)	2	(19)	1	(6)
Noninsects	5	(123)	3	(56)	3	(69)
Density: Quantitative (RTH) samples						
Total	8,426	(51)	−3,107	(−39)	−9,853	(−32)
EPT	2,074	(63)	−2,730	(−67)	−93	(−2)
Ephemeroptera	−1,153	(−90)	−1,888	(−88)	−67	(−6)
Plecoptera	−286	(−100)	−59	(−100)	−344	(−75)
Trichoptera	3,513	(202)	−783	(−42)	318	(8)
Odonata	−57	(−91)	14	(144)	44	(NA)
Diptera	1,595	(50)	768	(54)	4,604	(154)
Chironomidae	580	(21)	1,072	(116)	3,780	(141)
Noninsects	1,875	(314)	347	(37)	−13,045	(−64)

roads and buildings. Degradation of the invertebrate assemblage across the urban gradient followed the pattern expected for urban streams; that is, a decrease in insect taxa (particularly EPT taxa) and an increase in the numbers of noninsect taxa and oligochaetes as urban intensity increased.

Interpreting the Urban-Response Gradients

Many explanatory variables (BOS 156, BIR 153, SLC 178) were available to interpret invertebrate responses to increasing urban intensity. When combined with multiple studies, sample types, and response indicators, these explanatory variables constituted an un-

wieldy array of information. A more manageable subset of variables was derived by selecting the 12 variables that were most strongly correlated with each of three indicators of invertebrate assemblage responses: ordination site scores, richness-based tolerance (TOLr), and B-IBI-f. This reduced the number of explanatory variables to 30 for RTH data (Table 7) and 37 for QRC data (Table 8). Eight of these variables (bold type) were relatively consistent among urban study areas and sample types; the rest were restricted to a specific study area or sample type.

The explanatory variables most commonly associated with changes in invertebrate assemblages were related to land use, land cover, infrastructure, and popu-

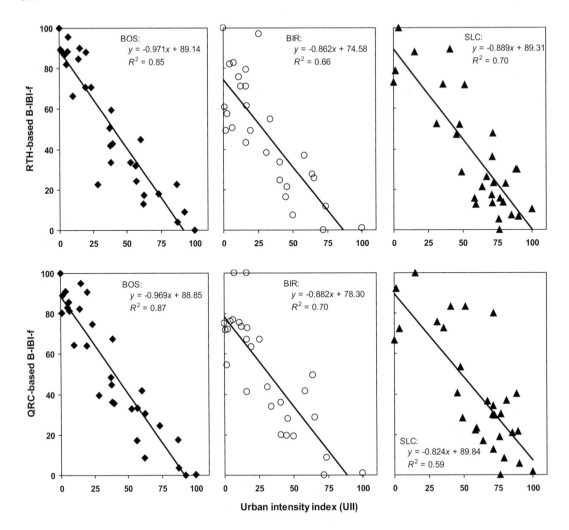

FIGURE 4. Relations between the B-IBI-f and urban intensity (UII) for assemblages based on RTH and QRC samples for the Boston (BOS), Birmingham (BIR), and Salt Lake City (SLC) urban study areas. All slopes are statistically significant ($b \neq 0$, $P < 0.05$).

lation. Urban intensity index, the percentage of developed (urban, low-intensity residential, commercial/industrial/transportation) land in the basin, the percentage of stream buffers in urban lands, road density, and population density (1990, 1999) were the most consistent explanatory variables across all study areas. Elevation, lithology and soils were important only for the SLC study area and then primarily for the qualitative samples. The importance of these factors in SLC is related to the pattern of urban development, which began on the valley floor and has been moving up the mountain benches.

Stream physical habitat variables (Short et al. 2005) were not important explanatory variables rela-

tive to land use, and only one variable (number of riffles in the sampling reach) made the top 12 associations and then only for one study area (SLC) and data type (QRC). The lack of correspondence between invertebrate responses and physical habitat structure variables is, in part, a result of our study design, which kept habitat structure consistent within each study area to maximize our ability to detect basin-scale effects versus local-scale effects.

A dozen chemical variables made the list of top explanatory variables. However, there was little consistency among study areas, and the chemical variables that were important tended to be specific to a particular study area. No common set of chemical variables

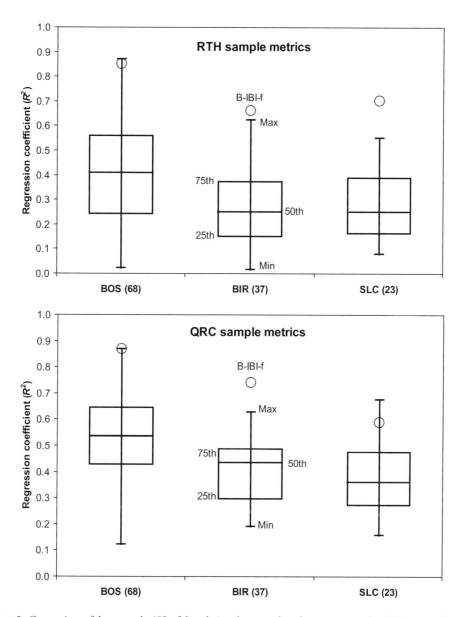

FIGURE 5. Comparison of the strengths (R^2) of the relations between the urban intensity index (UII), B-IBI-f (o), and the invertebrate assemblage metrics comprising the B-IBI-f (box plot) based on RTH and QRC samples. Minimum (min), maximum (max), 25th, 50th, and 75th percentiles are represented in the box plots. The values in parentheses indicate the number of assemblage metrics comprising the B-IBI-f for the Boston (BOS), Birmingham (BIR), and Salt Lake City (SLC) urban studies.

were associated with invertebrate responses across all three urban study areas.

Comparing Responses Among Urban Areas

Invertebrate assemblage responses were compared among study areas using both the UII and the CUII.

Relations between response variables (ordination axis site scores and assemblage metrics) and urban intensity (UII and CUII) were evaluated by comparing the slopes of linear regressions. The response variables investigated were limited to those that were at least moderately correlated ($|\rho| \geq 0.5$) with the UII, had statistically significant slopes ($b \neq 0$, $P \leq 0.01$), rela-

TABLE 5. Assemblage metrics that were used in constructing the "common" and "reduced" variations of the B-IBI.

Metric	RTH B-IBI		QRC B-IBI	
	Common	Reduced	Common	Reduced
Richness				
RICH			X	X
PLECOr	X	X		
TRICHr			X	X
EPTr	X	X	X	X
EPT_CHr			X	X
COLEOPr	X	X	X	X
% richness				
PLECOrp	X			
TRICHrp			X	
EPTrp			X	
EPT_CHrp			X	
NONINSrp	X	X	X	X
ODIPNIrp			X	X
OLIGOrp			X	X
Functional group richness				
FCr			X	X
Density				
PLECO	X			
COLEOP	X			
% density				
COLEOPp	X			

TABLE 6. Relations between UII and B-IBIs based on all metrics that were correlated with the UII ($|\rho| \geq 0.5$) for each study (B-IBI-f), on a common set of metrics shared by all three studies (B-IBI-c), and on common metrics with no redundancy (B-IBI-r). Relations are derived from linear regressions: $Y = a + bX$ where Y is the B-IBI and X is the UII. N is the number of metrics used to calculate the B-IBI for the Boston (BOS), Birmhingham (BIR), and Salt Lake City (SLC) urban study areas.

RTH metrics					QRC metrics				
Model	N	a	b	R^2	Model	N	a	b	R^2
BOS					BOS				
B-IBI-f	68	89.14	−0.97	0.85	B-IBI-f	37	88.85	−0.97	0.87
B-IBI-c	8	74.70	−0.84	0.75	B-IBI-c	12	94.43	−0.93	0.80
B-IBI-r	4	91.40	−1.03	0.85	B-IBI-r	9	94.44	−0.95	0.81
BIR					BIR				
B-IBI-f	37	74.58	−0.86	0.66	B-IBI-f	25	76.10	−0.85	0.74
B-IBI-c	8	49.73	−0.64	0.48	B-IBI-c	12	71.73	−0.79	0.65
B-IBI-r	4	60.31	−0.70	0.56	B-IBI-r	9	77.44	−0.79	0.66
SLC					SLC				
B-IBI-f	23	89.31	−0.89	0.70	B-IBI-f	23	89.84	−0.82	0.59
B-IBI-c	8	78.27	−0.85	0.67	B-IBI-c	12	88.03	−0.81	0.52
B-IBI-r	4	84.01	−0.91	0.63	B-IBI-r	9	86.26	−0.79	0.51

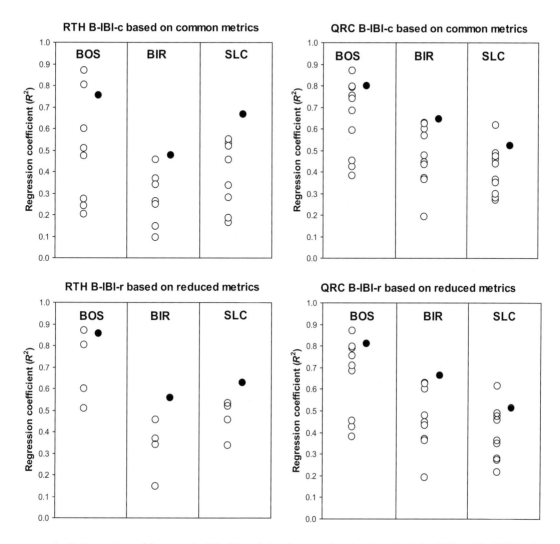

FIGURE 6. Comparison of the strengths (R^2) of the relations between the urban intensity index (UII) and the B-IBI-c, the B-IBI-r (•), and the invertebrate assemblage metrics comprising these indices (o) based on RTH and QRC samples for the Boston (BOS), Birmingham (BIR), and Salt Lake City (SLC) urban study areas.

tively even distributions across the gradient defined by the UII, included no outliers, and were common to all three study areas. Only 12 response variables (3 based on RTH data, 9 based on QRC data) possessed these characteristics.

Response rates (slopes) for most metrics (8 of 12) did not differ significantly ($P \leq 0.05$) among study areas when urban intensity was expressed as UII (Table 9). Four metrics that did differ significantly were all QRC richness metrics with higher response rates in BOS than in BIR or SLC. The significantly higher rates in BOS are a consequence of the higher taxa richness associated with background sites in BOS com-

pared to BIR and SLC (Figure 1). Areas with higher background taxa richness have more taxa that can be lost along the urban gradient. Consequently, the numbers of taxa lost per unit of urban intensity (slope) are higher in these areas (BOS) than in areas with lower background richness (BIR, SLC).

When response rates were based on the CUII most of the metrics (8 of 12) were statistically different among study areas (Table 9). All of these differences were associated with higher response rates in BOS. Response rates in BIR and SLC were not statistically different from one another. The higher response rates in BOS are a result of differences in the maxi-

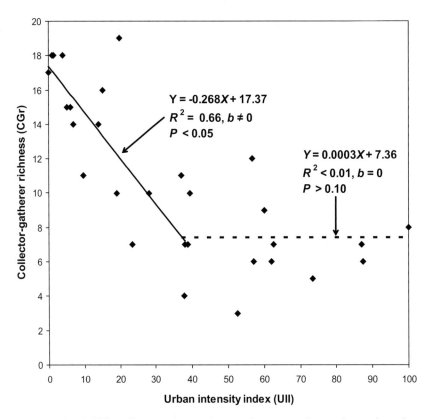

FIGURE 7. Response threshold for collector-gatherer richness in the Boston urban study area derived using a two-step regression analysis.

mum levels of urban intensity measured by CUII and UII, which were substantially different in BOS (CUII = 74, UII = 100) but not in BIR (CUII = 100, UII = 100) or SLC (CUII = 95, UII = 100). These differences are reflected in the relation between CUII and UII (Tate et al. 2005). There is almost a 1:1 relation in BIR (UII = 1.06 × CUII − 1.93, R^2 = 0.97) and SLC (UII = 1.19 × CUII − 5.69, R^2 = 0.86), but in BOS a unit of CUII corresponds to 1.52 units of UII (UII = 1.52 × CUII − 1.90, R^2 = 0.98). Consequently, the rate of change in BOS is substantially higher when expressed as CUII than as UII because the same magnitude of invertebrate response occurs over a smaller range of urban intensity. The average ratio (CUII:UII) of slopes for the response variables in Table 9 (BOS: 1.50, BIR: 1.04, SLC: 1.18) match the slopes of the regressions relating CUII and UII for each study area.

The strong relation between CUII and UII in each urban study area dictates that the correlations between urban intensity and assemblage metrics are virtually the same regardless of whether urban inten-

sity is characterized by CUII or UII. Linear regressions relating correlations between metrics based on CUII and UII show a nearly 1:1 correspondence (BOS: b = 0.99, R^2 = 0.99; BIR: b = 0.97, R^2 = 0.99; SLC: b = 0.94, R^2 = 0.99). Consequently, expressing urban intensity using the CUII had no effect on determining which metrics were most strongly correlated with urbanization. The value of CUII is that it places the response rates of the three study areas on a common basis by using a common set of urban indicator variables.

Urban Optima and Tolerance Values

The inference models used to estimate taxa optima performed well with a close correspondence (R^2) between observed and modeled urban intensity (ca. 0.89 for BOS and BIR and 0.75 for SLC) and root mean-square errors for optima of ca. 7 units of intensity for BOS and BIR and 12 for SLC. There was a high degree of correspondence between the optima derived from UII and CUII (BOS: CUII = 0.60 × UII + 3.21,

TABLE 7. Spearman rank correlations between indicators of invertebrate response and explanatory variables based on RTH samples for the Boston (BOS), Birmingham (BIR), and Salt Lake City (SLC) urban study areas. Only the 12 explanatory variables having the highest correlations ($|\rho|$) with the ordination axis representing urbanization, richness-based tolerance (TOLr), or B-IBI-f are shown. Explanatory variables in bold type were relatively consistent among study areas and sample types. Stream buffer area is based on a 180 m wide (90 m per side) buffer throughout the basin.

Explanatory variable	BOS			BIR			SLC		
	Axis 1	TOLr	B-IBI-f	Axis 1	TOLr	B-IBI-f	Axis 2	TOLr	B-IBI-f
Urban intensity (UII) index	0.91	0.85	−0.91	0.78	0.70	−0.81	−0.74	0.60	−0.75
Lithology and soils (% basin area)									
Lake sediment and playa							−0.64	0.58	−0.70
Land use/land cover (% basin area)									
Developed	0.87	0.79	−0.91	0.78	0.70	−0.80	−0.73	0.62	−0.71
Low intensity residential	0.86	0.78	−0.91	0.72	0.63	−0.76		0.62	
High intensity residential				0.75	0.66	−0.77			
Commercial/industrial/ transportation	0.84		−0.88	0.78	0.75	−0.79		0.60	
Forested	−0.90	−0.83	0.89			−0.64			
Mixed				−0.72	−0.59	0.71			
Shrub lands							0.65		
Deciduous							0.67		
Herbaceous planted/cultivated									
Pasture/hay				−0.71		0.72			
Urban/recreational grasses					0.60	−0.72		0.70	
Stream buffers (% buffer area)									
Urban	0.85	0.76	−0.90	0.78	0.70	−0.81	−0.72	0.61	−0.73
Forested	−0.86	−0.79	0.86						
Shrub land							0.72		0.69
Infrastructure									
Roads (km/km²)	0.89	0.82	−0.92	0.74	0.64	−0.75			
Toxic release inverntory (no./ 100 km²)		0.80	−0.87						
Sewers (% of households)				0.78		−0.76	−0.67	0.60	
Population and socioeconomic factors									
Population, 1990 (no./km²)	0.86	0.82	−0.88	0.78	0.65	−0.77	−0.71		−0.67
Population, 1999 (no./km²)	0.86	0.81	−0.88	0.79	0.65	−0.78	−0.72		−0.69
Population change: 1990– 1999 (no./km²)							−0.65		
Housing units built before 1980 (%)		0.78							
Socioeconomic factor 2 (PCA factor 2)					0.57		−0.74		−0.73
Chemistry									
Alkalinity (mg/L CaCO₃)	0.91		−0.89						
Ammonia (mg/L)		0.83							
Ammonia+organic nitrogen (mg/L)	0.76						0.65	0.60	
Chloride (mg/L)				0.70				0.75	−0.70
Conductance (microsiemens/ cm at 25°C)	0.85		−0.84				0.69		−0.75
Magnesium (mg/L)	0.89								−0.69
Sodium (mg/L)								0.70	−0.71
Periphyton									
biomass (g ash free dry mass/m²)								0.67	−0.78

$R^2 = 0.98$; BIR: CUII = $0.90 \times$ UII + 3.28, $R^2 = 0.99$; SLC: CUII = $0.63 \times$ UII + 16.81, $R^2 = 0.88$). The CUII optima based on QRC data were used to derive invertebrate tolerances (Appendix 5) because the CUII is the most consistent representation of urban intensity across the three study areas and QRC data include more invertebrate taxa than do either QMH or RTH. Tolerances derived from QMH and RTH samples were

TABLE 8. Spearman rank correlations between indicators of invertebrate response and explanatory variables based on QRC data for the Boston (BOS), Birmingham (BIR), and Salt Lake City (SLC) urban study areas. Only the 12 explanatory variables having the highest correlations ($|\rho|$) with the ordination axis representing urbanization, richness-based tolerance (TOLr), or B-IBI-f are shown. Explanatory variables in bold type were relatively consistent among study areas and sample types. Stream buffer area is based on a 180-m-wide (90 m per side) buffer thoughout the basin.

Explanatory variable	BOS			BIR			SLC		
	Axis 1	TOLr	B-IBI-f	Axis 1	TOLr	B-IBI-f	Axis 2	TOLr	B-IBI-f
Urban intensity (UII) index	0.92	0.88	−0.91	0.84	0.74	−0.83	−0.53	0.58	−0.70
Elevation (m)									
Site							0.77	−0.62	
Mean in basin							0.62		
Range in basin							−0.72	0.62	
Lithology and soils (% basin area)									
Lake sediment and playa							−0.63	0.63	−0.65
Soil: proportion of sand							−0.52		
Land use/land cover (% basin area)									
Developed	0.88	0.86	−0.91	0.83	0.75	−0.82		0.60	−0.68
Low intensity residential	0.87	0.85	−0.90	0.78	0.72	−0.77			
High intensity residential				0.82	0.75	−0.81			
Commercial/industrial/ transportation		0.83	−0.87	0.83	0.74	−0.84			
Forested	−0.90	−0.86	0.91	−0.75		0.68			
Mixed				−0.76	−0.75				
Herbaceous planted/cultivated									
Pasture/hay					−0.71	0.72			
Urban/recreational grasses				0.78	0.69	−0.75			
Stream buffers (% buffer area)									
Urban	0.85	0.83	−0.88	0.84	0.74	−0.84			−0.68
Forested	−0.87	−0.81	0.86				0.52		
Infrastructure									
Roads (km/km²)	0.89	0.87	−0.91	0.79	0.68	−0.80			
Toxic release inverntory (no./ 100 km²)	0.90	0.88	−0.90						
Sewers (% households)				0.82	0.75	−0.75			
Population and socioeconomic factors									
Population, 1990 (no./km²)	0.87	0.86	−0.89	0.84	0.68	−0.82			−0.63
Population, 1999 (no./km²)	0.87	0.86	−0.90	0.84	0.67	−0.81			−0.64
Population change: 1990– 1999 (no./km²)			−0.84						
Housing units built before 1980 (%)	0.83								
Socioeconomic factor 2 (PCA factor 2)									−0.68
Physical habitat structure and chemistry									
Number of riffles							0.71	−0.57	
Alkalinity (mg/L CaCO₃)	0.85	0.85	−0.85						
Ammonia (mg/L)	0.83								
Ammonia+organic nitrogen (mg/L)		0.83					−0.68	0.63	
Chloride (mg/L)							−0.53	0.74	−0.69
Conductance (micro- siemens/cm at 25°C)								0.68	−0.77
Magnesium (mg/L)									−0.72
Phosphorus (mg/L)							−0.67		

Table 8. Continued.

Explanatory variable	BOS Axis 1	TOLr	B-IBI-f	BIR Axis 1	TOLr	B-IBI-f	SLC Axis 2	TOLr	B-IBI-f
Sodium (mg/L)							−0.59	0.76	−0.69
Sulphate (mg/L)									−0.67
Turbidity (NTU)								0.66	
Temperature (°C)							−0.81	0.57	
Periphyton biomass (g ash free dry mass/m²)								0.65	−0.77

Table 9. Comparison of slopes (b) and regression coefficients (R^2) for linear regressions relating the two urban intensity indices (UII and CUII) to selected indicators of invertebrate response for the Boston (BOS), Birmingham (BIR), and Salt Lake City (SLC) urban study areas. All slopes are statistically significant ($b \neq 0$, $P \leq 0.01$). Slopes of study areas connected by a line are not statistically different from one another ($P \leq 0.05$). Metric abbreviations are explained in Table 1.

Metrics	Regressions with UII			Regressions with CUII		
Quantitative (RTH) sample metrics						
Ordination axis	SLC	BOS	BIR	SLC	BIR	BOS
b, R^2	−0.017, 0.51	−0.019, 0.87	−0.020, 0.74	−0.019, 0.42	−0.021, 0.71	−0.029, 0.77
Tolerance (TOLr)	BIR	BOS	SLC	BIR	SLC	BOS
b, R^2	0.016, 0.51	0.023, 0.81	0.025, 0.56	0.017, 0.50	0.029, 0.44	0.034, 0.72
B-IBI-f	BIR	SLC	BOS	BIR	SLC	BOS
b, R^2	−0.862, 0.66	−0.889, 0.70	−0.971, 0.85	−0.895, 0.61	−1.038, 0.58	−1.443, 0.79
Qualitative (QRC) data metrics						
Ordination axis	SLC	BOS	BIR	SLC	BIR	BOS
b, R^2	−0.012, 0.45	−0.016, 0.87	−0.017, 0.80	−0.013, 0.30	−0.018, 0.76	−0.024, 0.80
Richness metrics						
RICH	SLC	BIR	BOS	SLC	BIR	BOS
b, R^2	−0.183, 0.27	−0.266, 0.60	−0.459, 0.68	−0.256, 0.32	−0.285, 0.59	−0.693, 0.66
EPTr	BIR	SLC	BOS	BIR	SLC	BOS
b, R^2	−0.168, 0.63	−0.169, 0.46	−0.268, 0.75	−0.174, 0.58	−0.204, 0.40	−0.400, 0.71
TRICHr	BIR	SLC	BOS	BIR	SLC	BOS
b, R^2	−0.058, 0.37	−0.077, 0.36	−0.131, 0.79	−0.059, 0.33	−0.098, 0.36	−0.191, 0.72
% richness metrics						
EPTrp	BIR	BOS	SLC	BIR	SLC	BOS
b, R^2	−0.242, 0.57	−0.245, 0.74	−0.268, 0.44	−0.249, 0.52	−0.310, 0.36	−0.369, 0.71
EPT_CHrp	BOS	SLC	BIR	BIR	SLC	BIR
b, R^2	−0.009, 0.42	−0.011, 0.49	−0.013, 0.48	−0.012, 0.40	−0.013, 0.43	−0.014, 0.44
NONINSrp	BIR	SLC	BOS	BIR	SLC	BOS
b, R^2	0.162, 0.45	0.194, 0.48	0.309, 0.87	0.174, 0.45	0.219, 0.37	0.455, 0.79
Tolerance (TOLr)	BIR	SLC	BOS	BIR	SLC	BOS
b, R^2	0.015, 0.58	0.021, 0.49	0.021, 0.86	0.015, 0.53	0.023, 0.35	0.032, 0.80
B-IBI-f	SLC	BIR	BOS	BIR	SLC	BOS
b, R^2	−0.824, 0.59	−0.882, 0.70	−0.969, 0.87	−0.910, 0.65	−0.988, 0.52	−1.427, 0.79

strongly related (R^2 = 0.80–0.93) to QRC tolerances except for tolerances derived from RTH samples in SLC (R^2 = 0.52). Tolerance values derived from CUII (Appendix 5) were not closely associated (R^2: BOS 0.43, BIR 0.18, SLC 0.42) with tolerances reported by Barbour et al. (1999). However, despite the lack of correspondence at the taxa level, there was a strong relation between the mean of the tolerances for taxa at a site based on CUII optima and the tolerance metric (TOLr) derived from tolerances reported in Barbour et al. (1999; Figure 8A). These relations differed by study area with SLC assemblages showing much higher mean tolerances than BOS and BIR. There was little overlap between sites in SLC and those in BIR and BOS regardless of whether tolerances were based on CUII or literature values (TOLr). The similarity in site characterization based on CUII and literature (Barbour et al. 1999) tolerances (TOLr) indicate that the differences between SLC and BOS and BIR are real and not artifacts associated with the derivation of CUII, species optima, and tolerances. The cumulative distribution of CUII tolerance values within each study area (Figure 8B) also indicates that distributions of tolerances in BOS and BIR are similar to one another, but in SLC, the tolerances are skewed toward the high urban tolerances. Approximately 90% of the taxa in BOS and BIR had tolerance values of 5 or less, whereas only 31% of the taxa in SLC had optima below 5. These data imply that the invertebrate assemblages from SLC are more tolerant to urbanization than are assemblages from BOS or BIR.

Discussion

The responses of invertebrate assemblages observed in BOS, BIR, and SLC were generally consistent with those observed in other studies of urbanization. Taxa richness and many of its components (e.g., EPTr, EPEMr, PLECOr) decreased as urbanization increased (Garie and McIntosh 1986; Kennen 1999; Paul and Meyer 2001; Huryn et al. 2002; Kennen and Ayers 2002; Roy et al. 2003). B-IBI decreased and TOLr increased as urban intensity increased, consistent with other urban studies (May et al. 1997; Paul and Meyer 2001; Morley and Karr 2002; Roy et al. 2003). However, many studies have shown that diversity index values decreased with increasing urbanization (Klein 1979; Pratt et al. 1981; Duda et al. 1982; Whiting and Clifford 1983; Pedersen and Perkins 1986; Jones and Clark 1987; Schueler and Galli 1992; Shaver et al. 1995; Paul and Meyer 2001). This finding was not consistent with our results. Only BOS had a statis-

tically significant ($P \le 0.05$) decrease in diversity with increasing urbanization. Neither the BIR nor SLC urban study areas had any statistically ($P > 0.05$) meaningful relations between diversity and urban intensity.

Assemblage characteristics based on qualitative measures (i.e., taxa richness) had better and more consistent relations with urbanization than did quantitative measures (i.e., density) in all three urban study areas regardless of whether responses were assessed based on assemblage metrics or ordinations. Results of several other studies (Garie and McIntosh 1986; Huryn et al. 2002) also indicate that quantitative measures (e.g., density and biomass) are not as closely associated with changes in urbanization as are measures of taxa richness. This is likely a result of adding the errors associated with estimating density and biomass to that associated with detecting the taxon, which increases total variability and makes it more difficult to discern associations with urbanization. Our data (Figure 1) show that quantitative metrics are much more variable than are qualitative metrics. This may account for the generally poor performance of quantitative metrics. Quantitative samples also present numerous compromises when attempting to resolve taxonomic ambiguities (Cuffney 2003); the method used to do this can strongly affect both richness and abundance metrics and associations with environmental variables. Given the generally poor results observed with quantitative metrics, additional costs associated with generating these metrics may not be justified because they do not appear to increase our ability to detect responses along the urban gradient.

Effect thresholds for invertebrate assemblages at 5–18% total impervious surface area have been reported previously (Klein 1979; Jones and Clark 1987; Schueler 1994; Shaver et al. 1995; Booth and Jackson 1997; Maxted and Shaver 1997; May et al. 1997; Kennen and Ayers 2002; Morse et al. 2003). However, the results of our urban studies did not indicate that an effect threshold exists at low levels of urbanization. That is, the assemblages did not show any evidence of being able to resist or compensate for changes brought about during the initial phases of urbanization. Instead, responses can best be described as linear, with degradation of the invertebrate assemblage beginning as soon as the native vegetation begins to be replaced with roads and buildings. Our data provided no evidence to suggest that there is a level of urban intensity that has no effect on invertebrate assemblages. Thresholds at higher levels of urban intensity (Figure 7) also are rare for invertebrates. Only three high-level (exhaustion) thresholds were evident in more than

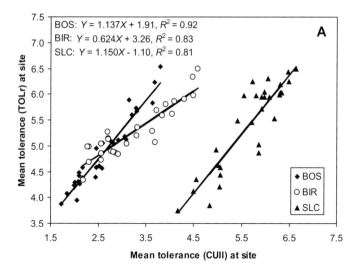

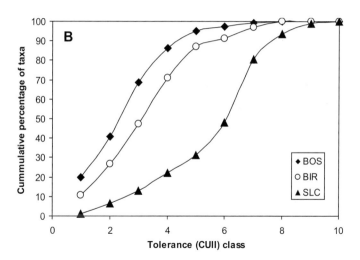

FIGURE 8. Relation between mean tolerance of invertebrates at a site based on literature values (TOLr) and tolerances derived from weighted-average calibration using CUII (A). All slopes are statistically significant ($b \neq 0$, $P < 0.05$). The cumulative distribution of CUII tolerances across 10 tolerance classes are compared for the Boston (BOS), Birmingham (BIR), and Salt Lake City (SLC) urban study areas (B).

400 responses (metrics, indices, ordinations) examined, and all of these occurred in BOS. Consequently, response thresholds cannot be described as a common feature of invertebrate responses to urbanization.

Four impairment categories for invertebrate assemblages have been identified (Schueler 1994) based on percent total impervious surface area (PTIA): unaffected at ≤ 5%, stressed at levels of 5–10%, impacted at levels of 11–25%, and degraded at levels above 26%. The corresponding impairment categories based on UII are unaffected—BOS≤ 11,

BIR ≤ 8, and SLC ≤ 5; stressed—BOS: 11–22, BIR: 8–17, and SLC: 5–17; impacted—BOS 22–56, BIR 17–45, and SLC 17–52; and degraded—BOS > 56, BIR > 45, and SLC > 52. These impairment categories indicate that assemblages in BOS, BIR, and SLC are degraded over about half of the urban gradient, impacted in the first quarter of the gradient, and stressed in the first 5–10% of the urban gradient. Only sites at the very low end of the urban gradient are unimpaired. If we accept Schueler's categories, about 67% of our study basins are in the impaired or degraded classifications and only 15% can be classified as unimpaired.

There was a strong commonality among study areas in terms of the environmental factors that are important in driving changes in invertebrate assemblages. In each area, the amount of developed land, land devoted to commercial/industrial/transportation activities, stream buffers in urban land use, road density, and population density are the paramount factors driving changes in the invertebrate assemblages. At a gross level, the responses of invertebrate assemblages to urbanization also are the same with a continual loss of taxa richness as urban-intensity increases. However, the components of the invertebrate assemblages that are most strongly affected by urbanization and that best serve as indicators of effect differed substantially among the three urban areas in our study. These differences arise because, while the driving factors associated with urbanization are consistent among regions, these factors are acting on an ecological template (i.e., climate, topography, geology, chemistry, habitat, and biology) that differs substantially among regions. It is this variation in the underlying ecological template that results in the variation in assemblage responses and lack of commonality in the biological indicators of urbanization.

Despite the lack of commonality in the response of assemblage metrics, we were able to extract indices (B-IBI-c and B-IBI-r) that were representative of the response of the invertebrate assemblages in each study area, based on a common set of metrics, and comparable among study areas. These indices suggest that it may be possible to derive nationally consistent IBIs that can be used to compare urban responses across the United States. The B-IBI-r was particularly interesting because this index was based on as few as four metrics (RTH), yet it was almost as strongly related to UII as were IBIs based on a much larger number of metrics (e.g., 20–68). Tolerance metrics (TOLr and the CUII-based tolerances derived from WA calibration) and ordinations provided another set of assemblage characteristics that were good indicators of urbanization and that were consistent and comparable among studies. The tolerances values that were derived by WA calibration varied by study area (Appendix 5), and there was relatively low correspondence among tolerance values derived for the same taxon in different study areas. This is consistent with tolerance values reported in Barbour et al. (1999), which also varied by region. Even though there was little correspondence between the tolerances derived from WA calibration and those reported in Barbour et

al. (1999), site characterizations based on average taxa tolerances at a site using these two methods were strongly related. This indicates that, while these tolerances differ at the level of the taxon, they both provide a meaningful representation of the assemblage response.

Ordinations provided valuable insights into assemblage responses to urbanization and were critical in the development of urban tolerances. However, the strengths (eigenvalues) of the ordinations were less than anticipated given that the study design was based on an urban intensity gradient. A strong eigenvalue occurs when there is a continual replacement of species along the environmental gradient (McCune et al. 2002) as conditions become more favorable for some species and less favorable for others. Data from our urban studies indicate that this is not the pattern associated with urban gradients. Rather than a continual replacement of taxa along the gradient, there is a continual loss of taxa richness with little replacement by new taxa. Data from BOS (Figure 9) illustrate the steady loss of taxa richness across the urban intensity gradient and very low recruitment of new taxa.

Further insight into the pattern of taxa distribution across the urban gradient in BOS was obtained by modeling the distribution of taxa along the primary (i.e., urban) ordination axis extracted from qualitative (QRC) data using CA. These models were developed by calculating Gaussian response curves for each taxon based on the optima and tolerances (i.e., the variance of the optima; ter Braak 1996) obtained from CA:

$$\text{Relative occurrence} = c_k - \frac{\left(x_i - \mu_k\right)^2}{2t_k^2} \text{ (ter Braak 1996)}$$

where μ_k = optima for taxon k

x_i = value of urbanization at site i

t_k = tolerance for taxon k

c_k = maximum of curve for taxon k (set to 100)

Displaying individual response curves for all taxa was not feasible, so the 140 response curves were reduced to 12 by ordering taxa from lowest to highest optima and averaging response curves for groups of 11 taxa, except for the last curve, which was based on 8 taxa. Response curves were converted to units of UII using the relation between taxa optima (taxa ordination scores) and taxa tolerances (i.e., WA-derived tolerances) derived from UII ($Y = 10.983x + 30.481$, $R^2 = 0.95$).

The modeled responses do not show a consistent replacement of taxa over the gradient. Instead, most of

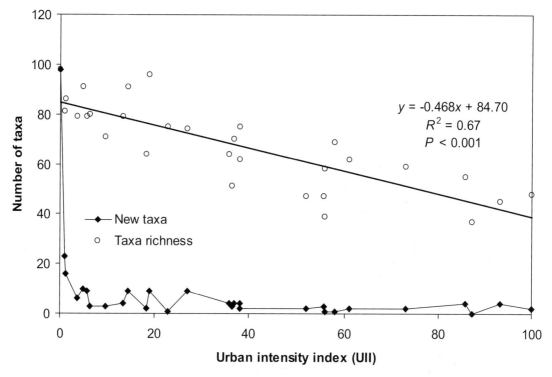

$$y = -0.468x + 84.70$$
$$R^2 = 0.67$$
$$P < 0.001$$

FIGURE 9. Taxa richness and number of new taxa encountered at sites along the urban gradient for the Boston urban study area.

the taxa drop out completely by UII = 55, and there are relatively few taxa that have optima above this level of urban intensity (Figure 10). This type of response is more typical of exposure to a toxicant where there is a loss of taxa over the gradient with no recruitment of new taxa, and all taxa that occur at the high end of the gradient are very tolerant and occur over a very large range of the gradient (i.e., the t_k is very large relative to m_k). Unfortunately, the chemical data collected as part of these studies are not sufficiently rigorous to determine if chemical toxicity was responsible for this distribution pattern. However, toxicants (e.g., pesticides, metals, polyaromatic hydrocarbons, and other organic compounds) are known to be common occurrences in urban runoff (Seaburn 1969; Andrea et al. 1997; Sansalone and Buchberger 1997a, 1997b; Sansalone et al. 1998; Hoffman et al. 2000; Beasley and Kneale 2002). The taxa that comprise the response curves with the highest optima are generally noninsect taxa (Turbellaria, Megadrile, Erpobdellidae, *Glossiphonia complanata*, *Physella* sp., *Laevapex* sp., *Musculium*, *Caecidotea* sp., and *Gammarus* sp.), with the exception of one species of elimid beetle *Ancyronyx variegate*. In contrast, the taxa that comprise the re-

sponse curves with the lowest optima are all insect taxa that typically are considered to be forms that are intolerant of pollutants (*Epeorus* sp., *Stenonema vicarium*, *Paraleptophlebia* sp., *Eurylophella* sp., *Psilotreta labida*, *Helicopsyche borealis*, *Rhyacophila fuscula*, *Ectopria* sp., *Hexatoma* sp., *Atherix lantha*, *Stempellina* sp., *Stempellinella* sp., *Parachaetocladius* sp., and *Hagenius brevistylus*).

The very strong linear relations ($R^2 = 0.6$–0.9) that we detected between assemblage responses and urban intensity are one of the most important results of our studies. Other studies (May et al. 1997; Morley and Karr 2002; Morse et al. 2003; Roy et al. 2003) have identified significant relations between invertebrate responses and urban intensities, but generally these relations were not as strong, or were not linear, or required many explanatory variables (i.e., multiple regression) to form a strong relation. The success of our studies lies in several aspects of our study and program design. Perhaps most important was our effort to control for natural sources of variability by dividing candidate sites into relatively homogeneous environmental settings (Appendix 2). The criteria used to select sampling reaches also helped by reducing local-scale sources

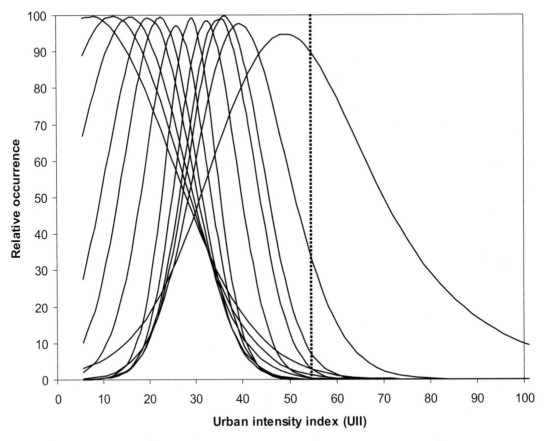

FIGURE 10. The distribution of taxa over the urban gradient modeled from Gaussian response curves based on QRC data for the Boston urban study area.

of disturbance, which allowed us to focus on basin-scale disturbances. While this enhanced our ability to detect the effects of urbanization, it may have reduced the importance of instream physical habitat variables in favor of land-use variables. The use of a simple multimetric index of urban intensity (UII) also was important because it allowed us to achieve a relatively even distribution of sites along the urban intensity gradient. Also important was our ability to use standard sample collection and processing protocols that allowed direct comparisons of invertebrate assemblages among urban areas. The NAWQA Program invertebrate collection (Cuffney et al. 1993) and processing (Moulton et al. 2000) methods are designed to provide a comprehensive characterization of invertebrates in the sampling reach. These methods are somewhat unusual in that samples are collected from a fairly large area of the sampling reach, which results in large numbers of taxa. This enhanced our ability to measure change (Cao et al. 2002a, 2002b).

We can illustrate how sampling area affects the ability to detect change along a gradient using three hypothetical sampling scenarios and the EPT taxa richness data from BOS (Figure 11). Sampling scenario 1 corresponds to the actual EPT taxa richness collected from BOS. Scenarios 2 and 3 represent sampling methods (e.g., smaller sampling areas) that produce one-half and one-quarter, respectively, of the taxa encountered in scenario 1. The response along the urban gradient is simulated using two methods. The first method (Figure 11A) sets the number of EPT taxa collected at each site to a constant proportion of the richness originally collected (i.e., 1, 0.5, and 0.25). The second method (Figure 11B) models the rate of EPT loss across the gradient as a constant regardless of how many taxa are collected by the sampling method. In the first method, the slopes and intercepts of the regression lines change as the initial number of taxa collected decreases from scenario 1–3 and our ability to detect change decreases as the magnitude of change

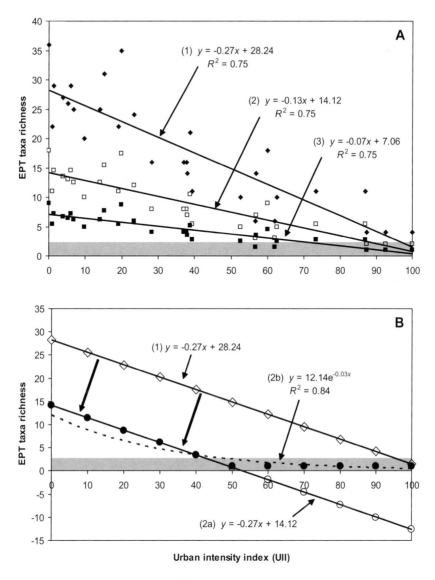

FIGURE 11. Three hypothetical sampling methods that sample progressively smaller proportions of the initial EPT taxa richness: (1) 1.0×, (2) 0.5×, and (3) 0.25×. The first scenario (A) simulates the recovery of a constant proportion of EPT taxa richness over the gradient, and the second scenario (B) simulates a constant rate of EPT taxa loss over the gradient.

in EPT taxa over the gradient (i.e., slope of the response line) decreases. In other words, it is much easier to detect the loss of 26 taxa over the gradient (scenario 1) than it is to detect the loss of 6 taxa (scenario 3), particularly as the number of taxa recovered approaches the zone (gray area) in which the method can no longer reliably detect changes in taxa richness.

The intercept changes, but the slope is constant in simulations using the second method. Only the first two scenarios (1× and 0.5) are shown in Figure 11B. In this example, the number of EPT taxa col-

lected using the second method (equation (2a) falls below the detection level (gray zone) about half way along the gradient. This has two consequences for understanding and detecting responses. First, the response can be detected only over a small portion of the urban gradient. Second, the form of the apparent response (equation (2b) is not linear, but corresponds to a negative exponential curve created when the response is lost in the "noise" associated with the method (gray zone), and the response slope is essentially zero.

The scenarios presented in Figure 11 are illustrative of some of the problems associated with comparing urban responses derived from different studies. Not only can the method used to estimate urban intensity make comparisons difficult, but the method used to collect and process invertebrates also may affect the ability to detect change, quantify the rate of response, and determine the form of the response. Caution is advised when comparing results among studies that differ markedly not only in terms of the area sampled, but also in the number of different habitat types sampled. These problems may account for some of the nonlinear relationships reported for responses to urbanization that have been reported in the literature.

Effective management, protection, and restoration of urban streams is dependent on a comprehensive understanding of physical, chemical, and biological responses and a clear understanding of the similarities and differences in responses among urban areas. Such information is essential if effective monitoring procedures are to be developed, and effective rules and regulations are implemented for urban areas in vastly different natural settings. While the factors (e.g., land-use changes) driving urbanization are similar among regions, our results indicate that elements of the invertebrate assemblages that respond are strongly affected by the local environmental setting in which urbanization is acting. Despite differences in responses among urban areas, there are a few indicators of invertebrate responses (e.g., B-IBIs, tolerance metrics, and ordinations) that can be used to compare responses among disparate environmental settings. These indicators may form the basis for nationally consistent biological indicators of urbanization.

Acknowledgments

We thank the many USGS colleagues who helped with fieldwork and sample collection. We also thank the numerous property owners and municipalities for granting us permission to access and sample the rivers. Without their generous support, none of this would have been possible. This work also was aided by the many USGS scientists who offered expertise and guidance during the design, execution, and analysis of the studies. We also thank Robert Hughes, Ian Waite, and two anonymous reviewers for providing suggestions and criticism to earlier drafts of the manuscript. Funding was provided by the U.S. Geological Survey's National Water-Quality Assessment (NAWQA) Program.

References

Andrea, R., T. Striebel, and R. Herrmann. 1997. Modeling of dissolved and particle-bound pollutants in urban street runoff. Water Science Technology 36:77–82.

Arnold, C. L., and C. J. Gibbons. 1996. Impervious surface coverage: the emergence of a key environmental indicator. American Planners Association Journal 62:243–258.

Barbour, M. T., J. Gerritsen, B. D. Snyder, and J. B. Stribling. 1999. Rapid bioassessment protocols for use in streams and wadeable rivers: periphyton, benthic macroinvertebrates, and fish. 2nd edition. U.S. Environmental Protection Agency, Office of Water, EPA Report 841-B-99–002, Washington, D.C.

Beasley, G., and P. Kneale. 2002. Reviewing the impact of metals and PAHs on macroinvertebrates in urban watercourses. Progress in Physical Geography 26:236–270.

Booth, D. B., and C. R. Jackson. 1997. Urbanization of aquatic systems: degradation thresholds, stormwater detection, and the limits of mitigation. Journal of the American Water Resources Association 33:1077–1090.

Cao, Y., D. P. Larsen, R. M. Hughes, P. L. Angermeier, and T. M. Patton. 2002a. Sampling effort affects multivariate comparisons of stream communities. Journal of the North American Benthological Society 21:701–714.

Cao, Y., D. D. Williams, and D. P. Larsen. 2002b. Comparison of ecological communities: the problem of sample representativeness. Ecological Monographs 72:41–56.

Coles, J. F., T. F. Cuffney, G. McMahon, and K. Beaulieu. 2004. The effects of urbanization on the biological, physical, and chemical characteristics of coastal New England streams. U.S. Geological Survey Professional Paper 1695, Denver.

Cuffney, T. F. 2003. User's manual for the National Water-Quality Assessment Program Invertebrate Data Analysis System (IDAS) software: Version 3. U.S. Geological Survey Open-File Report 03–172, Raleigh, North Carolina. Available: ftp://ftpext.usgs.gov/pub/er/nc/raleigh/tfc/IDAS/. (March 2004)

Cuffney, T. F., M. E. Gurtz, and M. R. Meador. 1993. Methods for collecting benthic invertebrate samples as part of the National Water-Quality Assessment Program. U.S. Geological Survey Open-File Report 93–406, Raleigh, North Carolina.

Davis, W. S., and T. P. Simon, editors. 1995. Biological assessment and criteria: tools for water resource planning and decision making. Lewis Publishers, Boca Raton, Florida.

Duda, A. M., D. R. Lenat, and D. L. Penrose. 1982. Water quality in urban streams; what can we expect? Journal of the Water Pollution Federation 54:1139–1147.

Fitzpatrick, F. A., I. R. Waite, P. J. D'Arconte, M. R. Meador, M. A. Maupin, and M. E. Gurtz. 1998. Revised methods for characterizing stream habitat in the National Water-Quality Assessment Program. U.S. Geological Survey Water-Resources Investigations Report 98–4052, Raleigh, North Carolina.

Fore, L. S., J. R. Karr, and R. W. Wisseman. 1996. Assessing invertebrate responses to human activities: evaluating alternative approaches. Journal of the North American Benthological Society 15:212–231.

Garie, H. L., and A. McIntosh. 1986. Distribution of benthic macroinvertebrates in a stream exposed to urban runoff. Water Resources Bulletin 22:447–455.

Hoffman, R. S., P. D. Capel, and S. J. Larson. 2000. Comparison of pesticides in eight U.S. urban streams. Environmental Toxicology and Chemistry 19:2249–2258.

Horner, R. R., B. D. Booth, A. Azous, and C. W. May. 1997. Watershed determinants of ecosystem functioning. Pages 251–274 in C. Roessner, editor. Effects of watershed development and management on aquatic ecosystems. American Society of Civil Engineers, New York.

Huryn, A. D., V. M. B. Huryn, C. J. Arbuckle, and L. Tsomides. 2002. Catchment land-use, macroinvertebrates and detritus processing in headwater streams: taxonomic richness versus function. Freshwater Biology 47:401–415.

Jones, R. C., and C. C. Clark. 1987. Impact of watershed urbanization on stream insect communities. Water Resources Bulletin 23:1047–1055.

Juggins, S. 2003. C² user guide. Software for ecological and palaeoecological data analysis and visualisation. University of Newcastle, Newcastle-upon-Tyne, UK.

Karr, J. R. 1981. Assessment of biotic integrity using fish communities. Fisheries 6(6):21–27.

Karr, J. R., and E. W. Chu. 1999. Restoring life in running waters: better biological monitoring. Island Press, Washington, D.C.

Karr, J. R., and E. W. Chu. 2000. Sustaining living rivers. Hydrobiologia 422:1–14.

Kerans, B. L., and J. R. Karr. 1994. Development and testing of a benthic index of biotic integrity (B-IBI) for rivers of the Tennessee Valley. Ecological Applications 4:768–785.

Kemp, S. J., and J. R. Spotila. 1997. Effects of urbanization on brown trout Salmo trutta, other fishes and macroinvertebrates in Valley Creek, Valley Forge, Pennsylvania. American Midland Naturalist 138:55–68.

Kennen, J. G. 1999. Relation of macroinvertebrate community impairment to catchment characteristics in New Jersey streams. Journal of the American Water Resources Association 36:939–955.

Kennen, J. G., and M. A. Ayers. 2002. Relation of environmental characteristics to the composition of aquatic assemblages along a gradient of urban land use in New Jersey, 1996–98. U.S. Geological Survey Water-Resources Investigations Report 02–4069, West Trenton, New Jersey.

Klein, R. D. 1979. Urbanization and stream quality impairment. Water Resources Bulletin 15:948–963.

Lenat, D. R., and J. K. Crawford. 1994. Effects of land use on water quality and aquatic biota of three North Carolina Piedmont streams. Hydrobiologia 294:185–199.

May, C. W., R. Horner, J. R. Karr, B. Mar, and E. Welch. 1997. Effects of urbanization on small streams in the Puget Sound Lowland ecoregion. Watershed Protection Techniques 2:483–494.

Maxted, J.R. and E. Shaver. 1997. The use of retention basins to mitigate stormwater on aquatic life. Pages 494–512 in L.A. Roesner, editor. Effects of watershed development and management on aquatic ecosystems. American Society of Civil Engineers, New York.

McCune, B., J. B. Grace, and D. L. Urban. 2002. Analysis of ecological communities. MjM Software Design, Gleneden Beach, Oregon.

McMahon, G., and T. F. Cuffney. 2000. Quantifying urban intensity in drainage basins for assessing stream ecological conditions. Journal of American Water Resources Association 36:1247–1261.

Meador, M. R., J. F. Coles, and H. Zappia. 2005. Fish assemblage responses to urban intensity gradients in contrasting metropolitan areas: Birmingham, Alabama, and Boston, Massachusetts. Pages 409–423 in L. R. Brown, R. H. Gray, R. M. Hughes, and M. R. Meador, editors. Effects of urbanization on stream ecosystems. American Fisheries Society, Symposium 47, Bethesda, Maryland.

Morley, S. A., and J. R. Karr. 2002. Assessing and restoring the health of urban streams in the Puget Sound basin. Conservation Biology 16:1498–1509.

Morse, C. C., A. D. Huryn, and C. Cronan. 2003. Impervious surface area as a predictor of the effects of urbanization on stream insect communities in Maine, U.S.A. Environmental Monitoring and Assessment 89:95–127.

Moulton, S. R., J. L. Carter, S. A. Grotheer, T. F. Cuffney, and T. M. Short. 2000. Methods for analysis by the U.S. Geological Survey National Water Quality Laboratory – processing, taxonomy, and quality control of benthic macroinvertebrate samples. U.S.

Geological Survey Open-File Report 00–212, Denver.

Natural Resources Conservation Service. 2000. Summary report, 1997 National resources inventory, revised December 2000. U.S. Department of Agriculture, Washington, D.C.

NCDENR (North Carolina Department of Environment and Natural Resources). 2003. Standard operating procedures for benthic macroinvertbrates, Raleigh, North Carolina. Available: http://www.esb.enr.state.nc.us/BAUwww/benthossop.pdf. (August, 2001)

Ourso, R. T., and S. A. Frenzel. 2003. Identification of linear and threshold responses in streams along a gradient of urbanization in Anchorage, Alaska. Hydrobiologia 501:117–131.

Paul, M. J., and J. L. Meyer. 2001. Streams in the urban landscape. Annual Review of Ecology and Systematics 32:333–365.

Pedersen, E. R., and M. A. Perkins. 1986. The use of benthic macroinvertebrate data for evaluating impacts of urban runoff. Hydrobiologia 139:13–22.

Potapova, M., J. C. Coles, E. M. P. Giddings, and H. Zappia. 2005. A comparison of the influences of urbanization in contrasting environmental settings on stream benthic algal assemblages. Pages 333–359 in L. R. Brown, R. H. Gray, R. M. Hughes, and M. R. Meador, editors. Effects of urbanization on stream ecosystems. American Fisheries Society, Symposium 47, Bethesda, Maryland.

Pratt, J. M., R. A. Coler, and P. J. Godfrey. 1981. Ecological effects of urban stormwater runoff on benthic macroinvertebrates inhabiting the Green River, Massachusetts. Hydrobiologia 83:29–42.

Rosenberg, D. M., and V. H. Resh, editors. 1993. Freshwater biomonitoring and benthic macroinvertebrates. Routledge, Chapman and Hall, Inc., New York.

Roy, A. H., A. D. Rosemona, M. J. Paul, D. S. Leigh, and J. B. Wallace. 2003. Stream macroinvertebrate response to catchment urbanization (Georgia, U.S.A.). Freshwater Biology 48:329–346.

Sansalone, J. J., and S. G. Buchberger. 1997a. Characterization of solid and metal element distributions in urban highway stormwater. Water Science and Technology 36(8–9):155–160.

Sansalone, J. J., and S. G. Buchberger. 1997b. Partitioning and first flush of metals in urban roadway stormwater. Journal of Environmental Engineering 123:134–143.

Sansalone, J. J., J. M. Koran, J. A., Smithson, and S. G. Buchberger. 1998. Physical characteristics of urban roadway solids transported during rain events. Journal of Environmental Engineering 124:427–440.

Schueler, T. 1994. The importance of imperviousness. Watershed Protection 1:100–111.

Schueler, T. R., and J. Galli. 1992. Environmental impacts of stormwater ponds. Pages 159–180 in P. Kumble and T. Schueler, editors. Watershed restoration source book. Metropolitan Washington Council of Governments, Publication 92705, Washington, D.C.

Seaburn, G. E. 1969. Effects of urban development on direct runoff to East Meadow Brook, Nassau County, New York. U.S. Geological Survey Professional Paper 627-B, Washington, D.C.

Shaver, E. J., G. C. Maxted, and D. Carter. 1995 Watershed protection using an integrated approach. Pages 435–459 in H. C. Torno, editor. Stormwater NPDES related monitoring needs. American Society of Civil Engineers, Crested Butte, Colorado.

Shelton, L. R. 1994. Field guide for collecting and processing stream-water samples for the National Water-Quality Assessment Program. U.S. Geological Survey Open-File Report 94–455, Sacramento, California.

Short, T. M., E. M. P. Giddings, H. Zappia, and J. F. Coles. 2005. Urbanization effects on stream habitat characteristics in Boston, Massachusetts; Birmingham, Alabama; and Salt Lake City, Utah. Pages 317–332 in L. R. Brown, R. H. Gray, R. M. Hughes, M. R. Meador, editors. Effects of urbanization on stream ecosystems. American Fisheries Society, Symposium 47, Bethesda, Maryland.

SPSS. 1999. SYSTAT 9 statistics I & II. SPSS Inc., Chicago.

Tate, C. M., T. F. Cuffney, G. McMahon, E. M. P. Giddings, J. F. Coles, and H. Zappia. 2005. Use of an urban intensity index to assess urban effects on streams in three contrasting environmental settings. Pages 291–315 in L. R. Brown, R. H.Gray, R. M. Hughes, and M. R. Meador, editors. Effects of urbanization on stream ecosystems. American Fisheries Society, Symposium 47, Bethesda, Maryland.

ter Braak, C. J. F. 1995. Chapter 5, Ordination. Pages 91–173 in R. H. G. Jongman, C. J. F. ter Braak, and O. F. R. Van Tongeren, editors. Data analysis in community and landscape ecology. Cambridge University Press, New York.

ter Braak, C. J. F. 1996. Unimodal models to relate species to environment. DLO-Agricultural Mathematics Group, Wageningen, Netherlands.

ter Braak, C. J. F. and P. Šmilauer. 1998. CANOCO manual and user's guide to CANOCO for windows: software for CANOCO community ordination (version 4). Microcomputer Power, Ithaca, New York.

U.S. Environmental Protection Agency. 2000. The quality of our nation's waters. EPA Report 841-S-00-001, Washington, D.C.

U.S. Geological Survey. 2003. National elevation dataset. U.S. Geological Survey EROS Data Center, Sioux Falls, South Dakota. Available: http://gisdata.usgs.gov/ned/. (May 2003)

Vølstad, J. H., N. E. Roth, G. Mercurio, M. T. Southerland, and D. E. Strebel. 2003. Using environmental stressor information to predict the ecological status of Maryland non-tidal streams as measured by biological indicators. Environmental Monitoring and Assessment 84:219–242.

Whiting, E. R., and H. J. Clifford. 1983. Invertebrates and urban runoff in a small northern stream, Edmonton, Alberta, Canada. Hydrobiologia 102:73–80.

Yoder, C. O., R. J. Miltner, and D. White. 1999. Assessing the status of aquatic life designated uses in urban and suburban watersheds. Pages 16–28 in A. Everson, S. Minamyer, J. Dye, P. Heimbrock, and S.Wilson, editors. National Conference on Retrofit Opportunities for Water Resource Protection in Urban Environments. U.S. Environmental Protection Agency, EPA/625/R-99/002, Washington, DC.

Yoder, C. O., and E. T. Rankin. 1996. Assessing the condition and status of aquatic life designated uses in urban and suburban watersheds. Pages 201–227 in L. A. Roesner, editor. Effect of watershed development and management on aquatic ecosystems. American Society of Civil Engineers, New York.

Zar, J. H. 1974. Biostatistical analysis. Prentice-Hall, Inc., Englewood Cliffs, New Jersey.

APPENDIX 1. Occurrence (% of sites) of taxa across the urban gradient based on QRC samples for the Boston (BOS) Birmingham (BIR) and Salt Lake City (SLC) urban study areas; all sites (ALL: BOS n = 30, BIR n = 28, and SLC n = 30), background sites with UII ≤ 10 (BOS n = 8, BIR n = 7, SLC n = 3) and highly urbanized sites with UII ≥ 70 (BOS n = 5, BIR n = 3, SLC n = 11).

| | BOS | | | BIR | | | SLC | | |
| | All | UII ≤ 10 | UII ≥ 70 | All | UII ≤ 10 | UII ≥ 70 | All | UII ≤ 10 | UII ≥ 70 |
Taxon									
Hydra sp.	3.3	0.0	20.0				6.7	0.0	0.0
Turbellaria	46.7	12.5	100.0	25.0	14.3	100.0	60.0	100.0	63.6
Prostoma sp.	16.7	0.0	40.0				6.7	0.0	18.2
Nematoda	83.3	75.0	80.0	53.6	42.9	66.7	70.0	33.3	54.5
Campeloma sp.	16.7	12.5	20.0	10.7	14.3	0.0			
Hydrobiidae	60.0	37.5	100.0						
Fluminicola sp.							60.0	66.7	54.5
Elimia sp.				67.9	100.0	0.0			
Leptoxis sp.				7.1	0.0	0.0			
Pleurocera sp.				7.1	0.0	33.3			
Ferrissia sp.	6.7	0.0	0.0	32.1	0.0	66.7			
Hebetancylus excentricus				35.7	0.0	100.0			
Laevapex sp.	30.0	12.5	80.0						
Lymnaeidae	6.7	0.0	20.0						
Pseudosuccinea columella				3.6	14.3	0.0	3.3	0.0	9.1
Stagnicola sp.							23.3	0.0	27.3
Physella sp.	46.7	37.5	100.0	32.1	28.6	66.7	60.0	33.3	63.6
Gyraulus sp.	6.7	0.0	0.0				20.0	0.0	45.5
Helisoma sp.	40.0	37.5	40.0						
Planorbella sp.	16.7	0.0	20.0		25.0	0.0	33.3		
Planorbula armigera	13.3	0.0	20.0						
Elliptio complanata	23.3	12.5	0.0						
Corbicula sp.				53.6	42.9	33.3			
Pisidium sp.	93.3	100.0	100.0	3.6	0.0	0.0	63.3	66.7	45.5
Musculium sp.	50.0	12.5	100.0						
Sphaerium sp.				32.1	28.6	0.0			
Megadrile	30.0	0.0	60.0	78.6	57.1	100.0	86.7	66.7	90.9
Lumbriculidae	90.0	87.5	80.0	46.4	42.9	66.7	40.0	0.0	63.6
Naididae				35.7	0.0	100.0	83.3	0.0	100.0

APPENDIX 1. Continued.

Taxon	BOS All	BOS UII ≤ 10	BOS UII ≥ 70	BIR All	BIR UII ≤ 10	BIR UII ≥ 70	SLC All	SLC UII ≤ 10	SLC UII ≥ 70
Dero sp.	73.3	87.5	80.0						
Tubificidae	40.0	25.0	60.0				93.3	100.0	100.0
Branchiura sowerbyi				67.9	57.1	66.7			
Enchytraeidae	26.7	37.5	40.0	7.1	14.3	33.3	73.3	66.7	90.9
Glossiphonia complanata	20.0	0.0	80.0						
Helobdella stagnalis	16.7	0.0	60.0				43.3	33.3	54.5
Placobdella ornata	3.3	12.5	0.0						
P. parasitica	6.7	0.0	0.0	7.1	0.0	33.3			
Erpobdellidae	50.0	37.5	80.0	21.4	14.3	66.7	76.7	33.3	90.9
Acari	86.7	100.0	60.0	100.0	100.0	100.0	96.7	100.0	100.0
Cambaridae							3.3	0.0	9.1
Cambarus sp.				57.1	100.0	33.3			
Orconectes sp.	63.3	50.0	80.0						
O. rusticus				35.7	14.3	33.3			
Procambarus sp.	3.3	0.0	0.0						
Caecidotea sp.	60.0	37.5	100.0	17.9	28.6	0.0	46.7	33.3	54.5
Lirceus sp.				32.1	42.9	33.3			
Crangonyx sp.	16.7	0.0	40.0	21.4	14.3	0.0	13.3	0.0	18.2
Synurella sp.	36.7	62.5	20.0						
Gammaridae				3.6	0.0	0.0			
Gammarus sp.	30.0	0.0	80.0				23.3	0.0	0.0
Hyalella azteca	53.3	37.5	20.0	14.3	28.6	0.0	23.3	0.0	27.3
Collembola	3.3	0.0	0.0	17.9	0.0	66.7	20.0	33.3	9.1
Choroterpes sp.				10.7	42.9	0.0			
Paraleptophlebia sp.	36.7	87.5	0.0	10.7	42.9	0.0	10.0	0.0	0.0
Hexagenia atrocaudata				3.6	0.0	0.0			
H. bilineata				17.9	28.6	0.0			
H. limbata				3.6	14.3	0.0			
Caenis sp.	20.0	37.5	40.0						
C. diminuta group				3.6	14.3	0.0			
C. hilaris group				3.6	14.3	0.0			
C. anceps				17.9	42.9	0.0			
Drunella coloradensis							3.3	0.0	9.1
D. doddsi							6.7	66.7	0.0
D. flavilinea							10.0	66.7	9.1
Ephemerella inermis							6.7	0.0	0.0
Eurylophella sp.	26.7	62.5	0.0						
E. aestiva				21.4	57.1	0.0			
Serratella deficiens	33.3	75.0	0.0	17.9	42.9	0.0			
S. serrata	33.3	75.0	0.0						
S. tibialis							13.3	66.7	18.2
Timpanoga lita				3.6	14.3	0.0			
Tricorythodes sp.	26.7	25.0	0.0	46.4	14.3	0.0	30.0	0.0	36.4
Ameletus sp.							6.7	66.7	0.0
Centroptilum/Procloeon sp.	16.7	37.5	0.0	10.7	14.3	0.0			
Acentrella turbida	6.7	0.0	0.0	14.3	42.9	0.0			
Acerpenna pygmaea	23.3	25.0	0.0	10.7	28.6	0.0			

APPENDIX 1. Continued.

Taxon	BOS			BIR			SLC		
	All	UII ≤ 10	UII ≥ 70	All	UII ≤ 10	UII ≥ 70	All	UII ≤ 10	UII ≥ 70
Baetis bicaudatus							3.3	33.3	0.0
B. flavistriga	76.7	87.5	40.0	82.1	71.4	66.7			
B. intercalaris	6.7	12.5	0.0	39.3	57.1	0.0			
B. tricaudatus	13.3	12.5	0.0				93.3	100.0	100.0
Callibaetis sp.				7.1	0.0	0.0	6.7	0.0	9.1
Diphetor hageni							3.3	33.3	0.0
Heterocloeon curiosum				7.1	14.3	0.0			
Plauditus sp.	36.7	37.5	0.0						
Pseudocloeon sp.	30.0	12.5	0.0						
P. propinquum				3.6	14.3	0.0			
Siphlonurus sp.	13.3	37.5	0.0				10.0	0.0	18.2
Cinygmula sp.							13.3	66.7	0.0
Epeorus sp.	20.0	50.0	0.0						
E. longimanus							26.7	66.7	9.1
Leucrocuta sp.	3.3	0.0	0.0	14.3	57.1	0.0			
Nixe sp.							3.3	0.0	0.0
Rhithrogena sp.							3.3	0.0	0.0
Stenacron sp.	10.0	0.0	0.0						
S. interpunctatum				35.7	100.0	0.0			
Stenonema modestum/ smithae	60.0	37.5	40.0						
S. exiguum				3.6	14.3	0.0			
S. femoratum				10.7	14.3	0.0			
S. mediopunctatum				3.6	14.3	0.0			
S. pulchellum				46.4	71.4	0.0			
S. terminatum				10.7	28.6	0.0			
S. vicarium	26.7	75.0	0.0						
Isonychia sp.	63.3	100.0	0.0	60.7	100.0	0.0			
Calopteryx maculata	66.7	87.5	0.0	14.3	42.9	0.0			
Hetaerina americana	10.0	0.0	0.0	3.6	0.0	0.0			
Coenagrion/Enallagma sp.	6.7	0.0	20.0						
Argia fumipennis	43.3	62.5	0.0	10.7	0.0	33.3			
A. moesta				3.6	0.0	0.0			
A. sedula				71.4	71.4	66.7			
A. vivida							20.0	0.0	18.2
Enallagma sp.	6.7	0.0	40.0						
Enallagma weewa				3.6	14.3	0.0			
Ischnura sp.	3.3	0.0	20.0						
Aeshna sp.	16.7	12.5	20.0				10.0	0.0	9.1
Basiaeschna janata	13.3	25.0	0.0						
Boyeria grafiana	23.3	37.5	0.0						
Boyeria vinosa	83.3	100.0	40.0	78.6	100.0	33.3			
Nasiaeschna pentacantha	3.3	0.0	0.0						
Epitheca princeps				7.1	14.3	0.0			
Helocordulia uhleri	20.0	50.0	0.0						
Neurocordulia obsoleta	3.3	12.5	0.0						

APPENDIX 1. Continued.

Taxon	BOS			BIR			SLC		
	All	UII ≤ 10	UII ≥ 70	All	UII ≤ 10	UII ≥ 70	All	UII ≤ 10	UII ≥ 70
Dromogomphus sp.				3.6	0.0	0.0			
Erpetogomphus sp.				3.6	0.0	0.0			
Gomphus sp.	36.7	87.5	0.0	42.9	28.6	33.3			
Hagenius brevistylus	33.3	75.0	0.0	39.3	28.6	33.3			
Lanthus sp.				7.1	28.6	0.0			
Ophiogomphus sp.	16.7	25.0	0.0						
O. severus							13.3	0.0	18.2
Progomphus sp.				3.6	0.0	0.0			
Stylogomphus albistylus	43.3	87.5	0.0	7.1	14.3	0.0			
Libellulidae				3.6	0.0	0.0			
Libellula sp.							3.3	0.0	0.0
Macromia illinoiensis	6.7	0.0	0.0	28.6	42.9	0.0			
Capniidae							10.0	33.3	0.0
Paracapnia sp.	10.0	37.5	0.0						
Leuctra sp.	33.3	50.0	40.0	3.6	14.3	0.0			
Paraleuctra sp.							3.3	33.3	0.0
Amphinemura sp.							6.7	0.0	0.0
Malenka sp.							6.7	0.0	0.0
Zapada sp.							13.3	66.7	9.1
Suwallia sp.							6.7	33.3	0.0
Sweltsa sp.	13.3	50.0	0.0				16.7	66.7	18.2
Peltoperlidae				3.6	14.3	0.0			
Tallaperla sp.	10.0	0.0	0.0						
Acroneuria sp.				14.3	42.9	0.0			
A. lycorias	66.7	100.0	40.0						
Hesperoperla pacifica							30.0	100.0	0.0
Perlesta sp.	10.0	0.0	0.0	21.4	28.6	0.0			
Perlinella drymo	3.3	0.0	0.0						
Paragnetina immarginata	3.3	12.5	0.0						
P. media	40.0	75.0	40.0						
Perlodidae	3.3	0.0	0.0						
Isoperla sp.							10.0	0.0	0.0
Skwala sp.							10.0	33.3	0.0
Pteronarcella badia							10.0	0.0	0.0
Pteronarcys californica							20.0	33.3	0.0
Belostoma sp.				3.6	14.3	0.0			
B. flumineum	13.3	0.0	20.0						
Corisella decolor							6.7	0.0	9.1
Hesperocorixa laevigata							6.7	0.0	18.2
Sigara sp.	6.7	12.5	20.0				16.7	0.0	9.1
Trichocorixa sp.	6.7	0.0	40.0	3.6	0.0	0.0			
Aquarius conformis	20.0	25.0	0.0	17.9	0.0	0.0			
A. nyctalis							60.0	33.3	54.5
A. remigis	50.0	75.0	60.0						
Gerris marginatus				3.6	0.0	0.0			
Limnoporus canaliculatus				3.6	14.3	0.0			
Rheumatobates sp.	6.7	0.0	20.0	7.1	0.0	0.0			

APPENDIX 1. Continued.

Taxon	BOS All	BOS UII ≤ 10	BOS UII ≥ 70	BIR All	BIR UII ≤ 10	BIR UII ≥ 70	SLC All	SLC UII ≤ 10	SLC UII ≥ 70
Metrobates sp.				14.3	0.0	0.0			
M. hesperius	16.7	25.0	0.0						
Trepobates pictus				32.1	28.6	0.0			
Ranatra fusca	3.3	12.5	0.0						
R. kirkaldyi	3.3	0.0	20.0						
Notonecta sp.				3.6	0.0	0.0	3.3	0.0	0.0
N. irrorata	13.3	12.5	40.0						
Microvelia sp.	3.3	12.5	0.0						
Rhagovelia distincta							16.7	0.0	9.1
R. obesa	66.7	75.0	60.0	39.3	71.4	0.0			
Chauliodes rastricornis	13.3	0.0	60.0						
Nigronia fasciatus				3.6	14.3	0.0			
N. serricornis	73.3	100.0	0.0	32.1	57.1	0.0			
Corydalus cornutus	30.0	25.0	0.0	71.4	71.4	0.0			
Sialis sp.	56.7	87.5	60.0	25.0	57.1	0.0			
Glossosoma sp.	56.7	87.5	20.0	10.7	28.6	0.0	3.3	0.0	0.0
Protoptila sp.				17.9	14.3	0.0			
Hydroptila sp.	36.7	37.5	60.0	57.1	28.6	100.0			
H. arctia							60.0	33.3	81.8
Leucotrichia sp.							3.3	0.0	0.0
L. pictipes				7.1	0.0	0.0			
Mayatrichia ayama	3.3	0.0	0.0						
Ochrotrichia sp.				3.6	0.0	0.0	13.3	33.3	0.0
Oxyethira sp.	3.3	0.0	0.0						
Rhyacophila coloradensis group							30.0	66.7	18.2
R. hyalinata group							3.3	33.3	0.0
R. rotunda group							3.3	33.3	0.0
R. brunnea							30.0	33.3	18.2
R. coloradensis							3.3	0.0	0.0
R. fuscula	43.3	100.0	0.0	3.6	14.3	0.0			
Chimarra sp.	93.3	100.0	60.0	57.1	85.7	33.3			
Dolophilodes sp.				3.6	0.0	0.0	10.0	33.3	0.0
D. distinctus	30.0	50.0	0.0						
Wormaldia sp.							6.7	33.3	0.0
Phylocentropus sp.	3.3	12.5	0.0						
Arctopsyche grandis							20.0	33.3	18.2
Parapsyche elsis							3.3	33.3	0.0
Diplectrona modesta	3.3	12.5	0.0						
Ceratopsyche cf. *alhedra*	3.3	12.5	0.0						
C. alhedra	3.3	12.5	0.0						
C. bronta	20.0	50.0	0.0						
C. cheilonis				14.3	28.6	0.0			
C. cockerelli							36.7	66.7	9.1
C. morosa	10.0	12.5	0.0						
C. oslari							36.7	66.7	9.1
C. sparna	63.3	75.0	0.0	25.0	57.1	0.0			

APPENDIX 1. Continued.

Taxon	BOS			BIR			SLC		
	All	UII ≤ 10	UII ≥ 70	All	UII ≤ 10	UII ≥ 70	All	UII ≤ 10	UII ≥ 70
Cheumatopsyche sp.	90.0	75.0	100.0	96.4	85.7	100.0	10.0	0.0	9.1
Hydropsyche rossi/simulans				3.6	0.0	0.0			
H. depravata group	100.0	100.0	100.0	64.3	28.6	33.3			
H. betteni	3.3	0.0	20.0						
H. californica							3.3	0.0	0.0
H. occidentalis							63.3	33.3	72.7
Macrostemum sp.	23.3	25.0	0.0						
Neureclipsis sp.	3.3	0.0	0.0						
Paranyctiophylax sp.	3.3	0.0	0.0						
Polycentropus sp.	40.0	50.0	20.0	35.7	85.7	0.0			
Lype diversa	40.0	75.0	0.0	17.9	28.6	0.0			
Psychomyia flavida	6.7	0.0	0.0	7.1	14.3	0.0			
Tinodes sp.							10.0	0.0	9.1
Limnephiloidea	13.3	25.0	0.0						
Apatania sp.							3.3	0.0	0.0
Brachycentrus americanus							16.7	0.0	9.1
B. appalachia	13.3	25.0	0.0						
B. numerosus	26.7	62.5	0.0						
B. occidentalis							3.3	0.0	0.0
Micrasema sp.	56.7	87.5	0.0				10.0	33.3	0.0
M. wataga				35.7	57.1	0.0			
Goera sp.	3.3	0.0	0.0	3.6	14.3	0.0			
Lepidostoma sp.	16.7	37.5	0.0				43.3	100.0	27.3
Onocosmoecus unicolor							3.3	0.0	0.0
Frenesia sp.	3.3	0.0	0.0						
Hesperophylax sp.							13.3	0.0	0.0
Pycnopsyche sp.	63.3	75.0	0.0						
Neophylax sp.	33.3	25.0	0.0				3.3	0.0	0.0
Neothremma alicia							3.3	33.3	0.0
Anisocentropus pyraloides				3.6	14.3	0.0			
Ceraclea sp.	10.0	12.5	0.0						
Mystacides sepulchralis	13.3	25.0	0.0	7.1	14.3	0.0			
Oecetis sp.	30.0	62.5	40.0						
O. avara group							10.0	0.0	18.2
O. disjuncta							13.3	33.3	9.1
O. persimilis				10.7	14.3	0.0			
Triaenodes sp.	3.3	0.0	20.0						
T. cumberlandensis/ melaca				7.1	14.3	0.0			
T. ignitus				3.6	0.0	0.0			
Molanna sp.	23.3	25.0	0.0	3.6	0.0	0.0			
Psilotreta labida	20.0	62.5	0.0						
Helicopsyche borealis	20.0	50.0	0.0	7.1	14.3	0.0			
Lepidoptera	33.3	37.5	20.0						
Petrophila sp.				25.0	0.0	0.0			
Agabus sp.				3.6	14.3	0.0	30.0	0.0	36.4
Liodessus affinis						3.3	0.0	0.0	

APPENDIX 1. Continued.

Taxon	BOS All	BOS UII ≤ 10	BOS UII ≥ 70	BIR All	BIR UII ≤ 10	BIR UII ≥ 70	SLC All	SLC UII ≤ 10	SLC UII ≥ 70
Hydroporini	13.3	0.0	0.0						
Oreodytes sp.							6.7	0.0	9.1
Laccophilus sp.	3.3	0.0	20.0						
Dineutus ciliatus	3.3	0.0	0.0						
D. discolor	46.7	37.5	0.0	17.9	28.6	0.0			
Gyrinus bifarius							3.3	0.0	0.0
G. lecontei	16.7	37.5	0.0						
G. marginellus	16.7	25.0	0.0						
Brychius sp.							13.3	0.0	0.0
Haliplus sp.	6.7	0.0	0.0						
Peltodytes sp.	13.3	0.0	60.0	21.4	14.3	0.0			
P. callosus							6.7	33.3	0.0
Staphylinidae				14.3	42.9	0.0	6.7	33.3	0.0
Helophorus sp.							3.3	0.0	0.0
Ametor scabrosus							20.0	33.3	9.1
Berosus sp.				25.0	0.0	66.7			
Cymbiodyta sp.	6.7	12.5	0.0	3.6	14.3	0.0			
Hydrobius sp.	6.7	12.5	0.0						
Laccobius sp.							3.3	0.0	0.0
Paracymus sp.	3.3	0.0	20.0	3.6	0.0	0.0			
Sperchopsis tessellata	16.7	12.5	0.0	10.7	14.3	0.0			
Tropisternus sp.	3.3	0.0	20.0	7.1	0.0	0.0			
Scirtidae				10.7	0.0	0.0			
Helichus basalis				7.1	28.6	0.0			
H. fastigiatus	6.7	0.0	0.0	7.1	0.0	0.0			
H. lithophilus				3.6	0.0	0.0			
H. striatus							16.7	33.3	9.1
Ancyronyx variegata	53.3	25.0	80.0	21.4	14.3	0.0			
Cleptelmis addenda							10.0	33.3	0.0
Dubiraphia sp.	63.3	87.5	40.0	75.0	100.0	0.0			
Heterlimnius corpulentus							16.7	66.7	18.2
Lara avara							3.3	33.3	0.0
Macronychus glabratus	80.0	87.5	40.0	35.7	42.9	0.0			
Microcylloepus pusillus	26.7	12.5	0.0	42.9	42.9	0.0			
Narpus concolor							20.0	66.7	27.3
Optioservus castanipennis							16.7	0.0	9.1
O. divergens							6.7	0.0	0.0
O. fastiditus	3.3	0.0	0.0						
O. ovalis	43.3	62.5	0.0	10.7	14.3	0.0			
O. quadrimaculatus							43.3	66.7	9.1
O. trivittatus				57.1	85.7	0.0			
Oulimnius latiusculus	56.7	87.5	0.0	25.0	42.9	0.0			
Promoresia tardella	40.0	62.5	0.0	3.6	14.3	0.0			
Stenelmis concinna	6.7	12.5	0.0						
S. crenata	80.0	87.5	60.0	89.3	100.0	100.0			
S, mera	3.3	0.0	0.0						

APPENDIX 1. Continued.

Taxon	BOS All	BOS UII ≤ 10	BOS UII ≥ 70	BIR All	BIR UII ≤ 10	BIR UII ≥ 70	SLC All	SLC UII ≤ 10	SLC UII ≥ 70
Zaitzevia parvula							26.7	33.3	0.0
Ectopria sp.	23.3	62.5	0.0	3.6	0.0	0.0			
Psephenus herricki	60.0	75.0	0.0	64.3	100.0	0.0			
Anchytarsus bicolor	3.3	0.0	0.0						
Lampyridae							3.3	0.0	9.1
Curculionidae				3.6	0.0	0.0	10.0	0.0	0.0
Blephariceridae				3.6	14.3	0.0			
Ceratopogonidae	6.7	0.0	0.0	14.3	14.3	0.0			
Bezzia/Palpomyia sp.							6.7	0.0	0.0
Probezzia sp.							20.0	0.0	27.3
Phaenopsectra/Tribelos sp.	23.3	25.0	20.0	28.6	28.6	0.0			
Chironomus sp.	10.0	0.0	0.0	57.1	57.1	66.7	53.3	0.0	72.7
Cryptochironomus sp.	20.0	12.5	40.0	67.9	71.4	66.7	66.7	0.0	81.8
Demicryptochironomus sp.							3.3	0.0	0.0
Dicrotendipes sp.	13.3	12.5	40.0	53.6	42.9	100.0	33.3	0.0	45.5
Glyptotendipes sp.	3.3	0.0	20.0	3.6	0.0	0.0			
Lauterborniella agrayloides	6.7	12.5	0.0						
Microtendipes sp.	63.3	100.0	0.0	32.1	85.7	0.0	6.7	0.0	0.0
Nilothauma sp.	3.3	12.5	0.0						
Parachironomus sp.	3.3	0.0	0.0				6.7	0.0	18.2
Paracladopelma sp.							10.0	33.3	0.0
Paratendipes sp.	40.0	50.0	20.0	35.7	42.9	0.0	16.7	0.0	27.3
Phaenopsectra sp.	20.0	25.0	20.0	67.9	71.4	33.3	93.3	66.7	100.0
Polypedilum sp.	100.0	100.0	100.0	96.4	100.0	100.0	73.3	100.0	63.6
Stelechomyia perpulchra	3.3	12.5	0.0						
Stenochironomus sp.	46.7	37.5	40.0	25.0	28.6	0.0	6.7	0.0	18.2
Stictochironomus sp.	3.3	0.0	0.0	14.3	28.6	0.0			
Tribelos sp.	23.3	50.0	0.0	32.1	28.6	0.0			
Xenochironomus xenolabis	13.3	25.0	0.0	3.6	14.3	0.0	3.3	0.0	9.1
Xestochironomus sp.				3.6	0.0	0.0			
Pseudochironomus sp.	3.3	0.0	0.0	17.9	28.6	0.0			
Micropsectra/Tanytarsus sp.	46.7	75.0	40.0	14.3	14.3	0.0	50.0	66.7	36.4
Cladotanytarsus sp.				7.1	0.0	0.0			
Micropsectra sp.	30.0	75.0	20.0				63.3	66.7	54.5
Paratanytarsus sp.	3.3	0.0	0.0	28.6	42.9	33.3	6.7	0.0	9.1
Rheotanytarsus sp.	93.3	100.0	80.0	92.9	100.0	100.0	40.0	33.3	36.4
Stempellina sp.	23.3	62.5	0.0						
Stempellinella sp.	30.0	62.5	0.0	17.9	14.3	0.0	6.7	33.3	0.0
Sublettea coffmani	3.3	0.0	0.0	7.1	0.0	0.0			
Tanytarsus sp.	56.7	87.5	40.0	64.3	85.7	100.0	10.0	0.0	18.2
Diamesa sp.	6.7	0.0	20.0						
Pagastia sp.	30.0	50.0	20.0				63.3	100.0	45.5
Pseudodiamesa sp.							6.7	33.3	9.1
Cricotopus/ Orthocladius sp.	63.3	75.0	60.0	53.6	42.9	66.7	70.0	66.7	90.9
Eukiefferiella/Tvetenia sp.	30.0	62.5	20.0						

APPENDIX 1. Continued.

Taxon	BOS All	BOS UII ≤ 10	BOS UII ≥ 70	BIR All	BIR UII ≤ 10	BIR UII ≥ 70	SLC All	SLC UII ≤ 10	SLC UII ≥ 70
Brillia sp.	66.7	87.5	40.0	14.3	28.6	0.0	60.0	66.7	63.6
Cardiocladius sp.	16.7	0.0	20.0	28.6	14.3	33.3	10.0	33.3	0.0
Corynoneura sp.	16.7	12.5	20.0				10.0	0.0	18.2
Cricotopus bicinctus group	53.3	37.5	40.0	57.1	28.6	100.0	80.0	66.7	90.9
C. trifascia group				7.1	0.0	33.3	53.3	33.3	45.5
Eukiefferiella sp.	56.7	75.0	40.0	10.7	14.3	0.0	90.0	100.0	90.9
Heleniella sp.							3.3	33.3	0.0
Heterotrissocladius sp.				3.6	14.3	0.0			
Hydrobaenus sp.							6.7	33.3	0.0
Limnophyes sp.							6.7	0.0	9.1
Lopescladius sp.	6.7	25.0	0.0	7.1	14.3	0.0			
Nanocladius sp.	40.0	75.0	60.0	14.3	0.0	100.0	16.7	0.0	36.4
Orthocladius lignicola	33.3	75.0	0.0	3.6	0.0	0.0	6.7	33.3	0.0
Parachaetocladius sp.	30.0	87.5	0.0						
Parakiefferiella sp.	6.7	12.5	0.0				13.3	0.0	9.1
Parametriocnemus sp.	83.3	100.0	40.0	67.9	100.0	33.3	76.7	33.3	90.9
Paraphaenocladius sp.	13.3	0.0	0.0	3.6	0.0	0.0			
Psectrocladius sp.	3.3	12.5	0.0						
Rheocricotopus sp.	56.7	62.5	40.0	71.4	57.1	100.0	66.7	100.0	90.9
Synorthocladius sp.	6.7	12.5	0.0	25.0	14.3	0.0	10.0	0.0	0.0
Thienemanniella sp.	53.3	75.0	40.0	28.6	28.6	0.0	40.0	33.3	45.5
Tvetenia sp.	80.0	100.0	40.0	35.7	57.1	0.0	53.3	100.0	27.3
Xylotopus par	33.3	62.5	0.0	10.7	14.3	0.0			
Zalutschia sp.							3.3	0.0	0.0
Odontomesa sp.							16.7	33.3	0.0
Prodiamesa sp.	3.3	0.0	0.0				60.0	33.3	54.5
Clinotanypus sp.	10.0	0.0	20.0	3.6	14.3	0.0			
Alotanypus sp.							6.7	0.0	9.1
Apsectrotanypus sp.				3.6	14.3	0.0			
Psectrotanypus sp.	3.3	0.0	20.0						
Radotanypus submarginella							46.7	33.3	45.5
Natarsia sp.				14.3	14.3	0.0			
Thienemannimyia group	93.3	100.0	100.0	92.9	100.0	100.0	50.0	66.7	45.5
Ablabesmyia sp.	73.3	62.5	80.0	96.4	85.7	100.0			
Labrundinia sp.	6.7	0.0	0.0	3.6	0.0	0.0			
Larsia sp.	3.3	12.5	0.0				6.7	33.3	0.0
Nilotanypus sp.	40.0	37.5	0.0	10.7	14.3	0.0			
Paramerina sp.				14.3	14.3	33.3	3.3	0.0	0.0
Pentaneura sp.	20.0	0.0	20.0	14.3	14.3	0.0			
Zavrelimyia sp.	3.3	12.5	0.0	3.6	14.3	0.0			
Procladius sp.	16.7	25.0	40.0	46.4	14.3	66.7	10.0	0.0	27.3
Culex sp.	3.3	0.0	0.0				10.0	0.0	18.2
Dixidae							3.3	0.0	0.0
Dixa sp.				10.7	14.3	0.0			
Dixella sp.				7.1	0.0	0.0			
Pericoma/ Telmatoscopus sp.							13.3	0.0	9.1

APPENDIX 1. Continued.

Taxon	BOS			BIR			SLC		
	All	UII ≤ 10	UII ≥ 70	All	UII ≤ 10	UII ≥ 70	All	UII ≤ 10	UII ≥ 70
Maruina sp.							6.7	33.3	0.0
Psychoda sp.							3.3	0.0	0.0
Simulium sp.	100.0	100.0	100.0	85.7	85.7	66.7	80.0	66.7	90.9
Tanyderidae				3.6	14.3	0.0			
Thaumalea sp.							6.7	33.3	0.0
Prionocera sp.							6.7	33.3	9.1
Tipula sp.	56.7	37.5	60.0	50.0	57.1	0.0	53.3	66.7	36.4
Antocha sp.	46.7	50.0	20.0	71.4	71.4	33.3	26.7	66.7	0.0
Dicranota sp.	23.3	37.5	0.0				13.3	33.3	9.1
Hexatoma sp.	33.3	87.5	0.0	7.1	28.6	0.0	20.0	33.3	0.0
Limonia sp.	3.3	0.0	0.0				26.7	0.0	18.2
Pedicia sp.							10.0	66.7	0.0
Atherix lantha	23.3	62.5	0.0	10.7	28.6	0.0			
A. pachypus							13.3	33.3	0.0
Clinocera sp.							3.3	33.3	0.0
Wiedemannia sp.							6.7	33.3	0.0
Chelifera/Metachela sp.				3.6	14.3	0.0			
Hemerodromia sp.	83.3	87.5	80.0	75.0	71.4	100.0	36.7	0.0	54.5
Neoplasta sp.							33.3	66.7	0.0
Ephydridae							3.3	33.3	0.0
Muscidae							6.7	0.0	9.1
Sciomyzidae	3.3	0.0	0.0						
Myxosargus sp.				3.6	14.3	0.0			
Eristalis sp.							6.7	0.0	0.0
Chrysops sp.	3.3	0.0	0.0						
Tabanus sp.				7.1	28.6	0.0			

APPENDIX 2. Minimum and maximum values for selected site characteristics and assemblage metrics (see Table 1 for explanation of abbreviations).

Basin characteristics	BOS		BIR		SLC	
	Minimum	Maximum	Minimum	Maximum	Minimum	Maximum
Basin area (km^2)	46	125	5	66	4	1,764
Stream order	2	5	2	4	2	6
Population density (no./km^2)	25	1,261	10	1,543	13	2,251
Urban intensity (UII)	0	100	0	100	0	100
Sampling reach characteristics						
Area (m^2)	750	1,879	628	4,051	99	3,511
Riffle (%)	18	64	5	77	3	92
Gradient (m/m)	0.001	0.016	<0.001	0.007	0.004	0.166
Dominant substrate (size-class)	5.1	8.6	2.3	8.8	0.5	8.0
Fines (%)	0	45	0	79	2	21
Silt cover (%)	0	15	0	45	0	100
Canopy closure (%)	77	100	51	100	40	80
Richness metrics						
Total	37	98	32	65	31	62
EPTr	4	36	2	21	1	24
PLECOr	0	6	0	3	0	9
TRICHr	3	17	2	10	1	13
COLEOPr	0	14	1	10	0	7
DIPr	10	32	13	26	12	27
CHr	7	28	9	22	10	23
ORTHO_CHr	0.20	0.74	0.14	0.67	0.18	0.59
NONINSr	6	19	4	13	3	14
ODIPNIr	10	22	7	17	10	19
MOLCRUr	2	12	2	9	0	7
OLIGOr	0	4	1	5	1	5
Density metrics						
DENSITY	2,177	29,699	1,939	12,390	1,673	88,832
EPT	544	14,302	146	9,839	2	26,725
PLECO	0	1,254	0	243	0	1,358
TRICH	524	13,870	67	4,315	2	22,021
COLEOP	0	2,965	0	5,001	0	4,516
DIP	822	14,947	92	5,774	806	40,417
CH	296	12,368	0	5,678	538	33,642
ORTHO_CH	0	1	0	1	0.12	0.93
NONINS	97	9,261	181	8,852	195	60,368
ODIPNI	446	11,840	371	8,982	422	60,686
MOLCRU	0	3,773	9	8,723	0	59,741
OLIGO	0	4,944	0	908	2	12,042
Tolerance metrics						
TOL	3.2	6.4	3.4	6.6	3.1	6.9
TOLr	3.9	6.5	4.3	6.5	3.8	6.5
Diversity index						
SHANND	0.68	1.49	0.46	1.23	0.36	1.31

APPENDIX 3. Spearman rank correlations between the UII and assemblage metrics based on richness and percent richness. Metrics in bold type are strongly correlated ($|\rho| \geq 0.7$) with the UII. Metrics marked with an ampersand (@) are among the 12 metrics most strongly correlated with the UII in each study area. Metrics marked with an asterisk (*) were used to construct the B-IBI-f for each study area. NA indicates that the metric could not be calculated in that study. Abbreviations are explained in Table 1.

Metric	Quantitative (RTH) samples			Qualitative (QRC) data		
	BOS	BIR	SLC	BOS	BIR	SLC
Richness						
RICH	@*−0.85	−0.41	−0.39	@*−0.86	@*−0.78	*−0.51
EPTr	@*−0.89	@*−0.71	*−0.47	@*−0.88	@*−0.83	*−0.53
EPT_CHr	−0.24	@*−0.69	*−0.48	*−0.63	@*−0.77	@*−0.57
EPEMr	@*−0.82	@*−0.77	−0.25	@*−0.83	@*−0.80	−0.19
PLECOr	@*−0.88	*−0.49	@*−0.63	*−0.68	−0.39	@*−0.61
PTERYr	NA	NA	*−0.46	NA	NA	*−0.46
TRICHr	@*−0.83	−0.39	*−0.49	@*−0.86	*−0.65	@*−0.60
ODONOr	*−0.53	−0.11	0.06	*−0.70	−0.32	0.07
COLEOPr	*−0.66	*−0.61	@*−0.65	*−0.56	@*−0.72	@*−0.57
DIPr	*−0.82	0.24	−0.13	*−0.78	−0.11	−0.25
CHr	*−0.81	*0.46	<−0.01	*−0.73	0.03	0.03
ORTHOr	*−0.79	0.32	0.04	*−0.73	0.28	0.02
ORTHO_CHr	0.13	0.01	0.06	−0.15	0.33	0.01
TANYr	*−0.65	0.20	−0.31	*−0.58	−0.02	−0.23
TANY_CHr	−0.27	−0.23	−0.35	−0.35	−0.03	−0.24
NCHDIPr	*−0.45	−0.31	*−0.47	*−0.69	−0.41	*−0.54
NONINSr	*0.62	*0.45	0.33	*0.78	0.34	0.40
ODIPNIr	*0.52	0.13	0.14	*0.65	−0.09	0.05
MOLCRUr	*0.71	−0.06	−0.03	*0.78	−0.21	0.13
GASTROr	*0.52	0.32	−0.04	*0.71	0.41	0.24
BIVALr	0.27	−0.15	−0.04	*0.49	−0.15	−0.25
CORBICr	NA	−0.09	NA	NA	−0.09	NA
AMPHIr	*0.59	0.13	−0.25	0.23	−0.40	0.03
ISOPr	*0.54	−0.06	0.18	*0.45	−0.18	0.11
OLIGOr	−0.01	*0.61	0.42	0.23	*0.46	@*0.78
% richness						
EPTrp	*−0.62	@*−0.66	−0.40	@*−0.84	@*−0.77	*−0.51
EPT_CHrp	−0.24	@*−0.70	*−0.49	*−0.62	@*−0.77	@*−0.57
EPEMrp	*−0.64	@*−0.69	−0.15	*−0.75	@*−0.75	−0.04
PLECOrp	*−0.78	*−0.49	@*−0.64	*−0.58	−0.38	@*−0.60
PTERYrp	NA	NA	*−0.47	NA	NA	*−0.46
TRICHrp	−0.32	−0.25	−0.38	*−0.74	*−0.48	*−0.51
ODONOrp	−0.35	−0.10	0.07	−0.40	0.12	0.07
COLEOPrp	−0.35	*−0.54	@*−0.57	−0.24	*−0.57	*−0.48
DIPrp	−0.29	*0.52	0.37	−0.09	*0.56	0.42
CHrp	−0.43	*0.58	*0.47	−0.08	@*0.65	@*0.66
ORTHOrp	−0.27	*0.47	0.44	−0.22	*0.61	*0.49
ORTHO_CHrp	0.15	<0.01	0.04	−0.15	0.34	0.02
TANYrp	−0.42	0.40	−0.16	−0.33	0.32	−0.04
TANY_CHrp	−0.26	−0.23	−0.35	−0.34	−0.04	−0.24
NCHDIPrp	0.31	−0.18	−0.29	−0.14	−0.15	−0.39
NONINSrp	*0.81	@*0.68	@*0.50	@*0.91	*0.64	@*0.63
ODIPNIrp	*0.81	*0.51	0.37	@*0.85	*0.56	*0.53
MOLCRUrp	@*0.86	0.10	0.02	@*0.90	0.29	0.26
GASTROrp	*0.63	*0.47	−0.04	@*0.82	@*0.65	0.37

APPENDIX 3. Continued.

Metric	Quantitative (RTH) samples			Qualitative (QRS) data		
	BOS	BIR	SLC	BOS	BIR	SLC
BIVALrp	*0.53	−0.11	−0.04	***0.77**	<−0.01	−0.09
CORBICrp	NA	0.06	NA	NA	0.10	NA
AMPHIrp	***0.65**	0.13	−0.25	*0.61	−0.37	0.07
ISOPrp	*0.58	−0.01	0.20	***0.69**	−0.04	0.22
OLIGOrp	0.37	**@*0.71**	@*0.52	*0.61	*0.63	**@*0.75**
Functional groups						
Richness						
PAr	−0.02	0.21	−0.10	0.04	0.31	−0.14
PRr	***−0.80**	−0.22	−0.29	***−0.69**	*−0.53	−0.44
OMr	***0.67**	−0.15	−0.16	0.30	*−0.63	−0.14
GCr	***−0.75**	0.15	−0.09	**@*−0.79**	*−0.52	−0.04
FCr	***−0.71**	*−0.46	−0.30	**@*−0.80**	*−0.50	*−0.54
SCr	***−0.80**	*−0.56	−0.43	***−0.71**	**@*−0.69**	−0.44
SHr	−0.33	−0.11	@*−0.56	−0.40	−0.37	*−0.49
PIr	NA	NA	NA	NA	NA	NA
% richness						
PArp	*0.48	0.33	0.15	*0.53	*0.57	0.18
PRrp	−0.33	0.05	0.15	−0.14	0.09	−0.04
OMrp	***0.67**	−0.15	−0.16	***0.78**	−0.32	0.13
GCrp	−0.14	*0.50	0.35	−0.17	0.28	@*0.60
FCrp	0.37	−0.27	−0.04	−0.03	−0.02	−0.42
SCrp	−0.22	*−0.46	−0.32	−0.37	−0.40	−0.26
SHrp	0.13	0.05	@*−0.51	0.21	−0.16	−0.39
PIrp	NA	NA	NA	NA	NA	NA
Tolerance						
TOLr	**@*0.85**	**@*0.70**	@*0.60	**@*0.88**	**@*0.74**	@*0.58
Number of correlations |ρ| ≥ 0.7						
Positive	8	3	0	11	3	3
Negative	15	6	1	17	10	0
Total	23	9	1	28	13	3

Appendix 4. Spearman rank correlations between UII and assemblage metrics based on density and percent density. Metrics in bold type are strongly correlated (\|ρ\| ≥ 0.7) with the UII. Metrics marked with an ampersand (@) are among the 12 metrics most strongly correlated with the UII in each study area. Metrics marked with an asterisk (*) were used to construct the B-IBI-f for each study area. NA indicates that the metric could not be calculated in that study. Abbreviations are explained in Table 1.

Metric	Density			Metric	% density		
	BOS	BIR	SLC		BOS	BIR	SLC
Taxonomic groupings							
DEN	0.13	−0.44	−0.13				
EPT	0.38	−0.36	−0.07	EPTp	0.34	−0.27	0.02
EPT_CH	0.35	*−0.56	−0.02	EPT_CHp	0.35	*−0.56	−0.02

Appendix 4. Continued.

Metric	Density			Metric	% density		
	BOS	BIR	SLC		BOS	BIR	SLC
EPEM	*–0.76	–0.40	–0.31	EPEMp	*–0.74	–0.28	–0.21
PLECO	@*–0.89	*–0.49	@*–0.55	PLECOp	@*–0.90	*–0.50	*–0.49
PTERY	NA	NA	*–0.47	PTERYp	NA	NA	*–0.47
TRICH	*0.57	–0.31	0.05	TRICHp	*0.61	–0.18	0.17
ODONO	*–0.48	–0.06	0.07	ODONOp	*–0.48	–0.08	0.07
COLEOP	*–0.61	@*–0.72	@*–0.68	COLEOPp	*–0.70	–0.62	@*–0.64
DIP	–0.05	0.28	0.02	DIPp	–0.10	*0.61	0.11
CH	–0.18	0.28	0.07	CHp	–0.28	*0.61	0.16
ORTHO	*–0.59	0.38	0.08	ORTHOp	*–0.73	*0.55	0.20
ORTHO_CH	*–0.54	0.03	0.26	ORTHO_CHp	*–0.54	0.05	0.26
TANY	–0.22	0.12	–0.44	TANYp	–0.22	0.36	–0.35
TANY_CH	–0.03	–0.12	–0.32	TANY_CHp	–0.03	–0.11	–0.32
NCHDIP	0.27	–0.22	–0.13	NCHDIPp	0.19	0.02	–0.14
NONINS	0.23	0.01	0.02	NONINSp	0.27	0.21	0.22
ODIPNI	0.34	–0.10	–0.07	ODIPNIp	0.38	0.19	0.15
MOLCRU	0.43	–0.16	–0.06	MOLCRUp	*0.46	–0.04	–0.02
GASTRO	*0.54	0.01	–0.28	GASTROp	*0.53	0.10	–0.27
BIVAL	0.14	–0.03	–0.11	BIVALp	0.14	–0.03	–0.03
CORBIC	NA	–0.02	NA	CORBICp	NA	0.01	NA
AMPHI	*0.60	0.13	–0.25	AMPHIp	*0.59	0.13	–0.25
ISOP	*0.57	–0.14	0.19	ISOPp	*0.56	–0.03	0.21
OLIGO	0.04	*0.58	0.33	OLIGOp	0.06	*0.61	*0.48
Functional group metrics							
PA	0.10	0.13	–0.09	PAp	0.08	0.20	–0.07
PR	–0.37	0.16	0.09	PRp	*–0.59	@*0.66	0.24
OM	*0.67	–0.16	–0.17	OMp	*0.67	–0.15	–0.17
GC	*–0.62	–0.04	–0.12	GCp	*–0.66	0.19	0.05
FC	*0.53	–0.20	–0.02	FCp	*0.64	0.20	0.14
SC	*–0.61	@*–0.63	–0.39	SCp	*–0.68	*–0.58	*–0.45
SH	–0.09	0.11	0.01	SHp	–0.15	0.33	0.18
PI	NA	NA	NA	PIp	NA	NA	NA
Dominance metrics							
				DOM1	*0.67	–0.34	0.06
				DOM2	*0.75	–0.29	–0.01
				DOM3	*0.79	–0.23	0.01
				DOM4	@*0.82	–0.15	0.08
				DOM5	@*0.84	–0.12	0.12
Tolerance metrics							
TOL	@*0.86	*0.45	0.34				
Number of correlations |ρ| ≥ 0.7							
Positive	8	1	0				
Negative	8	1	1				
Total	16	2	1				

APPENDIX 5. CUII derived optima and tolerance values for invertebrates collected at five or more sites within the Boston (BOS), Birmingham (BIR), and Salt Lake City (SLC) urban study areas. National tolerances are averages of regional tolerance values reported by Barbour et al. (1999) and NCDENR (2003).

Taxon	Optima (CUII)			Tolerances (CUII)			National tolerance
	BOS	BIR	SLC	BOS	BIR	SLC	
Minor taxa							
Turbellaria	36.7	55.7	55.1	5.0	7.8	6.3	4.0
Prostoma sp.	41.2			5.7			
Nematoda	24.1	37.1	52.4	2.9	4.7	5.5	5.5
Mollusca							
Campeloma sp.	27.3			3.5			
Hydrobiidae	33.3			4.4			7.0
Fluminicola sp.			52.6			5.6	5.0
Elimia sp.		18.2			1.5		2.7
Ferrissia sp.		44.9			6.0		6.2
Hebetancylus excentricus		50.4			6.9		
Laevapex sp.	41.4			5.8			
Stagnicola sp.			54.7			6.2	8.4
Physella sp.	35.2	46.7	55.7	4.7	6.3	6.5	8.1
Gyraulus sp.			67.4			9.7	6.1
Helisoma sp.	28.5			3.7			
Planorbella sp.	33.3	47.9		4.4	6.5		6.4
Elliptio complanata	19.9			2.3			5.1
Corbicula sp.		28.5			3.2		
Pisidium sp.	25.1		52.6	3.1		5.6	6.8
Musculium sp.	38.7			5.3			5.0
Sphaerium sp.		25.0			2.6		6.1
Oligochaeta							
Megadrile	34.0	35.9	54.7	4.6	4.5	6.2	
Lumbriculidae	24.8	31.5	63.2	3.1	3.8	8.6	7.5
Naididae		54.8	60.4		7.7	7.8	
Dero sp.	26.1			3.3			9.5
Tubificidae	31.5		55.9	4.1		6.5	9.0
Branchiura sowerbyi		30.7			3.6		8.3
Enchytraeidae	26.4		59.7	3.3		7.6	9.9
Glossiphonia complanata	50.7			7.3			
Helobdella stagnalis	48.4		53.1	6.9		5.7	8.6
Erpobdellidae	32.8	45.9	56.9	4.4	6.2	6.8	8.0
Mites							
Acari	22.5	31.5	54.2	2.7	3.7	6.1	
Crustacea							
Cambarus sp.		22.4			2.2		7.6
Orconectes sp.	30.4			4.0			2.6
Orconectes rusticus		34.5			4.3		
Caecidotea sp.	32.8	21.3	56.1	4.4	2.0	6.6	7.7
Lirceus sp.		29.4			3.4		7.9
Crangonyx sp.	44.2	20.1		6.2	1.8		5.9
Synurella sp.	16.6			1.7			
Gammarus sp.	46.1		48.0	6.5		4.3	6.6
Hyalella azteca	19.9		48.4	2.3		4.4	7.9
Ephemeroptera							
Paraleptophlebia sp.	8.4			0.4			1.3
Hexagenia bilineata		17.0			1.3		

APPENDIX 5. Continued.

Taxon	Optima (CUII)			Tolerances (CUII)			National tolerance
	BOS	BIR	SLC	BOS	BIR	SLC	
Caenis sp.	20.9			2.4			6.3
Caenis anceps		14.7			0.9		
Eurylophella sp.	8.6			0.4			3.5
Eurylophella aestiva		11.0			0.3		
Serratella deficiens	11.6	11.9		0.9	0.4		2.2
Serratella serrata	10.0			0.7			1.4
Tricorythodes sp.	18.0	28.7	55.2	1.9	3.3	6.3	4.2
Centroptilum/Procloeon sp.	12.2			1.0			
Acerpenna pygmaea	14.1			1.3			3.4
Baetis flavistriga	20.7	31.9		2.4	3.8		4.4
Baetis intercalaris		24.8			2.6		4.9
Baetis tricaudatus			54.7			6.2	1.6
Plauditus sp.	21.9			2.6			
Pseudocloeon sp.	18.4			2.0			3.4
Epeorus sp.	8.0			0.3			0.4
Epeorus longimanus			38.6			1.7	0.0
Stenacron interpunctatum		11.5			0.4		6.9
Stenonema modestum/smithae	26.1			3.3			
Stenonema pulchellum		16.6			1.2		2.3
Stenonema vicarium	7.1			0.2			1.9
Isonychia sp.	14.4	17.7		1.4	1.4		2.3
Odonata							
Calopteryx maculata	18.1			2.0			
Argia fumipennis	19.8			2.2			
Argia sedula		32.5			3.9		8.5
Argia vivida			57.8			7.1	
Aeshna sp.	24.3			3.0			5.0
Boyeria grafiana	16.5			1.7			6.1
Boyeria vinosa	20.8	23.7		2.4	2.4		3.8
Helocordulia uhleri	8.7			0.4			4.9
Gomphus sp.	14.7	32.8		1.4	4.0		5.4
Hagenius brevistylus	11.7	29.6		0.9	3.4		2.5
Ophiogomphus sp.	13.7			1.2			2.5
Stylogomphus albistylus	12.1			1.0			4.7
Macromia illinoiensis		25.1			2.7		
Plecoptera							
Leuctra sp.	17.2			1.8			0.3
Sweltsa sp.			40.9			2.4	
Acroneuria lycorias	17.5			1.9			2.3
Hesperoperla pacifica			33.5			0.3	1.0
Perlesta sp.		17.3			1.3		4.7
Paragnetina media	16.1			1.6			2.1
Pteronarcys californica			40.7			2.3	0.0
Hemiptera							
Sigara sp.			55.9			6.5	
Aquarius conformis	20.0	33.1		2.3	4.0		
Aquarius nyctalis			51.6			5.3	
Aquarius remigis	24.9			3.1			

APPENDIX 5. Continued.

Taxon	Optima (CUII)			Tolerances (CUII)			National tolerance
	BOS	BIR	SLC	BOS	BIR	SLC	
Metrobates hesperius	13.9			1.3			
Trepobates pictus		27.6			3.1		
Rhagovelia distincta			53.8			5.9	
Rhagovelia obesa	23.6	12.7		2.9	0.6		
Megaloptera	16.9	17.8					
Nigronia serricornis				1.8	1.4		2.9
Corydalus cornutus	19.5	26.6		2.2	2.9		4.5
Sialis sp.	18.9	9.5		2.1	0.0		4.8
Trichoptera							
Glossosoma sp.	17.6			1.9			0.8
Protoptila sp.		19.7			1.8		1.5
Hydroptila sp.	28.6	38.3		3.7	4.9		5.5
Hydroptila arctia			55.8			6.5	6.0
Rhyacophila coloradensis group			47.6			4.2	
Rhyacophila brunnea			46.2			3.8	
Rhyacophila fuscula	10.5			0.7			0.9
Chimarra sp.	23.1	24.2		2.8	2.5		3.6
Dolophilodes distinctus	10.0			0.7			
Arctopsyche grandis			52.7			5.6	2.0
Ceratopsyche bronta	10.6			0.7			3.7
Ceratopsyche cockerelli			39.5			2.0	
Ceratopsyche oslari			38.2			1.6	
Ceratopsyche sparna	16.9	22.0		1.8	2.1		2.5
Cheumatopsyche sp.	28.1	32.4		3.6	3.9		4.8
Hydropsyche depravata group	25.9	31.3		3.2	3.7		
Hydropsyche occidentalis			58.9			7.4	4.0
Macrostemum sp.	19.5			2.2			3.2
Polycentropus sp.	17.3	12.1		1.8	0.5		4.8
Lype diversa	15.3	15.2		1.5	1.0		3.0
Brachycentrus americanus			44.3			3.3	
Brachycentrus numerosus	9.9			0.6			1.4
Micrasema sp.	14.7			1.4			1.5
Micrasema wataga		14.5			0.9		2.3
Lepidostoma sp.	12.6		41.8	1.1		2.6	1.0
Pycnopsyche sp.	18.5			2.0			3.5
Neophylax sp.	21.5			2.5			2.7
Oecetis sp.	23.8			2.9			6.3
Molanna sp.	16.1			1.6			6.0
Psilotreta labida	7.7			0.3			0.0
Helicopsyche borealis	7.0			0.2			2.0
Lepidoptera	21.2			2.5			
Petrophila sp.		38.8			5.0		3.3
Coleoptera							
Agabus sp.			62.1			8.2	7.3
Dineutus discolor	18.2	15.9		2.0	1.1		
Gyrinus lecontei	8.4			0.4			
Gyrinus marginellus	15.7			1.6			
Peltodytes sp.		33.8			4.1		6.9

APPENDIX 5. Continued.

Taxon	Optima (CUII)			Tolerances (CUII)			National tolerance
	BOS	BIR	SLC	BOS	BIR	SLC	
Ametor scabrosus			47.9			4.3	
Berosus sp.		53.0			7.4		6.7
Sperchopsis tessellata	16.4			1.7			
Helichus striatus			47.8			4.3	
Ancyronyx variegata	33.8	22.8		4.5	2.3		
Dubiraphia sp.	22.1	21.2		2.6	2.0		5.3
Heterlimnius corpulentus			52.1			5.5	
Macronychus glabratus	22.7	17.3		2.7	1.3		3.8
Microcylloepus pusillus	24.2	24.7		3.0	2.6		2.4
Narpus concolor			46.6			3.9	4.0
Optioservus castanipennis		37.3				1.4	
Optioservus ovalis	14.2			1.3			2.4
Optioservus quadrimaculatus			45.6			3.7	4.0
Optioservus trivittatus		20.9			1.9		
Oulimnius latiusculus	16.9	21.2		1.8	2.0		1.8
Promoresia tardella	11.3			0.9			1.0
Stenelmis crenata	23.5	30.9		2.8	3.6		
Zaitzevia parvula			44.3			3.3	4.0
Ectopria sp.	7.7			0.3			4.5
Psephenus herricki	16.4	17.4		1.7	1.4		3.3
Diptera							
Probezzia sp.			57.8			7.1	6.0
Phaenopsectra/Tribelos sp.	27.0	31.0		3.4	3.7		
Chironomus sp.		36.3	63.4		4.6	8.6	9.5
Cryptochironomus sp.	32.9	33.1	58.6	4.4	4.0	7.3	6.8
Dicrotendipes sp.		41.1	58.4		5.4	7.2	7.4
Microtendipes sp.	15.2	11.5		1.5	0.3		6.2
Paratendipes sp.	20.2	17.0	57.4	2.3	1.3	6.9	7.0
Phaenopsectra sp.	19.2	30.3	56.3	2.1	3.5	6.6	6.9
Polypedilum sp.	25.9	32.1	53.0	3.2	3.8	5.7	6.0
Stenochironomus sp.	25.6	21.9		3.2	2.1		5.0
Tribelos sp.	11.5	22.3		0.9	2.2		5.4
Pseudochironomus sp.		25.0			2.6		5.0
Micropsectra/Tanytarsus sp.	18.8		50.7	2.1		5.1	
Micropsectra sp.	11.8		50.4	0.9		5.0	5.2
Paratanytarsus sp.		30.0			3.5		6.1
Rheotanytarsus sp.	25.1	31.0	50.5	3.1	3.7	5.0	5.4
Stempellina sp.	10.9			0.8			1.3
Stempellinella sp.	9.2	16.5		0.5	1.2		3.8
Tanytarsus sp.	22.1	35.4		2.6	4.4		5.7
Pagastia sp.	16.7		52.1	1.7		5.5	1.3
Cricotopus/Orthocladius sp.	25.8	38.5	59.4	3.2	4.9	7.5	
Eukiefferiella/Tvetenia sp.	21.9			2.6			
Brillia sp.	20.0		55.6	2.3		6.4	5.0
Cardiocladius sp.	33.7	41.0		4.5	5.4		5.3
Corynoneura sp.	30.0			3.9			6.1
Cricotopus bicinctus group	29.2	43.6	57.1	3.8	5.8	6.9	7.4
Cricotopus trifascia group		58.4				7.2	4.9

APPENDIX 5. Continued.

Taxon	Optima (CUII)			Tolerances (CUII)			National tolerance
	BOS	BIR	SLC	BOS	BIR	SLC	
Eukiefferiella sp.	22.6		55.5	2.7		6.4	8.0
Nanocladius sp.	24.2		56.6	3.0		6.7	4.3
Orthocladius lignicola	10.9			0.8			
Parachaetocladius sp.	8.2			0.4			2.7
Parametriocnemus sp.	21.7	20.7	55.8	2.5	1.9	6.5	4.3
Rheocricotopus sp.	24.7	36.9	55.6	3.0	4.7	6.4	6.1
Synorthocladius sp.		44.4			5.9		2.8
Thienemanniella sp.	22.8	22.5	54.4	2.7	2.2	6.1	5.5
Tvetenia sp.	20.5	26.9	43.7	2.3	3.0	3.1	5.0
Xylotopus par	10.7			0.8			4.0
Prodiamesa sp.			42.5			2.8	3.0
Odontomesa sp.			58.7			7.3	
Radotanypus submarginella			52.5			5.6	
Thienemannimyia group	25.7	33.1	54.3	3.2	4.0	6.1	6.0
Ablabesmyia sp.	26.7	32.5		3.4	3.9		6.8
Nilotanypus sp.	20.6			2.4			5.3
Pentaneura sp.	30.2			3.9			5.6
Procladius sp.	35.3	38.0		4.8	4.8		8.5
Simulium sp.	25.9	31.3	55.0	3.2	3.7	6.3	5.2
Tipula sp.	24.3	22.7	55.6	3.0	2.3	6.4	5.3
Antocha sp.	22.6	27.9	40.1	2.7	3.1	2.1	3.1
Dicranota sp.	8.5			0.4			2.0
Hexatoma sp.	8.1		48.1	0.3		4.4	2.5
Limonia sp.			56.1			6.6	7.2
Atherix lantha	8.1			0.3			2.4
Hemerodromia sp.	25.4	35.5	61.9	3.2	4.4	8.2	6.0
Neoplasta sp.			43.8			3.2	

American Fisheries Society Symposium 47:409–423, 2005

Fish Assemblage Responses to Urban Intensity Gradients in Contrasting Metropolitan Areas: Birmingham, Alabama and Boston, Massachusetts

MICHAEL R. MEADOR*

U.S. Geological Survey, 12201 Sunrise Valley Drive, Mail Stop 413, Reston, Virginia 20192, USA

JAMES F. COLES

U.S. Geological Survey, c/o USEPA New England, Suite 1100 (HBS)
1 Congress Street, Boston, Massachusetts 02114, USA

HUMBERT ZAPPIA

1162 Rock Cliff Drive, Martinsburg, West Virginia 25401, USA

Abstract.—We examined fish assemblage responses to urban intensity gradients in two contrasting metropolitan areas: Birmingham, Alabama (BIR) and Boston, Massachusetts (BOS). Urbanization was quantified by using an urban intensity index (UII) that included multiple stream buffers and basin land uses, human population density, and road density variables. We evaluated fish assemblage responses by using species richness metrics and detrended correspondence analyses (DCA). Fish species richness metrics included total fish species richness, and percentages of endemic species richness, alien species, and fluvial specialist species. Fish species richness decreased significantly with increasing urbanization in BIR ($r = -0.82$, $P = 0.001$) and BOS ($r = -0.48$, $P = 0.008$). Percentages of endemic species richness decreased significantly with increasing urbanization only in BIR ($r = -0.71$, $P = 0.001$), whereas percentages of fluvial specialist species decreased significantly with increasing urbanization only in BOS ($r = -0.56$, $P = 0.002$). Our DCA results for BIR indicate that highly urbanized fish assemblages are composed primarily of largescale stoneroller *Campostoma oligolepis*, largemouth bass *Micropterus salmoides*, and creek chub *Semotilus atromaculatus*, whereas the highly urbanized fish assemblages in BOS are dominated by yellow perch *Perca flavescens*, bluegill *Lepomis macrochirus*, yellow bullhead *Ameiurus natalis*, largemouth bass, pumpkinseed *L. gibbosus*, brown bullhead *A. nebulosus*, and redfin pickerel *Esox americanus*. Differences in fish assemblage responses to urbanization between the two areas appear to be related to differences in nutrient enrichment, habitat alterations, and invasive species. Because species richness can increase or decrease with increasing urbanization, a general response model is not applicable. Instead, response models based on species' life histories, behavior, and autecologies offer greater potential for understanding fish assemblage responses to urbanization.

Introduction

Fish assemblage responses to urbanization have been less studied than those of other stream biota, particularly invertebrates (Paul and Meyer 2001). However, much is known about the negative effects of urbanization on fish assemblages. Urban streams have been reported to support fish assemblages that are functionally less diverse than nonurban streams (Weaver and Garman 1994; May et al. 1997). In addition, stream reaches above or below urban areas are vulnerable to invasion by alien fish species (DeVivo 1996). Urbanization also is associated with increases in tolerant species and the decline of sensitive species (Onorato et al. 2000; Wang et al. 2000; Scott and Helfman 2001).

Despite our understanding of fish assemblage responses to urbanization, a general response model does not exist (Paul and Meyer 2001). Studies of the

---

* Corresponding author: mrmeador@usgs.gov

effects of urbanization on stream fish assemblages have included examining multiple sites along single streams (e.g., Matthews and Gelwick 1990; Weaver and Garman 1994; Kemp and Spotila 1997) and analysis of multiple streams in an ecoregion (e.g., Steedman 1988; Wang et al. 2000, 2001; Snyder et al. 2003). Few examinations have been made of fish assemblage responses to urbanization in contrasting ecoregions and zoogeographic areas (Paul and Meyer 2001).

A nationally applicable understanding of fish assemblage responses to urbanization is challenged by the need to simplify the complexity of urban influences on stream biota. Urbanization is a complex environmental gradient that can serve as a framework for assessing effects of urban influences on ecosystems (McDonnell and Pickett 1990). Understanding urbanization effects is complicated by multiple approaches for quantifying ecosystem effects and urbanization (e.g., human population density, urban land use, percentage of impervious surface). Although most studies of the effects of urbanization on stream biota have been based on single measures of urban influences, Yoder et al. (1999) noted that interpretations of ecosystem effects varied with the measures used.

In 2000, the U.S. Geological Survey's National Water-Quality Assessment (NAWQA) Program initiated a series of studies that used a common design to examine the effects of urbanization on aquatic biota in major metropolitan areas (Tate et al. 2005, this volume). The goal of our study was to examine fish assemblage responses to urban gradients in two of these study areas—Birmingham, Alabama (BIR) and Boston, Massachusetts (BOS), which represent different ecoregions, zoogeographic regions, and urban-development histories. Specific objectives were to (1) determine relations between various measures of fish species richness and an urban intensity index (UII, Tate et al. 2005), (2) identify fish assemblages associated with the most and least disturbed sites along a gradient of urbanization, (3) compare fish assemblage responses between the two urban areas, and (4) relate these responses to existing stressor-response models.

Study Areas

To reduce potential sources of natural variation within each study area, the BIR sites were located within the Ridge and Valley ecoregion in Alabama (Omernik 1987). The BOS sites were located within the Northeastern Coastal Zone ecoregion in Maine, New Hampshire, Massachusetts, and Connecticut (Omernik 1987). Surface waters at the BOS sites were classified according

to whether they contained predominantly warmwater fish species, coldwater fish species, or a mixture of both (Flanagan et al. 1999). The geographical distinction between cold- and warmwater fisheries closely follows the distinction between the colder-water streams of the Northeastern Highlands and the warmer-water streams of the Northeastern Coastal Zone ecoregions.

In addition to ecoregion differences, the two study areas represent contrasting ichthyogeographic regions. Many factors, including a subtropical climate and freshwater habitat diversity, are combined to make the Mobile River basin, where the BIR study area is located, one of the most diverse natural faunistic regions in North America. Mettee et al. (1996) reported 404 fish species for the state of Alabama and Mobile River basin tributaries in adjacent states. Within Alabama's Ridge and Valley ecoregion alone (the BIR study area), there are about 117 fish species, of which 25 are endemic (Mettee et al. 1996). In contrast, the native fish fauna in the BOS study area is species poor because freshwater habitats were limited during glaciation, and physical barriers precluded colonization following glaciation (Halliwell et al. 1999). Of the 51 fish species reported in the Northeastern Coastal Zone, none are considered endemic (Halliwell et al. 1999)

The BOS study area has more alien fish species compared to the BIR study area, reflecting the longer period of urban development in BOS relative to BIR. Urban development in BIR dates to the late 1800s and is related to industrial development of agricultural land (Lewis 1994). Although urban development in BOS is also related to industrial development of agricultural land, European settlement in BOS dates to the 1600s (Halliwell et al. 1999). Of the 95 fish species introduced into New England (Maine, New Hampshire, Vermont, Massachusetts, Connecticut, and Rhode Island; U.S. Geological Survey 2000a), 49 have become established. Many of these introductions occurred prior to 1900, including goldfish *Carassius auratus* in the late 1600s, largemouth bass *Micropterus salmoides* in the mid-1800s, and rainbow trout *Oncorhynchus mykiss* and brown trout *Salmo trutta* in the late 1800s (Hartel et al. 2002). The U.S. Geological Survey (2000a) lists 55 fish species introduced into Alabama, and most were introduced after World War II (Mettee et al. 1996). Of these, 18 species are reported to be established (Mettee et al. 1996).

Site Selection

In both study areas, sites were selected from a pool of candidate watersheds representing a gradient from low to high urban intensity. Details about the site-selection process are provided by Tate et al. (2005). Boundaries for the candidate watersheds were delineated using 30-m digital elevation model data in conjunction with geographic information programs (U.S. Geological Survey 2000b), and drainage areas were determined.

Multiple anthropogenic variables describing infrastructure (such as road and housing density), land use, and human population density were normalized by drainage area and used to construct the UII. The UII was formed by standardizing each of the variables so that they ranged from 0 to 1. For each site, a mean of all of the range-standardized variables combined was calculated and then multiplied by 100 to produce an index that ranged from 0 (low urbanization) to 100 (high urbanization). The rationale for, and calculation of, the UII is described in greater detail in McMahon and Cuffney (2000) and Tate et al. (2005).

Candidate sites were visited to assess local stream conditions, such as riparian land use and stream habitat characteristics. This information was used to select sites that represented a gradient from low to high urbanization, while minimizing natural environmental variability and anthropogenic variability that were not directly associated with urbanization, (e.g., agricultural or forestry related activities; Tate et al. 2005). Twenty-one sites were selected in BIR and 30 sites in BOS (Table 1). Sites consisted primarily of 3rd- to 5th-order streams (Short et al. 2005, this volume). In the BIR study area, bed substrates consisted of relatively similar proportions of sand, gravel, and cobble, whereas in the BOS study area, streambed substrate particle size was dominated by cobble-sized particles (Short et al. 2005). The selected sites represented a narrow range in drainage area and elevation and a broad range in population density, percent urban land, and UII (Table 1). Additional information regarding site selection and locations can be found in Tate et al. (2005). Additional information regarding stream habitat characteristics in the study sites can be found in Short et al. (2005).

Methods

We sampled fish in the BIR study area 7–17 May 2001 and in the BOS study area 3 August–5 September 2000. The sampling reach lengths at each site were 20 times the mean wetted channel width, roughly equivalent to one meander wavelength (Fitzpatrick et al. 1998). A sampling distance of at least one meander wavelength is likely to include at least two examples each of two different habitat types (pools, riffles, runs; Leopold et al. 1964). A minimum reach length of 150 m and a maximum reach length of 300 m also were established. Electrofishing a minimum reach length of 150 m in streams less than 4 m wide has been reported to be sufficient to yield accurate and precise estimates of species richness and percentage of abundance (Patton et al. 2000; Reynolds et al. 2003)

We sampled fish with a single backpack electrofisher at 30–60 pulses per second (Meador et al. 1993). Operators of electrofishing equipment received training in the sampling protocol (Meador et al. 1993) and in electrofishing principles, such as power transfer theory, to aid in standardizing the effort and increasing the efficiency of electrofishing operations (Reynolds 1996).

Electrofishing crews usually consisted of four people, all well experienced at electrofishing streams in the respective study areas. All backpack electrofishing was conducted in an upstream direction. Block nets were not used to isolate the sampling area because studies have indicated that using block nets did not improve estimates of species richness or abundance (Vadas and Orth 1993; Simonson and Lyons 1995; Edwards et al. 2003). Fish were removed from the water with dip nets, and upon completion of the first pass, fish that could be identified in the field were counted and transported downstream from the sampling reach. A second pass was then conducted, and the data from each pass were combined. Meador et al. (2003a) indicated that a single backpack electrofishing pass may under represent cyprinids and centrarchids. Fish that could not be identified in the field were

TABLE 1. Site characteristics for streams in the BIR (N = 21) and BOS (N = 30) study areas.

	BIR			BOS		
	Mean	Range	SD	Mean	Range	SD
Drainage area (km²)	36.6	6–66	15.2	75.7	46–125	23.2
Elevation (m above mean sea level)	228	163–315	40	115	31–237	59
1999 population density (people/km²)	340	10–1,543	363	337	25–1,261	359
Developed land (percent)	22.2	0–73.4	19.8	19.5	1.5–66.7	18.9
UII	36.0	1.7–100	26.8	36.4	0–100	30.5

retained for identification and enumeration in the laboratory (Walsh and Meador 1998).

In each study area, we classified fish species as native, endemic, or alien based on Mettee et al. (1996), U.S. Geological Survey (2000a), and Hartel et al. (2002). In addition, we classified all fish species as either fluvial specialists or macrohabitat generalists based on information in Kinsolving and Bain (1993), Mettee et al. (1996), Hartel et al. (2002), and Ipswich River Watershed Association (2002). Fluvial specialists are fish species that generally require flowing-water habitats throughout their lives, though occasionally individuals may be found or stocked in a reservoir or lake. In contrast, macrohabitat generalists are adaptable to a wide variety of habitats and often are found in both lotic and lentic environments.

Data Analysis

Data analysis included a combination of metric and multivariate approaches. The metric approach included total fish species richness, and percentages of richness of endemic species (for BIR only), alien species, and fluvial specialist species. Total fish species richness has been used commonly in bioassessment studies (e.g., Davis and Simon 1995), and alien fish species richness has been shown to be related to increased population density (Meador et al. 2003b). Analysis of fluvial specialist species has been used in both Alabama (Kinsolving and Bain 1993) and New England (e.g., Ipswich River Watershed Association 2002) to assess recovery of fish assemblages along gradients of anthropogenic disturbance. Yoder et al. (1999) suggested that analysis of endemic species richness could lead to improved understanding of fish assemblage responses to urbanization. Percentage calculations were arcsine-square root transformed to improve normality, and we used Pearson correlation analyses to examine relations between species richness metrics and the UII.

Detrended correspondence analysis (DCA, Gauch 1982) was used to quantify fish assemblage structure and identify fish assemblages associated with the most and least disturbed sites in both study areas. Species abundances were log transformed ($\log_{10} x + 1$) and rare species (defined as those occurring in less than 20% of the number of collections as the most frequently occurring species) were downweighted in proportion to their frequency.

Ordination techniques, such as DCA, reduce the dimensionality of multivariate data sets while attempting to preserve the structure inherent in the data. The resulting ordination represents the relative differences among sites along derived environmental gradients (DCA axes) where sites with similar compositions are located close together along an axis and sites with very different compositions are located far apart. The primary ordination axis (DCA axis 1) explains the most variation (structure) in the data with each succeeding axis explaining less of the variation. For this study, responses associated with the first two axes of the ordinations (DCA axes 1 and 2) were examined based on the following hypothesis: if urban intensity were an important factor in determining community structure and natural factors had been controlled in the study design, DCA axis 1 should be correlated with measures of urban intensity.

To determine if the primary measure of fish assemblage structure (defined by DCA axis 1) corresponded to urbanization, Pearson correlation analysis was conducted to examine the relation between site scores from DCA axes 1 and 2 and the UII. Assuming that DCA axis-1 site scores represented a gradient of urbanization, whereas DCA axis-2 site scores did not, we wanted to examine the fish assemblages most associated with DCA axis-1 site scores while minimizing associations with nonurban gradients represented by DCA axis-2 site scores. High and low DCA axis-1 site scores were defined by determining the 75th and 25th percentiles of site scores along DCA axis 1, and the mean and standard deviation of DCA axis-2 site scores also were determined. Fish species scores occurring within one standard deviation of DCA axis-2 site scores and greater than the 75th percentile of DCA axis-1 site scores were considered to be high and assumed to represent the fish assemblage most associated with high DCA axis-1 site scores. Similarly, fish species scores occurring within one standard deviation of DCA axis-2 site scores and less than the 25th percentile of DCA axis 1 site scores were considered to be low and assumed to represent the fish assemblage most associated with low DCA axis-1 site scores.

To test that the site-selection process limited natural variation related to drainage area and elevation, Pearson correlation analyses were conducted to examine relations between species richness metrics and log-transformed ($\log_{10} x$) drainage area and elevation. Pearson correlation analysis also was conducted to examine relations between DCA axis-1 and 2 site scores and log-transformed drainage area and elevation. An assessment of relations between fish assemblage measures and urbanization independent of stream-size effects (drainage area and elevation) is desired because fish assemblage composition often is correlated with stream size (Smogor and Angermeier 1999).

To compare linear relations between species richness and urbanization for the two study areas, analysis of covariance (ANCOVA) was conducted by using the model species richness = UII + study area + (UII x study area).

This ANCOVA model fits separate linear regressions of species richness and urbanization for each of the study areas. This linear model assumes that within a study area, species richness varies with urbanization at a constant rate—the slope of the regression line. The inclusion of the interaction term, however, allows the slope to vary between study areas. A significance level of 0.05 was used for all statistical tests.

Locally weighted regression smoothing (LOESS) of data scatter plots was conducted to examine nonlinear patterns in relations between species richness and urbanization. Patterns based on LOESS smoothing were compared to patterns in relations between species richness and stressors based on three response models. Carlisle et al. (2003) provided an example of a dose–response relation, based on a negative, nonlinear response of species richness to a chemical stressor (dose–response model, Figure 1A). Such a response curve illustrates resistance and exhaustion components (Selye 1973). Using data from Ohio, Yoder et al. (1999) suggested a negative, nearly linear fish species richness response to urbanization consisting of three components: (1) loss of endemic species, (2) loss of additional species primarily as a result of habitat degradation, and (3) continued loss of fish species richness as a result of toxicity and organic enrichment (Ohio model, Figure 1B). Scott and Helfman (2001) provided a response model for the southeastern United States, which indicated that habitat destruction associated with anthropogenic activity can result in simultaneous loss of endemic species and an increase in species richness as a result of exploitation of the altered habitat by native and alien invasive species (habitat-disturbance model, Figure 1C).

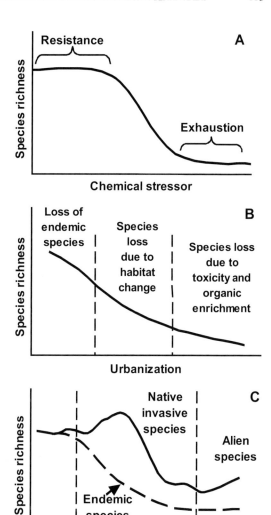

FIGURE 1. Examples of three stressor-response models based on species richness: (A) dose–response model (Carlisle et al. 2003); (B) Ohio model, based on data from Yoder et al. (1999); and (C) habitat-disturbance model (Scott and Helfman 2001).

Results

BIR Study Area

A total of 48 species representing 5,625 fish individuals was collected in the BIR study area (Appendix A; data collected as part of the NAWQA Program can be accessed at http://water.usgs.gov/nawqa/). Species richness per site ranged from 6 to 26 (mean = 15). Overall, the most abundant species was largescale stoneroller *Campostoma oligolepis*, representing 64.5% of the total individuals collected. Two other species represented

greater than 5% of the total abundance—longear sunfish *Lepomis megalotis* (11.3%) and western mosquitofish *Gambusia affinis* (5.5%). Two species, largescale stoneroller and bluegill *L. macrochirus*, were collected at all 21 sites. Five additional species were collected at greater than 50% of the 21 sites: green sunfish *L. cyanellus* (95.2%), longear sunfish (95.2%), Alabama hog sucker *Hypentelium etowanum* (90.5%), black-banded darter *Percina nigrofasciata* (57.1%), and banded sculpin *Cottus carolinae* (52.4%). No alien

species were collected. Nine of the species collected are
endemic to the BIR study area: Alabama darter
Etheostoma ramseyi, Alabama shiner *Cyprinella callistia*,
burrhead shiner *Notropis asperifrons*, Coosa darter *E.
coosae*, Coosa shiner *N. xaenocephalus*, greenbreast darter
E. jordani, Mobile logperch *P. kathae*, riffle minnow
Phenacobius catostomus, and tricolor shiner *C.
trichroistia* (Appendix A).

The UII was significantly negatively related to
species richness ($r = -0.82$, $P = 0.001$) and percentage
of endemic species richness ($r = -0.71$, $P = 0.001$).
The UII was not significantly related to the percentage of fluvial specialist species richness ($r = -0.41$, $P =
0.064$). Drainage area was not significantly related to
species richness ($r = 0.40$, $P = 0.074$), the percentage
of endemic species richness ($r = 0.23$, $P = 0.312$), or
the percentage of fluvial specialist species richness ($r =
0.41$, $P = 0.066$). Elevation also was not significantly
related to species richness ($r = -0.09$, $P = 0.709$), the
percentage of endemic species richness ($r = -0.03$, $P =
0.887$), or the percentage of fluvial specialist species
richness ($r = 0.32$, $P = 0.162$).

Eigenvalues were 0.26 and 0.14 for the first and
second DCA axes, respectively. The UII was significantly related to DCA axis-1 site scores ($r = 0.99$, $P =
0.001$) but not to DCA axis-2 site scores ($r = 0.08$, $P
= 0.929$). Three species—largescale stoneroller, large-
mouth bass, and creek chub *Semotilus atromaculatus*—
had high species scores for DCA axis 1 (Figure 2).
Seven species—Alabama darter, Alabama shiner, spot-
ted sunfish *L. punctatus*, tricolor shiner, speckled darter

E. stigmaeum, Mobile logperch, and warmouth *L.
gulosus*—had low species scores for DCA axis 1 (Figure 3). Drainage area was not significantly related to
DCA axis-1 site scores ($r = -0.28$, $P = 0.220$) or DCA
axis-2 site scores ($r = 0.08$, $P = 0.719$). Elevation also
was not significantly related to DCA axis-1 site scores
($r = 0.34$, $P = 0.136$) or DCA axis-2 site scores ($r = -
0.32$, $P = 0.133$).

BOS Study Area

A total of 29 fish species representing 6,431 individuals was collected in the BOS study area (Appendix B). Overall, six species accounted for greater than
5% of the total abundance—fallfish *S. corporalis*
(18.8%), common shiner *Luxilus cornutus* (17.2%),
white sucker *Catostomus commersoni* (11.9%),
blacknose dace *Rhinichthys atratulus* (10.9%),
longnose dace *R. cataractae* (8.6%), and bluegill
(6.2%). Seven species were collected at greater than
50% of the 30 sites sampled—white sucker (89.7%),
pumpkinseed *L. gibbosus* (86.2%), American eel
Anguilla rostrata (75.9%), fallfish (72.4%), largemouth bass (58.6%), bluegill (55.2%), and chain
pickerel *Esox niger* (55.2%). Nine species are considered alien—black crappie *Pomoxis nigromaculatus*,
bluegill, brown trout, green sunfish, largemouth bass,
margined madtom *Noturus insignis*, rainbow trout,
smallmouth bass *M. dolomieu*, and yellow bullhead
Ameiurus natalis. Atlantic salmon *Salmo salar*, once
native but extirpated, have been reintroduced into
New England.

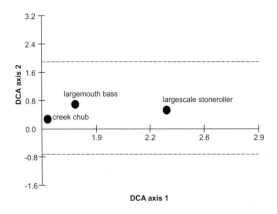

FIGURE 2. Plot of BIR fish species scores greater than the
75th percentile of DCA axis-1 site scores and within one
standard deviation of DCA axis-2 site scores. Dashed line
represents bounds of one standard deviation of DCA axis-2
site scores. Fish species within these bounds can be considered tolerant of urbanization.

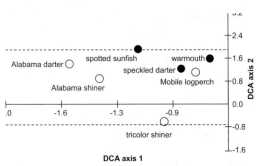

FIGURE 3. Plot of BIR fish species scores less than the
25th percentile of DCA axis-1 site scores and within one
standard deviation of DCA axis-2 site scores. Dashed line
represents bounds of one standard deviation of DCA axis-2
site scores. Open circles indicate species identified as endemic
(Mettee et al. 1996). Fish species within these bounds can be
considered intolerant of urbanization.

The UII was significantly negatively related to species richness ($r = -0.48$, $P = 0.008$) and percentage of fluvial specialist species richness ($r = -0.56$, $P = 0.002$), but was not significantly related to the percentage of alien species richness ($r = 0.07$, $P = 0.446$). Drainage area was not significantly related to species richness ($r = -0.06$, $P = 0.772$), the percentage of alien species richness ($r = 0.19$, $P = 0.306$), or the percentage of fluvial specialist species richness ($r = 0.32$, $P = 0.089$). Elevation was not significantly related to species richness ($r = 0.33$, $P = 0.079$), the percentage of alien species richness ($r = 0.24$, $P = 0.214$), or the percentage of fluvial specialist species richness ($r = 0.31$, $P = 0.096$).

Eigenvalues were 0.43 and 0.17 for the first and second DCA axes, respectively. The UII was significantly related to DCA axis-1 site scores ($r = 0.73$, $P = 0.001$), but was not significantly related to DCA axis-2 site scores ($r = 0.23$, $P = 0.237$). Seven species—yellow perch *Perca flavescens*, bluegill, yellow bullhead, largemouth bass, pumpkinseed, brown bullhead *A. nebulosus*, and redfin pickerel *Esox americanus*—had high DCA axis-1 species scores (Figure 4). Nine species—common shiner, blacknose dace, longnose dace, sea lamprey *Petromyzon marinus*, brook trout *Salvelinus fontinalis*, white sucker, swamp darter *E. fusiforme*, fallfish, and creek chubsucker *Erimyzon oblongus*—had low DCA axis-1 species scores (Figure 5). Drainage area was not significantly related to DCA axis-1 site scores ($r = 0.27$, $P = 0.157$) or DCA axis-2 site scores ($r = -0.11$, $P = 0.575$). Elevation was also not significantly related to DCA axis-1 site scores ($r = -0.32$, $P = 0.080$) or DCA axis-2 site scores ($r = -0.01$, $P = 0.976$).

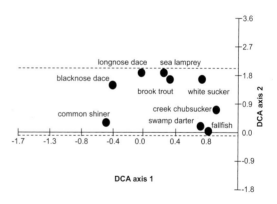

FIGURE 5. Plot of BOS fish species scores less than the 25th percentile of DCA axis-1 site scores and within one standard deviation of DCA axis-2 site scores. Dashed line represents bounds of one standard deviation of DCA axis-2 site scores. Fish species within these bounds can be considered intolerant of urbanization. All species except swamp darter are considered fluvial specialists.

Combined Analyses

The full ANCOVA model of fish species richness, UII values, and study area was significant ($P = 0.001$), and the UII by study area interaction term in the model also was significant ($P = 0.004$, Table 2). The scatter plot of the relations between fish species richness and the UII for both study areas indicates possible variation in relations between species richness and UII scores less than 50 compared to scores greater than 50 (Figure 6). In addition, of the 19 BOS sites with UII values less than 50, 9 sites had relatively low species richness values (BOS1<50), whereas 10 sites had relatively high species richness values for the same UII scores (BOS2<50).

A total of 18 species were collected from all sites in the BOS1<50 group. Overall, six species accounted for greater than 5% of the total abundance for this group (3,450) and included common shiner (23.8%), fallfish (23.5%), blacknose dace (15.3%), longnose dace (12.9%), white sucker (11.7%), and margined madtom (6.4%). A total of 25 species were collected from all sites in the BOS2<50 group. Overall, eight species accounted for greater than 5% of the total abundance for this group (1,650) and included common shiner (17.5%), fallfish (17.2%), blacknose dace (9.7%), white sucker (8.9%), Atlantic salmon (8.5%), bluegill (8.1%), longnose dace (6.5%), and redbreast sunfish *L. auritus* (6.2%). Eight species were collected in the BOS2 < 50 that were not collected in the BOS1<50, including black crappie, green sunfish, rainbow trout, redfin pickerel, sea lamprey, smallmouth

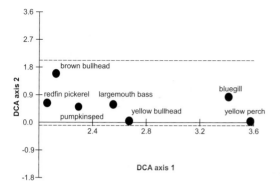

FIGURE 4. Plot of BOS fish species scores greater than the 75th percentile of DCA axis-1 site scores and within one standard deviation of DCA axis-2 site scores. Dashed line represents bounds of one standard deviation of DCA axis-2 site scores. Fish species within these bounds can be considered tolerant of urbanization.

TABLE 2. Analysis of covariance models of fish species richness with the urban intensity index (UII), study area, and the interaction of the UII and study area. The BIR and BOS study areas were divided into five groups—BIR UII values < 50 (BIR<50), BOS with relatively low species richness and UII values < 50 (BOS1<50), BOS with relatively high species richness and UII values < 50 (BOS2<50), BIR UII values > 50 (BIR>50), and BOS UII values > 50 (BOS>50).

Model	Model P-value	UII P-value	Study area P-value	UII × study area P-value
BIR, BOS	0.001	0.001	0.001	0.004
BIR < 50, BOS1 < 50, BOS2 < 50	0.001	0.001	0.001	0.099
BIR > 50, BOS > 50	0.607	0.307	0.595	0.620

bass, swamp darter, and tessellated darter *E. olmstedi*. Of these, black crappie, green sunfish, and small-mouth bass are alien species and macrohabitat generalists; rainbow trout is an alien species and fluvial specialist, whereas swamp darter is a native macro-habitat generalist.

An ANCOVA was conducted on species richness data for sites with UII values less than 50 for three groups—BIR<50, BOS1<50, and BOS2<50. The full ANCOVA model was significant (*P* = 0.001) and the UII by study area (group) interaction term in the model was not significant (*P* = 0.099, Table 2). An ANCOVA was also conducted for UII values greater than 50 on species richness data for the BIR>50 and BOS>50. For these sites, the full ANCOVA model was not significant (*P* = 0.607, Table 2).

Locally weighted regression smoothing plots for the BIR UII scores illustrate a negative, nearly linear pattern with total species richness and with endemic species richness, particularly for UII values less than 75 (Figure 7A). In contrast, LOESS plots for the BOS UII suggested a nonlinear pattern with total species richness, indicating periodic increases and decreases in species richness (Figure 7B). The corresponding LOESS plot of BOS UII values and fluvial specialist richness indicates that, following an initial decline, the

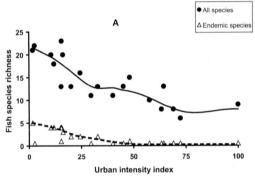

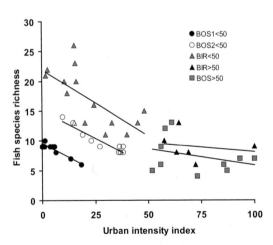

FIGURE 6. Scatter plot showing relations between fish species richness and UII values for five groups: BIR < 50, BOS1<50, BOS2<50, BIR>50, and BOS>50. See Table 2 for group definitions. Lines represent linear trends.

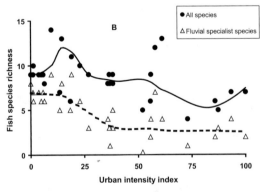

FIGURE 7. LOESS plots of relations between fish species richness, endemic species richness, and richness of fluvial specialist species, and the UII for the BIR (A) and the BOS (B) study areas.

number of fluvial specialist species remained relatively stable for UII scores greater than 40.

Discussion

Species richness decreases with increasing urbanization in the BIR and BOS study areas, similar to results reported elsewhere (Onorato et al. 2000; Wang et al. 2000; Paul and Meyer 2001). In our study, species richness measures are not related to drainage area or elevation, suggesting that variability related to these factors is limited along the gradients of urbanization.

In BIR, the decline in species richness related to increasing urbanization appears to result from a decline in endemic species richness. Similar findings were reported by Walters et al. (2005, this volume) in the Etowah River basin, Georgia. Endemic species tend to be prone to extinction because of their small geographic ranges and specific habitat requirements (Meffe and Carroll 1997). In a study of the upper Cahaba River system in Alabama, Onorato et al. (2000) reported that the decline of Alabama shiner and tricolor shiner, endemic species that require silt-free substrates for crevice spawning, may be attributed to siltation associated with urban development.

In the BOS study area, which lacks endemic species, the decline in species richness appears to be a function of the loss of fluvial specialists. Similar results have been reported for the Ipswich River, Massachusetts (Armstrong et al. 2001). As noted by Halliwell et al. (1999), many coldwater, flowing habitats in the northeastern United States were degraded by the mid-1800s by the construction of small mill dams and canals, many of which still exist. Thus, historical alterations to hydrology and habitat combined with present-day alterations of flow (Armstrong et al. 2001), which are related to increased urbanization, may explain the decline in fluvial specialists in the BOS study area.

Assessment of the relations between fish assemblages and urbanization based on DCA reveals that eigenvalues for the first DCA axes are relatively low, particularly for the BIR study area. An eigenvalue represents a relative measure of the strength of an axis, the amount of variation along an axis, and ideally, the importance of an ecological gradient. In general, higher eigenvalues for DCA axes are related to higher beta diversities or species turnover along environmental gradients (McCune et al. 2002). Thus, an axis or gradient with relatively low eigenvalues may suggest that some species will be common to both ends of an environmental gradient or that relatively few species are being added along the gradient. Cuffney et al. (2005,

this volume) conducted ordination analyses of invertebrate assemblage data for the BIR and BOS study areas and also reported relatively low eigenvalues for DCA. Cuffney et al. (2005) noted that the relatively low eigenvalues may reflect a continual loss of species richness along the urban gradient with little replacement by more adaptable taxa. Similarly, we noted a continual loss of fish species richness along the urban gradient in our study.

Though increasing urbanization is related to changes in fish assemblages in both BIR and BOS, differences occurred in the fish assemblages most strongly associated with urbanization. In the BIR study area, the urban fish assemblage is characterized by three species and dominated by a single species, the largescale stoneroller. Largescale stonerollers tend to congregate in large schools during spawning, typically in April in Alabama (Mettee et al. 1996), a factor that may have contributed to the collection of largescale stonerollers at all 21 sites in the BIR study area. Walters et al. (2005) reported that centrarchids were associated with increasing urbanization in the Etowah River and suggested that centrarchids, classified as macrohabitat generalists, are more resilient to disturbance than other stream fishes. Walters et al. (2005) also suggested that the presence of centrarchids with increasing urbanization in the Etowah River was primarily related to changes in hydrology. One centrarchid species in the BIR study area, the macrohabitat generalist largemouth bass, is associated with increasing urbanization. However, the largescale stoneroller, classified as a fluvial specialist, is an herbivore that can persist in streams chronically stressed both chemically and physically (Mettee et al. 1996).

Extensive urban development in BIR has increased water use and point-source discharges in the upper Cahaba River system (Shepard et al. 1997). During low flow periods, nearly 100% of the flow in the upper Cahaba River is removed for municipal water supply (Onorato et al. 1998). Twenty-six municipal wastewater-treatment plants each discharge secondarily treated water into the upper Cahaba River system (Shepard et al. 1997). Whereas secondarily treated wastewater removes particulate matter and oxygen-consuming wastes, it generally contains elevated nutrient concentrations that contribute to eutrophication. El-Kaddah and Carey (2004) suggest that such point-source discharges may account for significant nitrogen input into the Cahaba River, greater than the input from nonpoint sources. Shepard et al. (1997) reported that biodiversity has decreased in the upper Cahaba River system and that eutrophication may be a contributing factor. Onorato et al. (2000) reported that the largescale stoneroller was collected in a larger percentage of samples from the upper Cahaba River system in 1997 compared to historical records and attributed the increase in this disturbance-tolerant species to the fact that it can persist in streams disturbed by wastewater. Eutrophication provides an abundant source of nutrients to sustain the production of algae consumed by these herbivores.

In contrast to BIR, the urban fish assemblage in BOS consisted of seven macrohabitat generalists. Alterations in hydrology and associated increased water temperature have been suggested as causative factors related to a reduction in the ranges of coldwater fluvial specialists, such as brook trout, and the expansion of ranges of warmer-water macrohabitat generalists, such as redfin pickerel, in the Ipswich River basin (Armstrong et al. 2001). Increased urbanization and concomitant increased water withdrawals for public water supply have increased the severity and duration of low flows in streams in the Ipswich River basin (Armstrong et al. 2001). These authors determined that groundwater withdrawals, wastewater transfers, and land-use alterations that increase impervious areas combined to result in flow reductions of more than 90% in the upper Ipswich River. These hydrological alterations result in lower base flows, which support streamflow between precipitation events. Diminished base flows during the summer will likely result in warmer water temperatures because when cool inflow is reduced, the reduced volume of water in the river heats more rapidly. In addition to increases in stream temperature caused by direct heating of reduced volumes of streamflow, groundwater withdrawals can cause the loss of coldwater springs that provide important areas of refuge during low-flow periods.

Analysis of covariance of fish species richness indicates that the linear rate of species-richness decrease with increasing urbanization varied between the relatively species-rich BIR and the comparatively species-poor BOS. Further examination of the data reveals two distinct patterns in the relation between species richness and urbanization in the BOS study area for UII values less than 50. The greater number of species in the BOS2<50 compared with the BOS1<50 resulted from the addition of alien species and native macrohabitat generalists, such as black crappie, green sunfish, and smallmouth bass. Thus, even at relatively low levels of urbanization, increases in species richness were noted in the BOS study area.

When the data were divided into groups based on urban intensity, ANCOVA indicates that linear patterns in responses of fish species richness to urbanization are similar between the BIR and BOS study areas. ANCOVA indicates that for relatively low UII values, slopes of relations between fish species richness and UII values do not vary significantly among the BIR study area and the two groups of BOS sites. These results indicate that despite the addition of species at some BOS sites at relatively low levels of urbanization, the linear rate of species loss is similar. Results of the ANCOVA also indicate that at UII values greater than 50, there is insignificant loss of species richness with increased urbanization for BIR and BOS.

Examination of patterns in LOESS plots indicates differences in relations between species richness and urbanization for BIR and BOS compared to species-richness stressor models. In the BIR study area, the response appeared to be nearly linear, similar to the response using the Ohio model. Although there was no evidence to suggest a resistance response, as suggested by the dose–response model, there appeared to be an exhaustion response.

In contrast, patterns in LOESS plots suggest a nonlinear response in relations between species richness and urbanization in BOS. This nonlinear response suggests periodic decreases and increases in species richness. This pattern is similar to that of the habitat-disturbance model, a model developed for the species-rich southeastern United States. Patterns in responses of total species richness and the number of fluvial specialist species indicate resistance. An exhaustion response is evident in the relation between fluvial specialist richness and urbanization. An exhaustion response in the relation between total species richness and urbanization is not as clear and follows the proposed slight increase in species richness as indicated by the habitat-disturbance model.

Despite contrasts in ecoregions and ichthyogeographic regions, similarities exist in the responses of fish assemblages to urbanization in BIR and BOS. In both study areas, species richness declined, and the rate of species decline was similar regardless of large-scale differences (BIR and BOS) or smaller-scale differences (groups within the BOS study area) in relations between species richness and urbanization. In both study areas, declines in total species richness were associated with declines of species expected to be sensitive to urbanization—endemic species in BIR and fluvial specialists in BOS.

Although increased urbanization in both study areas may be related to changes associated with altered hydrology, increased urbanization results in different fish assemblage structures in the BIR and BOS. These differences appear to be the result of differences in native invasive and alien species between the two study areas, resulting in periodic increased species richness with increasing urbanization. Increased species richness can result from the addition of alien species and because of tolerant, generalist, native species that can invade from downstream areas (Scott and Helfman 2001). This increase in species richness is likely a function predominantly of physical habitat changes that provide more suitable conditions for new species. An absence of habitat changes or the presence of increased chemical toxicity and organic enrichment at high levels of urbanization may prohibit the addition of new species.

Differences noted in fish assemblage responses may be the result of differences in urban-development histories between the two study areas. Understanding the effects of urban influences on ecosystems can often be complicated by factors including antecedent land use (e.g., urbanization of agricultural areas as opposed to urbanization of forested land). Harding et al. (1998) noted the importance of antecedent land use as a determinant for understanding the effects of human influences on stream fishes. Whereas a multimetric UII may provide a better understanding of the effects of urbanization on stream biota compared to single-dimension measures of spatial variation in urban influences, a better understanding of temporal aspects of urban influences is needed.

Because species richness can increase or decrease with increasing urbanization, depending on factors such as physical and chemical alterations associated with urbanization, the presence of alien species, and the ability of tolerant native species to invade altered habitats, a single general-response model of fish species richness to urbanization may not be broadly applicable. Whereas the Ohio model may describe species richness responses to urbanization in the BIR study area, the habitat-disturbance model appears to be more applicable in the BOS study area. However, response models based on total species richness may be misleading because aquatic ecosystem integrity can degrade despite increases in species richness (Scott and Helfman 2001). Thus, developing response models based on life history and behavioral and ecological requirements may provide a better understanding of fish assemblage responses to urbanization than approaches using total species richness.

Acknowledgments

We thank the biologists, hydrologists, and technicians, too numerous to name individually, who collected data as part of the NAWQA Program. This study was conducted as part of ecological synthesis through the NAWQA Program.

References

Armstrong, D. S., T. A. Richards, and G. W. Parker. 2001. Assessment of habitat, fish communities, and streamflow requirements for habitat protection, Ipswich River, Massachusetts. U.S. Geological Survey, Water-Resources Investigations Report 01–4161, Northborough, Massachusetts.

Carlisle, D. M., P. M. Stewart, and J. T. Butcher. 2003. Macroinvertebrate assemblages associated with patterns in land use and water quality. Pages 271–285 in T. P. Simon, editor. Biological response signatures: indicator patterns using aquatic communities. CRC Press, New York.

Cuffney, T. F., H. Zappia, E. M. P. Giddings, and J. F. Coles. 2005. Effects of urbanization on benthic macroinvertebrate assemblages in contrasting environmental settings: Boston, Massachusetts; Birmingham, Alabama; and Salt Lake City, Utah. Pages 361–407 in L. R. Brown, R. M. Hughes, R. Gray, and M. R. Meador, editors. Effects of urbanization on stream ecosystems. American Fisheries Society, Symposium 47, Bethesda, Maryland.

Davis, W. S., and T. P. Simon, editors. 1995. Biological assessment and criteria—tools for water resource planning and decision making. Lewis Publishers, Boca Raton, Florida.

DeVivo, J. C. 1996. Fish assemblages as indicators of water quality within the Apalachicola-Chattahoochee-Flint (ACF) River basin. Master's thesis. University of Georgia, Athens.

Edwards, M. R., D. L. Combs, and S. B. Cook. 2003. Comparison of single-pass electrofishing to depletion sampling for surveying fish assemblages in small warmwater streams. Journal of Freshwater Ecology 18:625–634.

El-Kaddah, D. N., and A. E. Carey. 2004. Water quality modeling of the Cahaba River, Alabama. Environmental Geology 45:323–338.

Fitzpatrick, F. A., I. R. Waite, P. J. D'Arconte, M. R. Meador, M. A. Maupin, and M. E. Gurtz. 1998. Revised methods for characterizing stream habitat—National Water-Quality Assessment Program. U.S. Geological Survey, Water-Resources Investigations Report 98–4052, Raleigh, North Carolina.

Flanagan, S. M., K. W. Nielsen, K. W. Robinson, and J. F. Coles. 1999. Water-quality assessment of the New England coastal basins in Maine, Massachusetts, New Hampshire, and Rhode Island: environmental settings and implications for water quality and aquatic biota. U.S. Geological Survey Water-Resources Investigations Report 98–4249, Pembroke, New Hampshire.

Gauch, H. G. 1982. Multivariate analysis in community ecology. Cambridge University Press, Cambridge, Massachusetts.

Halliwell, D. B., R. W. Langdon, R. A. Daniels, J. P. Kurtenbach, and R. A. Jacobson. 1999. Classification of freshwater fish species of the northeastern United States for use in the development of indices of biological integrity, with regional applications. Pages 301–337 *in* T.P. Simon, editor. Assessing the sustainability and biological integrity of water resources using fish communities. CRC Press, Lewis Publishers, Boca Raton, Florida.

Harding, J. S., E. F. Benfield, P.V. Bolstad, G.S. Helfman, and E. B. D. Jones. 1998. Stream biodiversity: the ghost of land use past. Proceedings of the National Academy of Sciences 95:14843–14847.

Hartel, K. E., D. B. Halliwell, and A. E. Launer. 2002. Inland fishes of Massachusetts. Massachusetts Audubon Society, Lincoln.

Ipswich River Watershed Association. 2002. Ipswich River target fish community. Available: http://www.ipswichriver.org/policy.html. (March 2003).

Kemp, S. J., and J. R. Spotila. 1997. Effects of urbanization on brown trout *Salmo trutta*, other fishes and macroinvertebrates in Valley Creek, Valley Forge, Pennsylvania. American Midland Naturalist 138:55–68.

Kinsolving, A. D., and M. B. Bain. 1993. Fish assemblage recovery along a riverine disturbance gradient. Ecological Applications 3:531–544.

Leopold, L. B., M. G. Wolman, and J. P. Miller. 1964. Fluvial processes in geomorphology. W.H. Freeman, San Francisco.

Lewis, W. D. 1994. Sloss furnaces and the rise of the Birmingham district: an industrial epic: University of Alabama Press, Tuscaloosa.

Matthews, W. J., and F. P. Gelwick. 1990. Fishes of Crutcho Creek and the North Canadian River in central Oklahoma: effects of urbanization. The Southwestern Naturalist 35(4):403–410.

May, C. W., R. R. Horner, J. R. Karr, B. W. Mar, and E. B. Welch. 1997. Effects of urbanization on small streams in the Puget Sound Lowland ecoregion. Watershed Protection Techniques 2:483–494.

McCune, B., J. B. Grace, and D. L. Urban. 2002. Analysis of ecological communities. MjM Software Design, Gleneden Beach, Oregon.

McDonnell, M. K., and S. T. A. Pickett. 1990. Ecosystem structure and function along urban-rural gradients: an unexploited opportunity for ecology. Ecology 71:1232–1237.

McMahon, G., and T. F. Cuffney. 2000. Quantifying urban intensity in drainage basins for assessing stream ecological conditions. Journal of the American Water Resources Association 36:1247–1261.

Meador, M. R., T. F. Cuffney, and M. E. Gurtz. 1993. Methods for sampling fish communities as part of the National Water-Quality Assessment Program. U.S. Geological Survey, Open-File Report 93–104, Raleigh, North Carolina.

Meador, M. R., L. R. Brown, and T. M. Short. 2003b. Relations between introduced fish and environmental conditions at large geographic sales. Ecological Indicators 3:81–92.

Meador, M. R., J. P. McIntyre, and K. H. Pollock. 2003a. Assessing the efficacy of single-pass backpack electrofishing to characterize fish community structure. Transactions of the American Fisheries Society 132:39–46.

Meffe, G. K., and C. R. Carroll. 1997. Principals of conservation biology. Sinauer Associates Inc, Sunderland, Massachusetts.

Mettee, M. F., P. E. O'Neil, and J. M. Pierson. 1996. Fishes of Alabama and the Mobile basin. Oxmoor House, Inc., Birmingham, Alabama.

Omernik, J. M. 1987. Ecoregions of the conterminous United States. Annals of the Association of American Geographers 77:118–125.

Onorato, D., K. R. Marion, and R. A. Angus. 1998. Longitudinal variations in the ichthyofaunal assemblages of the upper Cahaba River: possible effects of urbanization in the watershed. Journal of Freshwater Ecology 13:139–154.

Onorato, D., R. A. Angus, and K. R. Marion. 2000. Historical changes in the ichthyofaunal assemblages of the upper Cahaba River in Alabama associated with extensive urban development in the watershed. Journal of Freshwater Ecology 15:47–63.

Patton, T. M., W. A. Hubert, F.J. Rahel, and K. G. Gerow. 2000. Effort needed to estimate species richness in small streams on the Great Plains in Wyoming. North American Journal of Fisheries Management 20:394–398.

Paul, M. J., and J. L. Meyer. 2001. Streams in the urban landscape. Annual Review of Ecology and Systematics 32:333–365.

Reynolds, J. B. 1996. Electrofishing. Pages 221–254 *in* B. R. Murphy and D. W. Willis, editors. Fisheries techniques, 2nd edition. American Fisheries Society, Bethesda, Maryland.

Reynolds, L., A. T. Herlihy, P. R. Kaufmann, S. V. Gregory, and R. M. Hughes. 2003. Electrofishing effort requirements for assessing species richness and biotic integrity in western Oregon streams. North American Journal of Fisheries Management 23:450–461.

Robins, C. R., R. M. Bailey, C. E. Bond, J. R. Brooker, E. A. Lachner, R. N. Lea, and W. B. Scott. 1991. Common and scientific names of fishes from the United States and Canada. 5th Edition. American Fisheries Society, Special Publication 20, Bethesda, Maryland.

Scott, M. C., and G. S. Helfman. 2001. Native invasions, homogenization, and the mismeasure of integrity of fish assemblages. Fisheries 26(11):6–15.

Selye, H. 1973. The evolution of the stress concept. American Scientist 61:629–699.

Shepard, T. E., P. E. O'Neil, S. W. McGregor, M. F. Mettee, and S. C. Harris. 1997. Biomonitoring and water-quality studies in the upper Cahaba River drainage of Alabama, 1989–1994. Geological Survey of Alabama, Bulletin 165, Tuscaloosa.

Short, T. M., E. M. P. Giddings, H. Zappia, and J. F. Coles. 2005. Urbanization effects on stream habitat characteristics in Boston, Massachusetts; Birmingham, Alabama; and Salt Lake City, Utah. Pages 317–332 in L. R. Brown, R. M. Hughes, R. Gray, and M. R. Meador, editors. Effects of urbanization on stream ecosystems. American Fisheries Society, Symposium 47, Bethesda, Maryland.

Simonson, T. D., and J. Lyons. 1995. Comparison of catch per effort and removal procedures for sampling stream fish assemblages. North American Journal of Fisheries Management 15:419–427.

Smogor, R. A., and P. L. Angermeier. 1999. Relations between fish metrics and measures of anthropogenic disturbance in three IBI regions in Virginia. Pages 585–610 in T. P. Simon, editor. Assessing the sustainability and biological integrity of water resources using fish communities. CRC Press, Boca Raton, Florida.

Snyder, C. D., J. A. Young, R. Villella, and D. P. Lemarié. 2003. Influences of upland and riparian land use patterns on stream biotic integrity. Landscape Ecology 18:647–664.

Steedman, R. J. 1988. Modification and assessment of an index of biotic integrity to quantify stream quality in southern Ontario. Canadian Journal of Fisheries and Aquatic Sciences 45:492–501.

Tate, C. M., T. F. Cuffney, G. McMahon, E. M. P. Giddings, J. F. Coles, and H. Zappia. 2005. Use of an urban intensity index to assess urban effects on streams in three contrasting environmental settings. Pages 291–315 in L. R. Brown, R. M. Hughes, R.

Gray, and M. R. Meador, editors. Effects of urbanization on stream ecosystems. American Fisheries Society, Symposium 47, Bethesda, Maryland.

U.S. Geological Survey. 2000a. Nonindigenous fish distribution information. Available: http://nas.er.usgs.gov/fishes/. (March 2003)

U.S. Geological Survey. 2000b. National Water-Quality Assessment (NAWQA) - digital map products. Available: http://water.usgs.gov/nawqa/digmap.html. (March 2003)

Vadas, R. L., and D. J. Orth. 1993. A new technique for estimating the abundance and habitat use of stream fishes. Journal of Freshwater Ecology 8:305–317.

Walters, D. M., M. C. Freeman, D. S. Leigh, B. J. Freeman, and C. M. Pringle. 2005. Urbanization effects on fishes and habitat quality in a southern piedmont river basin. Pages 69–85 in L. R. Brown, R. M. Hughes, R. Gray, and M. R. Meador, editors. Effects of urbanization on stream ecosystems. American Fisheries Society, Symposium 47, Bethesda, Maryland.

Walsh, S. J., and M. R. Meador. 1998. Guidelines for quality assurance and quality control of fish taxonomic data collected as part of the National Water-Quality Assessment Program. U.S. Geological Survey, Water-Resources Investigations Report 98–4239, Raleigh, North Carolina.

Wang, L., J. Lyons, P. Kanehl, and R. Bannerman. 2001. Impacts of urbanization on stream habitat and fish across multiple spatial scales. Environmental Management 28:255–266.

Wang, L., J. Lyons, P. Kanehl, R. Bannerman, and E. Emmons. 2000. Watershed urbanization and changes in fish communities in southeastern Wisconsin streams. Journal of the American Water Resources Association 36:1173–1189.

Weaver, L. A., and G. C. Garman. 1994. Urbanization of a watershed and historical changes in a stream fish assemblage. Transactions of the American Fisheries Society 123:162–172.

Yoder, C. O., R. J. Miltner, and D. White. 1999. Assessing the status of aquatic life designated uses in urban and suburban watersheds. Pages 16–28 in A. Everson, editor. National conference on retrofit opportunities for water resource protection in urban environments. U.S. Environmental Protection Agency, Report EPA/625/R-99/002, Washington, D.C.

APPENDIX A. Scientific and common names of fish collected in the BIR study area. ([E] indicates species identified as endemic [Mettee et al. 1996]; [FS] indicates species identified as fluvial specialists; [MG] indicates species identified as macrohabitat generalists [Kinsolving and Bain 1993; Mettee et al. 1996]. Scientific names follow Robins et al. [1991]).

Family	Scientific name	Common name
Petromyzontidae	*Ichthyomyzon gagei*	southern brook lamprey[FS]
Cyprinidae	*Campostoma oligolepis*	largescale stoneroller[FS]
	Cyprinella callistia	Alabama shiner[E, FS]
	C. trichroistia	tricolor shiner[E, FS]
	C. venusta	blacktail shiner[MG]
	Luxilus chrysocephalus	striped shiner[FS]
	Lythrurus bellus	pretty shiner[FS]
	Notropis asperifrons	burrhead shiner[E, FS]
	N. chrosomus	rainbow shiner[FS]
	N. stilbius	silverstripe shiner[FS]
	N. xaenocephalus	Coosa shiner[E, FS]
	Phenacobius catostomus	riffle minnow[E, FS]
	Semotilus atromaculatus	creek chub[MG]
Catostomidae	*Hypentelium etowanum*	Alabama hog sucker[FS]
	Minytrema melanops	spotted sucker[MG]
	Moxostoma duquesnei	black redhorse[MG]
	M. erythrurum	golden redhorse[MG]
	M. poecilurum	blacktail redhorse[MG]
Ictaluridae	*Ameiurus natalis*	yellow bullhead[MG]
	Ictalurus punctatus	channel catfish[MG]
	Noturus leptacanthus	speckled madtom[FS]
Esocidae	*Esox niger*	chain pickerel[MG]
Fundulidae	*Fundulus olivaceus*	blackspotted topminnow[MG]
	F. stellifer	southern studfish[FS]
Poeciliidae	*Gambusia affinis*	western mosquitofish[MG]
Cottidae	*Cottus carolinae*	banded sculpin[FS]
Centrarchidae	*Ambloplites ariommus*	shadow bass[FS]
	Lepomis auritus	redbreast sunfish[MG]
	L. cyanellus	green sunfish[MG]
	L. gulosus	warmouth[MG]
	L. macrochirus	bluegill[MG]
	L. megalotis	longear sunfish[MG]
	L. microlophus	redear sunfish[MG]
	L. miniatus	redspotted sunfish[MG]
	L. punctatus	spotted sunfish[MG]
	Micropterus coosae	redeye bass[FS]
	M. punctulatus	spotted bass[MG]
	M. salmoides	largemouth bass[MG]
	Pomoxis nigromaculatus	black crappie[MG]
Percidae	*Etheostoma coosae*	Coosa darter[E, FS]
	E. jordani	greenbreast darter[E, FS]
	E. ramseyi	Alabama darter[E, FS]
	E. stigmaeum	speckled darter[FS]
	E. swaini	Gulf darter[FS]
	E. whipplei	redfin darter[FS]
	Percina caprodes	logperch[FS]
	P. kathae	Mobile logperch[E, FS]
	P. nigrofasciata	blackbanded darter[FS]

APPENDIX B. Scientific and common names of fish collected in the BOS study area. ([A] indicates fish species identified as alien [Hartel et al. 2002]; [FS] indicates species identified as fluvial specialists; [MG] indicates species identified as macrohabitat generalists [Hartel et al. 2002; Ipswich River Watershed Association 2002]. Atlantic salmon, once native but extirpated, have been reintroduced into New England. Scientific names follow Robins et al. [1991]).

Family	Scientific name	Common name
Petromyzontidae	*Petromyzon marinus*	sea lamprey[FS]
Anguillidae	*Anguilla rostrata*	American eel[FS]
Cyprinidae	*Luxilus cornutus*	common shiner[FS]
	Notemigonus crysoleucas	golden shiner[MG]
	Notropis hudsonius	spottail shiner[MG]
	Rhinichthys atratulus	eastern blacknose dace[FS]
	R. cataractae	longnose dace[FS]
	Semotilus corporalis	fallfish[FS]
Catostomidae	*Catostomus commersonii*	white sucker[FS]
	Erimyzon oblongus	creek chubsucker[FS]
Ictaluridae	*Ameiurus natalis*	yellow bullhead[A, MG]
	A. nebulosus	brown bullhead[MG]
	Noturus insignis	margined madtom[A, FS]
Esocidae	*Esox americanus*	redfin pickerel[MG]
	E. niger	chain pickerel[MG]
Salmonidae	*Oncorhynchus mykiss*	rainbow trout[A, FS]
	Salmo salar	Atlantic salmon[FS]
	S. trutta	brown trout[A, FS]
	Salvelinus fontinalis	brook trout[FS]
Centrarchidae	*Lepomis auritus*	redbreast sunfish[MG]
	L. cyanellus	green sunfish[A, MG]
	L. gibbosus	pumpkinseed[MG]
	L. macrochirus	bluegill[A, MG]
	Micropterus dolomieu	smallmouth bass[A, MG]
	M. salmoides	largemouth bass[A, MG]
	Pomoxis nigromaculatus	black crappie[A, MG]
Percidae	*Etheostoma fusiforme*	swamp darter[MG]
	E. olmstedi	tessellated darter[FS]
	Perca flavescens	yellow perch[MG]